HEBREW SHORT STORIES:

Dual Language Hebrew-English

Interlinear & Parallel Text

HEBREW SHORT STORIES:

Dual Language Hebrew-English Interlinear & Parallel Text

PRESS

ISBN 978-1-952161-00-1

www.L2Press.com

First Edition

Contents

PART II
STORIES IN HEBREW ONLY

Introduction

DEAR LANGUAGE LEARNER: This is a dual language book of Modern Hebrew and English stories presented in a combined *interlinear + parallel text* format. The combination of parallel text with interlinear is the best of both worlds — the word-by-word translations and pronunciation guide of the interlinear and the broad translations of the parallel text. This single volume streamlines the process of reading in a foreign language by giving you everything needed to read, pronounce, and understand.

Reading is highly beneficial to acquiring a foreign language. Exposure to new words and phrases in the context of a larger story is productive and interesting. But reading in a foreign language, especially if the writing system is different from your native language, can be slow and frustrating. The typical process of reading in a foreign language involves continuously stopping to look up the meaning of words and phrases, which is a slow process that interferes with comprehending the story. Even if all the words in a sentence are familiar, sometimes the meaning of the sentence remains elusive because it contains unfamiliar grammar concepts or idioms. Furthermore, pronunciation is not always obvious. Interlinear text combined with parallel text solves these problems in a compact and convenient way.

The page layout is consistent and logical, with parallel text located next to the corresponding interlinear text. Parallel text occupies the outer section of each page while interlinear text occupies the inner section. The translation style of the interlinear is essentially literal, whereas the parallel text is a free translation. Linguistically speaking, this is an interlinear gloss containing three lines of interlinear text: (1) the first line is the Hebrew source text; (2) the second line is the romanization, which improves speaking and provides a better overall understanding of the word; and (3) the third line is the translation. The interlinear translations give more context-specific information than a dictionary possibly could.

This book is intended for those who want to learn Modern Hebrew as spoken in Israel. The language style is conversational and not overly formal or particularly different from the register that you would encounter in the everyday life of an educated person, yet the grammar is proper.

Intensive and Extensive Reading

Language learners use two methods to read stories – intensive reading and extensive reading. **Intensive reading** is a way of reading a small amount of text in a detailed manner with the goal of understanding as much as possible while extracting new vocabulary and grammar. **Extensive reading** is reading quickly, for pleasure, without looking up anything, for as long as you want, with the goal of gaining massive exposure to the language. Intensive reading is typically utilized in the early stages of language learning, while extensive reading is utilized in the later stages of language learning.

This book allows language learners at any stage to easily perform both intensive and extensive reading. The practice of intensive reading involves looking up the meaning and pronunciation of every unfamiliar word and phrase in a reading session. Even with the help of a dictionary, the meaning can remain elusive, particularly if the word is conjugated, if there are multiple words with the same spelling, or if the word has multiple meanings in English. Professionally edited translations and romanizations eliminate such problems and allow for reading intensively in an efficient and less frustrating manner. Similarly, this book assists learners with extensive reading by providing a large amount of engaging text in story form. Even though extensive reading does not involve stopping to look up words, the compact and convenient nature of the interlinear + parallel text allows for quick clarifications that won't distract from your extensive reading flow.

Active Listening

Written text with a corresponding audio file is a powerful combination of language learning tools. This book has an associated Hebrew audio file (available for purchase at L2Press.com) that was recorded by a professional voice actor. By hearing the language spoken, you can appreciate and imitate the prosody, melody, and intonation of the language. Combined, the audio and romanization will instill confidence, consistency, and clarity in how the language is spoken.

Prioritize active listening, which requires all of your attention and concentration, over passive listening, which requires little effort and yields minimal results. Productive active listening exercises include:

- *Shadowing*: listen to audio while repeating it nearly simultaneously, directly following the sound like a shadow. Ideally do this both with and without looking at a written version of the audio. Try to speak, as best as you can, like the native speaker, focusing on vowel sounds, vowel length, new consonant sounds, stress, and intonation.

- *Repeating*: listen to audio and then pause to repeat. Like shadowing, ideally do this both with and without looking at a written version of the audio, and try to mimic the native speaker as closely as possible. This technique, along with shadowing, is useful for developing a good accent.

- *Listening-Reading*: listen to Hebrew audio while reading English text. Following along in English while listening to Hebrew audio helps you understand what is being said. Can also combine this technique with shadowing (Listen to Hebrew, shadow in Hebrew, read English). This technique is great for developing your ability to understand spoken Hebrew.

- *Transcribing*: listen to an audio file while pausing frequently to write down exactly what you heard. Correct your transcription against the original text. This technique is good for *focused* listening comprehension.

- *Summarizing*: listen to a short piece of audio and summarize what you heard. Summarize in either written or spoken form. Ideally, summarize in front of a tutor/teacher for immediate feedback. This technique is good for *global* listening comprehension.

How To Use This Book

Mastering the meaning, pronunciation, and usage of every word, phrase, and sentence in this book will unavoidably yield a high level of Hebrew proficiency because there is so much material - roughly 3600 sentences. Considering that books containing 1000 or fewer sentences claim learners can reach CEFR level B2 by mastering their material, imagine the results of mastering 3600 sentences. That said, it is unrealistic for a single work to give you full proficiency in a foreign language, but mastering everything in this book through consistent effort will get you farther than almost anything else. This begs the question: How does one master all of the material in this book? Here are tips to get you started:

1. *Extensive and Intensive reading.* As described above, both extensive and intensive reading are made much easier with this book, and they are the main techniques that you will use when reading. If you want to improve your speaking abilities, then read aloud. If you aren't sure of the correct pronunciation, then

look at the line below for immediate feedback and correction. And if you don't know the meaning of the word, look at the third line for immediate feedback and correction of the meaning. If you don't understand the meaning of a phrase or sentence, then look at the parallel text. This constant cycle of instant feedback and correction is a key attribute of deliberate practice and will accelerate your learning like never before.

2. *Active listening.* Use techniques such as Shadowing, Repeating, Listening-Reading, Transcribing, and Summarizing, as described above.

3. *Spaced repetition with chunks.* Spaced repetition software (SRS) is an electronic flashcard system with a built-in algorithm that shows you the cards at optimal times for memorizing. If you are having trouble remembering certain words, phrases, and sentences after reading them many times, and you like to review flashcards, then put them into an SRS, such as Anki or Memrise, and review daily. "Chunks" are groups of two or more words that you should learn as a single unit. Chunks give you vocabulary, context, and grammar all in a short phrase. As an example, take the simple sentence "Last night I ate dinner with my family." Instead of breaking up the sentence into eight individual words and learning them all separately, it would be far more productive to learn it in three chunks - "last night", "I ate dinner", and "with my family". Now you know three chunks of words that work together and can be applied in new situations. "I was at my friend's house *last night*", "*I ate dinner* already", "I'm visiting New York *with my family*". Intuiting the grammar through context is more enjoyable and useful than laboring through tedious grammar exercises.

4. *Converse with a speaking partner.* In parallel to mastering the content of this book using the above techniques, find a native speaker and converse with them on a consistent basis, preferably at least one hour per week. The ideal practice partner is patient and will not simply correct your errors but will prompt you to self-correct. If you desire to speak fluently, there is no substitute for conversation practice.

5. *Part 1 vs Part 2.* This book is divided into two Parts. Part 1 contains the Hebrew stories formatted with interlinear and parallel translations. Part 2 contains the same stories but purely in Hebrew with no translations. Part 2 has been provided so that you can test your learning progress and accustom yourself to reading in Hebrew without any help from translations. Continuously cycle between the two Parts of the book to build further confidence in your new language skills.

Special notes about the Hebrew

1. There are no vowels points, or nikkud, used in this book. Instead, there is the romanization in the second line of the interlinear gloss. This was an intentional choice meant to get you used to reading Modern Hebrew without vowels points, which is the normal status of written Modern Hebrew in any situation outside of books for children.

2. The direct object particle את - *et* does not have an English translation and is therefore labeled "D.O.", for "direct object", in the third line of the interlinear. את is used only before *definite* direct objects and not before *indefinite* direct objects. See the *Hebrew Grammar By Example* book for a more comprehensive description with examples.

Alphabet and Pronunciation

The Hebrew Alphabet and Romanization

Letter[1]	Pronunciation[2]	IPA[3]	Romanization[4]
א	<u>a</u>lef	*takes vowel sound or silent*	
ב	bet	/b/ or /v/	b/v
ג	<u>g</u>imel	/g/	g
ד	<u>d</u>alet	/d/	d
ה	he	/h/	h
ו	vav	/v/	v/o/u
ז	<u>za</u>'in	/z/	z
ח	khet	/χ/	kh
ט	tet	/t/	t
י	yud	/j/	y/i
כ	kaf	/k/ or /χ/	k/kh
ך	kaf sofit	/χ/	kh
ל	<u>la</u>med	/l/	l
מ	mem	/m/	m
ם	mem sofit	/m/	m
נ	nun	/n/	n
ן	nun sofit	/n/	n
ס	<u>sa</u>mekh	/s/	s
ע	<u>a</u>'in	*takes vowel sound or silent*	
פ	pe	/p/ or /f/	p/f
ף	pe sofit	/f/	f
צ	<u>tsa</u>di	/t͡s/	ts
ץ	<u>tsa</u>di sofit	/t͡s/	ts
ק	kuf	/k/	k
ר	resh	/ʁ/	r
ש	shin	/ʃ/ or /s/	sh/s
ת	tav	/t/	t

(1) The first column of the table shows the Hebrew letters in alphabetical order, including the five special final (*sofit*) forms, which are letters that occur only at the end of a word.

(2) The second column lists the name of each letter, as pronounced in Modern Hebrew.

(3) The third column shows the phonemic notation for each letter in Modern Hebrew as described by the International Phonetic Alphabet equivalent.

(4) The fourth and final column shows the method of romanization as used in this book.

NOTE: In Hebrew, word stress usually falls on either the final syllable (מלרע - *milra*) or the penultimate syllable (מלעיל - *mileil*). In this book, any stress that does not fall on the last syllable is noted with an <u>und</u>erline.

Romanized Vowels and Pronunciation

Romanized Vowel[A]	IPA[B]	Similar to this English sound[C]
a	/a/	f<u>a</u>ther
e	/e/	p<u>e</u>t
i	/i/	gl<u>ee</u>
o	/o/	gl<u>o</u>ry
u	/u/	fl<u>u</u>te
ai	/aɪ/	<u>eye</u>
ei	/eɪ/	p<u>ay</u>
oi	/ɔɪ/	j<u>oy</u>
ui	/uɪ/	g<u>ooey</u>

(A) The first column lists vowels used in the romanization of Hebrew in this book.
(B) The middle column shows the phonemic notation for each romanized vowel.
(C) The third and final column lists English words with comparable vowel sounds. The relevant vowel is underlined. Keep in mind that comparable Hebrew vowel sounds are shorter than the English versions.
NOTE: Double vowels, such as *a'a* or *e'e*, represent long vowels, which are common and key for proper pronunciation and clarity in speech. For example, מערכת - *ma'arekhet* not *marekhet*.

Representing Foreign Sounds with Hebrew

Hebrew[1]	Sounds like[2]	IPA[3]	Romanization[4]
'ג	<u>J</u>erusalem	/dʒ/	j
'ד	<u>th</u>e	/ð/	th
וו	<u>W</u>ashington	/w/	w
'ז	mea<u>s</u>ure	/ʒ/	zh
'צ	<u>ch</u>ip	/tʃ/	ch
'ת	<u>th</u>ank	/θ/	th

(1) The first column of the table above shows some of the modified Hebrew letters used to create foreign (non-Hebrew) sounds. Aside from the double *vav*, which yields the /w/ sound, the letters are followed by a sharp apostrophe called a *geresh*.
(2) The second column lists example words that demonstrate the sounds created by the letters in the first column.
(3) The third column shows the phonetic notation for each letter as described by the International Phonetic Alphabet equivalent.
(4) The fourth and final column shows the method of romanization as used in this book.

Part I

STORIES IN INTERLINEAR AND PARALLEL TEXT

STORY 1

Garden Variety

Having a garden is not a good way to save money. You think that all the produce will lower your grocery costs. But you forget about the cost of actually growing the garden. So you should raise vegetables only for the psychological benefits.

שהיבול לך נדמה כסף לחסוך טובה דרך לא זה גינה טיפוח
shehayevul *lekha* *nidme* *kesef* *lakhsokh* *tova* *derekh* *lo* *ze* *gina* *tipu'akh*
that the produce / to you / it seems / money / to save / good / way / not / this / garden / cultivation of

הטיפול עלות את שוכח אתה אבל שלך. הקניות עלות את יוריד
hatipul *alut* *et* *shokhe'akh* *ata* *aval* *shelkha* *hakniyot* *alut* *et* *yorid*
the care / cost of / D.O. / you forget / you / but / your / the shopping / cost of / D.O. / would lower

הפסיכולוגי הערך בשביל רק ירקות לגדל מוטב לכן, בגינה.
hapsikhologi *ha'erekh* *bishvil* *rak* *yerakot* *legadel* *mutav* *lakhen* *bagina*
the psychological / the value / for / only / vegetables / to grow / it is advisable / so / in the garden

שבדבר.
shebadavar
that's in the thing

I can't believe how much my wife loves her garden. She gets an incredible sense of satisfaction seeing the vegetables grow. In contrast, I get a different sense. It's called pain!

נמלאת היא שלה. הגינה את אוהבת אשתי כמה עד יאומן לא
nimlet *hi* *shela* *hagina* *et* *ohevet* *ishti* *ad kama* *ye'uman* *lo*
she gets filled / she / her / the garden / D.O. / she loves / my wife / to the extent / I will believe / no

אני לעומתה. גדלים הירקות את מלראות עצומה סיפוק תחושת
ani *le'umata* *gdelim* *hayerakot* *et* *milirot* *atsuma* *sipuk* *tkhushat*
I / in contrast / they grow / the vegetables / D.O. / from seeing / tremendous / satisfaction / feeling of

נמלא תחושה אחרת. היא נקראת כאב!
nimla *tkhusha* *akheret* *hi* *nikret* *ke'ev*
I get filled / feeling / different / it / it is called / pain

---

Putting a fence around the garden is not fun. It costs about 1000 shekels in materials for a 2.5 meter high fence to surround a 5 by 6 meter garden. It's got to be 2.5 meters high to discourage the porcupines from turning the garden into a salad bar.

לגדר החומרים עלות כיף. לא זה לגינה מסביב גדר לשים
legader *hakhomarim* *alut* *kef* *lo* *ze* *lagina* *mesaviv* *gader* *lasim*
to fence / the materials / cost of / fun / not / this / to the garden / around / fence / to put

5 בגודל גינה להקיף המיועדת 2.5 מטרים, בגובה
khamisha *begodel* *gina* *lehakif* *hameyu'edet* *shnei metrim va'khetsi* *bagova*
five / in size / a garden / to surround / that is designated / two and a half meters / at the height of

בגובה גדר נדרשת שקל. כ-1000 היא מטרים, 6 על
bagova *gader* *nidreshet* *shekel* *ke'elef* *hi* *metrim* *shisha* *al*
for the height / fence / required / shekel / about one thousand / she / meters / six / by

הגינה את להפוך מהדורבנים למנוע כדי 2.5 מטרים
hagina *et* *lahafokh* *mehadorbanim* *limno'a* *kedei* *shnei metrim va'khetsi*
the garden / D.O. / to turn into / from the porcupines / to prevent / in order to / two and a half meters

למזנון סלטים.
salatim *lemiznon*
salads / to a buffet of

Story 1

Even then, they can get in via other methods. Sometimes they hang around near the gate, hiding behind the shrubs. They slip in unnoticed when you go to weed. One porcupine tried to parachute in last summer. Luckily the wind shifted and he wound up putting a hole through the neighbor's roof.

אפילו אז, הם יכולים להיכנס בדרכים אחרות. לפעמים הם מסתובבים
afilu az, hem yekholim lehikanes bidrakhim akherot. lifamim hem mistovevim
even then they can to enter in ways other sometimes they they wander around

ליד השער, מתחבאים מאחורי השיחים. הם חומקים פנימה
leyad hasha'ar, mitkhabim me'akhorei hasikhim. hem khomkim pnima
next to the gate they hide themselves behind the shrubs they they escape inside

כשאתה יוצא לנכש עשבים. בקיץ האחרון ניסה דורבן אחד
kshe'ata yotse lenakesh asabim. bakaits ha'akharon nisa dorban ekhad
when you you go out to uproot weeds in the summer the last it tried a porcupine one

לצנוח פנימה. למרבה המזל כיוון הרוח השתנה והוא סיים את
litsno'akh pnima. lemarbe hamazal kivun haru'akh hishtana vehu siyem et
to parachute inside very luckily direction of the wind it changed and it it finished D.O.

הצניחה בפעירת חור בתקרה של השכנים.
hatsnikha bifirat khor batikra shel hashkhenim.
the descent by opening a hole in the roof of the neighbors

Tilling the soil is not a small matter. First, you have to go to the local rental place and find a tiller that fits in your car. Unless you have a four by four truck, you wind up with a little one.

עיבוד הקרקע אינו עניין של מה בכך. ראשית, צריך ללכת למשתלה
ibud hakarka eino inyan shel ma bekhakh. reshit, tsarikh lalekhet lamishtala
working of the soil it isn't matter inconsequential first you need to go to the nursery

הקרובה ולמצוא מכונת עיבוד קרקע שנכנסת למכונית שלך.
hakrova velimtso mekhonat ibud karka shenikhneset lamekhonit shelkha.
the nearby and to find machine of working of soil that it fits into the car your

אלא אם יש לך טנדר ארבע על ארבע, תמצא שתוכל לקחת
ela im yesh lekha tender arba al arba, timtsa shetukhal lakakhat
unless you have truck four by four you will find that you will be able to take

רק מכונה קטנה.
rak mekhona ktana.
only machine small

The little ones weigh about a kilo and just skip along the top of the soil. This means you have to push the blades of the tiller into the hard ground as they are spinning.

הקטנות שוקלות בערך קילו, והן סתם מקפצות על פני השטח.
haktanot shoklot be'erekh kilo, vehen stam mekaptsot al pnei hashetakh.
the small ones they weigh approximately kilo and they just they skip on the surface

כלומר, אתה צריך לדחוף את להבי המכונה אל תוך האדמה
klomar, ata tsarikh lidkhof et lehavei hamekhona el tokh ha'adama
that is to say you you need to push D.O. blades of the machine into the ground

הקשה בזמן שהם מסתובבים.
hakasha bizman shehem mistovevim.
the hard while that they they spin around

Try doing this for two hours when your usual exercise is only lifting a wine glass and zipping through tv channels.

נסה לעשות זאת במשך שעתיים כששיגרת האימון שלך ביום-יום
nase la'asot zot bemeshekh sha'ata'im ksheshigrat ha'imun shelkha bayom-yom
try to do this for two hours when routine of the exercise your in the daily

מסתכמת בהנפת כוסות יין וזפזופ מול הטלוויזיה.
mistakemet behanafat kosot ya'in vezipzup mul hatelevizya.
it amounts to in raising glasses of wine and zipping in front of the television

Then you have to help your wife dig holes for the seeds. OK, they are small holes. But digging is not fun unless

ואז אתה צריך לעזור לאישתך לחפור בורות עבור הזרעים. אוקיי,
ve'az ata tsarikh la'azor la'ishtekha lakhpor borot avur hazra'im. okei,
and then you you need to help to your wife to dig holes for the seeds okay

אלה גומות קטנות. אבל חפירה איננה עניין מהנה, אלא אם אתה מוצא
ele gumot ktanot aval khafira einena inyan mehane ela im ata motse
these holes small but digging it isn't issue enjoyable unless you you find

אוצר שהוטמן באדמה.
otsar shehutman ba'adama
treasure that is buried in the ground

you find buried treasure.

כמה שבועות אחר כך אם לא יורד יותר מדי גשם, אבל יורד מספיק
kama shavu'ot akhar kakh im lo yored yoter midai geshem aval yored maspik
a few weeks later if no it falls too much rain but it falls enough

גשם, ואם הארנבות לא מתגנבות דרך הגדר, אתה זוכה לנכש
geshem ve'im ha'arnavot lo mitganvot derekh hagader ata zokhe lenakesh
rain and if the rabbits no they sneak in through the fence you you get to uproot

עשבים שוטים ולקטוף קצת יבול.
asabim shotim veliktof ktsat yevul
weeds and to pick a little produce

After a few weeks, if it doesn't rain too much, but it rains enough, and the rabbits don't sneak through the fence, you then get to pull weeds and harvest a little produce.

אני משתדל לצאת מהעיר כשהעשבים השוטים מגיחים
ani mishtadel latset meha'ir ksheha'asabim hashotim megikhim
I I make efforts to leave from the town when the weeds they burst out

מהקרקע, אבל לפעמים אני לא מצליח לקחת חופשה, ואני נאלץ
mehakarka aval lifamim ani lo matsli'akh lakakhat khufsha va'ani ne'elats
from the ground but sometimes I no I succeed to take vacation and I I am forced

לשנס מותניים ולנכש.
leshanes motna'im ulenakesh
to buckle down and to pull weeds

I try to be out of town when the weeds burst out of the ground, but sometimes I can't take the time off and get roped into the weeding.

ואז אני זוכה להעביר כמה פגישות אצל הכירופרקט, כדי
ve'az ani zokhe leha'avir kama pgishot etsel hakhiroprakt kedei
and then I I get to spend several sessions at the chiropractor in order to

שיעשה לי כמה תיקונים שאוכל לעמוד שוב באופן נורמלי.
sheya'ase li kama tikunim she'ukhal la'amod shuv be'ofen normali
that he will do to me a few adjustments that I will be able to stand again in a manner normal

Then I get to spend several sessions at the chiropractor's office while he makes a few adjustments so I can stand normally again.

האסיף גם הוא דורש עבודה רבה בכפיפה. רק הרמת שק אחד
ha'asif gam hu doresh avoda raba bikhfifa rak haramat sak ekhad
the harvest also it it requires labor much stooped just lifting of sack one

של שעועית ובחזרה לכירופרקט שזה עתה רכש יאכטה קטנה
shel she'u'it uvakhazara lakhiroprakt sheze ata rakhash yakhta ktana
of beans and back to the chiropractor that just now he bought yacht small

מהתשלומים שקיבל ממני בעונת הגינון.
mehatashlumim shekibel mimeni be'onat haginun
from the payments that he received from me in season the gardening

Harvesting also requires a lot of stooped labor. Just pick one bag of beans and it's back to the chiropractor, who just bought a small yacht from the fees I've paid him during the gardening season.

כשהילדים היו קטנים היתה לנו גינה גדולה הרבה יותר, ותמיד
kshehayeladim hayu ktanim haita lanu gina gdola harbe yoter vetamid
when the kids they were young we had garden big much more and always

שתלנו יותר מדי. נהגנו לגדל ארבעה שיחי קישוא בכל שנה.
shatalnu yoter midai nahagnu legadel arba'a sikhei kishu bekhol shana
we planted too much we used to to grow four bushes of zucchini in every year

When the kids were younger we had a much bigger garden and always planted too much. We used to grow four zucchini plants each year. What normal family can possibly eat the output of four zucchini plants?

3

Story 1

איזו משפחה נורמלית יכולה לאכול את התוצרת של ארבעה שיחי
eizo mishpakha normalit yekhola le'ekhol et hatotseret shel arba'a sikhei
what family normal it can to eat D.O. the produce of four bushes of

קישוא ?
kishu
zucchini

We had so much zucchini that we had to give it away. We loaded the kids into a little red wagon, covered them with zucchini, gave them snorkels so they wouldn't suffocate, and marched down the street.

היו לנו כל כך הרבה קישואים שנאלצנו לחלק לאחרים. העמסנו
hayu lanu kol kakh harbe kishu'im shene'elatsnu lekhalek la'akherim. he'emasnu
we had so much much zucchinis that we had to distribute to the others we loaded

את הילדים בעגלה קטנה אדומה, כיסינו אותם בקישואים, נתנו
et hayeladim be'agala ktana aduma, kisinu otam bekishu'im, natanu
D.O. the kids in a wagon little red we covered them with zucchinis we gave

להם שנורקלים כדי שלא יחנקו וצעדנו במורד הרחוב.
lahem shnorkelim kedei shelo yekhanku vetsa'adnu bemorad harekhov.
to them snorkels so that not they will suffocate and we marched down the street

All of our neighbors got vegetables. After a week or two, the neighbors heard the squeak of the wagon wheels as we made our rounds. They drew their curtains and locked their doors. Nobody was at home in the whole neighborhood.

כל השכנים קיבלו ירקות. שבוע או שבועיים אחר כך, השכנים
kol hashkhenim kiblu yerakot. shavu'a o shvu'a'im akhar kakh, hashkhenim
all the neighbors they received vegetables week or two weeks later the neighbors

שמעו שוב את חריקת גלגלי העגלה כשיצאנו לסיבוב שלנו.
shamu shuv et kharikat galgalei ha'agala kisheyatsanu lasivuv shelanu.
they heard again D.O. squeak of wheels of the wagon when we went out to the rounds our

הם סגרו את הוילונות ונעלו את הדלתות. אף אחד לא היה
hem sagru et havilonot vena'alu et hadlatot. af ekhad lo haya
they they closed D.O. the curtains and they locked D.O. the doors nobody no he was

בבית בשכונה כולה.
baba'it bashkhuna kula.
at home in the neighborhood whole

What to do with the extra zucchini? We set up a zucchini stand in our driveway. Our daughter, who can sell anything to anyone, was not able to sell our produce.

מה עושים עם הקישואים המיותרים? הצבנו דוכן קישואים בכביש
ma osim im hakishu'im hameyutarim? hetsavnu dukhan kishu'im bikhvish
what we do with the zucchinis the extras we placed stand of zucchinis at the road of

הגישה לביתנו. בתנו, שיכולה למכור כל דבר לכל אחד, לא
hagisha leveteinu. biteinu, sheyekhola limkor kol davar lekhol ekhad, lo
the access to our house our daughter who (she) can to sell anything to anyone no

הצליחה למכור את התוצרת.
hitslikha limkor et hatotseret.
she succeeded to sell D.O. the output

So the wife uncovered recipes for zucchini soup, zucchini fritters, zucchini cookies, zucchini popcorn, etc.

אז האישה גילתה מתכונים למרק קישואים, לביבות קישואים,
az ha'isha gilta matkonim lemarak kishu'im, levivot kishu'im,
so the wife she discovered recipes for soup of zucchinis latkes of zucchinis

עוגיות קישואים, פופקורן קישואים, וכו'.
ugiyot kishu'im, popkorn kishu'im, vekhule.
cookies of zucchinis popcorn of zucchinis etc

At night, I would sneak out to our garden and secretly feed birth control pills to the zucchini plants, anything

בלילה הייתי מתגנב לגינה ונותן לשיחי הקישואים בחשאי
balaila ha'iti mitganev lagina venoten lesikhei hakishu'im bakhashai
in the night I would I sneak to the garden and I give to bushes of the zucchinis secretly

4

גלולות למניעת הריון, כל דבר כדי למנוע מהם להתרבות.
glulot | limniyat herayon | kol davar | kedei | limno'a | mehem | lehitrabot
pills | birth control | anything | in order to | to prevent | from them | to reproduce

to stop them from reproducing.

אשתי גידלה גם הרבה חצילים. מעולם לא שמעתי על חצילים עד
ishti | gidla | gam | harbe | khatsilim | me'olam | lo | shamati | al | khatsilim | ad
my wife | she grew | also | lots of | eggplants | never | no | I heard | of | eggplants | until

שעברתי ממרכז תל אביב למרחבי הטבע של גבעתיים. כמובן,
she'avarti | mimerkaz | tel aviv | lemerkhavei | hateva | shel | givata'im | kamuvan
that I moved | from center | Tel Aviv | to wide open space of | the nature | of | Givatayim | of course

לרוב תושבי גבעתיים לא היה מושג מהו מוקצ'ינו, כך שהדברים
lerov | toshavei | givata'im | lo | haya | musag | mahu | mokatschino | kakh shehadvarim
to most | residents of | Givatayim | no | it was | idea | what is | mochachino | so the things

התאזנו מעט.
hitaznu | me'at
they evened out | a little

My wife also grew lots of eggplant. I had never heard of eggplant until I moved from central Tel Aviv to the wilds of Givatayim. Of course, most people in Givatayim didn't know what a mochachino was, so that evened things out a bit.

מאחר ואשתי ממצפה רמון, אין לי מושג מאיפה היא קבלה את
me'akhar ve'ishti | memitspe ramon | ein li | musag | me'eifo | hi | kibla | et
since my wife | from Mitzpe Ramon | I don't have | idea | from where | she | she got | D.O.

הרעיון שחצילים הם משהו שאנשים נורמליים אוכלים. אף אחד
hara'ayon | shekhatsilim | hem | mashehu | she'anashim | normalim | okhlim | af ekhad
the idea | that eggplants | are | something | that people | normal | they eat | nobody

במצפה רמון לא אוכל חצילים.
bemitspe ramon | lo | okhel | khatsilim
in Mitzpe Ramon | no | he eats | eggplants

Since my wife is from Mitzpe Ramon, I have no idea where she ever got the idea that eggplants were something that normal people ate. Nobody in Mitzpe Ramon ate eggplant.

בכל אופן, לא אהבתי את הרעיון לגדל חצילים או לאכול משהו
bekhol ofen | lo | ahavti | et | hara'ayon | legadel | khatsilim | o | le'ekhol | mashehu
anyway | no | I liked | D.O. | the idea | to grow | eggplants | or | to eat | something

שמכיל חצילים. היה להם צבע מוזר. מי שמע על ירקות
shemekhil | khatsilim | haya lahem | tseva | muzar | mi | shama | al | yerakot
that (it) contains | eggplants | they had | color | strange | who | he heard | about | vegetables

סגולים? הם היו רכים מדי כשהיו מבושלים. זה עשה לי
sgulim | hem | hayu | rakim | midai | kshehayu | mevushalim | ze | asa li
purple | they | they were | soft | too | when they were | cooked | this | it made me

כולרה, או יבלות, או משהו כזה.
kholera | o | yabalot | o | mashehu | kaze
cholera | or | warts | or | something | like that

Anyway, I didn't like the idea of growing eggplant or eating anything that contained eggplant. It had a funny color. Who ever heard of purple vegetables? It was too mushy when it was cooked. It gave me cholera, or warts, or something like that.

לא חשוב, גידלנו הרבה חצילים. בכל ערב שיחקנו מחבואים.
lo | khashuv | gidalnu | harbe | khatsilim | bekhol | erev | sikhaknu | makhbo'im
not | important | we grew | much | eggplants | in every | evening | we played | hide-and-seek

האישה הייתה מחביאה חצילים איפשהו בארוחה, והילדים ואני ניסינו
ha'isha | haita | makhbi'a | khatsilim | eifoshehu | ba'arukha | vehayeladim | va'ani | nisinu
the wife | she would | she hides | eggplants | somewhere | in the meal | and the kids | and I | we tried

לזהות אותם ולזרוק אותם על הרצפה.
lezahot | otam | velizrok | otam | al | haritspa
to identify | them | and to throw | them | on | the floor

No matter, we grew plenty of eggplant. Every night we played hide and seek. The wife would hide eggplant somewhere in the dinner, and the kids and I would try to identify it and drop it on the floor.

5

Story 1

We complained so much that the wife went on a cooking strike. That was bad. We survived for three days eating my cooking. Then the kids threw in the towel. I held out for another twenty minutes, to show them what I was made of. Then I also gave up. After that, it was eggplants day and night.

זה. בישול בשביתת שהאישה פצחה הרבה כך כל התלוננו
ze bishul bishvitat sheha'isha patskha harbe kol kakh hitlonanu
that cooking on a strike of she broke into much so we complained

הילדים ואז שלי. התבשילים על ימים שלושה שרדנו רע. היה
hayeladim ve'az sheli hatavshilim al yamim shlosha saradnu ra haya
the kids and then my the dishes on days three we survived bad it was

להם להראות כדי נוספות, דקות עשרים מעמד החזקתי נכנעו.
lahem leharot kedei nosafot dakot esrim ma'amad hekhzakti nikhne'u
to them to show in order to additional minutes twenty I held on they surrendered

היה זה כך אחר קורצתי. אני גם ואז ידיים. הרמתי חומר מאיזה
haya ze akhar kakh koratsti ani gam ve'az heramti yada'im khomer me'eize
it was that after I was made I also and then I gave up stuff from which

ולילה. יום חצילים
valaila yom khatsilim
and night day eggplants

The tomatoes were the coup de grace in the garden. Each year we planted twelve, yes I said twelve, tomato plants.

עשר, שנים שתלנו שנה בכל בגינה. המוות מכת היו העגבניות
shneim asar shatalnu shana bekhol bagina makat hamavet hayu ha'agvaniyot
twelve we planted year in each in the garden the coup de grace they were the tomatoes

עגבניות. שיחי עשר, שנים אמרתי כן
agvaniyot sikhei shneim asar amarti ken
tomatoes bushes of twelve I said yes

I tried to cage them. I thought it would limit the output. But the suckers grew right through the bars of the cages.

אבל התפוקה. את יגביל שזה חשבתי בכלוב. אותם לסגור ניסיתי
aval hatfuka et yagbil sheze khashavti bikluv otam lisgor nisiti
but the output D.O. it would limit that this I thought in a cage them to close in I tried

הכלובים. סורגי דרך גדלו הממזרות
hakluvim sorgei derekh gadlu hamamzerot
the cages grates of through they grew the bastards

Every year, all the tomatoes ripened within eight minutes of each other, on the third Thursday in August. This has always meant one thing - tomato sauce. I hate making tomato sauce. It takes about three days.

מזו, זו דקות שמונה בתוך הבשילו העגבניות כל שנה, בכל
zo mizo dakot shmone betokh hivshilu ha'agvaniyot kol shana bekhol
of each other minutes eight within they ripen the tomatoes all year in every

רוטב — תמיד הייתה הדבר משמעות אוגוסט. של השלישי חמישי ביום
rotev tamid haita hadavar mashma'ut ogust shel hashlishi beyom khamishi
sauce of always it was the thing meaning of August of the third on Thursday

ימים. שלושה בערך לוקח זה עגבניות. רוטב להכין שונא אני עגבניות.
yamim shlosha be'erekh loke'akh ze agvaniyot rotev lehakhin sone ani agvaniyot
days three about it takes this tomatoes sauce of to make I hate I tomatoes

First you have to pick about three thousand tomatoes. Then you have to throw them in a pot of boiling water. We usually build a fire under the upstairs jacuzzi and use that as our pot.

עליך ואז עגבניות. אלפים שלושת בערך לאסוף עליך כל קודם
aleikha ve'az agvaniyot shloshet alafim be'erekh le'esof aleikha kodem kol
you have to and then tomatoes 3000 about to pick you have to first of all

מדורה מקימים כלל בדרך אנחנו רותחים. מים עם לסיר אותן לזרוק
medura mekimim bederekh klal anakhnu rotkhim ma'im im lesir otan lizrok
bonfire we build usually we boiling water with to a pot them to throw

סיר. בתור בו ומשתמשים העליונה, בקומה לג׳קוזי מתחת
sir betor bo umishtamshim ha'elyona bakoma lajakuzi mitakhat
pot as a in it and we use the upper on the story to the jacuzzi under

6

העגבניות צורחות כשאתה זורק אותן פנימה. זה דבר נוראי לשמוע.
ha'agvaniyot tsorkhot kshe'ata zorek otan pnima. ze davar nora'i lishmo'a.
the tomatoes | they scream | when you | you throw | them | inside | this | thing | terrible | to hear

כשחושבים על זה הקול בעצם מגיע ממני. אני תמיד זורק את
kshekhoshvim al ze hakol be'etsem magi'a mimeni. ani tamid zorek et
when thinking | about | this | the noise | actually | it comes | from me | I | always | I throw | D.O.

העגבניות לג'קוזי קצת יותר מדי חזק, ומתיז על עצמי רסס רותח.
ha'agvaniyot lajakuzi ktsat yoter midai khazak, umatiz al atsmi reses rote'akh.
the tomatoes | in the jacuzzi | a little | too much | hard | and I splash | on | myself | spray | boiling

זה כואב!
ze ko'ev!
that | it hurts

The tomatoes scream when you throw them in. It's a terrible thing to hear. Come to think of it, the noise actually comes from me. I always throw the tomatoes into the jacuzzi a little too hard and splatter myself with scalding spray. That hurts!

אחרי כמה דקות, עליך להוציא את העגבניות מהמים הרותחים
akharei kama dakot, aleikha lehotsi et ha'agvaniyot mehama'im harotkhim
after | a few | minutes | you have to | to remove | D.O. | the tomatoes | from the water | the boiling

ולקלף אותן. הן לא אוהבות שמקלפים אותן. הן מתפתלות
ulekalef otan. hen lo ohavot shemekalfim otan. hen mitpatlot
and to peel | them | they | no | they like | that we are peeling | them | they | they squirm

ומחליקות ומנסות להתחמק.
umakhlikot umenasot lehitkhamek.
and they slide | and they try | to escape

After a few minutes, you have to take the tomatoes out of the hot water and peel them. They don't like being peeled. They squirm and slide and try to get away.

אתה לא יכול לתת להן להחליק מהאחיזה שלך או שתקבל
ata lo yakhol latet lahen lehakhlik meha'akhiza shelkha o shetekabel
you | no | you can | to let | to them | to slip | from the grasp | your | or | that you will receive

את המבט. המבט הוא הבעה שאבא שלי ערך בה ניסויים
et hamabat. hamabat hu haba'a she'aba sheli arakh ba nisu'im
D.O. | the glare | the glare | is | the look | that father | my | he conducted | with it | experiments

ואשתי שכללה לכדי שלמות. אני יכול להרגיש את המבט בוער
ve'ishti shikhlela likhdei shlemut. ani yakhol lehargish et hamabat bo'er
and my wife | she improved | to | perfection | I | I can | to feel | D.O. | the glare | it burns

דרכי כשאני רודף אחר עגבניה נמלטת, עירומה למחצה, אל תוך
darki kshe'ani rodef akhar agvaniya nimletet, eroma lemekhetsa, el tokh
through me | when I | I chase | after | tomato | escaping | half-naked | to | inside

חדר האוכל.
khadar ha'okhel.
the dining room

You can't let them slip from your grasp or you get *The Glare*. *The Glare* is a look that my father experimented with, and my wife has perfected. I can feel *The Glare* burn through me as I chase an escaping, half-naked tomato into the dining room.

כשהעגבניות מקולפות כולן ושוכבות ורועדות על דופן הג'קוזי,
ksheha'agvaniyot mekulafot kulan veshokhvot ro'adot al dofen hajakuzi,
when the tomatoes | peeled | all | and they lie down | they shiver | on | side | the jacuzzi

עליך להוציא את הגרעינים. אני לא יכול לתאר את הייסורים שאני
aleikha lehotsi et hagarinim. ani lo yakhol leta'er et hayisurim she'ani
you have to | to remove | D.O. | the seeds | I | no | I can | to describe | D.O. | the suffering | that I

חש כשאני לוקח בזה אחר זה את היצורים הקטנים האומללים
khash kshe'ani loke'akh baze akhar ze et hayetsurim haktanim veha'umlalim
I feel | when I | to take | one after another | D.O. | the creatures | the little | and the unfortunate

When the tomatoes are all peeled and lie shivering on the side of the jacuzzi, you have to take out the seeds. I can't tell you the anguish I feel as I take one after another of the poor little things and squeeze them until their many little seeds pop out. I can't tell you how many future generations of these tomatoes have been squashed by my calloused fingers.

וסוחט אותם עד שהגרעינים הקטנים והרבים קופצים החוצה.
vesokhet otam ad shehagarinim haktanim veharabim koftsim hakhutsa
and I squeeze · them · until · that the seeds · the little · and the many · they pop · outside

לא אוכל לומר כמה דורות עתידיים של העגבניות האלה
lo ukhal lomar kama dorot atidiyim shel ha'agvaniyot ha'ele
no · I will be able · to tell · how many · generations · future · of · the tomatoes · the these

נמעכו בין אצבעותיי המחוספסות.
nimakhu bein etsbe'otai hamekhuspasot
they were squashed · between · my fingers · rough

Finally, you pulverize the tomatoes in a blender, turn them into puree, and hand them to your wife, the master sauce maker. I do not know what unspeakable acts she commits from that point on.

לבסוף אתה מרסק את העגבניות בבלנדר, הופך אותן לפירה
levasof ata merasek et ha'agvaniyot biblender, hofekh otan lepire
finally · you · you pulverize · D.O. · the tomatoes · in a blender, · you turn into · them · to puree

ונותן אותן לאשתך, מכינת הרטבים הראשית. אני לא יודע מהם
venoten otan le'ishtekha, mekhinat haretavim harashit. ani lo yode'a mahem
and you give · them · to your wife, · preparer of · the sauces · the chief. · I · no · I know · what are

אותם המעשים שאין להעלותם על דל השפתיים שהיא מבצעת בהן
otam hama'asim she'ein leha'alotam al dal hasfata'im shehi mevatsa'at bahen
them · the actions · that are not · to articulate · that she · she performs · on them

מנקודה זו ואילך.
minekuda zo va'elakh
from point · that · onward

I usually run from the kitchen after the puree part. But I do know that the result is very tasty, so I don't lose too much sleep. Unfortunately, three days work with thousands of tomatoes results in about a half a cup of sauce, so the rewards are fleeting.

אני בדרך כלל בורח מהמטבח אחרי החלק של הפירה. אבל אני
ani bederekh klal bore'akh mehamitbakh akharei hakhelek shel hapire. aval ani
I · usually · I run away · from the kitchen · after · the part · of · the puree. · but · I

כן יודע שהתוצאה טעימה מאוד כך שזה לא מדיר שינה מעיני.
ken yode'a shehatotsa'a te'ima me'od kakh sheze lo madir shena me'enai
yes · I know · that the result · tasty · very · this way · that this · no · it causes me to lose sleep

לרוע המזל, שלושה ימי עבודה עם אלפי עגבניות מסתכמים
lero'a hamazal, shlosha yemei avoda im alfei agvaniyot mistakmim
unfortunately · three · days of · work · with · thousands of · tomatoes · they amount to

בכחצי כוס רוטב, כך שהפיצוי הוא קצרצר.
bekekhatsi kos rotev, kakh shehapitsui hu ktsartsar
in about half · cup of · sauce, · so that the compensation · it · very brief

As I write this, I am remembering the smell of tomato sauce coming from the kitchen. It was a wonderful smell.

כשאני כותב, אני נזכר בריח רוטב העגבניות המגיע מהמטבח.
kshe'ani kotev, ani nizkar berei'akh rotev ha'agvaniyot hamagi'a mehamitbakh
as I · I write, · I · I remember · in smell · sauce of · the tomatoes · that comes · from the kitchen

זה היה ריח נפלא.
ze haya rei'akh nifla
this · it was · smell · wonderful

These days, our garden is a lot smaller. Thank God for little favors.

בימים אלה הגינה שלנו הרבה יותר קטנה. תודה לאל על חסדים
beyamim ele hagina shelanu harbe yoter ktana. toda la'el al khasadim
in days · these · the garden · our · much · more · small. · thanks · to god · for · favors

קטנים.
ktanim
small

העגלה מחלידה במרתף, הגלגלים עדיין חורקים. הילדים כבר לא
ha'agala *makhlida* *bamartef* *hagalgalim* *ada'in* *khorkim* *hayeladim* *kvar lo*
the wagon / it rusts / in the basement / the wheels / still / they squeak / the kids / no longer

כאן לשחק 'החבא את החציל'. השכנים מחוץ לעיר, למקרה
kan *lesakhek* *hakhbe* *et* *hakhatsil* *hashkhenim* *mikhuts la'ir* *lemikre*
here / to play / hide / D.O. / the eggplant / the neighbors / out of town / in case

שננסה לחלוק איתם ירקות.
shenenase *lakhlok* *itam* *yerakot*
that we will try / to share / with them / vegetables

The wagon is rusting in the basement, the wheels still squeak. The kids no longer are here to play 'hide the eggplant'. The neighbors are out of town, just in case we try to share vegetables with them.

אבל תחזוקת הגינה עדיין עולה הרבה יותר משהיא חוסכת בחשבון
aval *takhzukat* *hagina* *ada'in* *ola* *harbe* *yoter* *mishehi* *khosekhet* *bekheshbon*
but / maintenance of / the garden / still / it costs / much / more / than it / it saves / in the bill of

הקנייה במכולת.
hakniya *bamakolet*
the shopping / at the grocery

But the garden still costs a lot more money to maintain than it saves you on grocery bills.

באפריל האחרון עיבדתי את הקרקע לקבלת יבולי השנה, ואני
be'april *ha'akharon* *ibadeti* *et* *hakarka* *lekabalat* *yevulei* *hashana* *va'ani*
in April / the last / I worked / D.O. / the soil / in the obtaining of / produce of / this year / and I

עדיין הולך כמו אדם שסוחב 20 קילו אבנים על הגב. אני
ada'in *holekh* *kmo* *adam* *shesokhev* *esrim* *kilo* *avanim* *al* *hagav* *ani*
still / I walk / like / man / that (he) carries / twenty / kilograms of / stones / on / the back / I

חייב לחזור לכירופרקט!
khayav *lakhzor* *lakhiroprakt*
I have to / to go back / to the chiropractor

Last April I did the tilling for this year's crop and I'm still walking like a man carrying a 20 kilo stone on his back. I've got to go back to the chiropractor!

9

STORY 2

A Good Sport

"תפסיקו לזרוק בוץ אחד על השני," צעקתי.
tsa'akti ekhad al hasheni bots lizrok tafsiku
I yelled / one on the second / mud / to throw / stop

"Stop throwing mud at each other," I yelled.

"תומר השפריץ עלי מבקבוק המים שלו."
shelo hama'im mibakbuk alai hishprits tomer
his / the water / from bottle / on me / he squirted / Tomer

"Tomer squirted me with his water bottle."

"תומר, אל תעשה את זה."
ze et ta'ase al tomer
that / D.O. / you will do / don't / Tomer

"Tomer, don't do that."

תומר, הבן שלי, היה אמור לשמש דוגמה לילדים האחרים.
ha'akherim layeladim dugma leshamesh amur haya sheli haben tomer
the others / to the boys / example / to serve / supposed to / he was / my / the son / Tomer

Tomer, my son, was supposed to be setting a good example for the other boys.

"המאמן דן, אני לא יכול לבוא למשחק בשבת," אמר רועי. "אני לא
lo ani ro'i amar beshabat lamiskhak lavo yakhol lo ani dan hame'amen
no / I / Roi / he said / on Saturday / to the game / to come / I can / no / I / Dan / the coach

"Coach Dan, I can't come to the game Saturday," said Roi. "I don't want to practice any more."

רוצה להתאמן יותר."
yoter lehitamen rotse
more / to practice / I want

"למה לא?" שאלתי.
sha'alti lo lama
I asked / not / why

"Why not?" I asked.

"אני לא אוהב כדורגל."
kaduregel ohev lo ani
soccer / I like / no / I

"I don't like soccer."

"אז למה הצטרפת לקבוצה?"
lakvutsa hitstarafta lama az
to the team / you joined / why / then

"Then why did you join the team?"

"אמא שלי הכריחה אותי."
oti hikhrikha sheli ima
me / she forced / my / mother

"My mother made me."

בדיוק אז פגע בי גוש של בוץ.
bots shel gush bi paga az bediyuk
mud / of / chunk / at me / it hit / then / just

Just then I was hit with a chunk of mud.

Story 2

"Stop throwing mud," I yelled. "We have our first game in two days. Everyone sit and listen for a few minutes."

"תפסיקו לזרוק בוץ," צעקתי. "המשחק הראשון שלנו בעוד יומיים.
yoma'im be'od shelanu harishon hamiskhak tsa'akti bots lizrok tafsiku
two days in our the first the game I yelled mud to throw stop

כולם לשבת ולהקשיב כמה דקות."
dakot kama ulehakshiv lashevet kulam
minutes few and to listen to sit everyone

My team of nine and ten year old boys finally sat down on the grass, sweaty and tired after running hard.

קבוצת בני התשע והעשר שלי התיישבה לבסוף על הדשא, מזיעים
mazi'im hadeshe al levasof hityashva sheli veha'eser hatesha bnei kvutsat
sweaty the grass on finally she sat down my and the ten the nine boys of team of

ועייפים לאחר ריצה מתישה.
metisha ritsa le'akhar ve'ayefim
exhausting running after and tired

I spoke quickly. Boys don't sit for long. After five minutes of explaining strategy, we were running again.

דיברתי זריז. בנים אינם מסוגלים לשבת בשקט לאורך זמן. לאחר
le'akhar le'orekh zman besheket lashevet mesugalim einam banim zariz dibarti
after for a length of time in silence to sit capable they are not boys quickly I spoke

חמש דקות של הסברים על אסטרטגיה, חזרנו לרוץ.
laruts khazarnu astrategya al hesberim shel dakot khamesh
to run we returned strategy about explanations of minutes five

An hour later practice was over. I had to wait twenty minutes before the last mother showed up to pick up her child.

שעה לאחר מכן, הסתיים האימון. היה עלי להמתין עשרים דקות עד
ad dakot esrim lehamtin haya alai ha'imun histayem le'akhar miken sha'a
until minutes twenty to wait it was on me the practice it ended afterward hour

שהופיעה האמא האחרונה לאסוף את בנה.
bna et le'esof ha'akharona ha'ima shehofiya
her boy D.O. to collect the last the mother that showed up

"If you are late next time, I'm selling him," I told her.

"אם תאחרי בפעם הבאה, אני מוכר אותו," אמרתי לה.
la amarti oto mokher ani haba'a bapa'am te'akhri im
to her I told him I sell I next in the instance you will be late if

---
2

Eleven of the fifteen boys on our team showed up for our first game.

אחד עשר מתוך חמישה עשר הילדים בקבוצה הגיעו למשחק הראשון.
harishon lamiskhak higi'u bakvutsa hayeladim khamisha asar mitokh akhad asar
the first to the game they came on the team the boys fifteen out of eleven

"Where is everyone?" my wife Gilat asked.

"איפה כולם?" שאלה אשתי גילת.
gilat ishti sha'ala kulam eifo
Gilat my wife she asked everyone where

"This is just a town league," one of the fathers said. "The parents and kids don't take it seriously. It's just something for them to do on Saturdays if they don't have other plans."

"זו בסך הכל הליגה העירונית," אמר אחד האבות. "ההורים והילדים
vehayeladim hahorim ha'avot ekhad amar ha'ironit haliga besakh hakol zo
and the kids the parents the fathers one he said the municipal the league in the total sum this

לא לוקחים את זה ברצינות. זה רק עיסוק לשבתות אם אין להם
ein lahem im leshabatot isuk rak ze birtsinut ze et lok'khim lo
they don't have if for Saturdays occupation only this seriously this D.O. they take no

תוכניות אחרות."
akherot tokhniyot
other plans

"זה לא הוגן כלפי אלה שכן הגיעו," אמרתי.
ze lo hogen klapei ele sheken higi'u amarti
this not fair towards those that yes they came I said

"It's unfair to the ones who do show up," I said.

צור ניגש אליי במהלך החימום.
tsur nigash elai bemahalakh hakhimum
Tsur he approached to me during the warm up

Tsur came over to me during the warm up.

"אני לא רוצה לשחק היום."
ani lo rotse lesakhek hayom
I no I want to play today

"I don't want to play today."

"למה?"
lama
why

"Why?"

"הילד הגדול ההוא מהקבוצה השנייה אמר לי שהוא יפיל
hayeled hagadol hahu mehakvutsa hashniya amar li shehu yapil
that boy the big that one from the team the second he told to me that he he will push down

"That big kid on the other team told me he's going to knock me down."

אותי."
oti
me

"גיל ישמור עליך."
gil yishmor aleikha
Gil he will protect you

"Gil will protect you."

"לא נכון," צעק גיל.
lo nakhon tsa'ak gil
not correct he yelled Gil

"No I won't," yelled Gil.

"רועי, למה אתה מוריד את נעלי הפקקים שלך?"
ro'i lama ata morid et na'alei hapkakim shelkha
Roi why you you take off D.O. the cleats your

"Roi, why are you taking off your cleats?"

"אני לא רוצה לשחק."
ani lo rotse lesakhek
I no I want to play

"I don't want to play."

בדיוק אז הגיעה אמא של רועי וצבטה באוזנו. הוא החל
bediyuk az higi'a ima shel ro'i vetsavta be'ozno hu hekhel
exactly then she arrived mother of Roi and she pinched on his ear he he began

Just then, Roi's mother came over and twisted his ear. He started putting his cleats back on.

לנעול שוב את נעלי הפקקים.
linol shuv et na'alei hapkakim
to put on again D.O. shoes of the plugs

כמה דקות מאוחר יותר, התחיל המשחק. צור רץ מיד אל מחוץ
kama dakot me'ukhar yoter hitkhil hamiskhak tsur rats miyad el mikhuts
a few minutes later more it started the game Tsur he ran promptly to out of

The game started a few minutes later. Tsur promptly ran off the field and hid behind a chair. We had to play a man down after that.

למגרש והסתתר מאחורי כיסא. משם היינו צריכים לשחק עם שחקן
lamigrash vehistater me'akhorei kise misham ha'inu tsrikhim lesakhek im sakhkan
from the field and he hid behind chair from there we had to to play with player

13

Story 2

Our team parents were very quiet. Most of the time they sat on folding chairs and talked with each other. I caught a few of them glancing at the game for a second or two. But most of the time they weren't too interested. They were annoyed at half time when they had to stop gossiping and give their kids a snack.

אחד פחות.
pakhot ekhad — less one

הורי הקבוצה שלנו היו שקטים מאוד. רוב הזמן הם ישבו על
horei hakvutsa shelanu hayu shketim me'od. rov hazman hem yashvu al

כסאות מתקפלים ושוחחו זה עם זה. תפסתי כמה מהם מציצים
kisot mitkaplim vesokhakhu ze im ze. tafasti kama mehem metsitsim

על המשחק לשנייה או שתיים אבל רוב הזמן הם לא ממש
al hamiskhak leshniya o shta'im aval rov hazman hem lo mamash

התעניינו. הם היו מוטרדים במחצית, כשהיה עליהם להפסיק
hitanyenu. hem hayu mutradim bamakhatsit, kshehaya aleihem lehafsik

לרכל ולתת לילדים חטיף.
lerakhel velatet layeladim khatif.

"Look on the bright side," Gilat said. "They could be like the other team parents."

"תסתכל על הצד החיובי," אמרה גילת. "הם היו יכולים להיות כמו
tistakel al hatsad hakhiyuvi, amra gilat. hem hayu yekholim lihiyot kmo

ההורים בקבוצה השנייה."
hahorim bakvutsa hashniya.

"Those people really are loud and not nice. I've never seen a father throw a chair at his own kid for getting a hand ball foul."

"האנשים האלה באמת קולניים ולא נעימים. אף פעם לא ראיתי אבא
ha'anashim ha'ele be'emet kolaniyim velo ne'imim. af pa'am lo ra'iti aba

שזורק כיסא על הילד שלו בגלל עבירת יד."
shezorek kise al hayeled shelo biglal averat yad.

"We did score on the penalty kick," Gilat reminded me.

"הבקענו גול בבעיטת העונשין," הזכירה לי גילת.
hivkanu gol bivitat ha'onshin, hizkira li gilat.

"Is Tomer going to play goalie again in this half?" she continued.

"תומר יהיה שוב שוער במחצית הזאת?" המשיכה.
tomer ihiye shuv sho'er bamakhatsit hazot? himshikha.

"No."

"לא".
lo

"Good. I don't want to see him getting his legs all tangled up in the net again."

"יופי. אני לא רוצה לראות את הרגליים שלו מסתבכות שוב
yofi. ani lo rotsa lirot et haragla'im shelo mistabkhot shuv

14

ברשת."
bareshet
in the net

איך הוא הצליח לעשות את זה בדיוק כשהקבוצה השנייה
eikh hu hitsli'akh la'asot et ze bediyuk kshehakvutsa hashniya
how he he succeeded to do D.O. that exactly when the team the second

פרצה קדימה?"
partsa kadima
it broke through forward

"How did he do that just when the other team had a breakaway?"

"אני לא יודעת, אבל טוב שדוד כל כך מהיר," אמרה גילת.
ani lo yoda'at, aval tov shedavid kol kakh mahir, amra gilat
I no I know, but good that David so fast, she said Gilat

"I don't know, but it's a good thing that David is so fast," Gilat said.

"אם הוא לא היה משיג את החלוץ שלהם ובועט את הכדור
im hu lo haya masig et hakhaluts shelahem uvo'et et hakadur
if he no he had caught up with D.O. the forward their and he kicks D.O. the ball

החוצה, תומר היה מרגיש נורא," אמרתי.
hakhutsa, tomer haya margish nora, amarti
out Tomer he would have felt terrible, I said

"If he hadn't caught up with their forward and kicked the ball out of bounds, Tomer would have felt terrible," I said.

— 3 —

הילד הגדול מהקבוצה השנייה היה איטי. איש אחד בצד השני
hayeled hagadol mehakvutsa hashniya haya iti. ish ekhad batsad hasheni
the boy the big from the team the second he was slow. man one on the side the second

של המגרש התחיל לרוץ הלוך ושוב לאורך המגרש, תוך שהוא צועק
shel hamigrash hitkhil laruts halokh vashov le'orekh hamigrash, tokh shehu tso'ek
of the field he started to run back and forth to the length the field, while that he he yells

עליו לרוץ מהר יותר.
alav laruts maher yoter
at him to run fast more

The big kid on the other team was slow. Some man on the other side of the field started running up and down the sideline yelling at him to run faster.

"מי זה המשוגע הזה?" שאלתי.
mi ze hameshuga haze? sha'alti
who this the crazy person the that I asked

"Who is that nut?" I asked.

"זה אבא שלו," אמרה גילת.
ze aba shelo, amra gilat
that father his, she said Gilat

"That's his father," Gilat said

עשר דקות לאחר מכן, הילד כעס כל כך שיצא מהמגרש. הוא
eser dakot le'akhar miken, hayeled ka'as kol kakh sheyatsa mehamigrash. hu
ten minutes afterwards, the boy he was angry so that he left from the field. he

התיישב ובכה בעוד אביו ואמו מתווכחים.
hityashev uvakha be'od aviv ve'imo mitvak'khim
he sat and he cried while his father and his mother they argued

After ten minutes, the kid was so angry that he left the field. He sat down and cried while his father and mother argued.

Story 2

"Since that big kid quit, I can play now," said Tsur.

"בגלל שהילד הגדול פרש, אני יכול לשחק עכשיו," אמר צור.
biglal shehayeled hagadol parash, ani yakhol lesakhek akhshav, amar tsur.
since that the boy the big he quit, I I can to play now, he said Tsur.

"Great. Go in at defender. We've been playing without a defender all game."

"מצוין, תיכנס כבלם. שיחקנו בלי בלם כל המשחק."
metsuyan, tikanes kevalam. sikhaknu bli balam kol hamiskhak.
excellent, you will go in as defender. we played without defender all the game.

Two minutes later, I noticed something.

שתי דקות לאחר מכן, הבחנתי במשהו.
shtei dakot le'akhar miken, hivkhanti bemashehu.
two of minutes afterwards, I noticed in something.

"Nobody is playing their position," I said. "They're all running after the ball."

"אף אחד לא משחק בעמדה שלו," אמרתי. "כולם רצים אחרי הכדור."
af ekhad lo mesakhek ba'emda shelo, amarti. kulam ratsim akharei hakadur.
no one no they play in the position his, I said. everyone they run after the ball.

"That happens a lot in this league," Guy's father said.

"זה קורה הרבה בליגה הזאת," אמר אביו של גיא.
ze kore harbe baliga hazot, amar aviv shel gai.
that it happens a lot in the league the this, he said father of Guy.

"How do I stop them?"

"איך אני עוצר אותם?"
eikh ani otser otam?
how I I stop them?

"I don't know. You're the coach."

"אני לא יודע. אתה המאמן."
ani lo yode'a. ata hame'amen.
I no I know. you the coach.

"Gilat, let Jessie off the leash."

"גילת, תשחררי את ג'סי מהרצועה."
gilat, teshakhreri et jesi meharetsu'a.
Gilat, you will release D.O. Jessie from the leash.

Jessie was our dog. We had brought her to the game.

ג'סי הייתה הכלבה שלנו. הבאנו אותה למשחק.
jesi haita hakalba shelanu. hevenu ota lamiskhak.
Jessie she was the dog our. we brought her to the game.

"She will run onto the field and chase the ball," Gilat said.

"היא תרוץ למגרש ותרדוף אחרי הכדור," אמרה גילת.
hi taruts lamigrash vetirdof akharei hakadur, amra gilat.
she she will run to the field and she will chase after the ball, she said Gilat.

"That's what I want her to do. The referee will stop the game and I can talk to the team."

"זה בדיוק מה שאני רוצה שתעשה. השופט יעצור את המשחק ואני אוכל לדבר עם הקבוצה."
ze bediyuk ma she'ani rotse sheta'ase. hashofet ya'atsor et hamiskhak va'ani ukhal ledaber im hakvutsa.
that exactly what that I I want that she will do. the referee he will stop D.O. the game and I I will be able to talk with the team.

"That's not fair. I'm not doing it."

"זה לא הוגן. אני לא עושה את זה."
ze lo hogen. ani lo osa et ze.
that no fair. I no I do D.O. that.

16

"תגיד לאחד הילדים לזייף פציעה," הציע אביו של גיא.
gai shel aviv hitsiya ptsiya lezayef hayeladim le'ekhad tagid
Guy of his father he suggested injury to fake the kids to one tell

"Tell one of the kids to fake an injury," Guy's father suggested.

"גם זה לא יפה," אמרה גילת.
gilat amra yafe lo ze gam
Gilat she said nice no this also

"That's not nice either," Gilat said.

"הם עושים את זה בליגות האירופיות כל הזמן," עניתי לה. "זה
ze la aniti hazman kol ha'eiropeiyot baligot ze et osim hem
this to her I replied the time all the European in the leagues this D.O. they do they

ממש אומנות אצל חלק מהשחקנים המקצוענים האלה."
ha'ele hamiktso'anim mehasakhkanim khelek etsel omanut mamash
the those the professional of the players some for art really

"They do it in the European leagues all the time," I told her. "It's really an art form with some of those professional players."

"אבל אלו ילדים בני עשר. אתה לא רוצה ללמד אותם דברים כאלה
ka'ele dvarim otam lelamed rotse lo ata eser bnei yeladim elu aval
like these things them to teach you want no you ten age of children these but

בגיל כל כך צעיר."
tsa'ir kol kakh begil
young so at age

"But these are ten year old children. You don't want to teach them things like that at such an early age."

"ובכן, לא, אבל הם רוצים לנצח."
lenatse'akh rotsim hem aval lo uvkhen
to win they want they but no well

"Well, no, but they want to win."

"לא אכפת להם מהניצחון," אמרה גילת. "לך אכפת."
ikhpat lekha gilat amra mehanitsakhon lahem ikhpat lo
care to you Gilat she said of the victory to them care no

"They don't care about winning," Gilat said. "You care."

בדיוק אז, הבקיעה הקבוצה היריבה שער.
sha'ar hayeriva hakvutsa hivki'a az bediyuk
goal the opponent the team she broke through then exactly

Just then, the opposing team scored.

—4—

"זה היה משחק כיפי, לא?" שאלתי את תומר.
tomer et sha'alti lo kefi miskhak haya ze
Tomer D.O. I asked no fun game it was that

"Wasn't that a fun game?" I asked Tomer.

"הוא היה ממש מגניב," הוא ענה.
ana hu magniv mamash haya hu
he answered he cool really it was it

"It was really cool," he replied.

"חבל על המאמן של הקבוצה השנייה," אמרה גילת.
gilat amra hashniya hakvutsa shel hame'amen al khaval
Gilat she said the second the team of the coach about too bad

"Too bad about the other team's coach," Gilat said.

"למה השופט הוציא אותו מהמשחק לקראת הסוף?" שאל תומר.
tomer sha'al hasof likrat mehamiskhak oto hotsi hashofet lama
Tomer he asked the end toward from the game him he ejected the referee why

"Why did the referee throw him out of the game near the end?" Tomer asked.

Story 2

"The coach didn't think the referee was doing a good job," I said.

"המאמן לא חשב שהשופט עושה עבודה טובה," אמרתי.

amarti	tova	avoda	ose	shehashofet	khashav	lo	hame'amen
I said	good	job	he does	that the referee	he thought	no	the coach

"He said a lot of bad words that you are not supposed to say in front of nice people," added Gilat.

"הוא אמר הרבה מילים לא יפות שאתה לא אמור לומר בפני

bifnei	lomar	amur	lo	she'ata	yafot	lo	milim	harbe	amar	hu
in the presence of	to say	supposed to	not	that you	nice	not	words	many	he said	he

אנשים נחמדים," הוסיפה גילת.

gilat	hosifa	nekhmadim	anashim
Gilat	she added	nice	people

"We didn't win," said Tomer. "But we played well. A tie is pretty good."

"לא ניצחנו," אמר תומר. "אבל שיחקנו טוב. תיקו זה טוב למדי."

lemadai	tov	ze	teiku	tov	sikhaknu	aval	tomer	amar	nitsakhnu	lo
quite	good	this	tie	well	we played	but	Tomer	he said	we won	no

"You looked funny jumping up and down after their goal," Tomer said.

"נראית מצחיק כשקפצת למעלה ולמטה אחרי השער שלהם," אמר

amar	shelahem	hasha'ar	akharei	ulemata	lemala	kshekafatsta	matskhik	nireta
he said	their	the goal	after	and down	up	when you jumped	funny	you looked

תומר.

tomer
Tomer

"Do you remember what I was screaming?"

"אתה זוכר מה צעקתי?"

tsa'akti	ma	zokher	ata
I screamed	what	you remember	you

"Stay in your positions, stay in your positions."

"תישארו בעמדות, תישארו בעמדות."

ba'amadot	tisha'aru	ba'amadot	tisha'aru
in the positions	stay	in the positions	stay

"Right. And you all did that for the rest of the game. So the jumping worked."

"נכון. וכולכם עשיתם את זה במשך שאר המשחק. אז

az	hamiskhak	sh'ar	be'meshekh	ze	et	asitem	vekulkhem	nakhon
so	the game	remainder	for the duration of	that	D.O.	you did	and you all	correct

הקפיצות עבדו."

avdu	hakfitsot
they worked	the jumps

"Did you like my header?"

"אהבת את הנגיחה שלי?"

sheli	hanegikha	et	ahavta
my	the header	D.O.	you liked

"It was pretty good. Next time try to use the top of your head. Not your face."

"היא הייתה טובה למדי. בפעם הבאה נסה לנגוח בעזרת החלק

hakhelek	be'ezrat	lingo'akh	nase	haba'a	bapa'am	lemadai	tova	haita	hi
the part	with	to butt	try	the next	in the occasion	quite	good	it was	it

העליון של הראש. לא הפנים."

hapanim	lo	harosh	shel	ha'elyon
the face	not	the head	of	the top

"My nose still hurts."

"האף שלי עדיין כואב."

ko'ev	ada'in	sheli	ha'af
it hurts	still	my	the nose

"הגלידה תשפר את הרגשתך."
haglida *teshaper* *et* *hargashat'kha*
the ice cream / it will improve / D.O. / your feeling

"The ice cream will make you feel better."

"מתי נלך הביתה?"
matai *nelekh* *habaita*
when / we will go / home(ward)

"When can we go home?"

"ברגע שהנפיחות תרד והדימום ייפסק," אמרה גילת. "אני
barega *shehanefikhut* *tered* *vehadimum* *yipasek* *amra* *gilat* *ani*
as soon as / that the swelling / it goes down / and the bleeding / it stops / she said / Gilat / I

לא רוצה שתלכלך את השטיח בדם."
lo *rotsa* *shetelakhlekh* *et* *hashati'akh* *bedam*
no / I want / that you will soil / D.O. / the rug / with blood

"As soon as the swelling goes down and the bleeding stops," Gilat said. "I don't want you getting blood on the rug."

STORY 3

Truth Will Out

התקשרתי לרז, השכן והברוקר שלי, ושאלתי אותו כמה שאלות
hitkasharti / *leraz* / *hashakhen* / *vehabroker* / *sheli* / *vesha'alti* / *oto* / *kama* / *she'elot*
I called / to Raz / the neighbor / and the broker / my / and I asked / him / a few / questions

על אודות אחת מקרנות הנאמנות שמכר לי.
al odot / *akhat* / *mikranot hane'emanut* / *shemakhar* / *li*
about / one / of the mutual funds / that he sold / to me

> I called Raz, my neighbor and stock broker, and asked him a few questions about one of the mutual funds he sold me.

״רפי, אני לא יכול לדבר איתך היום,״ הוא אמר לי.
rafi / *ani* / *lo* / *yakhol* / *ledaber* / *itkha* / *hayom* / *hu* / *amar* / *li*
Rafi / I / no / I can / to talk / with you / today / he / he said / to me

> "Rafi, I can't talk with you today," he said to me.

״למה לא?״ שאלתי.
lama / *lo* / *sha'alti*
why / not / I asked

> "Why not?" I asked.

״אני לוקח תרופה לכאבי גב. יש לה תופעת לוואי מוזרה. היא גורמת
ani / *loke'akh* / *trufa* / *likh'evei* / *gav* / *yesh la* / *tofa'at levai* / *muzara* / *hi* / *goremet*
I / I take / medication / for pain of / back / it has / side effect / strange / it / it causes

לי לומר את האמת.״
li / *lomar* / *et* / *ha'emet*
to me / to tell / D.O. / the truth

> "I'm taking drugs for my back pain. It has a strange side effect. It causes me to tell the truth."

״זה רע?״ שאלתי.
ze / *ra* / *sha'alti*
that / bad / I asked

> "Is that bad?" I asked.

״זה הדבר הגרוע ביותר שיכול לקרות לברוקר. אנחנו אף פעם לא
ze / *hadavar* / *hagaru'a* / *beyoter* / *sheyakhol* / *likrot* / *libroker* / *anakhnu* / *af pa'am* / *lo*
that / the thing / the bad / most / that can / to happen / to a broker / we / never / no

אומרים את האמת. אופס. לא הייתי צריך לומר את זה. אתה רואה איך
omrim / *et* / *ha'emet* / *ups* / *lo* / *ha'iti tsarikh* / *lomar* / *et* / *ze* / *ata* / *ro'e* / *eikh*
tell / D.O. / the truth / oops / no / I should have / to say / D.O. / that / you / you see / how

הגלולות האלה משפיעות עלי?״
haglulot / *ha'ele* / *mashpi'ot alai*
the pills / the these / they influence me

> "It's the worst thing that could happen to a stock broker. We never tell the truth. Oops. I shouldn't have said that. See how these pills are affecting me?"

״אני חבר ושכן שלך. אתה יכול לספר לי את האמת.״
ani / *khaver* / *veshakhen* / *shelkha* / *ata* / *yakhol* / *lesaper* / *li* / *et* / *ha'emet*
I / friend / and neighbor / your / you / you can / to tell / to me / D.O. / the truth

> "I'm your friend and neighbor. You can tell the truth to me."

״אני לא מדבר עם אף אחד עד שאסיים עם הגלולות. זה מסוכן
ani / *lo* / *medaber* / *im* / *af ekhad* / *ad* / *she'asayem* / *im* / *haglulot* / *ze* / *mesukan*
I / no / I talk / with / nobody / until / that I will finish / with / the pills / this / dangerous

> "I'm not talking to anyone until these pills are finished. It's too dangerous. The only reason I answered this call is

because I thought you wanted to set up a golf game. All my other calls are going straight to voice mail."

מדי. הסיבה היחידה שעניתי לשיחה הזאת היא בגלל שחשבתי
midai hasiba hayekhida she'aniti lasikha hazot hi biglal shekhashavti
too the reason the only that I answered the call the this it because of that I thought

שאתה רוצה לארגן משחק גולף. כל השיחות האחרות מגיעות היישר
she'ata rotse le'argen miskhak golf kol hasikhot ha'akherot magi'ot ha'isher
that you you want to arrange game golf all the calls the others they arrive directly

לתא הקולי."
lata hakoli
to the voice mail

I hung up the phone and walked into the kitchen.

סגרתי את הסלולרי והלכתי למטבח.
sagarti et haselulari vehalakhti lamitbakh
I hung up D.O. the cellphone and I walked to the kitchen

"Raz won't talk to me," I said to my wife Gilat.

"רז לא מוכן לדבר איתי," אמרתי לאשתי גילת.
raz lo mukhan ledaber iti amarti le'ishti gilat
Raz no ready to talk with me I said to my wife Gilat

"That's odd."

"זה נשמע מוזר."
ze nishma muzar
that it sounds strange

"He's taking pills for his back that make him tell the truth all the time," I said, "so he's afraid to talk to his clients."

"הוא לוקח כדורים לגב שגורמים לו לומר את האמת כל
hu loke'akh kadurim lagav shegormim lo lomar et ha'emet kol
he he takes pills for the back that (they) cause to him to tell D.O. the truth all

הזמן," אמרתי, "אז הוא מפחד לדבר עם הלקוחות שלו."
hazman amarti az hu mefakhed ledaber im halakokhot shelo
the time I said so he he is afraid to talk with the clients his

Gilat was sitting at the kitchen table eating a cookie. Her brow wrinkled. I could tell she was getting an idea.

גילת ישבה ליד שולחן המטבח ואכלה עוגייה. גבותיה התקמטו.
gilat yashva leyad shulkhan hamitbakh ve'akhla ugiya gaboteiha hitkamtu
Gilat she sat at table the kitchen and she ate cookie her eyebrow became wrinkled

שמתי לב שיש לה רעיון.
samti lev sheyesh la ra'ayon
I noticed that she has idea

"Now would be a great time to find out if Raz has been selling us the right investments," she said.

"עכשיו זה זמן מצוין לגלות אם רז מכר לנו את ההשקעות
akhshav ze zman metsuyan legalot im raz makhar lanu et hahashka'ot
now this time excellent to find out if Raz he sold to us D.O. the investments

הנכונות," אמרה.
hanekhonot amra
the correct she said

I thought about that for a minute.

חשבתי על זה לרגע.
khashavti al ze lerega
I thought about that for a minute

"You're right," I said. "Let's go visit him when he gets home. His wife is away on a business trip and won't be able to protect him."

"את צודקת," אמרתי. "בואי נלך לבקר אותו כשיחזור הביתה.
at tsodeket amarti bo'i nelekh levaker oto ksheyakhzor habaita
you correct I said let's we will go to visit him when he will return homeward

לְהָגֵן עָלָיו." תּוּכַל וְלֹא עֲבוֹדָה בְּעִנְיָנֵי נָסְעָה אִשְׁתּוֹ
lehagen alav — *tukhal* — *velo* — *avoda* — *be'inyanei* — *nasa* — *ishto*
to protect him — she will be able — and no — work — for matters of — she traveled — his wife

שֶׁהַבַּיִת מִכָּךְ נִדְאַג שֶׁלֹא כְּדֵי לַיְלָדִים שְׁמַרְטַף "אַזְמִין
shehaba'it — *mikakh* — *nidag* — *shelo* — *kedei* — *layeladim* — *shmartaf* — *azmin*
that the house — of this — we will worry — that not — in order to — for the kids — babysitter — I will order

גִּילַת. אָמְרָה הָאֱמֶת, אֶת מֵרָז מוֹצִיאִים שֶׁאֲנַחְנוּ בִּזְמַן יִישָׂרֵף
gilat — *amra* — *ha'emet* — *et* — *meraz* — *motsi'im* — *she'anakhnu* — *bizman* — *yisaref*
Gilat — she said — the truth — D.O. — from Raz — we extract — that we — when — he will be burned

"I'll call a sitter for the kids so we don't have to worry about the house burning down while we're forcing the truth out of Raz," said Gilat.

יָצָאנוּ וַאֲנִי גִּילַת בֵּיתוֹ. דֶּלֶת אֶת רָז פָּתַח יוֹתֵר מְאֻחָר שַׁעֲתַיִים
yatsanu — *va'ani* — *gilat* — *be'ito* — *delet* — *et* — *raz* — *patakh* — *yoter* — *me'ukhar* — *sha'ata'im*
we exited from — and I — Gilat — his house — door — D.O. — Raz — he opened — more — late — two hours

60 זִינֵק רָז הַדֶּלֶת. שֶׁלְּיַד הַגְּדוֹלָה הַחַיָּה הַגָּדֵר מֵאֲחוֹרֵי
shishim — *zinek* — *raz* — *hadelet* — *sheleyad* — *hagdola* — *hakhaya* — *hagader* — *me'akhorei*
sixty — he jumped away — Raz — the door — that next to — the large — the hedge — behind

אוֹתָנוּ. זִיהָה הוּא וְאָז בָּאֲוִיר. ס"מ
otanu — *ziha* — *hu* — *ve'az* — *ba'avir* — *sentimeter*
us — he recognized — he — and then — in the air — cm

Two hours later, Raz unlocked the front door of his house. Gilat and I stepped out from behind the large hedge next to the door. Raz jumped 60 cm into the air. Then he recognized us.

מִתְחַבְּאִים וְגִילַת אַתָּה לָמָה לֵב. הֶתְקֵף לִי גָּרַמְתֶּם כִּמְעַט "רָפִי,
mitkhabim — *vegilat* — *ata* — *lama* — *lev* — *hetkef* — *li* — *geramtem* — *kimat* — *rafi*
you hide yourselves — and Gilat — you — why — heart — attack of — to me — you caused — almost — Rafi

בַּשִּׂיחִים?"
basikhim
in the bushes

"Rafi, you almost gave me a heart attack. Why are you and Gilat hiding in the bushes?"

שֶׁלָּנוּ," הַהַשְׁקָעוֹת לְגַבֵּי שְׁאֵלוֹת כַּמָּה אוֹתְךָ לִשְׁאוֹל רוֹצִים "אֲנַחְנוּ
shelanu — *hahashka'ot* — *legabei* — *she'elot* — *kama* — *otkha* — *lishol* — *rotsim* — *anakhnu*
our — the investments — about — questions — a few — you — to ask — we want — we

אָמַרְתִּי.
amarti
I said

"We want to ask you a few questions about our investments," I said.

גִּילַת פָּתְחָה אֶת הַדֶּלֶת וְלִיוְּותָה אֶת רָז פְּנִימָה.
gilat — *patkha* — *et* — *hadelet* — *velivta* — *et* — *raz* — *pnima*
Gilat — she opened — D.O. — the door — and she escorted — D.O. — Raz — inside

Gilat opened the door and escorted Raz inside.

בַּסָּלוֹן. סַפָּה עַל הִצְבִּיעָה הִיא גִּילַת. הוֹרְתָה רָז," שָׁם "שֵׁב
basalon — *sapa* — *al* — *hitsbi'a* — *hi* — *gilat* — *horta* — *raz* — *sham* — *shev*
in the living room — sofa — at — she pointed — she — Gilat — she ordered — Raz — there — sit

"Sit over there, Raz," ordered Gilat. She pointed to a sofa in the living room.

מִדַּי." כּוֹאֵב שֶׁלִּי הַגַּב "הַגַּב רָז. אָמַר שֶׁאֶשְׁכַּב," כְּדַאי "אוּלַי
midai — *ko'ev* — *sheli* — *hagav* — *amar* — *raz* — *she'eshkav* — *kedai* — *ulai*
overly — aching — my — the back — he said — Raz — that I will lie down — worthwhile — maybe

"Maybe I should lie down," said Raz. "My back has been aching so much."

"בְּבַקָּשָׁה," אָמְרָה גִּילַת.
bevakasha — *amra* — *gilat*
please — she said — Gilat

"Go ahead," said Gilat.

"If only my wife was here," Rafi muttered as he lay down.

הלוואי שאשתי הייתה פה," מלמל רז תוך שהוא שוכב.
halevai she'ishti haita po," milmel raz tokh shehu shokhev
if only that my wife she was here he mumbled Raz while that he he lies down

"Don't look so worried," I said. "We're your friends."

אל תראה כל כך מודאג," אמרתי. "אנחנו חברים שלך."
al tera'e kol kakh mudag," amarti. anakhnu khaverim shelkha
don't you will look so worried I said we friends your

"Have you been selling us the right investments?" Gilat demanded to know.

"מכרת לנו את ההשקעות הנכונות?" דרשה גילת לדעת.
makharta lanu et hahashka'ot hanekhonot?" darsha gilat lada'at
you sold to us D.O. the investments the correct she demanded Gilat to know

"I shouldn't talk about work until I finish taking my pills," Raz said.

"אסור לי לדבר על העבודה עד שאסיים עם הכדורים," אמר רז.
asur li ledaber al ha'avoda ad she'asayem im hakadurim," amar raz
forbidden to me to talk about the work until that I will finish with the pills he said Raz

Gilat's eyes narrowed as she stared at our neighbor.

עיניה של גילת הצטמצמו כשבחנה את שכננו.
eineiha shel gilat hitstamtsemu kshebakhana et shkhenenu
her eyes of Gilat they narrowed when she examined D.O. our neighbor

"If you don't cooperate, I'll tell everyone in the neighborhood about your nose job and pec implants," Gilat said.

"אם לא תשתף פעולה, אספר לכל השכונה על ניתוח האף
im lo teshatef pe'ula, asaper lekhol hashkhuna al nitu'akh ha'af
if no you will cooperate I will tell to all the neighborhood about surgery of the nose

ושתל שרירי החזה שלך," אמרה גילת.
veshetel shrirei hekhaze shelkha," amra gilat
and implant of muscles of the chest your she said Gilat

"That's blackmail," Raz said.

"זו סחיטה," אמר רז.
zo skhita," amar raz
that blackmail he said Raz

"You have two choices," I said. "Talk to us or have the whole neighborhood laughing at you."

"יש לך שתי אפשרויות," אמרתי. "או שתדבר איתנו או שכל
yesh lekha shtei efsharuyot," amarti. o shetedaber itanu o shekol
you have two of possibilities I said either that you will talk with us or that all

השכונה תצחק עליך."
hashkhuna titskhak aleikha
the neighborhood she will laugh at you

I saw a look of resignation in Raz's eyes.

ראיתי מבט כנוע בעיניו של רז.
ra'iti mabat kanu'a be'einav shel raz
I saw look defeated in his eyes of Raz

"OK, I'll talk. To answer your question, I sell the products that pay me the biggest commissions. I don't care if they are the right investments for you."

"או קיי, אני אדבר. בתשובה לשאלתכם, אני מוכר את המוצרים
o kei, ani adaber. bitshuva leshe'elatkhem, ani mokher et hamutsarim
okay I I will talk in reply to your question I I sell D.O. the products

שמשלמים לי את העמלה הגבוהה ביותר. לא מעניין אותי אם
shemeshalmim li et ha'amla hagvoha beyoter. lo me'anyen oti im
that (they) pay to me D.O. the commission the high most no it interests me if

24

הם ההשקעה הנכונה עבורכם."
avurkhem hanekhona hahashka'a hem
for you the correct the investment they

"זה מה שאנחנו מקבלים על כך שאנחנו בוטחים בשכנים שלנו,"
shelanu beshkhenim botkhim she'anakhnu al kakh mekablim she'anakhnu ma ze
our in neighbors we trust that we about that we get that we what this

אמרה לי גילת.
gilat li amra
Gilat to me she said

"This is what we get for trusting our neighbors," Gilat said to me.

"מי סיפר לכם על הניתוחים הפלסטיים שלי?" שאל רז.
raz sha'al sheli haplastim hanitukhim al lakhem siper mi
Raz he asked my the plastics the surgeries about to you he told who

"Who told you about my plastic surgeries?" Raz asked.

"זה הסוד שלי," אמרה גילת. "אחרי מה שסיפרת לי עכשיו,
akhshav li shesiparta ma akharei gilat amra sheli hasod ze
now to me that you told what after Gilat she said my the secret that

מזלך שהאף החדש שלך לא שבור."
shavur lo shelkha hakhadash sheha'af mazalkha
broken not your the new that the nose you're lucky

"That's my secret," said Gilat. "After what you just told me, consider yourself lucky that your new nose isn't broken."

היא עמדה מעל הספה והביטה אל תוך עיניו של רז. ראיתי
ra'iti raz shel einav tokh el vehibita hasapa me'al amda hi
I saw Raz of his eyes inside to and she looked at the couch over she stood she

זיעה מבצבצת על מצחו.
mitskho al mevatsbetset zei'a
his forehead on it emerges slightly sweat

She stood over the couch and stared down into Raz's eyes. I could see sweat building up on his forehead.

"מה הדרך הטובה ביותר להשקיע את הכסף שלנו?" שאלה גילת.
gilat sha'ala shelanu hakesef et lehashkiya beyoter hatova haderekh ma
Gilat she asked our the money D.O. to invest most the good the way what

"What's the best way to invest our money?" Gilat asked.

"לקנות קרן אגרות חוב, קרן שמתמחה במניות מקומיות וקרן
vekeren mekomiyot bimenayot shemitmakha keren igrot khov keren liknot
and fund domestic in stocks that specializes fund bonds fund of to buy

נוספת שמשקיעה במניות זרות."
zarot bimenayot shemashkiya nosefet
foreign in stocks that (it) invests additional

"Buy a bond fund, a fund that specializes in domestic stocks, and another fund that invests in foreign stocks."

"כמה כסף אנחנו שמים בכל קרן?" שאלתי.
sha'alti keren bekhol samim anakhnu kesef kama
I asked fund in each put we money how much

"How much money do we put into each fund?" I asked.

"בגילכם, הייתי שם שלושים אחוז באגרות חוב, חמישה עשר אחוזים
akhuzim khamisha asar be'igrot khov akhuz shloshim sam ha'iti begilkhem
percent fifteen in bonds percent thirty I put I would at your age

במניות זרות והשאר במניות מקומיות."
mekomiyot bimenayot vehash'ar zarot bimenayot
domestic in stocks and the rest foreign in stocks

"At your age, I would put thirty percent into bonds, fifteen percent into foreign stocks, and the rest into domestic stocks."

Story 3

Gilat and I digested this new information for a few minutes.

גילת ואני עיכלנו את המידע החדש במשך זמן מה.
gilat va'ani ikalnu et hameida hakhadash bemeshekh zman ma
Gilat and I we digested D.O. the information the new during a while

"I really don't want to answer any more questions," Raz whined.

"אני באמת לא רוצה לענות על שאלות נוספות," אמר רז.
ani be'emet lo rotse la'anot al she'elot nosafot amar raz
I really no I want to answer about questions additional he said Raz

"Maybe I'll have to tell your wife about your weekly visits to the massage parlor near your office," Gilat mentioned.

"אולי אאלץ לספר לאשתך על הביקורים השבועיים שלך
ulai e'alets lesaper le'ishtekha al habikurim hashvu'i'im shelkha
maybe I will be forced to tell to your wife about the visits the weekly your

במכון העיסוי ליד המשרד שלך," ציינה גילת.
bimakhon ha'isui leyad hamisrad shelkha tsi'ina gilat
at the institute of the massage near the office your she mentioned Gilat

"Were you following me?" Raz gasped.

"עקבת אחרי?" התנשף רז.
akavt akharai hitnashef raz
you followed after me he gasped Raz

Gilat continued her merciless interrogation.

גילת המשיכה בחקירה חסרת הרחמים.
gilat himshikha bakhakira khasrat harakhamim
Gilat she continued with the investigation lacking of the mercy

"What are the best investments that we can buy?" she asked.

"מהן ההשקעות הטובות ביותר שאנחנו יכולים לקנות?" שאלה.
mahen hahashka'ot hatovot beyoter she'anakhnu yekholim liknot sha'ala
what are the investments the good most that we we can to buy she asked

"Low cost index funds."

"תעודת סל בעלות נמוכה."
te'udat sal be'alut nemukha
index fund at cost low

"This is also what you buy for yourself?" I asked.

"זה גם מה שקנית בשביל עצמך?" שאלתי.
ze gam ma shekanita bishvil atsmekha sha'alti
this also what that you bought for yourself I asked

"Of course. All stock brokers use index funds for their own investment portfolio."

"כמובן. כל הברוקרים משתמשים בתעודות סל בתיק ההשקעות
kamuvan kol habrokerim mishtamshim bete'udot sal betik hahashka'ot
of course all the brokers they use in index funds in portfolio of the investments

שלהם."
shelahem
their

"How come you never told us that before?" I asked.

"איך זה שמעולם לא סיפרת לנו על כך?" שאלתי.
eikh ze sheme'olam lo siparta lanu al kakh sha'alti
how that that never no you told to us about it I asked

"I don't sell index funds."

"אני לא מוכר תעודות סל."
ani lo mokher te'udot sal
I no I sell index funds

Gilat grabbed a large vase that was sitting on a nearby table.

גילת תפסה אגרטל גדול שהיה מונח על שולחן סמוך.
gilat tafsa agartal gadol shehaya munakh al shulkhan samukh
Gilat she grabbed vase large that it was placed on table nearby

26

"אל תחשבי אפילו לשבור את זה על הראש שלו," אמרתי לה.
al takhshevi afilu lishbor et ze al harosh shelo amarti la
don't you will think even to break D.O. that on the head his I said to her

"Do not even think of breaking that on his head," I told her.

רז נראה מתוח מאוד כשגילת אחזה באגרטל. לבסוף הניחה
raz nira matu'akh me'od kshegilat akhaza ba'agartal levasof hinikha
Raz he appeared nervous very when Gilat she held at the vase finally she set down

אותו בחזרה על השולחן.
oto bakhazara al hashulkhan
it back on the table

Raz looked very nervous while Gilat held the vase. Finally she set it back onto the table.

"אנחנו צריכים להחליף קרנות בכל שנה?" שאלתי.
anakhnu tsrikhim lehakhlif kranot bekhol shana sha'alti
we we need to switch funds in every year I asked

"Should we switch funds every year?" I asked.

"לא, רוב האנשים שמחליפים קרנות בכל שנה מפסידים כסף
lo rov ha'anashim shemakhlifim kranot bekhol shana mafsidim kesef
no most the people that (they) switch funds in every year they lose money

בטווח הארוך."
batvakh ha'arokh
in the long run

"No, most people who switch funds every year lose money in the long run."

"אז למה אתה מעביר את הכסף שלנו מקרן לקרן כל כמה
az lama ata ma'avir et hakesef shelanu mikeren lekeren kol kama
then why you you move D.O. the money our from fund to fund every few

חודשים?" צעקה גילת.
khodashim tsa'aka gilat
months she shouted Gilat

"Then why do you move our money from fund to fund every few months?" Gilat shouted.

"אני מקבל עמלה בכל פעם שאתם מבצעים פעולה. ככל שאתם
ani mekabel amla bekhol pa'am she'atem mevatsim pe'ula kekhol she'atem
I I get commission in every time that you you perform transaction the more that you

עושים יותר עסקאות אני מרוויח יותר כסף."
osim yoter iska'ot ani marvi'akh yoter kesef
you make more transactions I I earn more money

"I get a commission every time you make a transaction. The more trades you make, the more money I earn."

גילת העיפה בי מבט זועף. "החבר שלך עומד להיקשר לפגוש
gilat he'ifa bi mabat zo'ef hakhaver shelkha omed lehikasher lepagosh
Gilat she threw at me look angry the friend your is about to to be tied to the bumper

המכונית שלנו בתחתוניו ולהיגרר ברחבי העיר."
hamekhonit shelanu betakhtonav ulehigarer berakhavei ha'ir
the car our in his underwear and to be dragged all over the town

Gilat scowled at me. "Your friend is about to be tied to the bumper of our car in his underwear and dragged around town."

"בבקשה אל תפגעי בי," אמר רז. "אני רק מנסה להרוויח מספיק
bevakasha al tifge'i bi amar raz ani rak menase leharvi'akh maspik
please don't you will hurt at me he said Raz I only I try to earn enough

כסף לממן את הבית היפה הזה, בית נופש בגליל ושתי
kesef lemamen et haba'it hayafe haze beit nofesh bagalil ushtei
money to finance D.O. the house the nice the this vacation house in the Galilee and two of

"Please don't hurt me," Raz said. "I'm just trying to make enough money to afford this nice house, a summer place in the Galilee, and a couple of fancy cars."

מכוניות יקרות."
yekarot mekhoniyot
expensive cars

Gilat's face got really red. Her eyes became bloodshot. It was scary. Raz and I gaped at her. She breathed deeply until she got control of herself. Finally, she was able to speak in a normal voice.

פניה של גילת הפכו אדומים ממש. עיניה הוצפו בדם.
paneiha shel gilat hafkhu adumim mamash. eineiha hutsfu bedam.
her face / of / Gilat / it became / red / really / her eyes / they were flooded / with blood

זה היה מפחיד. רז ואני הבטנו בה בפה פעור. היא נשמה
ze haya mafkhid. raz va'ani hibatnu ba befe pa'ur. hi nashma
this / it was / scary / Raz / and I / we looked / at her / with mouth / gaping / she / she breathed

נשימות עמוקות עד ששליטתה העצמית שבה אליה. לבסוף הייתה
neshimot amukot ad sheshlitata ha'atsmit shava eleiha. levasof haita
breaths / deep / until / that her control of / the self / it returned / to her / finally / she was

מסוגלת לדבר בקול רגיל.
mesugelet ledaber bekol ragil.
able / to speak / in voice / normal

"I'm leaving now. Raz, if I see you again I am going to carve my initials into one of your fake pecs."

"אני עוזבת עכשיו. רז, אם אראה אותך שוב אחקוק את ראשי התיבות
ani ozevet akhshav. raz, im ere otkha shuv ekh'kok et rashei hatevot
I / I leave / now / Raz / if / I will see / you / again / I will engrave / D.O. / initials

של שמי על שרירי החזה המזוייפים שלך."
shel shmi al shrirei hekhaze hamezuyafim shelkha.
of / my name / on / muscles of / the chest / the fake / your

She stomped out of the front door.

היא יצאה החוצה מהדלת ברקיעת רגליים.
hi yatsa hakhutsa mehadelet birki'at ragla'im.
she / she left / outside / of the door / with stomping of / legs

"You were right," I said to Raz. "Those pills are really dangerous. Don't leave the house until they are finished."

"צדקת," אמרתי לרז. "הכדורים האלה באמת מסוכנים. אל תצא
tsadakta, amarti leraz. hakadurim ha'ele be'emet mesukanim. al tetse
you were right / I said / to Raz / the pills / the those / really / dangerous / don't / you will leave

מהבית עד שתסיים לקחת אותם."
mehaba'it ad shetesayem lakakhat otam.
from the house / until / that you will finish / to take / them

"How does she know all those things about me?" Raz asked.

"איך היא יודעת עלי את כל הדברים האלה?" שאל רז.
eikh hi yoda'at alai et kol hadvarim ha'ele? sha'al raz.
how / she / she knows / about me / D.O. / all / the things / the those / he asked / Raz

I could have told Raz the truth. That Gilat's sister works for Raz's plastic surgeon and her brother owns the massage parlor. Since Gilat talks to her siblings all the time, she knows which neighbors have had their tummies tucked and what type of massages they like to get. But I wanted Raz to squirm a little bit.

יכולתי לומר לרז את האמת. שאחותה של גילת עובדת אצל
yakholti lomar leraz et ha'emet. she'akhota shel gilat ovedet etsel
I could have / to tell / to Raz / D.O. / the truth / that her sister / of / Gilat / she works / for

המנתח הפלסטי שלו, ואחיה הוא בעל מכון העיסוי. היות
hamenate'akh haplasti shelo, ve'akhiha hu ba'al mekhon ha'isui. heyot
the surgeon / the plastic / his / and her brother / he / owner of / institute of / the massage / since

שגילת מדברת עם אחיה כל הזמן, היא יודעת אילו שכנים
shegilat medaberet im akhe'a kol hazman, hi yoda'at eilu shkhenim
that Gilat / she talks / with / her siblings / all / the time / she / she knows / which / neighbors

עברו מתיחת בטן ואיזה סוג עיסוי הם אוהבים. אבל רציתי

avru metikhat beten ve'eize sug isui hem ohavim. aval ratsiti

they underwent / tummy tucks / and which / type of / massage / they / they like. / but / I wanted

שרז יתפתל קצת.

sheraz yitpatel ktsat

that Raz / he will squirm / a little

"היא עובדת בסוכנות ממשלתית סודית," אמרתי לו.

hi ovedet besokhnut memshaltit sodit, amarti lo

she / she works / for agency / governmental / secret / I said / to him

"She works for a secret government agency," I told him.

הלכתי לכיוון הדלת.

halakhti lekhivun hadelet

I walked / to direction of / the door

I made my way to the door.

"עוד דבר אחד," אמרתי. "אני מתכוון להעביר את כל הכסף שלי

od davar ekhad, amarti. ani mitkaven leha'avir et kol hakesef sheli

another / thing / more / I said. / I / I plan / to transfer / D.O. / all / the money / my

לתעודות סל בעלות נמוכה. אני לא צריך שתהיה הברוקר שלי יותר."

lite'udot sal be'alut nemukha. ani lo tsarikh shetihiye habroker sheli yoter

to index funds / at cost / low / I / no / I need / that you will be / the broker / my / anymore

"One more thing," I said. "I plan to move all of my money into low cost index funds. I don't need you to be my stock broker anymore."

STORY 4

Child's Play

"למה אתה מקלל?" שאלה אותי גילת.
gilat oti sha'ala mekalel ata lama
Gilat me she asked you curse you why

"Why are you cursing?" Gilat asks me.

"האינטרנט לא עובד."
oved lo ha'internet
it works no the internet

"The internet isn't working."

"המחשב מחובר לחשמל?"
lakhashmal mekhubar hamakhshev
to the electricity it is connected the computer

"Is the computer plugged in?"

"למחשבים ניידים יש סוללה. בניגוד לטוסטרים, אין צורך לחבר
lekhaber tsorekh ein letosterim benigud solela lemakhshevim nayadim yesh
to connect need there isn't to toasters as opposed to battery laptops have

אותם לחשמל."
lakhashmal otam
to the electricity them

"Laptops have a battery. Unlike toasters, they don't need to be plugged in."

"רפי, אין צורך להיות סרקסטי. אני רק מנסה לעזור. למה שלא
shelo lama la'azor menasa rak ani sarkasti lihiyot tsorekh ein rafi
that no why to help I try only I sarcastic to be need there isn't Rafi

תתקשר לתמיכה הטכנית?"
hatekhnit latmikha titkasher
the technical to the support you will call

"Rafi, you don't have to be sarcastic. I'm just trying to help. Why don't you call technical support?"

"אולי קובי יוכל לעזור לי."
li la'azor yukhal kobi ulai
to me to help he will be able Kobi maybe

"Maybe Kobi will be able to help me."

"בפעם האחרונה שקובי עזר לך עם בעיה במחשב הוא שרף
saraf hu bemakhshev be'aya im lekha azar shekobi ha'akharona bapa'am
he burned he with computer problem with to you he helped that Kobi the last in the time

את הדיסק הקשיח."
hakashi'akh hadisk et
the hard the disk D.O.

"The last time Kobi helped you with a computer problem, he fried the hard drive."

"אה, נכון. אני אבקש מאחד הילדים לתקן את זה."
ze et letaken hayeladim me'ekhad avakesh ani a nakhon
this D.O. to fix the kids of one I will ask I ah correct

"Oh, right. I'll ask one of the kids to fix it."

"אני לא רוצה שהם יתעסקו עם המחשב שלנו. בפעם
bapa'am shelanu hamakhshev im yitasku shehem rotsa lo ani
at the time our the computer with they will fiddle with that they I want no I

"I don't want them fooling around with our computer. The last time you asked them to help, we ended up with SpongeBob as the background picture."

האחרונה שביקשת מהם לעזור סיימנו עם בובספוג בתור תמונת
ha'akharona shebikashta mehem la'azor siyamnu im bobsfog betor tmunat
the last that you asked of them to help we finished with SpongeBob as a picture of

הרקע."
hareka
background

"I'll call the computer company," I say.

"אתקשר לחברת המחשבים," אני אומר.
etkasher lekhevrat hamakhshevim ani omer
I will call to the company of the computers I I say

I wait on the phone for twenty minutes for the next available agent. He forces me to re-do all the steps I have already tried. After a few minutes, we find the problem.

אני ממתין בטלפון במשך עשרים דקות לנציג פנוי. הוא מכריח
ani mamtin batelefon bemeshekh esrim dakot lenatsig panui hu makhri'akh
I I wait on the phone for twenty minutes for agent free he he forces

אותי לחזור על כל הפעולות שכבר ניסיתי. לאחר כמה דקות,
oti lakhzor al kol hape'ulot shekvar nisiti le'akhar kama dakot
me to repeat about all the operations that already I tried after a few minutes

אנחנו מגלים את הבעיה.
anakhnu megalim et habe'aya
we we discover D.O. the problem

"I will email you software to download that will fix the problem," he tells me.

"אני אשלח לך בדוא"ל תוכנה להורדה שתפתור את
ani eshlakh lekha bado'ar elektroni tokhna lehorada shetiftor et
I I will send to you in the email software for downloading that (she) will fix D.O.

הבעיה," הוא אומר לי.
habe'aya hu omer li
the problem he he says to me

"That won't help, since I can't get onto the internet."

"זה לא יעזור, מכיוון שאני לא יכול להיכנס לאינטרנט."
ze lo ya'azor mikeivan she'ani lo yakhol lehikanes la'internet
that no he will help since that I no I can to enter to the internet

"I forgot about that," he says.

"שכחתי מזה," הוא אומר.
shakhakhti mize hu omer
I forgot of that he he says

"On second thought, send me the email. I'll open it at the neighbor's, copy the software onto a flash drive, and install it on my computer."

"במחשבה שנייה, שלח לי את המייל. אני אפתח אותו אצל השכנים,
bemakhshava shniya shlakh li et hameil ani eftakh oto etsel hashkhenim
on thought second send to me D.O. the email I I will open him at the neighbors

אעתיק את התוכנה לדיסק און קי ואתקין אותה במחשב שלי."
a'atik et hatokhna ledisk on ki ve'atkin ota bamakhshev sheli
I will copy D.O. the software to a flash drive and I will install her on the computer my

"Excellent."

"מצוין."
metsuyan
excellent

I ran over to Kobi's house to get the email. Forty minutes later my computer was updated.

רצתי לביתו של קובי לקבל את הדוא"ל. ארבעים דקות אחר כך
ratsti leveito shel kobi lekabel et hado'ar elektroni arba'im dakot akhar kakh
I ran to his house of Kobi to get D.O. the email forty minutes later

המחשב שלי היה מעודכן.
me'udkan haya sheli hamakhshev
updated it was my the computer

"תראי את זה," אמרתי לגילת.
legilat amarti ze et tiri
to Gilat I said this D.O. you will look

"Look at this," I say to Gilat.

"האינטרנט עדיין לא עובד?"
oved lo ada'in ha'internet
he works no still the internet

"Is the internet still not working?"

"זה בסדר עכשיו, אבל בדיוק קיבלתי הודעה ממיקרוסופט. הם מודיעים
modi'im hem mimaikrosoft hoda'a kibalti bediyuk aval akhshav beseder ze
they inform they from Microsoft notice I received exactly but now okay this

לי לא להוריד את העדכון האחרון של התוכנה כי זה מפריע
mafri'a ze ki hatokhna shel ha'akharon ha'idkun et lehorid lo li
it interrupts this because the software of the latest the update D.O. to download not to me

לאינטרנט."
la'internet
to the internet

"It's fine now, but I just received a notice from Microsoft. They tell me not to download their latest software upgrade because it interferes with the internet."

"עשית את זה לפני יומיים."
yoma'im lifnei ze et asita
two days ago that D.O. you did

"You did that two days ago."

"וזו הסיבה שהאינטרנט הפסיק לעבוד."
la'avod hifsik sheha'internet hasiba vezo
to work he stopped that the internet the reason and that

"And that's the reason the internet stopped working."

"אתה רוצה כוס יין?"
ya'in kos rotse ata
wine glass you want you

"Do you want a glass of wine?"

"נראה לי שכן."
sheken li nire
that yes to me it seems

"I think so."

2

יומיים מאוחר יותר, גילת תולשת את שיערה.
sei'ara et toleshet gilat yoter me'ukhar yoma'im
her hair D.O. she tears out Gilat more later two days

Two days later, Gilat is pulling her hair out.

"המדפסת לא עובדת."
ovedet lo hamadpeset
it works no the printer

"The printer isn't working."

"ניתקת את המחשב הנייד מהמדפסת היום?"
hayom mehamadpeset hanayad hamakhshev et nitakt
today from the printer the portable the computer D.O. you disconnected

"Did you disconnect the laptop from the printer today?"

"Yes. I was using it in the kitchen."

"כן, השתמשתי בו במטבח."
bamitbakh bo hishtamashti ken,
in the kitchen with it I used yes

"Sometimes that screws things up," I say.

"לפעמים זה משבש את העניינים," אני אומר.
omer ani ha'inyanim et meshabesh ze lifamim
I say I the matters D.O. it disrupts that sometimes

"Can you fix it?"

"אתה יכול לתקן את זה?"
ze et letaken yakhol ata
this D.O. to fix you can you

"I've already shown you how to correct that particular problem."

"כבר הראיתי לך איך לתקן את הבעיה הזאת."
hazot habe'aya et letaken eikh lakh hereti kvar
the that the problem D.O. to correct how to you I showed already

"I forgot."

"שכחתי."
shakhakhti
I forgot

"I'm reading right now," I tell her.

"אני קורא עכשיו," אני אומר לה.
la omer ani akhshav kore ani
to her I tell I now I read I

"Rafi, get over here and fix this printer, or I won't cook dinner tonight."

"רפי, בוא לכאן ותתקן את המדפסת הזאת, או שלא אבשל
avashel shelo o hazot hamadpeset et vetetaken lekhan bo rafi
I will cook that not or the this the printer D.O. and you will fix to here come Rafi

ארוחת ערב היום."
hayom arukhat erev
today dinner

I fix the problem immediately. Gilat is a great cook. I don't want her going on strike.

אני מתקן את הבעיה מיד. גילת טבחית מעולה. אני לא רוצה
rotse lo ani me'ula tabakhit gilat miyad habe'aya et metaken ani
I want not I wonderful chef Gilat immediately the problem D.O. I fix I

שתשבות.
shetishbot
that she will strike

"Why can't you remember when I show you how to correct minor problems with the computer and printer?" I ask Gilat during dinner.

"למה את לא מצליחה לזכור כשאני מראה לך איך לתקן
letaken eikh lakh mare kshe'ani lizkor matslikha lo at lama
to correct how to you I show when I to remember you are successful not you why

בעיות קטנות במחשב ובמדפסת?" אני שואל את גילת
gilat et sho'el ani uvamadpeset bamakhshev ktanot be'ayot
Gilat D.O. I ask I and with the printer with the computer small problems

בארוחת הערב.
be'arukhat ha'erev
at dinner

"That's your job. I don't want anything to do with fixing electronic devices."

"זה התפקיד שלך. אני לא רוצה להתעסק עם תיקון מכשירי
makhshirei tikun im lehitasek rotsa lo ani shelkha hatafkid ze
devices of repair with to be involved I want not I your the job that

אלקטרוניקה.״
elektronika
electronics

״זה לא הוגן,״ אני אומר.
| omer | ani | hogen | lo | ze |
| I say | I | fair | not | that |

"That's unfair," I say.

״החיים קשים. תתמודד עם זה.״
| ze | im | titmoded | kashim | hakhayim |
| it | with | you will deal with | hard | the life |

"Life is tough. Deal with it."

—— 3 ——

״אתה יכול להוסיף את דוד עמוס לרשימת אנשי הקשר בטלפון
| batelefon | hakesher | anshei | lirshimat | amos | dod | et | lehosif | yakhol | ata |
| on the telephone | the contact | people of | to the list of | Amos | uncle | D.O. | to add | you can | you |

שלי?״ אני שואל את בני בן השש.
| hashesh | ben | bni | et | sho'el | ani | sheli |
| the six | aged | my son | D.O. | I ask | I | my |

"Can you add Uncle Amos to the contact list on my cell phone?" I ask my six year old son.

״כבר הראיתי לך איך לעשות את זה,״ הוא אומר לי.
| li | omer | hu | ze | et | la'asot | eikh | lekha | hereti | kvar |
| to me | he says | he | this | D.O. | to do | how | to you | I showed | already |

"I showed you how to do this already," he says to me.

״תראה לי שוב.״
| shuv | li | tare |
| again | to me | you will show |

"Show me again."

״יש ספר הוראות הפעלה על השולחן שלך,״ הוא אומר.
| omer | hu | shelkha | hashulkhan | al | hafala | hora'ot | sefer | yesh |
| he says | he | your | the table | on | operating | instructions of | book | there is |

"There's an instruction book on your desk," he says.

״הרגל שלי כואבת. אני לא יכול ללכת לשולחן שלי.״
| sheli | lashulkhan | lalekhet | yakhol | lo | ani | ko'evet | sheli | haregel |
| my | to the table | to walk | I can | no | I | it hurts | my | the foot |

"My foot hurts. I can't walk to my desk."

״אתה עושה את עצמך?״ הוא שואל אותי.
| oti | sho'el | hu | ose et atsmekha | ata |
| me | he asks | he | you are pretending | you |

"Are you pretending?" he asks me.

״אולי.״
| ulai |
| maybe |

"Maybe."

״אם אתה לא אוהב שאמא לא זוכרת דברים שאתה מראה לה
| la | mare | she'ata | dvarim | zokheret | lo | she'ima | ohev | lo | ata | im |
| to her | you show | that you | things | she remembers | no | that mom | you like | no | you | if |

במחשב, למה אני צריך להסביר לך כל פעם איך לעדכן את
| et | le'adken | eikh | pa'am | kol | lekha | lehasbir | tsarikh | ani | lama | bamakhshev |
| D.O. | to update | how | time | every | to you | to explain | I need | I | why | for the computer |

"If you don't like it when mommy doesn't remember things you show her about the computer, why should I have to keep explaining how to update a contact list?"

"רשימת אנשי הקשר?"
reshimat anshei hakesher
list of / people of / the contact

Apparently, my son has very good hearing and an excellent memory. I make a mental note to be careful what I say in the future when he is nearby.

אני רושם מצוין. וזיכרון חדה מאוד שמיעה יש לבני ככל הנראה
kekhol hanire / yesh livni / shmi'a / khada / me'od / vezikaron / metsuyan / ani / roshem
apparently / my son has / hearing / sharp / very / and memory / excellent / I / I note

בזיכרוני להיזהר בדבריי בעתיד כשהוא בסביבה.
bezikhroni / lehizaher / bidvarai / be'atid / kshehu / basviva
in my memory / to be careful / in my words / in the future / when he / around

"Because I'm your father and drive you to soccer practice," I tell him.

"כי אני אבא שלך, ואני מסיע אותך לאימוני כדורגל," אני אומר
ki / ani / aba / shelkha / va'ani / masi'a / otkha / le'imunei / kaduregel / ani / omer
because / I / father / your / and I / I drive / you / to practice of / soccer / I / I say

לו.
lo
to him

"This is the last time I'm doing this. Now watch closely."

"זו הפעם האחרונה שאני עושה את זה. עכשיו תסתכל טוב."
zo / hapa'am / ha'akharona / she'ani / ose / et / ze / akhshav / tistakel / tov
this / the time / the last / that I / I do / D.O. / this / now / you will watch / good

He adds my brother's phone number to my contact list. I pretend to be concentrating very hard. Actually, I am noticing that his fingernails need to be cleaned. It's bad enough that I have to ask a kid who barely graduated kindergarten to help me with my cell phone. It's even worse when I tell him to fix the surround sound system two hours later.

הוא מוסיף את מספר הטלפון של אחי לרשימת אנשי
hu / mosif / et / mispar / hatelefon / shel / akhi / lirshimat / anshei
he / he adds / D.O. / number of / the telephone / of / my brother / to the list of / people of

הקשר שלי. אני מעמיד פנים שאני מרוכז מאוד. למעשה,
hakesher / sheli / ani / ma'amid panim / she'ani / merukaz / me'od / lema'ase
the contact / my / I / I pretend / that I / I am concentrating / very much / actually

אני שם לב שהוא זקוק לניקוי ציפורניים. מספיק גרוע שאני
ani / sam lev / shehu / zakuk / lenikui / tsiporna'im / maspik / garu'a / she'ani
I / I pay attention / that he / in need of / of cleaning of / fingernails / enough / bad / that I

צריך לבקש מילד שבקושי סיים את הגן לעזור לי עם
tsarikh / levakesh / miyeled / shebekoshi / siyem / et / hagan / la'azor / li / im
I need / to ask / from a kid / that barely / he finished / D.O. / the kindergarten / to help / to me / with

הטלפון הסלולרי שלי. זה גרוע אפילו יותר כשאני אומר לו לתקן
hatelefon / haselulari / sheli / ze / garu'a / afilu / yoter / kshe'ani / omer / lo / letaken
the telephone / the cellular / my / this / bad / even / more / when I / I tell / to him / to fix

את מערכת הסראונד שעתיים לאחר מכן.
et / ma'arekhet / hasaraund / sha'ata'im / le'akhar miken
D.O. / system / the surround / two hours / afterward

"What's the problem?" he asks.

"מה הבעיה?" הוא שואל.
ma / habe'aya / hu / sho'el
what / the problem / he / he asks

"There's no sound coming out of the four extra speakers," I say.

"אין צליל בארבעת הרמקולים הנוספים," אני אומר.
ein / tslil / be'arba'at / haramkolim / hanosafim / ani / omer
there isn't / sound / in four of / the speakers / the extra / I / I say

ובוחן הסלון, בפינת הטלוויזיה מאחורי לו מזדחל הוא
uvokhen hasalon befinat hatelevizya me'akhorei lo mizdakhel hu
and he examines the living room in the corner of the television behind to him he crawls he

ולממיר. לדי וי די לטלוויזיה, המחוברים הכבלים מאות ארבע את
ulamemir ladi vi di latelevizya hamekhubarim hakabelim me'ot arba et
and to the cable box to the DVD to the television connected the cables hundreds four D.O.

He worms himself behind the television set in the corner of the living room and examines the four hundred wires hooked into the TV, DVD player, and cable box.

"מישהו לחץ בטעות על הכפתור הזה," הוא אומר.
omer hu haze hakaftor al beta'ut lakhats mishehu
he says he the this the button on by mistake he pushed someone

"Someone pushed this button by accident," he says.

קן של חוטים יושב בתוך אותו ורואה הטלוויזיה מאחורי מציץ אני
khutim shel ken betokh yoshev oto vero'e hatelevizya me'akhorei metsits ani
wires of nest in he sits him and I see the television behind I peek I

הטיונר. של האחורי בחלקו קטן מתג על מצביע הוא וכבלים.
hatuner shel ha'akhori bekhelko katan meteg al matsbi'a hu vekabelim
the tuner of the rear on his part small switch at he points he and cables

I peek around the television and see him sitting in a nest of cords and cables. He is pointing to a small switch on the back of the tuner.

"זה במצב סגור," הוא אומר.
omer hu sagur bematsav ze
he says he off in position this

"It's in the off position," he says.

"אז תדליק אותו."
oto tadlik az
him you will turn on well

"Well, turn it on."

הוא לוחץ על הכפתור וארבעת הרמקולים הנוספים מתעוררים לחיים.
lekhayim mitorerim hanosafim haramkolim ve'arba'at hakaftor al lokhets hu
to life they wake up the extra the speakers and four of the button on he presses he

He pushes the button and the four extra speakers come alive with sound.

"אל תיגע בכפתור הזה שוב," הוא אומר.
omer hu shuv haze bakaftor tiga al
he says he again the this at the button you will touch don't

"Don't touch that button again," he says.

"לא נגעתי בו."
bo nagati lo
at it I touched no

"I didn't touch it."

"אם יהיו לך עוד בעיות תשאל את החנונית," הוא אומר לי.
li omer hu hakhnunit et tishal be'ayot od ihiyu lekha im
to me he says he the geek D.O. you will ask problems more you will have if

"If you have any more problems, ask the geek," he tells me.

"תפסיק לקרוא כך לאחותך. ולמה אני צריך לשאול אותה?"
ota lishol tsarikh ani velama la'akhotkha kakh likro tafsik
her to ask I need I and why to your sister like that to call you will stop

"Stop calling your sister that name. And why should I ask her?"

"היא יודעת יותר ממני. מר סלזר, השכן, משלם לה עשרים שקלים
shkalim esrim la meshalem hashakhen salazar mar mimeni yoter yoda'at hi
shekels twenty to her he pays the neighbor Salazar Mr than me more she knows she

יעבדו שלו והאזעקה הביתי שהקולנוע לדאוג לשבוע
ya'avdu shelo veha'azaka habeiti shehakolno'a lidog leshavu'a
they will function his and the alarm the residential that the cinema to take care of per week

"She knows more than I do. Mr. Salazar next door pays her twenty shekels a week to keep his home theater and house alarm working right."

37

כמו שצריך."
kmo shetsarikh
like that it should

4

"Technology is moving too fast for us," I tell Gilat later that night.

"הטכנולוגיה מתקדמת מהר מדי בשבילנו," אני אומר לגילת מאוחר
hatekhnologya mitkademet maher midai bishvilenu ani omer legilat me'ukhar
the technology it progresses fast too for us I I tell to Gilat later

יותר באותו לילה.
yoter be'oto laila
more in same night

"Are you having problems setting the alarm clock again?" she asks.

"אתה שוב מסתבך עם כיוון השעון המעורר?" היא שואלת.
ata shuv mistabekh im kivun hasha'on hame'orer hi sho'elet
you again you are having trouble with setting the alarm clock she she asks

"Yes. Why did we buy this digital thing? You need a master's degree in electronics to make it work."

"כן. למה קנינו את הדבר הדיגיטלי הזה? צריך תואר שני
ken lama kaninu et hadavar hadigitali haze tsarikh to'ar sheni
yes why we bought D.O. the thing the digital the this you need degree second

באלקטרוניקה כדי להפעיל אותו."
be'elektronika kedei lehafil oto
in electronics in order to to operate it

"You're just upset that the kids know more than you do."

"אתה סתם כועס כי הילדים יודעים יותר ממך."
ata stam ko'es ki hayeladim yodim yoter mimkha
you just you are angry that the kids they know more than you

"Our daughter has a tech consulting contract with Mr. Salazar."

"לבת שלנו יש חוזה ייעוץ טכני עם מר סלזר."
labat shelanu yesh khoze ye'uts tekhni im mar salazar
our daughter has contract of consulting technical with Mr. Salazar

"He doesn't have any kids, so he needs her expertise."

"אין לו ילדים, אז הוא צריך את המומחיות שלה."
ein lo yeladim az hu tsarikh et hamumkhiyut shela
he doesn't have kids so he he needs D.O. the expertise her

I sit in bed shaking my head in amazement.

אני מתיישב במיטה ומניד בראשי בפליאה.
ani mityashev bamita umenid beroshi bifli'a
I I sit down in the bed and I shake with my head in amazement

"The calculator she uses in her math class can solve equations," I tell Gilat. "I didn't even know how to spell the word 'equation' when I was ten."

"המחשבון שהיא משתמשת בו בשיעורי המתמטיקה יכול לפתור
hamakhshevon shehi mishtameshet bo beshi'urei hamatematika yakhol liftor
the calculator that she she uses in it in classes of the mathematics it can to solve

משוואות," אני אומר לגילת. "אני לא ידעתי אפילו לאיית את המילה
mishva'ot ani omer legilat ani lo yadati afilu le'ayet et hamila
equations I I say to Gilat I not I knew even to spell D.O. the word

'משוואה' כשהייתי בן עשר."
mishva'a ksheha'iti ben eser
equation when I was aged ten

"הילדים שלנו גדלים עם טכנולוגיה מתקדמת," אומרת גילת. "הם

hayeladim shelanu gdelim im tekhnologya mitkademet omeret gilat hem
the kids our they grow up with technology advanced she says Gilat they

לא חוששים ללחוץ על כל הכפתורים והם לומדים הרבה יותר מהר

lo khosheshim lilkhots al kol hakaftorim vehem lomdim harbe yoter maher
not they are afraid to press on all the buttons and they they learn much more fast

מאיתנו."

me'itanu
than us

"Our kids are growing up with advanced technology," Gilat says. "They aren't afraid to push all the buttons, and they learn a lot more quickly than we do."

"מעניין איך קשישים מסתדרים," אני אומר.

me'anyen eikh kshishim mistadrim ani omer
I wonder how elderly people they manage I I say

"I wonder how senior citizens manage," I say.

"הם מתקשרים לנכדים שלהם שיעזרו, או שהם פשוט לא

hem mitkashrim lanekhadim shelahem sheya'azru o shehem pashut lo
they they call to the grandchildren their that they will help or that they simply no

מתעסקים עם גאדג'טים מתוחכמים."

mitaskim im gajetim metukhkamim
they get involved with gadgets sophisticated

"They call their grandchildren for help, or they just don't bother with sophisticated gadgets."

"כמו אימא שלך, שמסרבת לגעת במחשב ולא קונה טלפון

kmo ima shelakh shemesarevet laga'at bamakhshev velo kona telefon
like mother your who (she) refuses to touch at the computer and no she buys telephone

סלולרי."

selulari
cellular

"Like your mother, who refuses to touch a computer and won't buy a cell phone."

"בדיוק," היא אומרת.

bediyuk hi omeret
exactly she she says

"Exactly," she says.

"אבל מה יקרה אם המכונית שלה תתקלקל והיא תצטרך

aval ma yikre im hamekhonit shela titkalkel vehi titstarekh
but what it will happen if the car her it breaks down and she she will need

להזמין גרר?"

lehazmin grar
to order tow truck

"But what if her car breaks down and she needs to call a tow truck?"

"היא כבר לא נוהגת."

hi kvar lo noheget
she already no she drives

"She doesn't drive any more."

"נכון, שכחתי."

nakhon shakhakhti
correct I forgot

"That's right. I forgot."

"מה תעשה כשהילדים יצאו מהבית?" שואלת גילת.

ma ta'ase kshehayeladim yetsu mehaba'it sho'elet gilat
what you will do when the kids they will leave from the house she asks Gilat

"What are you going to do when the kids move out of the house?" Gilat asks.

Story 4

"By then the manufacturers will be making devices that are so simple, that even a grown up can make them work. Either that, or you will need to give birth to a few more children."

"עד אז היצרנים ייצרו מכשירים פשוטים כל כך שאפילו
ad az — hayatsranim — yeyatsru — makhshirim — pshutim — kol kakh — she'afilu
by then — the manufacturers — they will create — devices — simple — so — that even

מבוגרים יצליחו להפעיל אותם. או זה, או שתצטרכי ללדת
mevugarim — yatslikhu — lehafil — otam — o — ze — o — shetitstarkhi — laledet
adults — they will succeed — to operate — them — either — that — or — that you will need — to give birth

עוד כמה ילדים."
od — kama — yeladim
another — few — children

"I think two is enough," Gilat said.

"אני חושבת ששניים זה מספיק," אמרה גילת.
ani — khoshevet — sheshna'im — ze — maspik — amra — gilat
I — I think — that two — this — enough — she said — Gilat

40

STORY 5

Selling Low

השעה שמונה וחצי בשבת בבוקר. מוקדם מכדי להיות ער.
hasha'a shmone vakhetsi beshabat baboker. mukdam mikhdei lihiyot er.
the hour eight and half on Saturday in the morning. too early to be awake.

ובכל זאת, הנה אני עם אשתי גילת, סוחבים סולחנות עמוסים
uvkhol zot, hine ani im ishti gilat, sokhavim shulkhanot amusim
and nevertheless here I am with I my wife Gilat, we drag tables loaded

גרוטאות מהחניה הפרטית אל כביש הגישה.
gruta'ot mehakhanaya hapratit el kvish hagisha.
junk from the parking the private to of road the access

It is eight thirty on Saturday morning. Much too early to be awake. Yet here I am with my wife Gilat, moving tables of junk from our garage into our driveway.

"איך הצלחנו לצבור את כל הגרוטאות האלה?" היא שואלת.
"eikh hitslakhnu litsbor et kol hagruta'ot ha'ele?" hi sho'elet.
"how we succeeded to accumulate D.O. all the junk the these?" she she asks.

"How did we ever accumulate all this junk?" she asks.

"זה מעגל קסמים. אנחנו קונים דברים שאנחנו לא צריכים כי
"ze ma'agal ksamim. anakhnu konim dvarim she'anakhnu lo tsrikhim ki
"this cycle of magic. we we buy things that we no we need because

הם במבצע. בסוף אנחנו מאחסנים את הדברים במחסן. אחרי כמה
hem bemivtsa. basof anakhnu me'akhsenim et hadvarim bamakhsan. akharei kama
they on sale. eventually we we store D.O. the things in the shed. after few

שנים המחסן מלא. אנחנו עורכים מכירת חצר כדי להיפטר
shanim hamakhsan male. anakhnu orkhim mekhirat khatser kedei lehipater
years the shed full. we we organize sale of yard in order to to get rid of

מהדברים במחסן, והמעגל מתחיל שוב."
mehadvarim bamakhsan, vehama'agal matkhil shuv."
from the things in the shed, and the cycle it begins again."

"It's a vicious cycle. We buy things we don't need because they are on sale. Eventually, we store the things in the shed. After a few years, the shed is full. We have a yard sale to get rid of everything in the shed. And the cycle begins again."

לפתע אני שומע קול נוסף.
lefeta ani shome'a kol nosaf.
suddenly I I hear voice additional.

Suddenly I hear another voice.

"אתן לכם שמונה שקלים עבור המנורה הזאת."
"eten lakhem shmona shkalim avur hamenora hazot."
"I will give to you eight shekels for the lamp the this."

"I'll give you eight shekels for this lamp."

אני מסתובב. אישה קטנה ואפורת שיער המרכיבה משקפי ראייה
ani mistovev. isha ktana ve'aforat sei'ar hamarkiva mishkefei re'iya
I I turn around. woman small and gray haired that (she) wears eyeglasses

גדולים ניצבת סמוך לאחד השולחנות שגררנו מהחניה. היא
gdolim nitsevet samukh le'akhad hashulkhanot shegararnu mehakhanaya. hi
big she stands next to to one the tables that we dragged from the parking. she

I turn around. A small woman with gray hair and large eyeglasses is standing next to one of the tables we dragged out of the garage. She is holding up one of the items we are trying to sell.

41

אוחזת באחד מהפריטים שאנחנו מנסים למכור.
limkor menasim she'anakhnu mehapritim be'akhad okhezet
to sell we try that we of the items at one she grasps

"It's a genuine Tiffany lamp," I say. "The price is eighty shekels."

"זו מנורת טיפאני מקורית," אני אומר. "המחיר הוא שמונים שקלים."
shkalim shmonim hu hamekhir omer ani mekorit tifani menorat zo
shekels eighty it the price I say I original Tiffany lamp of this

"You'll never get eighty shekels. Will you take twenty?"

"לא תצליחו לקבל שמונים שקלים. תיקחו עשרים?"
esrim tik'khu shkalim shmonim lekabel tatslikhu lo
twenty you will take shekels eighty to get you will succeed no

"Lady, the sale starts in thirty minutes. Come back then and we can talk."

"גברת, המכירה מתחילה בעוד שלושים דקות. תחזרי אז
az takhzeri dakot shloshim be'od matkhila hamekhira gveret
then you will come back minutes thirty in another it begins the sale lady

ונדבר."
unedaber
and we will talk

"The electrical wire is frayed," she says.

"חוט החשמל בלוי," היא אומרת.
omeret hi balui hakhashmal khut
she says she worn out the electricity wire of

She holds up the wire with her left hand and points to a worn part.

היא מחזיקה את החוט בידה השמאלית ומצביעה על קטע שחוק.
shakhuk keta al umatsbi'a hasmalit beyada hakhut et makhzika hi
worn part at and she points the left in her hand the wire D.O. she holds she

"She did that with her teeth while we were pulling this table out," Gilat says. "I saw her."

"היא עשתה את זה עם השיניים כשהוצאנו את השולחן הזה,"
haze hashulkhan et kshehotsenu hashina'im im ze et asta hi
the this the table D.O. when we took out the teeth with that D.O. she did she

אומרת גילת. "ראיתי אותה."
ota ra'iti gilat omeret
her I saw Gilat she says

"The penalty for tampering with the merchandise is double the price marked on the tag," I tell the lady. "One hundred and sixty shekels for the lamp."

"העונש על פגיעה בסחורה הוא תשלום כפול מהמחיר
mehamekhir kaful tashlum hu baskhora al pgi'a ha'onesh
of the price double payment it with the merchandise for tampering the punishment

המסומן בתג המחיר," אני אומר לגברת. "מאה שישים שקלים
shkalim shishim me'a lagveret omer ani hamekhir betag hamesuman
shekels sixty hundred to the lady I tell I the price on tag that is indicated

עבור המנורה."
hamenora avur
the lamp for

The lady stomps away, muttering something to herself. At the end of the driveway, she kicks our light pole.

הגברת מתרחקת בכבדות, ממלמלת לעצמה דבר-מה. בקצה כביש
kvish biktse dvar-ma le'atsma memalmelet bikhvedut mitrakheket hagveret
road of at the end something to herself she mumbles with heaviness she moves away the lady

הגישה היא בועטת בעמוד התאורה שלנו.
shelanu hate'ura be'amud bo'etet hi hagisha
our the lighting at the pole of she kicks she the access

עשר דקות אחר כך מגיע קהל ציידי מציאות במגוון
eser dakot akhar kakh magi'a kehal tsayadei metsi'ot bemigvan
ten minutes later it arrives clientele of hunters of bargains in a variety of

כלי רכב. הם מפשפשים בפיצ׳פקעס ומכשירי החשמל הקטנים
klei rekhev hem mefashpeshim bapichefkes umakhshirei hakhashmal haktanim
motor vehicles they they rummage with the trinkets and appliances of the electricity the small

שגילת ואני סידרנו על השולחנות.
shegilat va'ani sidarnu al hashulkhanot
that Gilat and I we arranged on the tables

Ten minutes later a crowd of bargain hunters arrives in assorted vehicles. They rummage through the trinkets and small appliances Gilat and I had arranged on the tables.

גילת צועדת לעבר שני אדונים מבוגרים הכפופים מעל הסחורה
gilat tso'edet le'ever shnei adonim mevugarim hakfufim me'al haskhora
Gilat she strolls toward two of gentlemen older that are hunched over the goods

שלנו. "ראיתי שהחלפתם את תגי המחיר," היא אומרת להם. פניהם
shelanu ra'iti shehekhlaftem et tagei hamekhir hi omeret lahem pneihem
our I saw that you switched D.O. tags of the price she she says to them their faces

מאדימים, והם פונים לדרכם, נבוכים.
ma'adimim vehem ponim ledarkam nevokhim
they turn red and they they turn on their way embarrassed

Gilat strolls over to two older gentlemen hunched over our goods. "I saw you switching the price tags," she tells them. Their faces turn red, and they walk away embarrassed.

גילת גוררת לכיווני נערה בת עשרה בעלת שיער קוצים כתום.
gilat goreret lekhivuni na'ara bat esre ba'alat sei'ar kotsim katom
Gilat she drags in my direction girl teenage having hair spikes orange

על זרועותיה כתובות קעקע אחדות, ושפתיה צבועות בליפסטיק שחור.
al zro'oteiha ktovot ka'aka akhadot usfateiha tsvu'ot belipstik shakhor
on her arms tattoos a few and her lips painted with lipstick black

בשתי גבותיה פירסינג עם טבעות רבות.
bishtei gaboteiha pirsing im taba'ot rabot
on two of her eyebrows piercing with rings multiple

Gilat drags a teenage girl with orange spiked hair over to me. The girl has a few tattoos on her arms and black lipstick. Both eyebrows are pierced with multiple rings.

"היא ניסתה להגניב את הדיסק הזה לתוך הארנק שלה," אומרת לי
hi nista lehagniv et hadisk haze letokh ha'arnak shela omeret li
she she tried to sneak D.O. the CD the this into the purse her she tells to me

גילת.
gilat
Gilat

"She tried to slip this CD into her purse," Gilat tells me.

אני מביט בדיסק. "הביץ׳ בויז — המיטב," אני אומר לנערה. "זה לא
ani mabit badisk habich boiz hameitav ani omer lana'ara ze lo
I I look at the CD The Beach Boys the best I I say to the girl this not

מוזיקה קלילה קצת בשבילך?"
muzika klila ktsat bishvilekh
music light a little for you

I look at the CD. "Best of The Beach Boys," I say to the girl. "Isn't this a little light for you?"

"זה בשביל חבר שלי," היא מייבבת.
ze bishvil khaver sheli hi meyabevet
this for boyfriend my she she whines

"It's for my boyfriend," she whines.

"Is he sixty years old?"

"הוא בן שישים?"
shishim ben hu
sixty aged he

"He's twenty. He likes surfing music."

"הוא בן עשרים. הוא אוהב מוזיקת גלישה."
glisha muzikat ohev hu esrim ben hu
surfing music of he likes he twenty aged he

"Go steal a Black Sabbath CD from the sale down the street."

"לכי תגנבי דיסק של בלאק סבאת' מהמכירה בהמשך הרחוב."
harekhov behemshekh mehamekhira sabath blak shel disk tignevi lekhi
the street further on from the sale Sabbath Black of CD you will steal go

"Run home, Sara, before I call your mother," Gilat says.

"רוצי הביתה, שרה, לפני שאתקשר לאימא שלך," אומרת גילת.
gilat omeret shelakh le'ima she'etkasher lifnei sara habaita rutsi
Gilat she says your to mother that I will call before Sara homeward run

"Do we know her?" I ask as we watch the girl run down the street.

"אנחנו מכירים אותה?" אני שואל בעוד אנו מביטים בנערה רצה
ratsa bana'ara mabitim anu be'od sho'el ani ota makirim anakhnu
she ran at the girl we watch we while I ask I her we know we

במורד הרחוב.
harekhov bemorad
the street down

"She used to babysit the kids."

"היא הייתה עושה בייביסיטר לילדים."
layeladim beibisiter haita osa hi
for the kids babysitter she used to do she

"Scary."

"מפחיד."
mafkhid
scary

For the next twenty minutes Gilat and I are really busy. Our junk sells a lot quicker than we expected.

בעשרים הדקות הבאות גילת ואני עסוקים מאוד. הגרוטאות שלנו
shelanu hagruta'ot me'od asukim va'ani gilat haba'ot hadakot be'esrim
our the junk very busy and I Gilat next the minutes for twenty

נמכרות מהר יותר מכפי שציפינו.
shetsipinu mikfi maher yoter nimkarot
that we expected than faster they are sold

"This sale is going so well that I think I will increase the prices for the remaining items by thirty percent," Gilat says as she grabs a marker.

"המכירה הזאת הולכת כל כך טוב שאני חושבת שאעלה את
et she'e'ele khoshevet she'ani tov kol kakh holekhet hazot hamekhira
D.O. that I will increase I think that I well so she is going the this the sale

מחיר החפצים שנותרו בשלושים אחוז," אומרת גילת תוך שהיא
shehi tokh gilat omeret akhuz bishloshim shenotru hakhafatsim mekhir
that she while Gilat she says percent by thirty that (they) remained the objects price of

מחזיקה את עט הסימון.
hasimun et et makhzika
the marking pen of D.O. she grabs

"Better not," I tell her. "These people are in a feeding frenzy. There may be a riot if you try to milk more money out of them."

"עדיף שלא," אני אומר לה. "האנשים האלה באמוק. עלולה
alula be'amok ha'ele ha'anashim la omer ani shelo adif
there may be in a state of frenzy the these the people to her I tell I that not preferable

להתעורר מהומה אם תנסי לחלוב מהם יותר כסף."
lehitorer mehuma im tenasi lakhlov mehem yoter kesef
to awaken riot if you will try to milk from them more money

גבר לבוש בהידור ניגש אלי.
gever lavush behidur nigash elai
man dressed elegantly he approached toward me

A well dressed gentleman approaches me.

"אני רוצה לקנות את השולחן המתרחב," הוא אומר במבטא קל.
ani rotse liknot et hashulkhan hamitrakhev hu omer bemivta kal
I want to buy D.O. the table that expands he he says with accent light

"I want to purchase the expanding table," he says with a slight accent.

"הוא עולה מאה עשרים ושמונה שקלים."
hu ole me'a esrim ushmona shkalim
it he costs hundred twenty and eight shekels

"That will be one hundred twenty eight shekels."

"תוכל לשים שלט 'נמכר' על השולחן ולשמור לי אותו עד
tukhal lasim shelet nimkar al hashulkhan velishmor li oto ad
you could to put sign sold on the table and to keep for me it until

שאחזור מאוחר יותר היום?"
she'ekhzor me'ukhar yoter hayom
that I will return later more today

"Will you put a 'Sold' sign on the table and hold it for me until I return later in the day?"

"בהחלט, אם תשלם לי מאה עשרים ושמונה שקלים."
behekhlet im teshalem li me'a esrim ushmona shkalim
sure if you will pay to me hundred twenty and eight shekels

"Sure, if you pay me one hundred twenty eight shekels."

"אתן לך מקדמה של עשרים שקלים."
eten lekha mikdama shel esrim shkalim
I will give to you down payment of twenty shekels

"I'll give you a down payment of twenty shekels."

"לא. שלם את כל הסכום אם אתה רוצה שאשמור לך אותו."
lo shalem et kol haskhum im ata rotse she'eshmor lekha oto
no pay D.O. all the sum if you you want that I will keep for you it

"No. Pay the full sum now if you want me to hold the table for you."

"אבל אני צריך ללכת הביתה להביא עוד כסף."
aval ani tsarikh lalekhet habaita lehavi od kesef
but I I need to go homeward to obtain more money

"But I have to go home to get more money."

"אתה מנסה להגיד לי שבאת למכירת חצר עם פחות ממאה
ata menase lehagid li shebata limkhirat khatser im pakhot mime'a
you you try to tell to me that you came to sale of yard with less than hundred

עשרים ושמונה שקלים?"
esrim ushmona shkalim
twenty and eight shekels

"Are you trying to tell me that you came to a yard sale with less than one hundred twenty eight shekels?"

"לא חשבתי שאקנה משהו יקר."
lo khashavti she'ekne mashehu yakar
no I thought that I will buy something expensive

"I didn't think I would buy anything expensive."

"אני מכיר את הטריק הזה," אמרתי. "אני שומר לך את השולחן עד
ani makir et hatrik haze amarti ani shomer lekha et hashulkhan ad
I I know D.O. the trick the this I said I I keep for you D.O. the table until

"I know this trick," I said. "I hold the table for you until the end of the day. You return and refuse to pay the price we agreed on. You figure you can steal it from me for forty shekels, since there are no more customers. That's an old scam. Go away."

סוף היום. אתה חוזר ומסרב לשלם את הסכום שהוסכם.
sof hayom ata khozer umesarev leshalem et haskhum shehuskam
end of the day you you return and you refuse to pay D.O. the sum that we were agreed

אתה חושב שתוכל לגנוב אותו ממני בארבעים שקלים, כי
ata khoshev shetukhal lignov oto mimeni be'arba'im shkalim, ki
you you think that you will be able to steal it from me for forty shekels because

אין יותר קונים. זה תרגיל ישן. לך מכאן."
ein yoter konim. ze targil yashan. lekh mikan
there aren't more buyers that trick old go from here

"You are not a nice person. I'm not coming to your next yard sale."

"אתה לא אדם נחמד. אני לא אבוא למכירת החצר הבאה שלך."
ata lo adam nekhmad. ani lo avo limkhirat hakhatser haba'a shelkha
you not nice person I not I will come to sale of the yard next your

"I'll take you off our mailing list," I say sarcastically.

"אוריד אותך מרשימת התפוצה שלנו," אני אומר בסרקזם.
orid otkha mirshimat hatfutsa shelanu, ani omer besarkazem
I will remove you from list of the distribution our I say I with sarcasm

The man walks away and kicks our light pole. I make an announcement.

האיש הולך לדרכו ובועט בעמוד התאורה שלנו. אני מכריז:
ha'ish holekh ledarko uvo'et be'amud hate'ura shelanu. ani makhriz
the man he goes on his way and he kicks at pole the lighting our I I announce

"If one more person kicks my light pole, I will lock them in the trunk of my car for a week."

"אם עוד מישהו יבעט בעמוד התאורה שלי, אנעל אותו
im od mishehu yivat be'amud hate'ura sheli, enal oto
if another someone he will kick at the pole of the lighting my I will lock him

בבגאז' של המכונית שלי למשך שבוע."
babagazh shel hamekhonit sheli lemeshekh shavu'a
in the trunk of the car my for week

Nobody pays any attention to me.

אף אחד לא שם לב אלי.
af ekhad lo sam lev elai
nobody no he pays attention to me

"Can I return this toaster if I don't like it?" one lady asks Gilat.

"אוכל להחזיר את הטוסטר אם הוא לא ימצא חן בעיני?" שואלת
ukhal lehakhzir et hatoster im hu lo yimtsa khen be'enai? sho'elet
I will be able to return D.O. the toaster if it no it will find grace in my eyes she asks

גברת אחת את גילת.
gveret akhat et gilat
lady one D.O. Gilat

"It's a toaster," Gilat says. "Decide now if you like it."

"זה טוסטר," אומרת גילת. "תחליטי עכשיו אם הוא מוצא חן בעינייך."
ze toster, omeret gilat. takhliti akhshav im hu motse khen be'enaikh
this toaster she says Gilat you will decide now if it you like

"It may not fit on my counter."

"יכול להיות שהוא לא יתאים על השיש שלי."
yakhol lihiyot shehu lo yatim al hashayish sheli
it can to be that it no it will fit on the counter my

"All sales are final. No returns."

"כל המכירות סופיות. אין החזרות."
kol hamekhirot sofiyot. ein hakhzarot
all the sales final there are no returns

"אשלם לך שני שקלים עבורו."
avuro shkalim shnei lakh ashalem
for it shekels two of to you I will pay

"I'll pay you two shekels for it."

"אני מעדיפה לרסק אותו בפטיש ולהשליך אותו לזבל מאשר
ma'asher lazevel oto ulehashlikh befatish oto lerasek ma'adifa ani
than in the garbage it and to throw with hammer it to smash I prefer I

למכור אותו בשני שקלים," אומרת גילת. "המחיר הוא חמישה
khamisha hu hamekhir gilat omeret shkalim bishnei oto limkor
five it the price Gilat she says shekels for two of it to sell

שקלים."
shkalim
shekels

"I'd rather smash it with a hammer and throw it in the garbage than sell it for two shekels," Gilat says. "The price is five shekels."

"מה דעתך על ארבעה?"
arba'a al da'atekh ma
four about your opinion what

"How about four?"

"נמכר. מזומן בלבד, בלי המחאות בבקשה."
bevakasha hamkha'ot bli bilvad mezuman nimkar
please checks no only cash sold

"Sold. Cash only, no checks, please."

הגברת משלמת עם שקית מלאה בכסף קטן. היא הולכת עם הטוסטר.
hatoster im holekhet hi katan bekhesef mele'a sakit im meshalemet hagveret
the toaster with she goes she small of money full bag with she pays the lady

The lady pays with a bag full of change. She walks away with her toaster.

"את אשת מכירות מצוינת," אני אומר לגילת.
legilat omer ani metsuyenet mekhirot eshet at
to Gilat I say I excellent sales woman of you

"You are a great saleslady," I say to Gilat.

היא זורחת מנחת.
minakhat zorakhat hi
with content she glows she

She beams with pleasure.

לקראת סוף היום נותרים רק חפצים אחדים. גילת ואני תשושים.
tshushim va'ani gilat akhadim khafatsim rak notarim hayom sof likrat
exhausted and I Gilat a few items only they remain the day end of towards

התמקחות עם קונים והתגוששות עם גנבים הם עבודה קשה.
kasha avoda hem ganavim im vehitgosheshut konim im hitmak'khut
hard work they are thieves with and wrestling buyers with bargaining

אנחנו קרובים לנקודת השבירה. מכירת חצר יכולה לגרום לבודהה
le'budha ligrom yekhola khatser mekhirat hashvira linkudat krovim anakhnu
to Buddha to cause she can yard sale of the breaking to the point of close we

לרצוח.
lirtsu'akh
to commit murder

Toward the end of the day, just a few items are left. Gilat and I are bone tired. Haggling with customers and wrestling with shoplifters is tough work. We are close to the breaking point. Running a yard sale could drive the Buddha to commit murder.

נותר קונה אחד.
ekhad kone notar
one buyer he remains

One customer remains.

47

"I will pay twelve shekels for this picture frame," he tells me.

> "אשלם לך שנים עשר שקלים עבור המסגרת הזאת," הוא אומר לי.
>
> li omer hu hazot hamisgeret avur shkalim shneim asar lekha ashalem
> to me he tells he the this the frame for shekels twelve to you I will pay

"The price is forty eight shekels. Since you are the last customer, I will give it to you for twenty four."

> "המחיר הוא ארבעים ושמונה שקלים. מאחר ואתה הלקוח האחרון
>
> ha'akharon halako'akh ve'ata me'akhar shkalim ushmona arba'im hu hamekhir
> the last the customer and you since shekels and eight forty it the price
>
> אתן לך אותה בעשרים וארבעה."
>
> ve'arba'a be'esrim ota lekha eten
> and four for twenty it to you I will give

"I only have twelve shekels."

> "יש לי רק שנים עשר שקלים."
>
> shkalim shneim asar rak yesh li
> shekels twelve only I have

I think for a second. I'm ready for a nice bottle of wine. Maybe I should just sell the frame for twelve shekels and get rid of this guy.

> אני חושב רגע. אני מוכן לבקבוק יין נחמד. אולי אני צריך פשוט
>
> pashut tsarikh ani ulai nekhmad ya'in levakbuk mukhan ani rega khoshev ani
> simply I need I maybe nice wine for bottle of ready I moment I think I
>
> למכור את המסגרת בשנים עשר שקלים ולהיפטר מהבחור הזה.
>
> haze mehabakhur ulehipater shkalim bishneim asar hamisgeret et limkor
> the this of the guy and to get rid of shekels for twelve the frame D.O. to sell

"Okay, twelve shekels," Gilat says. She must have been reading my thoughts.

> "או קיי, שנים עשר שקלים," אומרת גילת. כנראה קראה את מחשבותיי.
>
> makhshevotai et kara kanire gilat omeret shkalim shneim asar o kei
> my thoughts D.O. she read probably Gilat she says shekels twelve okay

"Is it acceptable to pay with change?" he asks.

> "אפשר לשלם באגורות?" הוא שואל.
>
> sho'el hu be'agorot leshalem efshar
> he asks he in agorot to pay possible

I uncork the wine as Gilat chases the man down the street with a shovel.

> אני פותח את הבקבוק היין בזמן שגילת, עם את חפירה בידיה,
>
> beyadeiha khafira et im bizman shegilat haya'in bakbuk et pote'akh ani
> in her hand digging shovel of with as Gilat the wine bottle of D.O. I open I
>
> רודפת אחרי האיש במורד הרחוב.
>
> harekhov bemorad ha'ish akharei rodefet
> the street down the man after she chases

STORY 6

Don't Stop and Smell the Roses

"הרגתי עוד שלושה," צעקתי לגילת.

haragti	od	shlosha	tsa'akti	legilat
I killed	another	three	I yelled	to Gilat

"I killed three more," I yelled to Gilat.

"תמשיך להילחם, אולי נצא מזה בחיים," היא צורחת בחזרה.

tamshikh	lehilakhem	ulai	netse	mize	bakhayim	hi	tsorakhat	bakhazara
you will continue	to fight	maybe	we will get out	of this	alive	she	she shrieked	back

"Keep fighting and we might get out of this alive," she shrieked back.

הפניתי את ראשי מתוקפיי לשבריר שנייה וראיתי שהאויב מקיף את גילת מכל הכיוונים. מיהרתי לעזרתה, מתעלם מביטחוני האישי.

hifneti	et	roshi	mitokfai	leshavrir	shniya	vera'iti	sheha'oyev
I turned	D.O.	my head	from my attackers	for a fraction of	second	and I saw	that the enemy

makif	et	gilat	mikol	hakivunim	miharti	le'ezrata	mitalem	mibitkhoni	ha'ishi
he surrounds	D.O.	Gilat	from all	the directions	I hurried	to her aid	I ignore	of my safety	the personal

I turned my head from my attackers for a split second and saw that Gilat was surrounded by the enemy on all sides. With no thought for my own safety I rushed to her aid.

"בואו, דפוקים," צעקתי לעבר יריבינו.

bo'u	dfukim	tsa'akti	le'ever	yeriveinu
come	suckers	I screamed	to	our opponents

"Bring it on, suckers," I screamed at our foes.

ניצבנו גב אל גב, חובטים ומכים ביריבינו, בעוד הם ממשיכים בהתקפתם. לאחר דקות אחדות היינו מותשים. אויבינו המשיכו במתקפה.

nitsavnu	gav	el	gav	khovtim	umakim	birivenu	be'od	hem	mamshikhim
we stood	back	to	back	we smack	and we hit	at our foes	while	they	they continue

behatkafatam	le'akhar	dakot	akhadot	ha'inu	mutashim	oyveinu	himshikhu	bamitkafa
with their attack	after	minutes	a few	we were	exhausted	our enemies	they continued	with the attack

We stood back to back, punching and smacking our adversaries as they continued their attack. After a few minutes, we were exhausted. Our enemies just kept coming.

"רפי, אין לנו ברירה," התנשפה גילת. "אנחנו חייבים להשתמש בכימיקלים רעילים."

rafi	ein lanu	breira	hitnashfa	gilat	anakhnu	khayavim	lehishtamesh
Rafi	we don't have	choice	she gasped	Gilat	we	we must	to use

bekhimikalim	re'ilim
with chemicals	toxic

"Rafi, we have no choice," Gilat gasped. "We have to use the toxic chemicals."

"There is very little left."

"נשאר ממש מעט."

me'at mamash nishar
little really it remains

"It's our only chance."

"זה הסיכוי היחיד שלנו."

shelanu hayakhid hasikui ze
our the only the chance this

The desperation in her voice made me turn to look at my lovely wife. Her eyes brimmed with tears. Her hair was unruly.

היאוש בקולה גרם לי להסב את ראשי ולהביט באשתי היפה.

hayafa be'ishti ulehabit roshi et lehasev li garam bekola haye'ush
the beautiful at my wife and to look my head D.O. to turn to me it caused in her voice the despair

עיניה היו מלאות דמעות. שיערה היה פרוע.

paru'a haya sei'ara dma'ot mele'ot hayu eineiha
unruly it was her hair tears full of they were her eyes

I pulled the can of mosquito repellent from the pocket of my shorts. I sprayed some on Gilat's bare arms and legs. Then I sprayed the rest on myself. I threw the can at the swarm of deadly little killers that was hovering in front of us.

הוצאתי את מכל דוחה היתושים מכיס מכנסיי הקצרים. ריססתי

risasti haktsarim mikhnesei mikis hayatushim dokhe mekhal et hotseti
I sprayed the short pants of from pocket of the mosquitoes repellent can of D.O. I took out

מעט על זרועותיה ורגליה החשופות של גילת. לאחר מכן ריססתי את

et risasti le'akhar miken gilat shel hakhasufot veragleiha zro'oteiha al me'at
D.O. I sprayed then Gilat of the bare and her legs her arms on a little

החומר הנותר על עצמי. השלכתי את המכל על נחיל היצורים

hayetsurim nekhil al hamekhal et hishlakhti atsmi al hanotar hakhomer
the creatures swarm of at the can D.O. I threw myself on the remaining the material

הקטלניים הזעירים שריחף מולנו.

muleinu sherikhef haze'irim hakatlaniyim
in front of us that (it) hovered the tiny the deadly

The mosquitoes pulled back to reform their lines. They knew better than to land on skin that had just been coated with spray. I could see the mosquito officers rally their troops for another onslaught.

היתושים נסוגו כדי לארגן את השורות מחדש. הם חכמים

khakhamim hem mekhadash hashurot et le'argen kedei nasogu hayatushim
wise they anew the lines D.O. to organize in order to they retreated the mosquitoes

מכדי לנחות על עור שזה או עתה כוסה בתרסיס. יכולתי לראות את

et lirot yakholti betarsis kusa ata sheze or al linkhot mikhdei
D.O. to see I could with spray it was covered now that this skin on to land too

היתושים הקצינים אוספים את הכוחות להסתערות נוספת.

nosefet lehista'arut hakokhot et osfim haktsinim hayatushim
additional for attack the strength D.O. they gather the officers the mosquitoes

"The protection only lasts for a few minutes," Gilat said. "Run to the car as fast as you can."

"ההגנה מספיקה רק לכמה דקות," אמרה גילת. "רוץ למכונית מהר

maher lamekhonit ruts gilat amra dakot lekhama rak maspika hahagana
fast to the car run Gilat she said minutes for a few only sufficient the protection

ככל שתוכל."

kekhol shetukhal
as much as you can

We were two kilometers from the parking lot. Deep in a swamp in the Hula Valley. We saw a small wooden sign with an arrow. The word "khruzh" was painted on it.

היינו שני קילומטר ממגרש החניה. עמוק בביצה בעמק החולה.

hakhula be'emek babitsa amok hakhanaya mimigrash kilometer shnei ha'inu
the Hula in valley of in the swamp deep the parking from lot of kilometer two of we were

לפנינו ראינו שלט עץ קטן שעליו מסומן חץ. המילה "כרוז" הייתה
lefaneinu *ra'inu* *shelet* *ets* *katan* *she'alav* *mesuman* *khets*. *hamila* "*khruzh*" *haita*
before us | we saw | sign of | wood | small | that on it | it is marked | arrow. | the word | khruzh | she was

כתובה עליו.
ktuva *alav*
written | on it

"Follow me!" I shouted. It was hard to make myself heard over the buzzing of millions of mosquito wings. I ran in the direction the arrow pointed. Gilat was close behind.

"בואי אחרי!" צעקתי. היה קשה להישמע בתוך זמזומם של מיליוני
bo'i *akharai*!" *tsa'akti*. *haya* *kashe* *lehishama* *betokh* *zimzumam* *shel* *milyonei*
come | after me | I shouted. | it was | hard | to be heard | within | their buzzing | of | millions of

כנפי יתושים. רצתי בכיוון שעליו הורה החץ. גילת הייתה
kanfei *yatushim*. *ratsti* *bakivun* *she'alav* *hora* *hakhets*. *gilat* *haita*
wings of | mosquitoes | I ran | in the direction | that at it | it instructed | the arrow. | Gilat | she was

מעט אחרי.
me'at *akharai*.
a little | behind me

"האם "כרוז" אומר שזו הדרך למגרש החניה?" התנשמה.
ha'im *khruzh* "*khruzh*" *omer* *shezo* *haderekh* *lemigrash* *hakhanaya*?" *hitnashma*.
is it that | khruzh | khruzh | it means | that this | the way | to lot of | the parking | she panted.

"Does 'khruzh' mean this is the way to the parking lot?" she panted.

"יכול להיות שהכוונה שיש בהמשך כרוב ענק," עניתי.
yakhol *lihiyot* *shehakavana* *sheyesh* *bahemshekh* *kruv* *anak*," *aniti*.
it can | to be | that the direction | that there is | further on | cabbage | huge | I answered.

"הערבית שלי לא טובה במיוחד."
ha'aravit *sheli* *lo* *tova* *bimyukhad*.
the Arabic | my | not | good | especially

"It might mean we are headed toward a large cabbage," I answered. "My Arabic is not very good."

בתחילת הטיול דרכתי על שורש של עץ ונקעתי את הקרסול.
bitkhilat *hatiyul* *darakhti* *al* *shoresh* *shel* *ets* *venakati* *et* *hakarsol*.
at the beginning of | the hike | I stepped on | on | root | of | tree | and I sprained | D.O. | the ankle

רגלי הלמה בכאב. ועדיין, הכאב לא עצר בעדי מלהימלט במלוא
ragli *halma* *bikha'ev*. *ve'ada'in*, *hake'ev* *lo* *atsar* *ba'adi* *milehimalet* *bimlo*
my foot | it pulsed | with pain. | and yet, | the pain | no | it stopped me | from escaping | with full

המהירות. זיעה מעורבת בקרם הגנה טיפטפה במורד מצחי אל
hamehirut. *ze'a* *me'orevet* *bekrem* *hagana* *tiftefa* *bemorad* *mitskhi* *el*
the speed. | sweat | it is mixed | with cream of | defense | it dripped | down | my forehead | to

תוך עיניי, שהחלו לצרוב. היער הפך מטושטש.
tokh *einai*, *shehekhelu* *litsrov*. *haya'ar* *hafakh* *metushtash*.
inside | my eyes | which (they) started | to burn. | the forest | it became | blurry.

At the beginning of our hike, I had stepped on a tree root and twisted my ankle. My foot throbbed with pain. This did not stop me from running with all of my speed to escape. Sweat mixed with suntan lotion ran down my forehead and into my eyes, which started to burn. The forest became blurry.

"אני לא רואה," אמרתי לגילת בקול שהכיל מידה רבה של
ani *lo* *ro'e*," *amarti* *legilat* *bekol* *shehekhil* *mida* *raba* *shel*
I | no | I see | I said | to Gilat | in a voice | that contained | characteristics | much | of

תבהלה. "לכי את ראשונה."
tavhela. "*lekhi* *at* *rishona*."
panic. | go | you | first

"I can't see," I said to Gilat in a voiced that contained a large dose of panic. "You go first."

We passed a man sitting on a chair and selling baklava and drinks from a multi-colored wagon.

חלפנו על פני אדם שישב על כיסא ומכר בקלאווה ושתייה
khalafnu al pnei adam sheyashav al kise umakhar baklawa ushtiya
we passed by man who (he) sat on chair and he sold baklava and beverage

בקרון צבעוני.
bekaron tsivoni
from a wagon multi-colored

"Run," I said to him. "They are right behind us."

"רוץ," אמרתי לו. "הם מאחורינו."
ruts amarti lo hem me'akhoreinu
run I said to him they behind us

"Would you like to purchase a Coca Cola?" asked the man.

"רוצים לקנות קוקה קולה?" שאל האיש.
rotsim liknot koka kola sha'al ha'ish
you want to purchase Coca Cola he asked the man

I had no time for a crazy man who was not concerned for his own safety. We left him and kept running.

לא היה לי זמן לאיש מטורף שלא דואג לביטחון שלו. עזבנו
lo haya li zman le'ish metoraf shelo do'eg labitakhon shelo azavnu
no I had time for a man crazy that no he is concerned for the safety his we left

אותו והמשכנו לרוץ.
oto vehimshakhnu laruts
him and we continued to run

A group of seven school children and two adult teachers passed us. They chatted happily to each other as they walked toward certain doom.

קבוצה של שבעה ילדים בגיל בית ספר ושני מורים מבוגרים חלפה
kvutsa shel shiva yeladim begil beit sefer ushnei morim mevugarim khalfa
group of seven kids at age of school and two of teachers adult she passed

על פנינו, מפטפטים בעליזות תוך שהם צועדים אל עבר גורלם המר.
al paneinu mefatpetim be'alizut tokh shehem tso'adim el ever goralam hamar
by us they chat happily as they they walk towards their fate the bitter

Gilat stopped for a second and grabbed the arm of one of the chaperones. "Go back. No human can survive in the swamp."

גילת עצרה לשנייה ואחזה בזרועו של אחד המלווים.
gilat atsra lishniya ve'akhaza bizro'o shel ekhad hamlavim
Gilat she stopped for a second and she grabbed by his arm of one of the chaperones

"תחזרו. אף אדם לא יכול לשרוד בביצה."
takhzeru af adam lo yakhol lisrod babitsa
you will go back no human no he can to survive in the swamp

He looked at us with a calm expression. I guess he was used to seeing sweaty tourists with wild expressions on their faces and thousands of mosquito bites erupting on their faces, arms, and legs.

הוא הביט בנו בשלווה. אני מניח שהיה מורגל לראות תיירים
hu hibit banu beshalva ani meni'akh shehaya murgal lirot tayarim
he he looked at us calmly I I assume that he was used to to see tourists

מזיעים העוטים הבעה פראית על פניהם, ואלפי עקיצות
mazi'im ha'otim haba'a pirit al pneihem ve'alfei akitsot
sweaty that (they) wear facial expression wild on their faces and thousands of bites of

יתושים על פניהם, ידיהם ורגליהם.
yatushim al pneihem yadeihem veragleihem
mosquitoes on their faces their arms and their legs

"Leave them," I said to Gilat. "Maybe our pursuers will devour them. It will give us a few extra seconds to get back to our rental car."

"עזבי אותם," אמרתי לגילת. "אולי רודפינו יטרפו אותם. זה
izvi otam amarti legilat ulai rodfeinu itrefu otam ze
leave them I said to Gilat maybe our pursuers they will devour them this

יתן לנו כמה שניות נוספות לחזור למכונית השכורה שלנו."

yiten	lanu	kama	shniyot	nosafot	lakhzor	lamekhonit	haskhura	shelanu
it will give	to us	a few	seconds	additional	to go back	to the car	the rented	our

"אבל הם רק ילדים," קראה גילת.

aval	hem	rak	yeladim	kara	gilat
but	they	just	children	she cried out	Gilat

"But they are just children," Gilat cried.

"זה הם או אנחנו," אמרתי ומשכתי אותה הרחק מקבוצת

ze	hem	o	anakhnu	amarti	umashakhti	ota	harkhek	mikvutsat
it	them	or	we	I said	and I pulled	her	far away	from the group of

"It's them or us," I said as I pulled her away from the school group.

בית הספר.

beit	hasefer
the school	

מעבר לעיקול הדרך הפך שביל העפר העמוס בסלעים לשביל

me'ever	le'ikul	haderekh	hafakh	shvil	he'afar	he'amus	bisla'im	lishvil
on the other side	to bend of	the path	it became	trail of	the dirt	the loaded	with rocks	to a trail

The rocky dirt trail became paved as we rounded a bend.

סלול.

salul
paved

"יש בניין לפנינו," צעקה גילת.

yesh	binyan	lefaneinu	tsa'aka	gilat
there is	building	in front of us	she yelled	Gilat

"There's a building ahead of us," Gilat howled.

רצנו עוד עשרים מטרים, פתחנו את הדלת המרושתת ומעדנו

ratsnu	od	esrim	metrim	patakhnu	et	hadelet	hamerushetet	uma'adnu
we ran	another	twenty	meters	we opened	D.O.	the door	the meshed	and we stumbled

We dashed another twenty meters, opened a screen door, and tumbled into a large room. Seven people were in the room. They looked up as I slammed the door shut behind us.

אל תוך חדר גדול. שבעה אנשים היו בחדר. הם הרימו את

el	tokh	kheder	gadol	shiva	anashim	hayu	bakheder	hem	herimu	et
to	inside	room	large	seven	people	they were	in the room	they	they raised	D.O.

מבטם כשתרקתי את הדלת מאחורינו.

mabatam	kshetarakti	et	hadelet	me'akhoreinu
their gazes	when I slammed	D.O.	the door	behind us

"תתקשרו למשטרה ולבית החולים," אמרתי, מתנשם בכבדות. "אנחנו

titkashru	lamishtara	uleveit hakholim	amarti	mitnashem	bikhvedut	anakhnu
you will call	to the police	and to the hospital	I said	I breathe	heavily	we

"Call the police and the hospital," I said, breathing heavily. "We need medical and psychiatric attention."

צריכים טיפול רפואי ופסיכיאטרי."

tsrikhim	tipul	refu'i	upsikhi'atri
we need	attention	medical	and psychiatrist

איש זקן דידה לעברנו.

ish	zaken	dida	le'evrenu
man	old	he moved unsteadily	toward us

An elderly man moved unsteadily toward us.

"הסתבכתם עם החרקים," אמר בעברית צחה.

histabakhtem	im	hakharakim	amar	be'ivrit	tsakha
you got into trouble	with	the bugs	he said	in Hebrew	clear

"You are having troubles with the bugs," he said in perfect Hebrew.

"Yes," I gasped, "we have been under attack since we left the reed area."

"כן," התנשפתי, "היינו תחת התקפה מאז שעזבנו את אזור קני הסוף."
ken hitnashafti ha'inu takhat hatkafa me'az she'azavnu et ezor knei hasuf
yes I gasped we were under attack since that we left D.O. area of reeds

"Did you not bring mosquito repellent?" the old man asked.

"לא הבאתם דוחה יתושים?" שאל הזקן.
lo hevetem dokhe yatushim sha'al hazaken
no you brought repellent of mosquitoes he asked the old man

"We brought some. It was supposed to last for six hours, but it only deterred our enemy for a few minutes," I said. "You can be sure I'm going to send a nasty letter to the manufacturer and demand a full refund. We kept re-spraying, until the can was empty. Then we made a run for the parking lot. We managed to get here before the swarm caught up with us again."

"הבאנו. זה היה אמור להספיק לשש שעות, אבל זה הרתיע את
hevenu ze haya amur lehaspik leshesh sha'ot aval ze hirti'a et
we brought it it was supposed to suffice for six hours but it it deterred D.O.

האויב רק לכמה דקות," אמרתי. "תהיה בטוח שאשלח מכתב
ha'oyev rak lekhama dakot amarti tihiye batu'akh she'eshlakh mikhtav
the enemy only for a few minutes I said you will be sure that I will send letter

חריף ליצרן ואדרוש החזר מלא. ריססנו שוב ושוב, עד
kharif layatsran ve'edrosh hekhzer male risasnu shuv vashuv ad
strong to the manufacturer and I will demand refund full we sprayed again and again until

שהמכל התרוקן. ואז רצנו אל מגרש החניה. הצלחנו להגיע
shehamekhal hitroken ve'az ratsnu el migrash hakhanaya hitslakhnu lehagi'a
that the can it became empty and then we ran to lot of the parking we succeeded to get to

לכאן לפני שהנחיל השיג אותנו שוב."
lekhan lifnei shehanekhil hisig otanu shuv
to here before that the swarm it caught up with us again

"There are children out there," Gilat said. "Someone needs to save them."

"יש שם ילדים," אמרה גילת. "מישהו צריך להציל אותם."
yesh sham yeladim amra gilat mishehu tsarikh lehatsil otam
there are there children she said Gilat someone he needs to save them

"It will be alright," the man explained. "We are used to the pests."

"יהיה בסדר," הסביר האיש. "אנחנו רגילים לחרקים."
ihiye beseder hisbir ha'ish anakhnu regilim lakharakim
it will be okay he explained the man we we are used to to the insects

"Where are we?" I asked.

"איפה אנחנו?" שאלתי.
eifo anakhnu sha'alti
where we I asked

"At the information center. We have a small library where you can read about the swamps and the different types of flora in our Gardens. The parking lot is a few meters from here. Would you like to drink something?"

"במרכז המידע. יש לנו ספרייה קטנה, שאתם יכולים לקרוא בה
bemerkaz hameida yesh lanu sifriya ktana she'atem yekholim likro ba
at center of the information we have library small that you you can to read in it

על הביצה ועל סוגי הצמחייה השונים בגנים שלנו. מגרש
al habitsa ve'al sugei hatsimkhiya hashonim baganim shelanu migrash
about the swamp and about types of the flora the different in the gardens our lot of

החנייה נמצא כמה מטרים מכאן. תרצו לשתות משהו?"
hakhanaya nimtsa kama metrim mikan tirtsu lishtot mashehu
the parking it is located a few meters from here you will want to drink something

"Do you have any arak?"

"יש לכם ערק?"
yesh lakhem arak
you have arak

הוא צחק. "אתם כל כך מצחיקים. יש לנו מיץ, מים, תה וקפה."
hu *tsakhak* *atem* *kol kakh* *matskhikim* *yesh lanu* *mits* *ma'im* *te* *vekafe*
he — he laughed — you — so — funny — we have — juice — water — tea — and coffee

He laughed. "You are so funny. We have juice, water, tea, and coffee."

גילת ואני התיישבנו על שרפרפים, לגמנו מבקבוקי המים וניסינו
gilat *va'ani* *hityashavnu* *al* *shrafrafim* *lagamnu* *mibakbukei* *hama'im* *venisinu*
Gilat — and I — we sat down — on — stools — we sipped — from bottles of — the water — and we tried

להשיב את רוחנו. דפדפנו בדפי הספר, שהסביר על אודות
lehashiv *et* *rukhenu* *difdafnu* *bedapei* *hasefer* *shehisbir* *al odot*
to return — D.O. — our spirit — we leafed through — in pages of — the book — that explained — about

סוגי הצמחים השונים בגן הבוטני. עיניי צרבו עדיין
sugei *hatsmakhim* *hashonim* *bagan* *habotani* *einai* *tsarvu* *ada'in*
types of — the plants — the different — in the garden — the botanical — my eyes — they burned — still

והקרסול שלי החל להתנפח.
vehakarsol *sheli* *hekhel* *lehitnape'akh*
and the ankle — my — it began — to swell

Gilat and I tried sat down on stools, sipped bottled water and tried to compose ourselves. We leafed through the pages of a book that explained all about the different types of plants that were contained in the Botanical Garden. My eyes still burned and my ankle was starting to swell.

"איך פיספסנו את הבניין הזה כשהגענו?" שאלה גילת.
eikh *fisfasnu* *et* *habinyan* *haze* *kshehiganu* *sha'ala* *gilat*
how — we missed — D.O. — the building — the this — when we arrived — she asked — Gilat

"How did we miss this building when we first got here?" Gilat asked.

"אין שלטים," אמרתי. "החניתי את המכונית בצד הלא נכון
ein *shlatim* *amarti* *hekhneti* *et* *hamekhonit* *batsad* *halo* *nakhon*
there aren't — signs — I said — I parked — D.O. — the car — on the side — the not — correct

של מגרש החניה."
shel *migrash* *hakhanaya*
of — lot of — the parking

"There are no signs," I said. "I parked the car at the wrong end of the parking lot."

"היינו צריכים לשאול את האנשים בכפר הנופש אם יש להם מפה
ha'inu tsrikhim *lishol* *et* *ha'anashim* *bikhfar* *hanofesh* *im* *yesh lahem* *mapa*
we should have — to ask — D.O. — the people — at village of — the vacation — if — they have — map

של המקום," אמרה גילת.
shel *hamakom* *amra* *gilat*
of — the place — she said — Gilat

"We should have asked the people at the resort if they had a map of this place," Gilat said.

"תוכלי לנהוג בדרך חזרה?" שאלתי אותה.
tukhli *linhog* *baderekh* *khazara* *sha'alti* *ota*
you will be able — to drive — on the way — the way back — I asked — her

"Can you drive back?" I asked her.

"אני לא יודעת לנהוג בהילוכים," ענתה גילת.
ani *lo* *yoda'at* *linhog* *bahilukhim* *anta* *gilat*
I — no — I know — to drive — with the gears — she answered — Gilat

"I don't know how to drive with a stick shift," she said.

"אבל הרגל שלי כואבת," התבכיינתי.
aval *heregel* *sheli* *ko'evet* *hitbakhyanti*
but — the leg — my — it hurts — I whined

"But my leg hurts," I whined.

"תוכל לטבול אותה באמבטיה חמה אחר כך."
tukhal *litbol* *ota* *be'ambatya* *khama* *akhar kakh*
you will be able — to soak — her — in bath — hot — later

"You can soak it in the hot tub later."

After a while we were ready to make a break for our rental car.

זמן מה מאוחר יותר היינו מוכנים לרוץ למכונית השכורה.
haskhura lamekhonit laruts mukhanim ha'inu yoter me'ukhar zman ma
the rented to the car to run ready we were more later a while

"I'm not going across the whole parking lot," Gilat said. "The mosquitos have probably set some kind of trap for us."

"אני לא חוצה את כל מגרש החניה," אמרה גילת. "היתושים בטח
betakh hayatushim gilat amra hakhanaya migrash kol et khotsa lo ani
surely the mosquitoes Gilat she said the parking lot of all D.O. I cross not I

הכינו לנו איזו מלכודת."
malkodet eizo lanu hekhinu
trap some for us they prepared

I argued with her, but it was useless. Once Gilat decides something, she will not change her mind.

התווכחתי איתה, אבל זה היה חסר טעם. כשגילת מחליטה משהו, היא
hi mashehu makhlita kshegilat khasar ta'am haya ze aval ita hitvakakhti
she something she decides when Gilat pointless it was it but with her I argued

לא תשנה את דעתה.
da'ata et teshane lo
her opinion D.O. she will change no

I ran to our car as fast as I could, watching over my shoulder for our enemies. Luckily, they were busy elsewhere. Probably stripping the carcass of another tourist that they had hunted down in the swamp. I drove the car to the entrance of the information center and Gilat jumped in.

רצתי אל עבר המכונית הכי מהר שיכולתי, מסתכל מעבר לכתפי
likhtefi me'ever mistakel sheyakholti hakhi maher hamekhonit el ever ratsti
to my shoulder over I watch that I could fastest the car towards I ran

אם האויב מתקרב. למרבה המזל, הם היו עסוקים במקום אחר.
akher bemakom asukim hayu hem lemarbe hamazal mitkarev ha'oyev im
another in a place busy they were they very luckily he approaches the enemy if

מן הסתם באכילת גווייתו של תייר אחר שצדו בביצה. הסעתי
hisati babitsa shetsadu akher tayar shel gviyato be'akhilat min hastam
I drove in the swamp that they hunted another tourist of his carcass in eating of probably

את המכונית לכניסת מרכז המידע וגילת קפצה פנימה.
pnima kaftsa vegilat hameida merkaz likhnisat hamkhonit et
inside she jumped and Gilat the information center of to the entrance of the car D.O.

As we sped back to our hotel, Gilat tried to count the number of bites on her body. She stopped at two hundred and punched me in the arm.

כשמיהרנו חזרה למלון, ניסתה גילת לספור את העקיצות שעל גופה.
gufa she'al ha'akitsot et lispor gilat nista lamalon khazara kshemiharnu
her body that on the bites D.O. to count Gilat she tried to the hotel back to as we hurried

היא הפסיקה במאתיים וחבטה בזרועי.
bizro'i vekhavta bemata'im hifsika hi
on my arm and she punched at two hundred she stopped she

"Ow," I said. "What was that for?"

"איי," אמרתי. "מה זה היה?"
haya ze ma amarti ai
it was that what I said ow

"For taking me to this stupid Botanical Garden," she said.

"על זה שהבאת אותי לגן הבוטני הטיפשי הזה," אמרה.
amra haze hatipshi habotani lagan oti al ze she'heveta
she said the this the stupid the botanical to the garden me for bringing

"You forced me to come here," I said. "I wanted to sit around the pool and drink wine."

"את הכרחת אותי לבוא לכאן," אמרתי. "אני רציתי לשבת ליד
leyad lashevet ratsiti ani amarti lekhan lavo oti hikhrakht at
next to to sit I wanted I I said to here to come me you forced you

הבריכה ולשתות יין."
ya'in   velishtot   habreikha
wine   and to drink   the pool

"זה מה שהיינו צריכים לעשות. זו אשמתך."
ashmatkha   zo   la'asot   sheha'inu tsrikhim   ma   ze
your fault   this   to do   we should have   what   that

"That's what we should have done. It's your fault."

STORY 7

Fool's Gold

"תיזהר מהמשאית!" צעקה גילת אשתי.
tizaher *mehamasa'it* *tsa'aka* *gilat* *ishti*
you will be careful | of the truck | she yelled | gilat | my wife

"Watch out for that truck!" my wife Gilat yelled.

"אני רואה אותה. את רוצה לנהוג?"
ani *ro'e* *ota* *at* *rotsa* *linhog*
I | see | it | you | you want | to drive

"I see it. Would you like to drive?"

"לא, רפי, נהיגה במנהטן מלחיצה אותי מדי."
lo *rafi* *nehiga* *bemanheten* *malkhitsa* *oti* *midai*
no | Rafi | driving | in Manhattan | it stresses out | me | too much

"No, Rafi, driving in Manhattan makes me too nervous."

"אז תפסיקי להתלונן. את מפריעה לי," אמרתי תוך שאני חותך נהג
az *tafsiki* *lehitlonen* *at* *mafri'a* *li* *amarti* *tokh* *she'ani* *khotekh* *nehag*
so | you will stop | to complain | you | you bother | to me | I said | while | that I | I cut off | driver of

מונית בשדרה העשירית.
monit *basdera* *ha'asirit*
taxi | on avenue | the tenth

"Well stop complaining. You're distracting me," I said as I cut off a taxi cab on Tenth Avenue.

"נהג המונית עשה תנועה מגונה לעברנו," אמרה גילת. "איזה חצוף."
nehag *hamonit* *asa* *tnu'a* *meguna* *le'evrenu* *amra* *gilat* *eize* *khatsuf*
driver | the taxi | he made | movement | offensive | toward us | she said | gilat | how | rude

"That taxi driver made an obscene gesture at us," Gilat said. "How rude."

"הוא רק נופף לשלום."
hu *rak* *nofef* *leshalom*
he | just | he waves | to hello

"He was just waving hello."

"למה כולם צופרים? יש בכל פינה שלטים שאומרים שזה קנס
lama *kulam* *tsofrim* *yesh* *bekhol* *pina* *shlatim* *she'omrim* *sheze* *knas*
why | everyone | they honk | there are | on every | corner | signs | that they say | that this | fine

של שלוש מאות וחמישים דולר."
shel *shlosh me'ot* *ve'khamishim* *dolar*
of | three hundred | and fifty | dollar

"Why does everyone honk their horns? There are signs on every corner saying it's a three hundred fifty dollar fine."

"השוטרים לא נותנים דוחות לנהגים מקומיים. בגלל שאין לנו
hashotrim *lo* *notnim* *dokhot* *linahagim* *mekomiyim* *biglal* *she'ein lanu*
the policemen | no | they give | tickets | to drivers | local | because of | that we don't have

לוחיות רישוי של ניו יורק, אנחנו נקבל דוח. אני מבטיח לך שאם
lukhiyot rishui *shel* *nyu* *york* *anakhnu* *nekabel* *dokh* *ani* *mavti'akh* *lakh* *she'im*
license plates | of | New | York | we | we will get | ticket | I | I promise | to you | that if

אצפור, תנחת עלינו להקת שוטרים ותרשום לנו דוחות ככל
etspor *tinkhat* *aleinu* *lahakat* *shotrim* *vetirshom* *lanu* *dokhot* *kekhol*
I will honk | it will land | on us | horde of | policemen | and it will write | to us | tickets | as many as

"The cops don't give tickets to local drivers. Since we don't have New York license plates, we would get a ticket. I guarantee that if I hit the horn one time, a horde of police officers would descend on us and write as many tickets as we could carry."

שנוכל לשאת.
shenukhal laset
that we will be able / to carry

"How come none of the drivers stay in their lane?" Gilat asked.

איך זה שאף אחד מהנהגים האלה לא נשאר בנתיב שלו?
eikh ze she'af ekhad mehanahagim ha'ele lo nishar banativ shelo
how this that not one of the drivers the these no he stayed in the lane his

שאלה גילת.
sha'ala gilat
she asked Gilat

"They are too busy avoiding potholes, double parked cars, and those crazy bicycle riders to pay attention to the lines on the street."

הם עסוקים מדי בהתחמקות מהמהמורות בכביש, מכוניות בחניה
hem asukim midai behitkhamkut mehamahamurot bakvish, mekhoniyot bekhanaya
they busy too evading from the potholes in the road, cars in parking

כפולה ורוכבי האופניים המטורפים האלה מכדי לשים לב לקווים
kfula verokhvei ha'ofana'im hametorafim ha'ele mikhdei lasim lev lakavim
double and riders of the bicycles the crazy the those in order to to pay attention to lines

על הכביש.
al hakvish
on the street

"You just went through a red light."

עברת עכשיו באור אדום.
avarta akhshav be'or adom
you went through just now in a light red

"So did the three cars behind us. If I had stopped, they would have rammed us."

וגם שלוש המכוניות שמאחורינו. אם הייתי עוצר, הם היו נכנסים
vagam shalosh hamekhoniyot sheme'akhoreinu. im ha'iti otser, hem hayu nikhnasim
and also three the cars that behind us. if I had stopped, they they would hit

בנו.
banu
into us

"I'm so glad we're driving an old car. It's got so many dents that any additional ones will be an improvement."

אני כל כך שמחה שאנחנו נוסעים במכונית ישנה. יש בה כל כך
ani kol kakh smekha she'anakhnu nosim bimkhonit yeshana. yesh ba kol kakh
I so glad that we we drive in car old. there is in it so

הרבה מכות שכל מכה נוספת תהיה שיפור.
harbe makot shekol maka nosefet tihiye shipur
many dents that any dent additional it will be improvement

"Yeah, the people with fancy new cars are at a disadvantage. They can't afford to be aggressive," I said.

כן, האנשים במכוניות החדשות והיקרות נמצאים בעמדת
ken, ha'anashim bamkhoniyot hakhadashot vehayekarot nimtsa'im be'emdat
yes the people in the cars the new and the expensive they are found at a position of

נחיתות. הם לא יכולים להרשות לעצמם להיות אגרסיבים, אמרתי.
nekhitut. hem lo yekholim leharshot le'atsmam lihiyot agresivim, amarti
inferiority they no they can to allow to themselves to be aggressive I said

"Why are you stopping?"

למה אתה עוצר?
lama ata otser
why you you stop

"אני רוצה נקניקייה."
ani *rotse* *naknikiya*
I / I want / hot dog

"I want a hot dog."

"לא צריך להחנות את המכונית?"
lo *tsarikh* *lehakhnot* *et* *hamkhonit*
no / you need / to park / D.O. / the car

"Shouldn't you park the car?"

"כל מקומות החנייה תפוסים. זה בסדר לחנות בחנייה כפולה כאן,
kol *mekomot* *hakhanaya* *tfusim* *ze* *beseder* *lakhanot* *bekhanaya* *kfula* *kan*
all / spaces of / the parking / taken / this / okay / to park / in parking / double / here

ליד המוכר."
leyad *hamokher*
next to / the vendor

"All the parking spaces are taken. It's okay to double park right here next to this vendor."

"אבל יש שני אוטובוסים ושלוש משאיות תקועים מאחורינו
aval *yesh* *shnei* *otobusim* *veshalosh* *masa'iyot* *tku'im* *me'akhoreinu*
but / there are / two of / buses / and three / trucks / stuck / behind us

וצופרים. הם לא יכעסו?"
vetsofrim *hem* *lo* *yikhasu*
and they honk / they / no / they will be angry

"But there are two buses and three trucks backed up behind us honking their horns. Won't they be angry?"

"זו מנהטן. הם צריכים לצפות לכמה עיכובים," אמרתי.
zo *manheten* *hem* *tsrikhim* *letsapot* *lekhama* *ikuvim* *amarti*
this / Manhattan / they / they should / to expect / to a few / delays / I said

"This is Manhattan. They have to expect a few delays," I said.

פתחתי את חלון הנהג. הריח שעלה מדוכן הנקניקיות מילא
patakhti *et* *khalon* *hanahag* *harei'akh* *she'ala* *midukhan* *hanaknikiyot* *mile*
I opened / D.O. / window of / the driver / the smell / that rose / from stand of / the hot dogs / it filled

את חלל המכונית.
et *khalal* *hamkhonit*
D.O. / space of / the car

I opened my window. The smell from the hot dog cart filled the car.

"נקניקייה עם כרוב כבוש וקטשופ," צעקתי באנגלית מבעד לרעש
naknikiya *im* *kruv kavush* *vekechup* *tsa'akti* *be'anglit* *miba'ad* *lera'ash*
hot dog / with / sauerkraut / and ketchup / I yelled / in English / through / to noise

פטישי האוויר.
patishei ha'avir
the jackhammers

"A hot dog with sauerkraut and ketchup," I yelled in English above the sound of jackhammers.

"אתה חושב שבטוח לאכול כאן?" שאלה גילת.
ata *khoshev* *shebatu'akh* *le'ekhol* *kan* *sha'ala* *gilat*
you / you think / that it is safe / to eat / here / she asked / gilat

"Do you think the food is safe to eat?" asked Gilat.

"בוודאי. זה אתר בנייה. רק לדוכני הנקניקיות הטובים ביותר
bevadai *ze* *atar* *bniya* *rak* *ledukhanei* *hanaknikiyot* *hatovim* *beyoter*
of course / this / site of / construction / only / to the stands of / the hot dogs / the good / most

מותר למכור כאן. את רוצה משהו?"
mutar *limkor* *kan* *at* *rotsa* *mashehu*
it is allowed / to sell / here / you / you want / something

"Sure. This is a construction site. Only the best hot dog vendors are allowed to sell their food here. Do you want anything?"

"I think I'll wait until later."

"אני חושבת שאחכה לאחר כך."
le'akhar kakh she'akhake khoshevet ani
for later that I will wait I think I

"You're missing out on a real treat," I said as I took my food from the friendly vendor and paid him four dollars.

את מפסידה מעדן אמיתי," אמרתי תוך שאני לוקח את המנה
hamana et loke'akh she'ani tokh amarti amiti ma'adan mafsida at
the dish D.O. I take that I while I said true delicacy you miss out on you

מהמוכר הידידותי ומשלם לו ארבעה דולרים.
dolarim arba'a lo umeshalem hayediduti mehamokher
dollars four to him and I pay the friendly from the seller

"The driver of the bus behind us got out of the bus and is walking toward you," Gilat said fearfully.

"נהג האוטובוס מאחורינו יצא מהאוטובוס והולך לעברך," אמרה
amra le'evrekha veholekh meha'otobus yatsa me'akhoreinu ha'otobus nehag
she said toward you and he walks from the bus he exited behind us the bus driver of

גילת בפחד.
befakhad gilat
fearfully Gilat

"He probably wants a hot dog too," I said.

"בוודאי גם הוא רוצה נקניקייה," אמרתי.
amarti naknikiya rotse hu gam bevadai
I said hot dog he wants he also probably

I hit the gas and pulled away just as the bus driver got to my window.

לחצתי על דוושת הגז והתרחקתי משם ממש כשנהג
kshenehag mamash misham vehitrakhakti hagaz davshat al lakhatsti
when driver of precisely from there and I pulled away the gas pedal of on I pressed

האוטובוס הגיע לחלון שלי.
sheli lakhalon higi'a ha'otobus
my to the window he arrived the bus

"He's shaking his fist at you," Gilat said.

"הוא מנופף לעברך באגרוף," אמרה גילת.
gilat amra be'egrof le'evrekha menofef hu
Gilat she said with fist toward you he waves he

"Quit looking through the rear window," I said. "You'll get a stiff neck."

"תפסיקי להסתכל בחלון האחורי," אמרתי. "ייתפס לך
lakh yitafes amarti ha'akhori bakhalon lehistakel tafsiki
to you he will be pulled I said the rear at the window to look you will stop

הצוואר."
hatsavar
the neck

I ate my hot dog as I drove up Tenth Avenue with one hand on the wheel. Gilat let out a few mild shrieks of fear. I don't know why. Traffic was pretty manageable today. I took a sharp left turn onto Forty-Ninth street.

אכלתי את הנקניקייה בעודי נוהג בשדרה העשירית עם יד אחת על
al akhat yad im ha'asirit basdera noheg be'odi hanaknikiya et akhalti
on one hand with the tenth on avenue I drive as I the hot dog D.O. I ate

ההגה. גילת השמיעה צווחות מבוהלות אחדות. אני לא יודע
yode'a lo ani akhadot mevohalot tsvakhot hishmi'a gilat hahege
I know no I a few frightened screams she made a sound Gilat the steering wheel

למה. התנועה הייתה יחסית סבירה היום. פניתי פנייה חדה שמאלה
smola khada pniya paniti hayom svira yakhasit haita hatnu'a lama
leftward sharp turn I turned today reasonable relatively it was the traffic why

לרחוב ארבעים ותשע.
lirkhov arba'im vatesha
to street / forty / and nine

"תראה את האנשים האלה שבורחים מהנתיב שלנו," אמרה גילת.
tire et ha'anashim ha'ele sheborkhim mehanativ shelanu, amra gilat
you will look / D.O. / the people / the those / that (they) run away / from the path / our / she said / Gilat

"Look at those people jump out of our way," Gilat said.

"הנזירות האלה זריזות למדי. אפילו זאת המבוגרת עם מקל ההליכה יודעת לרוץ די מהר."
hanezirot ha'ele zrizot lemadai. afilu zot hamevugeret im makel hahalikha yoda'at laruts dei maher.
the nuns / the those / quick / quite / even / that / the old lady / with / stick of / the walking / she knows how / to run / fairly / fast

"Those nuns are pretty quick. Even the old one with the cane can scurry pretty fast."

נכנסתי לתוך בניין חניה. הוא נראה כאילו גמר את הקריירה לפני עשר שנים, אבל היו להם המחירים הטובים ביותר בניו יורק. שילמנו לשומר הרוסי החביב וצעדנו מזרחה.
nikhnasti letokh binyan khanaya. hu nira ke'ilu gamar et hakaryera lifnei eser shanim, aval hayu lahem hamekhirim hatovim beyoter benyu york shilamnu lashomer harusi hakhaviv vetsa'adnu mizrakha.
I entered / into / building of / parking / it / it looked / like / it ceased / D.O. / the career / ago / ten / years / but / they had / the prices / the good / most / in New / York / we paid / to the guard / the Russian / the friendly / and we walked / eastward

I pulled into a parking garage. It looked like it had ceased operating ten years ago, but they had the best prices in New York City. We paid the friendly Russian attendant and walked east.

"אתה חושב שבטוח בשכונה הזאת?" שאלה גילת.
ata khoshev shebatu'akh bashkhuna hazot? sha'ala gilat
you / you think / that safe / in the neighborhood / the this / she asked / Gilat

"Do you think that this neighborhood is safe?" Gilat asked.

"אל תדאגי. הפושעים באזור הזה עובדים רק בלילה," אמרתי.
al tidagi. haposhim ba'ezor haze ovdim rak balaila, amarti
don't / you will worry / the criminals / in the area / the this / they work / only / at night / I said

"Don't worry. The criminals in this area only work at night," I said.

"אתה אומר את זה בסרקזם?" שאלה גילת.
ata omer et ze besarkazem? sha'ala gilat
you / you say / D.O. / this / sarcastically / she asked / Gilat

"Are you being sarcastic?" Gilat asked.

"כן."
ken
yes

"Yes."

עשר דקות מאוחר יותר היינו במתחם היהלומים. רחוב ארבעים ושבע, בין השדרה החמישית והשישית. עצרתי ונשענתי על ואן.
eser dakot me'ukhar yoter ha'inu be'mitkham hayahalomim. rekhov arba'im vasheva, bein hasdera hakhamishit vehashishit. atsarti venishanti al van.
ten / minutes / later / more / we were / in district of / the diamonds / street / forty / and seven / between / the avenue / the fifth / and the sixth / I stopped / and I leaned on / on / van

Ten minutes later we were in the Diamond District. Forty-seventh street, between Fifth Avenue and Sixth Avenue. I stopped and leaned against a parked van.

חונה.
khone
parked

"Give me some time to catch my breath," I said to Gilat.

"תני לי קצת זמן להסדיר את הנשימה," אמרתי לגילת.
legilat amarti haneshima et lehasdir zman ktsat li tni
to Gilat I said the breath D.O. to regularize time a little to me give

"You really are out of shape," Gilat said.

"אתה באמת לא בכושר," אמרה גילת.
gilat amra bekosher lo be'emet ata
Gilat she said in shape not really you

"How come we had to run all the way from Eighth Avenue to here?" I asked.

"איך זה שהיינו צריכים לרוץ את כל הדרך מהשדרה השמינית עד
ad hashminit mehasdera haderekh kol et laruts sheha'inu tsrikhim eikh ze
until the eighth from the avenue the way all D.O. to run that we had to how come

לכאן?" שאלתי.
sha'alti lekhan
I asked to here

"I thought someone was following us."

"חשבתי שמישהו עוקב אחרינו."
akhareinu okev shemishehu khashavti
after us he follows that someone I thought

"I almost got hit by a limousine when we sprinted across Broadway. We're supposed to wait for the green light." It took a while to get the words out, since I was still struggling to get air into my lungs.

"כמעט נדרסתי על ידי לימוזינה כשחצינו את רחוב ברודווי
brodwei rekhov et kshekhatsinu limuzina al yedei nidrasti kimat
Broadway road D.O. when we crossed limousine by I was run over almost

בריצה. אנחנו אמורים לחכות לאור הירוק." לקח קצת זמן
zman ktsat lakakh hayarok la'or lekhakot amurim anakhnu beritsa
time a little it took the green for the light to wait supposed to we by running

לפלוט את המילים, מאחר שעדיין נאבקתי להכניס אוויר לריאותיי.
lere'otai avir lehakhnis ne'evakti she'ada'in me'akhar hamilim et liflot
to my lungs air to bring in I struggled with that still since the words D.O. to utter

"Stop complaining," Gilat said. "We made it here without losing the gold chains. Let's go up and see how much they are worth."

"תפסיק להתלונן," אמרה גילת. "הגענו עד לכאן בלי לאבד את
et le'abed bli lekhan ad higanu gilat amra lehitlonen tafsik
D.O. to lose without to here as far as we arrived Gilat she said to complain you will stop

שרשראות הזהב. בוא נעלה ונראה כמה הן שוות."
shavot hen kama venire na'ale bo hazahav sharshera'ot
worth they how much and we will see we will go up let's the gold chains of

After a few more minutes I was able to breathe normally. We walked into a ten story building in the middle of the block and took the elevator to the sixth floor. Room 604 had a plaque on the door with the name of the business engraved in gold. We were buzzed into a little reception room. A young lady sat at a desk behind a bullet proof panel.

לאחר מספר דקות נוספות הצלחתי לנשום כרגיל. צעדנו אל תוך
tokh el tsa'adnu karagil linshom hitslakhti nosafot dakot mispar le'akhar
inside to we walked normally to breathe I was successful additional minutes a few after

בניין בן עשר קומות באמצע הבלוק ועלינו במעלית
bama'alit ve'alinu hablok be'emtsa komot eser ben binyan
in the elevator and we went up the block in middle of stories ten comprising building

לקומה השישית. על דלת חדר מספר 604 היה תלוי שלט
shelet talui haya shesh me'ot ve'arba mispar kheder delet al hashishit lakoma
sign hanging it was 604 number room door of on the sixth to the floor

עם שם העסק חרוט עליו באותיות מוזהבות. נשמע זמזום
im / *shem* / *ha'esek* / *kharut* / *alav* / *be'otiyot* / *muzhavot.* / *nishma* / *zimzum*
with / name of / the business / engraved / on it / in letters / gilded / it was heard / buzz

מהדלת והוכנסנו פנימה לחדר קבלה קטן. גברת צעירה
mehadelet / *vehukhnasnu* / *pnima* / *lekhadar* / *kabala* / *katan.* / *gveret* / *tse'ira*
from the door / and we were brought in / inside / to a room of / reception / little / lady / young

ישבה ליד שולחן שהוצב מאחורי מחיצה חסינת כדורים.
yashva / *leyad* / *shulkhan* / *shehutsav* / *me'akhorei* / *mekhitsa* / *khasinat kadurim.*
she sat / next to / table / that was positioned / behind / barrier / bulletproof

"אנחנו רוצים למכור כמה שרשראות זהב," אמרה גילת לגברת.
anakhnu / *rotsim* / *limkor* / *kama* / *sharshera'ot* / *zahav* / *amra* / *gilat* / *lagveret.*
we / we want / to sell / a few / necklaces of / gold / she said / Gilat / to the lady

"We want to sell some gold necklaces," Gilat said to the lady.

"תיכנסו לתא מספר אחת. תנעלו את הדלת מאחוריכם ואני
tikansu / *leta* / *mispar* / *akhat.* / *tinalu* / *et* / *hadelet* / *me'akhoreikhem* / *va'ani*
you will enter / to booth / number / one / you will lock / D.O. / the door / behind you / and I

"Step into booth number one. Lock the door behind you, and I'll send someone."

אשלח מישהו."
eshlakh / *mishehu.*
I will send / someone

על הקיר משמאלה של פקידת הקבלה היו שלוש דלתות ממוספרות.
al / *hakir* / *mismola* / *shel* / *pkidat hakabala* / *hayu* / *shalosh* / *dlatot* / *memusparot.*
on / the wall / to her left / of / the receptionist / they were / three / doors / numbered

נכנסנו בדלת מספר אחת. מולנו ניצבה מחיצה חסינת כדורים נוספת.
nikhnasnu / *bedelet* / *mispar* / *akhat.* / *muleinu* / *nitsva* / *mekhitsa* / *khasinat kadurim* / *nosefet.*
we entered / in door / number / one / opposite us / it stood / barrier / bulletproof / additional

תוך שלוש דקות הופיע מאחורי המחיצה גבר נמוך ורזה בעל
tokh / *shalosh* / *dakot* / *hofi'a* / *me'akhorei* / *hamekhitsa* / *gever* / *namukh* / *veraze* / *ba'al*
within / three / minutes / he appeared / behind / the barrier / man / short / and thin / having

שפמפם.
sfamfam.
small mustache

There were three numbered doors on a wall to the left of the receptionist. We walked through door number one. There was another bullet proof panel in front of us. Within three minutes a short, thin, young man with a small mustache appeared behind the panel.

"היי," אמר. "יש לכם זהב בשבילי?"
hai / *amar.* / *yesh lakhem* / *zahav* / *bishvili?*
hi / he said / you have / gold / for me

"Hi," he said. "You have gold for me?"

"יש לך מבטא מעניין," אמרתי בזמן שגילת דגה שקית פלסטיק
yesh lekha / *mivta* / *me'anyen,* / *amarti* / *bizman* / *shegilat* / *daga* / *sakit* / *plastik*
you have / accent / interesting / I said / when / that Gilat / she fished / bag of / plastic

מתוך ארנקה. "מאיפה אתה?"
mitokh / *arnaka.* / *me'eifo* / *ata?*
out of / her purse / from where / you

"You have an interesting accent," I said as Gilat fished a plastic bag out of her pocketbook. "Where are you from?"

"ליטא," ענה האיש.
lita / *ana* / *ha'ish.*
Lithuania / he answered / the man

"Lithuania," he answered.

"Is that near Chicago?" I asked.

"זה ליד שיקגו?" שאלתי.

ze	leyad	shikago	sha'alti
that	near	Chicago	I asked

"No," he laughed.

"לא," הוא צחק.

lo	hu	tsakhak
no	he	he laughed

Gilat produced her bag full of gold chains and pushed it through a slot in the barrier onto a countertop. Twenty minutes later, we walked out with four hundred dollars in cash.

גילת הוציאה את השקית המלאה בשרשראות זהב ודחפה אותה

gilat	hotsi'a	et	hasakit	hamele'a	besharshera'ot	zahav	vedakhafa	ota
Gilat	she took out	D.O.	the small bag	the full	with chains of	gold	and she pushed	it

בעד חרך במחיצה אל הדלפק. עשרים דקות מאוחר יותר יצאנו

ba'ad	kharakh	bamekhitsa	el	hadelpak	esrim	dakot	me'ukhar	yoter	yatsanu
through	slit	in the barrier	to	the counter	twenty	minutes	later	more	we left

עם ארבע מאות דולר במזומן.

im	arba me'ot	dolar	bimzuman
with	four hundred	dollar	in cash

"They paid us fifty percent more than the jewelry stores in New Jersey were willing to pay," Gilat said. "Let's treat ourselves to a nice dinner."

"הם שילמו לנו חמישים אחוז יותר ממה שחנויות התכשיטים

hem	shilmu	lanu	khamishim	akhuz	yoter	mima	shekhanuyot	hatakhshitim
they	they paid	to us	fifty	percent	more	than what	that stores of	the jewelry

בניו ג'רזי היו מוכנות לשלם," אמרה גילת. "בוא נתפנק

benyu	jerzi	hayu	mukhanot	leshalem	amra	gilat	bo	nitpanek
in New	Jersey	they were	ready	to pay	she said	Gilat	let's	we will treat ourselves

בארוחת ערב טובה."

be'arukhat erev	tova
with a dinner	good

"We should go eat hamburgers," I said. "Otherwise, we'll wind up spending our extra profits on fancy food and wine that we don't need."

"כדai לנו ללכת לאכול המבורגרים," אמרתי. "אחרת נבזבז את

kedai	lanu	lalekhet	le'ekhol	hamburgerim	amarti	akheret	nevazbez	et
worthwhile	to us	to go	to eat	hamburgers	I said	otherwise	we will waste	D.O.

כל הרווח על אוכל ויין יקרים שאנחנו לא צריכים."

kol	harevakh	al	okhel	veya'in	yekarim	she'anakhnu	lo	tsrikhim
all	the profit	on	food	and wine	expensive	that we	no	we need

"I made a dinner reservation before we left the hotel," Gilat said. "It's a French place just two blocks from here."

"הזמנתי מקומות במסעדה לפני שיצאנו מהמלון," אמרה גילת. "זו

hizmanti	mekomot	bemisada	lifnei	sheyatsanu	mehamalon	amra	gilat	zo
I reserved	spaces	at a restaurant	before	that we left	from the hotel	she said	Gilat	this

מסעדה צרפתית שני צמתים מכאן."

misada	tsarfatit	shnei	tsmatim	mikan
restaurant	French	two of	blocks	from here

I thought for a minute.

חשבתי לרגע.

khashavti	lerega
I thought	for a minute

"This whole adventure was all part of a clever plan to eat dinner at a fancy restaurant in Manhattan, wasn't it?" I said to Gilat.

"כל ההרפתקה הזאת היתה חלק מתוכנית מתוחכמת לאכול ארוחת ערב

kol	haharpatka	hazot	haita	khelek	mitokhnit	metukh'kemet	le'ekhol	arukhat erev
all	the adventure	the this	it was	part	of a plan	clever	to eat	dinner

במסעדה יוקרתית במנהטן, נכון?" אמרתי לגילת.
bemisada yukratit bemanheten nakhon amarti legilat
at a restaurant fancy in Manhattan right I said to Gilat

"ואם כן?"
ve'im ken
and if yes

"What if it was?"

"נלך לשם, בתנאי שלא תכריחי אותי לרוץ," אמרתי.
nelekh lesham bitnai shelo takhrikhi oti laruts amarti
we will go to there on the condition that no you will force me to run I said

"We can go there as long as you don't make me run," I said.

STORY 8

Dumbbells Everywhere

"תוריד קצת במשקל, רפי."
torid — you will lose
ktsat — a little
bamishkal — weight
rafi — Rafi

"Lose some weight, Rafi."

"זה הכל?" שאלתי. "ארבע מאות וחמישים שקלים עבור בדיקה
ze — that
hakol — everything
sha'alti — I asked
arba me'ot — four hundred
vakhamishim — and fifty
shkalim — shekels
avur — for
bdika — exam

מקיפה, וכל מה שאתה אומר לי זה שאני צריך לרדת במשקל?
makifa — comprehensive
vekhol ma — and all that
she'ata — that you
omer — you tell
li — to me
ze — that
she'ani — that I
tsarikh — I need
laredet bamishkal — to lose weight

בסכום הזה היית צריך למצוא לפחות ארבע בעיות נוספות.
baskhum — for sum of money
haze — the that
ha'ita tsarikh — you should have
limtso — to find
lefakhot — at least
arba — four
be'ayot — problems
nosafot — additional

אני רוצה חוות דעת נוספת."
ani — I
rotse — I want
khavat da'at — opinion
nosefet — additional

"That's it?" I asked. "Four hundred and fifty shekels for a complete physical and all you tell me is that I need to lose weight? For that kind of money, you should have found at least four other problems. I want a second opinion."

"או קיי," אמר חברי הטוב, ד"ר מיכה ווגנר, "גם האף שלך נראה
o kei — okay
amar — he said
khaveri — my friend
hatov — the good
doktor — doctor
mikha — Micha
vagner — Wagner
gam — also
ha'af — the nose
shelkha — your
nire — it looks

מוזר."
muzar — strange

"Okay," my good friend Dr. Micha Wagner said, "your nose looks funny, too."

"אתה עושה הופעות סטנד אפ בבית החולים בימי חמישי בערב?"
ata — you
ose — you do
hofa'ot — performances
stend ap — stand-up
beveit hakholim — at the hospital
biymei khamishi — on Thursdays
ba'erev — in the evening

שאלתי.
sha'alti — I asked

"Do you do standup comedy at the hospital on Thursday nights?" I asked.

"תשמע," הוא אמר, "אנחנו מכירים מאז האוניברסיטה. אתה יכול
tishma — you will listen
hu — he
amar — he said
anakhnu — we
makirim — we are familiar
me'az — since
ha'universita — the university
ata — you
yakhol — you can

לסמוך עליי. אני אומר לך שאתה צריך להתחיל להתאמן כל יום."
lismokh — to trust
alai — on me
ani — I
omer — I tell
lekha — to you
she'ata — that you
tsarikh — you need
lehatkhil — to start
lehitamen — to exercise
kol — every
yom — day

"Listen," he said, "we've known each other since college. You can trust me. I'm telling you that you have to start exercising every day."

"אני עובד כרגע חמישים שעות בשבוע," אמרתי. "יש לי שלושה
ani — I
oved — I work
karega — right now
khamishim — fifty
sha'ot — hours
beshavu'a — in a week
amarti — I said
yesh li — I have
shlosha — three

"I'm working fifty hours a week right now," I said. "I've got three small kids who I try to spend time with. And Gilat, my lovely wife, wants me to talk

69

with her every once in a while. I don't have any extra time to exercise."

ילדים קטנים שאני מנסה לבלות איתם קצת זמן יחד. וגילת,
yeladim ktanim she'ani menase levalot itam ktsat zman yakhad vegilat
children — small — that I — I try — to spend time — with them — a little — time — together — and Gilat

אשתי החביבה, רוצה שאדבר איתה מדי פעם. אין לי זמן
ishti hakhaviva rotsa she'adaber ita midei pa'am ein li zman
my wife — the lovely — she wants — that I will talk — with her — from time to time — I don't have — time

פנוי להתאמן."
panui lehitamen
free — to exercise

"What do you do after work?"

"מה אתה עושה אחרי העבודה?"
ma ata ose akharei ha'avoda
what — you — you do — after — the work

"I hope you don't intend to bill me for this conversation," I said. "I heard about how doctors charge patients just for talking with them."

"אני מקווה שאתה לא מתכוון לשלוח לי חשבון על השיחה
ani mekave she'ata lo mitkaven lishlo'akh li kheshbon al hasikha
I — I hope — that you — no — you intend — to send — to me — bill — for — the conversation

הזאת," אמרתי. "שמעתי על זה שרופאים מחייבים מטופלים רק על
hazot amarti shamati al ze sherofim mekhayvim metupalim rak al
the this — I said — I heard — about — this — that doctors — they charge — patients — just — for

שיחה."
sikha
conversation

"Do you want me to give you a couple of injections that you don't need?" he asked.

"אתה רוצה שאתן לך כמה זריקות שאתה לא צריך?" הוא
ata rotse she'eten lekha kama zrikot she'ata lo tsarikh hu
you — you want — that I will give — to you — a few — injections — that you — no — you need — he

שאל.
sha'al
he asked

Unfair. He knew I was afraid of needles.

לא הוגן. הוא ידע שאני מפחד ממחטים.
lo hogen hu yada she'ani mefakhed mimakhatim
not — fair — he — he knew — that I — afraid — of needles

"Okay, I'll talk," I said as I waved the imaginary needles away. "After work we eat dinner. We play with the kids, put them to bed, and then watch a few hours of television."

"בסדר, אני אדבר," אמרתי בעודי מנופף מעלי מחטים דמיוניות.
beseder ani amarti be'odi menofef me'alai mekhatim dimyoniyot
okay — I — I will talk — I said — as I — I wave — away from me — needles — imaginary

"אחרי העבודה אנחנו אוכלים ארוחת ערב. אנחנו משחקים עם הילדים,
akharei ha'avoda anakhnu okhlim arukhat erev anakhnu mesakhakim im hayeladim
after — the work — we — we eat — dinner — we — we play — with — the kids

משכיבים אותם לישון, ואז אנחנו צופים בטלוויזיה כמה שעות."
mashkivim otam lishon ve'az anakhnu tsofim batelevizya kama sha'ot
we put to bed — them — to sleep — and then — we — we watch — at the television — a few — hours

"There's the answer. Instead of watching television, you can exercise for an hour."

"והרי התשובה שלך. במקום לצפות בטלוויזיה אתה יכול להתאמן
veharei hatshuva shelkha bimkom litspot batelevizya ata yakhol lehitamen
and here is — the answer — your — instead of — to watch — at the television — you — you can — to exercise

שעה.
sha'a
hour

"כל כך מאוחר בלילה?" שאלתי.
kol kakh / me'ukhar / balaila / sha'alti
so / late / at night / I asked
"That late at night?" I asked.

"זה לא מושלם, אבל זה עדיף על להפוך למרשמלו."
ze / lo / mushlam / aval / ze / adif / al / lahafokh / lemarshmelo
this / not / perfect / but / this / preferable / over / to turn into / to a marshmallow
"It's not perfect, but it's better than turning into a marshmallow."

"רק עכשיו קניתי טלוויזיה בעלת מסך גדול ומערכת
rak / akhshav / kaniti / televizya / ba'alat / masakh / gadol / uma'arekhet
just / now / I bought / television / possessor of / screen / big / and set of
"I just bought a big screen television and surround sound speakers."

סראונד."
seraund
surround sound speakers

"תקליט את התוכניות האהובות עליך בזמן שאתה מתאמן
taklit / et / hatokhniyot / ha'ahuvot / aleikha / bizman / she'ata / mitamen
you will record / D.O. / the programs / the favorite / on you / when / that you / you exercise
"Record your favorite shows while you are exercising and watch them on weekends," he said.

ותצפה בהן בסופי השבוע," הוא אמר.
vetitspe / bahen / besofei / hashavu'a / hu / amar
and you will watch / at them / in end of / the week / he / he said

"זה לא אותו דבר בסוף השבוע," התלוננתי.
ze / lo / oto davar / besof hashavu'a / hitlonanti
this / not / same thing / on the weekend / I complained
"It's not the same on the weekend," I complained.

ד"ר מיכה נתן בי מבט חודר.
doktor / mikha / natan / bi / mabat / khoder
doctor / Micha / he gave / at me / look / piercing
Doctor Micha gave me a piercing look.

"תפסיק להמציא תירוצים ותמצא דרך להתאמן קצת במקום
tafsik / lehamtsi / terutsim / vetimtsa / derekh / lehitamen / ktsat / bimkom
you will stop / to make up / excuses / and you will find / way / to exercise / a little / instead of
"Quit making excuses and figure out a way to get some exercise instead of watching television."

לצפות בטלוויזיה."
litspot / batelevizya
to watch / at the television

הוא נטל פנקס מרשמים והחל לכתוב. "זה שם של ספר כושר
hu / natal / pinkas / mirshamim / vehekhel / likhtov / ze / shem / shel / sefer / kosher
he / he grasped / notepad / prescriptions / and he started / to write / this / name / of / book / fitness
He took out a prescription pad and started writing. "This is the name of a great exercise book. There are three or four simple routines that you can use to vary your workout. Buy this book and start sweating."

מצוין. יש שלוש או ארבע סדרות פשוטות שאתה יכול לעשות
metsuyan / yesh / shalosh / o / arba / sdarot / pshutot / she'ata / yakhol / la'asot
excellent / there are / three / or / four / routines / simple / that you / you can / to do

כדי לגוון את האימון. תקנה את הספר הזה ותתחיל
kedei / legaven / et / ha'imun / tikne / et / hasefer / haze / vetatkhil
in order to / to vary / D.O. / the training / you will buy / D.O. / the book / the this / and you will start

לְהַזִּיעַ."
lehazi'a
to sweat

"I don't like to sweat," I told him. "When I sweat, it makes me feel icky."

לִי גּוֹרֵם זֶה מַזִּיעַ כְּשֶׁאֲנִי לוֹ. אָמַרְתִּי לְהַזִּיעַ," אוֹהֵב לֹא "אֲנִי
li gorem ze mazi'a kshe'ani lo amarti lehazi'a ohev lo ani
to me it causes this I sweat when I to him I said to sweat I like no I

לְהַרְגִּישׁ אִיכְסָה."
ikhsa lehargish
icky to feel

"I don't want to hear excuses," he said.

אָמַר. הוּא תֵּירוּצִים," לִשְׁמֹעַ רוֹצֶה לֹא "אֲנִי
amar hu terutsim lishmo'a rotse lo ani
he said he excuses to hear I want no I

"My underwear sticks to my skin," I continued. "Funny smells come out of my armpits."

מוּזָר רֵיחַ יֵשׁ הִמְשַׁכְתִּי. לָאוֹר," לִי נִדְבָּקִים שֶׁלִּי "הַתַּחְתּוֹנִים
muzar rei'akh yesh himshakhti la'or li nidbakim sheli hatakhtonim
strange smell there is I continued to the skin to me they stick my the underwear

שֶׁלִּי מִבָּתֵּי הַשֶּׁחִי שֶׁלִּי."
sheli mibatei hashekhi
my from armpits

"Shower after you exercise. Gilat will appreciate that," he said.

הוּא זֶה אֶת תַּאֲרִיךְ גִּילַת מִתְאַמֵּן שֶׁאַתָּה אַחֲרֵי "תִּתְקַלֵּחַ
hu ze et ta'arikh gilat mitamen she'ata akharei titkale'akh
he that D.O. she will appreciate Gilat you exercise that you after you will take a shower

עָנָה.
ana
he answered

"Who wants to shower more than once a week? Nobody! It's a waste of good water."

שֶׁל בִּזְבּוּז זֶה אֶחָד! אַף בַּשָּׁבוּעַ? מִפַּעַם יוֹתֵר לְהִתְקַלֵּחַ רוֹצֶה "מִי
shel bizbuz ze af ekhad beshavu'a mipa'am yoter lehitkale'akh rotse mi
of waste this no one in a week than once more to take a shower he wants who

מַיִם טוֹבִים."
tovim ma'im
good water

"Now you've gotten me really annoyed," he said. "Just for that, I'm making a house call next week on Saturday at one o'clock."

עוֹרֵךְ אֲנִי זֶה, בִּגְלַל רַק אָמַר. הוּא בֶּאֱמֶת," אוֹתִי הִרְגַּזְתָּ "עַכְשָׁיו
orekh ani ze biglal rak amar hu be'emet oti hirgazta akhshav
I arrange I that because of just he said he really me you annoyed now

אַחַת." בְּשָׁעָה הַבָּא שַׁבָּת בְּיוֹם בִּיקּוּר בַּיִת אֶצְלְךָ
akhat besha'a haba shabat beyom bikur ba'it etslekha
one at o'clock next Saturday on day house call at your place

"Is it covered by insurance?"

זֶה?" אֶת מְכַסֶּה "הַבִּיטוּחַ
ze et mekhase habitu'akh
this D.O. it covers the insurance

"No. I'm bringing my doctor's bag and checking your blood pressure. I'm staying for the soccer game, too, since you have that nice new television. Finally, I'm sitting in your favorite re-

הַדָּם לַחַץ אֶת וְאֶבְדֹּק שֶׁלִּי הָרוֹפֵא תִּיק אֶת אָבִיא אֲנִי "לֹא.
hadam lakhats et ve'evdok sheli harofe tik et avi ani lo
the blood pressure D.O. and I will check my the doctor bag D.O. I will bring I no

שלך. אני גם אשאר למשחק הכדורגל, מאחר שיש לך טלוויזיה
shelkha / ani / gam / esha'er / lemiskhak / hakaduregel / me'akhar / sheyesh lekha / televizya
your / I / also / I will stay / for game / the soccer / since / that you have / television

כל כך נחמדה. בנוסף, אני אשב על כורסת הטלוויזיה החביבה עליך
kol kakh / nekhmada / benosaf / ani / eshev / al / kursat hatelevizya / hakhaviva / aleikha
so / nice / additionally / I / I will sit / on / the easy-chair / the favorite / on you

בזמן שאצפה במשחק."
bizman / she'etspe / bamiskhak
while / that I will watch / at the game

cliner while I watch."

"זאת עם מחזיק הכוסות המובנה במשענת היד בשביל פחית הבירה?"
zot / im / makhzik / hakosot / hamuvne / bemishenet hayad / bishvil / pakhit / habira
that / with / holder / the cups / the built-in / the armrest / for / small can / the beer

"The one with the cup holder built into the armrest for your beer can?"

"זאת. תוודא שיהיו לך הרבה בירות וחטיפים," הוא אמר.
zot / tevade / sheihiyu lekha / harbe / birot / vakhatifim / hu / amar
that / you will make sure / that you will have / much / beers / and snacks / he / he said

"That one. Make sure you have plenty of beer and snacks," he said.

"ומה אם לחץ הדם שלי לא ירד?"
uma / im / lakhats / hadam / sheli / lo / yered
and what / if / pressure / the blood / my / no / it will lower

"And what if my blood pressure isn't lower?"

"אני אבוא כל שבת עד שאראה שיפור משמעותי. אולי
ani / avo / kol / shabat / ad / she'ere / shipur / mashma'uti / ulai
I / I will come / every / Saturday / until / that I will see / improvement / significant / maybe

אביא את המשפחה. החטיפים יעלו לך הון."
avi / et / hamishpakha / hakhatifim / ya'alu / lekha / hon
I will bring / D.O. / the family / the snacks / they will cost / to you / fortune

"I'll come back every Saturday until I see a big improvement. Maybe I'll bring my family. The snacks will cost you a fortune."

—2—

"למה כל ריהוט הסלון במחסן מלבד הטלוויזיה ושתי
lama / kol / rihut / hasalon / bamakhsan / milvad / hatelevizya / ushtei
why / all / furniture of / the living room / in the garage / except for / the television / and two of

הכורסאות?" שאלה אותי גילת מאוחר יותר באותו ערב.
hakursa'ot / sha'ala / oti / gilat / me'ukhar / yoter / be'oto / erev
the armchairs / she asked / me / Gilat / late / more / in the same / evening

"Why is all the living room furniture in the garage except for the television and the two armchairs?" Gilat asked me later that evening.

"אני צריך מקום להתאמן."
ani / tsarikh / makom / lehitamen
I / I need / space / to exercise

"I need space to exercise."

"אתה לא יכול להתאמן בחוץ?"
ata / lo / yakhol / lehitamen / bakhuts
you / no / you can / to exercise / outside

"Can't you exercise outside?"

"אני מתכוון להתאמן אחרי שנשכיב את הילדים לישון. עד אז
ani / mitkaven / lehitamen / akharei / shenashkiv / et / hayeladim / lishon / ad / az
I / I intend / to exercise / after / that we will put to bed / D.O. / the kids / to sleep / until / then

"I'll be exercising after we put the kids to bed. It's too dark outside by then."

73

נהיה חשוך מדי."
nihiya khashukh midai
it will become dark too

"Go to a gym."

"לך למכון כושר."
lekh limekhon kosher
go to a gym

"I want to exercise at home, where I can watch the TV shows that I like."

"אני רוצה להתאמן בבית, איפה שאני יכול לצפות בתוכניות הטלוויזיה
ani rotse lehitamen baba'it eifo she'ani yakhol litspot betokhniyot hatelevizya
I I want to exercise at home where that I I can to watch at shows of the television

שאני אוהב."
she'ani ohev
that I I like

"This doesn't sound good," she said.

"זה לא נשמע טוב," היא אמרה.
ze lo nishma tov hi amra
this no it sounds good she she said

"Micha Wagner said he would come over every Saturday to watch sports and eat all our food until I start to get in better shape."

"מיכה ווגנר אמר שיבוא כל שבת לצפות בספורט ולאכול את
mikha vagner amar sheyavo kol shabat litspot bisport vele'ekhol et
Micha Wagner he said he will come every Saturday to watch at sport and to eat D.O.

כל האוכל שלנו עד שאתחיל להיכנס לכושר."
kol ha'okhel shelanu ad she'atkhil lehikanes lekhosher
all the food our until that I will start to get into to fitness

"Better him than your parents," she said.

"עדיף אותו מאשר ההורים שלך," היא אמרה.
adif oto me'asher hahorim shelkha hi amra
preferable him than the parents your she she said

"Don't start picking on my parents," I said. "Let's focus on exercising."

"אל תתחילי עם ההורים שלי," אמרתי. "בואי נתרכז באימון."
al tatkhili im hahorim sheli amarti bo'i nitrakez ba'imun
don't you will start with the parents my I said let's we will focus on at exercising

"You focus on exercising. I'm not going to do it," she said.

"אתה תתרכז באימון. אני לא מתכוונת להצטרף," אמרה.
ata titrakez ba'imun ani lo mitkavenet lehitstaref amra
you you will focus at exercising I no I intend to join she said

"Why not?" I asked.

"למה לא?" שאלתי.
lama lo sha'alti
why no I asked

"I exercise at a gym five days a week during my lunch hour."

"אני מתאמנת במכון כושר חמש פעמים בשבוע בהפסקת הצוהריים
ani mitamenet bimekhon kosher khamesh pe'amim beshavu'a behafsakat hatsohora'im
I I exercise at a gym five times in a week at break of the lunch

שלי."
sheli
my

"We could save lots of money if you exercised at home."

"יכולנו לחסוך הרבה כסף אם היית מתאמנת בבית."
yakholnu lakhsokh harbe kesef im ha'it mitamenet baba'it
we could to save a lot money if you would have exercised at home

"לא תודה. אני אוהבת להתאמן בצוהריים. אחר כך אני אוכלת
lo toda ani ohevet lehitamen batsohora'im akhar kakh ani okhelet
no thank you I I like to exercise at noon afterwards I I eat

ארוחת צוהריים בריאה. פירות ויוגורט. אתה צריך לנסות לאכול אוכל
arukhat tsohora'im bri'a peirot veyogurt ata tsarikh lenasot le'ekhol okhel
lunch healthy fruits and yogurt you you should to try to eat food

בריא יותר."
bari yoter
healthy more

"No thank you. I like exercising at noon. Afterwards I eat a healthy lunch. Fruit and yogurt. You should try eating healthier food."

"אני נהיה עצבני אם אני לא אוכל לפחות שני המבורגרים עם
ani nihiya atsbani im ani lo okhel lefakhot shnei hamburgerim im
I I become irritable if I no I eat at least two of hamburgers with

צ'יפס כל יום," אמרתי.
chips kol yom amarti
french fries every day I said

"I become irritable if I don't eat at least two hamburgers and fries every day," I said.

גילת נטלה את הספר שהיה מונח על כורסת הטלוויזיה והחלה
gilat natla et hasefer shehaya munakh al kursat hatelevizya vehekhela
Gilat she grasped D.O. the book that was placed on the easy-chair and she started

לדפדף בו.
ledafdef bo
to leaf in it

Gilat picked up the book that was sitting on the recliner and started leafing through the pages.

"מיכה המליץ על ספר הכושר הזה. אני אעשה את החלק
mikha himlits al sefer hakosher haze ani e'ese et hakhelek
Micha he recommended about book the fitness the that I I will do D.O. the part

האירובי של האימון בחלל הפנוי שבין הכורסה לטלוויזיה
ha'eirobi shel ha'imun bakhalal hapanui shebein hakursa latelevizya
the aerobic of the training in the space the empty that is between the easy-chair to the television

בזמן שאנחנו צופים בתוכניות שלנו בכל ערב."
bizman she'anakhnu tsofim batokhniyot shelanu bekhol erev
while that we we watch at the programs our in every evening

"Micha recommended that exercise book. I'll do the aerobic part of the workouts in this open space between the recliner and the television while we watch our shows each night."

"הסדרה בעמוד עשרים וחמש אומרת שאתה צריך ללכת במהירות
hasidra be'amud esrim vekhamesh omeret she'ata tsarikh lalekhet bimhirut
the routine on page twenty and five it says that you you need to walk fast

תוך הנפת משקולות יד," אמרה. "איך אתה מתכוון לעשות את זה
tokh hanafat mishkolot yad amra eikh ata mitkaven la'asot et ze
while lifting of weights of hand she said how you you intend to do D.O. that

כאן?"
kan
here

"The routine on page twenty five wants you to walk fast while you swing hand weights," she said. "How are you going to do that in here?"

"יש מספיק מקום ללכת הלוך חזור כמה צעדים."
yesh maspik makom lalekhet halokh khazor kama tse'adim
there is enough space to walk back and forth a few steps

"There's enough room to walk back and forth a few steps at a time."

"What if you hit one of the kids in the head while you're doing this? The hand weight would probably kill them."

מה יהיה אם תפגע באחד הילדים בראש בזמן שאתה עושה
ma *ihiye* *im* *tifga* *be'ekhad* *hayeladim* *barosh* *bizman* *she'ata* *ose*
what it will be if you will hit at one the kids on the head while that you you do

את זה? משקולת יד יכולה להרוג אותם."
et *ze* *mishkolet* *yad* *yekhola* *laharog* *otam*
D.O. this weight of hand it can to kill them

"The kids will be asleep."

הילדים יישנו."
hayeladim *yishnu*
the kids they will be asleep

She took another glance at the exercises.

היא הביטה בתרגילים שוב.
hi *hibita* *batargilim* *shuv*
she she looked at at the exercises again

"Jumping jacks," she said. "They want you to do twenty minutes of jumping jacks."

קפיצות פישוק," אמרה. "הם רוצים שתעשה עשרים דקות של
kfitsot *pisuk* *amra* *hem* *rotsim* *sheta'ase* *esrim* *dakot* *shel*
jumpings of spread she said they they want that you will do twenty minutes of

קפיצות פישוק."
kfitsot *pisuk*
jumpings of spread

"What's wrong with that?"

"מה לא בסדר בזה?"
ma *lo* *beseder* *beze*
what not okay with this

"It's noisy. The whole house will shake. I won't be able to hear the television."

"זה מרעיש. כל הבית ירעד. אני לא אוכל לשמוע את
ze *marish* *kol* *haba'it* *yirad* *ani* *lo* *ukhal* *lishmo'a* *et*
it noisy all the house it will shake I no I will be able to hear D.O.

הטלוויזיה."
hatelevizya
the television

"There's a rug in the room. That will muffle the sound. And I'll jump really lightly, like a ninja."

"יש שטיח בחדר. זה יעמעם את הרעש. ואני אקפוץ ממש
yesh *shati'akh* *bakheder* *ze* *ye'amem* *et* *hara'ash* *va'ani* *ekpots* *mamash*
there is rug in the room that it will muffle D.O. the noise and I I will jump really

בקלילות, כמו נינג'ה."
biklilut *kmo* *ninja*
light-footedly like ninja

Gilat shook her head.

גילת הנידה בראשה.
gilat *henida* *berosha*
Gilat she shook with her head

"I'll watch television in our bedroom while you're exercising," she decided. "It will be easier on both of us."

"אני אצפה בטלוויזיה בחדר השינה כשאתה מתאמן," החליטה.
ani *etspe* *batelevizya* *bakhadar hasheina* *kshe'ata* *mitamen* *hekhlita*
I I will watch at the television in the bedroom when you you exercise she decided

"כך יהיה קל יותר לשנינו."
kakh *ihiye* *kal* *yoter* *lishneinu*
this way it will be easy more to both of us

"מה עם זמן האיכות שלנו יחד?"
yakhad shelanu ha'eikhut zman im ma
together our the quality time with what

"What about our quality time together?"

"יש לנו זמן איכות כשאנחנו משחקים עם הילדים. צפייה בטלוויזיה
batelevizya tsfiya hayeladim im mesakhakim kshe'anakhnu eikhut zman yesh lanu
at the television watching the kids with we play when we quality time we have

זה זמן הרגעות. אני ארגע טוב יותר בחדר השינה."
bakhadar hasheina yoter tov eraga ani heragut zman ze
in the bedroom more good I will relax I relaxing time this

"We have our quality time when we play with the kids. Watching television is relaxing time. I'll relax better in the bedroom."

"אז אשים את אחת הכורסאות במחסן. כך יהיה לי יותר מקום,"
makom yoter ihiye li kakh bamakhsan hakursa'ot akhat et asim az
room more I will have that way in the garage the easy-chairs one D.O. I will put then

אמרתי.
amarti
I said

"Then I'll put one of the recliner chairs in the garage. That will give me more room," I said.

— 3 —

ד"ר מיכה הופיע בשבת הבאה עם בקבוק יין ושקית בייגלה.
beigale vesakit ya'in bakbuk im haba'a beshabat hofi'a mikha doktor
pretzels and a bag of wine bottle with next on Saturday he showed up Micha doctor

גילת הובילה אותו לחדר האורחים. כל הריהוט עמד שוב במקומו.
bimkomo shuv amad harihut kol lakhadar ha'orkhim oto hovila gilat
in its place again it was situated the furniture all into the living room him she led Gilat

אודי ונתי, שני חברים נוספים מהאוניברסיטה, כבר ישבו על הספה
hasapa al yashvu kvar meha'universita nosafim khaverim shnei venati udi
the couch on they sat already from the university additional friends two of and Nati Udi

ושתו בירה. ישבתי בכורסת הטלוויזיה כשתחבושת גדולה מכסה
mekhasa gdola kshetakhboshet bekhursat hatelevizya yashavti bira veshatu
it covers big as a bandage in the easy-chair I sat beer and they drank

את ראשי.
roshi et
my head D.O.

Doctor Micha showed up the next Saturday with a bottle of wine and a bag of pretzels. Gilat ushered him into our living room. All the furniture was back in place. Udi and Nati, two other college friends, were already sitting on the couch drinking beer. I was sitting in the recliner with a big bandage on the top of my head.

"מה קרה לך?" שאל מיכה.
mikha sha'al lekha kara ma
Micha he asked to you it happened what

"What happened to you?" Micha asked.

"אתה עשית לי את זה," אמרתי. "יש לך מזל שאני לא תובע אותך
otkha tove'a lo she'ani mazal yesh lekha amarti ze et li asita ata
you I sue no that I luck you have I said this D.O. to me you did you

על רשלנות מקצועית."
miktso'it rashlanut al
professional negligence for

"You did this to me," I said. "Consider yourself lucky I don't sue you for malpractice."

"איך עשיתי את זה?"
ze et asiti eikh
this D.O. I did how

"How did I do it?"

"You need to hear the whole story, Micha," Gilat said.

"אתה צריך לשמוע את כל הסיפור, מיכה," אמרה גילת.
gilat amra <u>mikha</u> hasipur kol et lishmo'a tsarikh ata
Gilat she said Micha the story all D.O. to hear you need you

"I better fortify myself with some alcohol."

"כדאי שאחזק את עצמי במעט אלכוהול."
alkohol bime'at atsmi et she'akhazek kedai
alcohol with a little myself D.O. that I will strengthen worthwhile

He sat down and unscrewed the cap on the wine bottle.

הוא התיישב ופתח את פקק ההברגה של בקבוק היין.
haya'in bakbuk shel hahavraga pkak et ufatakh hityashev hu
the wine bottle of the screwed on cap D.O. and he opened he sat down he

"Can't you afford wine that comes in bottles with corks?" asked Udi.

"אתה לא יכול להרשות לעצמך יין עם פקק שעם?" שאל אודי.
udi sha'al sha'am pkak im ya'in le'atsmekha leharshot yakhol lo ata
Udi he asked cork cap with wine to yourself to permit you can no you

"This is very good wine," Micha responded. "And it's a lot easier to open the bottle."

"זה יין מצוין," ענה מיכה. "והרבה יותר קל לפתוח את הבקבוק."
habakbuk et lifto'akh kal yoter veharbe <u>mikha</u> ana metsuyan ya'in ze
the bottle D.O. to open easy more and much Micha he answered excellent wine this

Micha picked up an empty wine glass from the coffee table, poured, and handed the half-full glass to Gilat.

מיכה נטל כוס יין ריקה משולחן הסלון, מזג והושיט
vehoshit mazag hasalon mishulkhan reika ya'in kos natal <u>mikha</u>
and he handed he poured the living room from table empty wine glass he grasped Micha

את הכוס החצי מלאה לגילת.
legilat mele'a hakhatsi hakos et
to Gilat full the half the glass D.O.

"Thank you, Micha. How did you know I needed this?"

"תודה, מיכה. איך ידעת שאני צריכה את זה?"
ze et tsrikha she'ani ya<u>da</u>ta eikh <u>mikha</u> toda
this D.O. I need that I you knew how Micha thank you

"When I see a bandage on Rafi's head and find out that there's a story behind it, I know that you have probably had a difficult week," he said.

"כשאני רואה תחבושת על הראש של רפי ומגלה שיש סיפור
sipur sheyesh umegale <u>rafi</u> shel harosh al takh<u>bo</u>shet ro'e kshe'ani
story that there is and I find out Rafi of the head on bandage I see when I

מאחורי זה, אני יודע שהיה לך ככל הנראה שבוע קשה," אמר.
amar kashe sha<u>vu</u>'a kekhol hanire shehaya lakh <u>yo</u>de'a ani ze me'akhorei
he said hard week probably that you had I know I this behind

He poured another glass for himself, sat down, and looked at me.

הוא מזג כוס נוספת לעצמו, התיישב והביט בי.
bi vehibit hityashev le'atsmo no<u>se</u>fet kos mazag hu
at me and he looked he sat down for himself additional glass he poured he

"Tell me the story."

"ספר לי את הסיפור."
hasipur et li saper
the story D.O. to me tell

"Ten minutes until the game starts," said Nati. "Tell it quickly."

"יש עשר דקות עד שהמשחק מתחיל," אמר נתי. "ספר מהר."
maher saper <u>na</u>ti amar matkhil shehamiskhak ad dakot eser yesh
quickly tell nati he said it starts that the game until minutes ten there are

"Wait a minute," said Micha. "What happened to the ceiling?" He pointed to a big hole in the ceiling above the

"חכה רגע," אמר מיכה. "מה קרה לתקרה?" הוא הצביע על חור
khor al hitsbi'a hu latikra kara ma <u>mikha</u> amar <u>re</u>ga khake
hole at he pointed he to the ceiling it happened what Micha he said minute wait

גדול בתקרה, ממש מעל הספה.
gadol / *batikra* / *mamash* / *me'al* / *hasapa*
big / in the ceiling / precisely / above / the couch

> couch.

"זה חלק מהסיפור," אמר נתי. "רפי לא רצה לספר לנו עד
ze / *khelek* / *mehasipur* / *amar* / *nati* / *rafi* / *lo* / *ratsa* / *lesaper* / *lanu* / *ad*
this / part / of the story / he said / Nati / Rafi / no / he wanted / to tell / to us / until

שתגיע."
shetagi'a
that you arrived

> "It's part of the story," said Nati. "Rafi didn't want to tell us until you got here."

עמדתי להסביר הכל כשגילת נכנסה לדבריי. "אני צריכה עוד יין,"
amadeti / *lehasbir* / *hakol* / *kshegilat* / *nikhnesa lidvarai* / *ani* / *tsrikha* / *od* / *ya'in*
I was about to / to explain / everything / when Gilat / she interrupted / I / I need / more / wine

היא אמרה.
hi / *amra*
she / she said

> I was just about to explain everything when Gilat interrupted. "I need more wine," she said.

היא נטלה את הבקבוק ומילאה שוב את הכוס שבידה.
hi / *natla* / *et* / *habakbuk* / *umila* / *shuv* / *et* / *hakos* / *shebeyada*
she / she grasped / D.O. / the bottle / and she filled / again / D.O. / the glass / that is in her hand

> She grabbed the bottle and refilled her glass.

"זה יעזור לי להקשיב שוב לסיפור בלי לזרוק על רפי את
ze / *ya'azor* / *li* / *lehakshiv* / *shuv* / *lasipur* / *bli* / *lizrok* / *al* / *rafi* / *et*
this / it will help / to me / to listen / again / to the story / without / to throw / at / Rafi / D.O.

השלט," אמרה לחבריי.
hashalat / *amra* / *lakhaverai*
the remote control / she said / to my friends

> "This will help me listen to the story again without throwing the remote control at Rafi," she said to my friends.

4

לרגע קצר תהיתי למה אשתי תרצה להשליך עליי חפץ קטן
lerega / *katsar* / *tahiti* / *lama* / *ishti* / *tirtse* / *lehashlikh* / *alai* / *khefets* / *katan*
for a moment / brief / I wondered / why / my wife / she will want / to hurl / at me / object / small

וקשיח. החלטתי להתעלם מהההערה ולספר את הסיפור.
vekashi'akh / *hekhlateti* / *lehitalem* / *mehahe'ara* / *ulesaper* / *et* / *hasipur*
and hard / I decided / to ignore / from the comment / and to tell / D.O. / the story

> For a brief moment I wondered why my wife would want to hurl a small, hard object at me. I decided to overlook her comment and told my story.

"קניתי את הספר שרשמת לי, רכשתי כמה משקולות והתחלתי
kaniti / *et* / *hasefer* / *sherashamta* / *li* / *rakhashti* / *kama* / *mishkolot* / *vehitkhalti*
I bought / D.O. / the book / that you prescribed / to me / I purchased / a few / weights / and I started

להתאמן."
lehitamen
to exercise

> "I bought the book you prescribed, bought some weights, and started exercising."

"מצוין," אמר מיכה.
metsuyan / *amar* / *mikha*
excellent / he said / Micha

> "Great," said Micha.

"Not so great," said Gilat. "He decided he could exercise in this room while he was watching television at night."

לא כל כך מצוין," אמרה גילת. "הוא החליט שהוא יכול להתאמן
lo kol kakh metsuyan amra gilat hu hekhlit shehu yakhol lehitamen
not so excellent Gilat she said he he decided that he he can to exercise

בחדר הזה בזמן שהוא צופה בטלוויזיה בלילה."
bakheder haze bizman shehu tsofe batelevizya balaila
in the room the this at the time that he he watches at the television at night

Micha's eyes opened wide. "Ahhh," he said, "suddenly things are becoming clear."

עיניו של מיכה התרחבו. "אהה," אמר, "פתאום הכל נהיה
einav shel mikha hitrakhavu aaa amar pitom hakol nihiya
his eyes of Micha they became wider ahhh he said suddenly everything it will become

ברור."
barur
clear

"One of the workout routines required marching in place and pumping the weights with my arms. I decided to combine the exercise with some step aerobics, so I put a small stool on the floor."

אחת מסדרות האימון כללה צעידה במקום והנפת משקולות.
akhat misdarot ha'imun kalela tse'ida bamakom vehanafat mishkolot
one of routines of the exercise it included marching in place and lifting of weights

החלטתי לשלב את התרגיל הזה עם תרגיל מדרגה אירובי, אז שמתי
hekhlateti leshalev et hatargil haze im targil madrega eirobi az samti
I decided to combine D.O. the exercise the this with exercise step aerobic so I put

שרפרף קטן על הרצפה."
shrafraf katan al haritspa
stool small on the floor

"He was watching one of those reality shows," interrupted Gilat.

הוא צפה באחת מתוכניות הריאליטי האלה," הפסיקה אותי גילת.
hu tsafa be'akhat mitokhniyot hare'aliti ha'ele hifsika oti gilat
he he watched at one of programs the reality the those she interrupted me Gilat

"I didn't even realize that I was swinging those weights right up to the ceiling," I continued.

אפילו לא שמתי לב לזה שאני מניף את המשקולות לכיוון
afilu lo samti lev leze she'ani menif et hamishkolot lekhivun
even no I paid attention to this that I I lift up D.O. the weights in direction of

התקרה," המשכתי.
hatikra himshakhti
the ceiling I continued

"He stepped on the stool and punched a one and a half kilo weight through the ceiling," Gilat concluded.

הוא עלה על השרפרף ותקע משקולת של קילו וחצי ישר
hu ala al hashrafraf vetaka mishkolet shel kilo vakhetsi yashar
he he rose up on the stool and he thrusted weight of kilo and a half straight

לתוך התקרה," סיכמה גילת.
letokh hatikra sikma gilat
into the ceiling she concluded Gilat

Micha, Udi, and Nati started laughing at me.

מיכה, אודי ונתי התחילו לצחוק עליי.
mikha udi venati hitkhilu litskhok alai
Micha Udi and Nati they started to laugh at me

"Who is telling this story?" I demanded.

מי מספר את הסיפור?" תבעתי לדעת.
mi mesaper et hasipur tavati lada'at
who he tells D.O. the story I demanded to know

"הייתי במיטה וצפיתי בדרמה רפואית מצוינת," אמרה גילת. "היה
haya gilat amra metsuyenet refu'it bedrama vetsafiti bamita ha'iti
there was Gilat she said excellent medical at a drama and I watched on the bed I was

רעש חזק, ופתאום היד של רפי הופיעה דרך הרצפה."
ra'ash khazak ufitom hayad shel rafi hofi'a derekh haritspa
noise strong and suddenly the hand of Rafi it appeared through the floor

"I was on our bed watching a good medical drama," said Gilat. "There was a big noise, and suddenly Rafi's hand was sticking through the floor."

הבחורים צחקו חזק יותר.
habakhurim tsakhaku khazak yoter
the guys they laughed strong more

The guys laughed harder.

"איזו הגזמה," צעקתי.
eizo hagzama tsa'akti
a what exaggeration I yelled

"That's an exaggeration," I yelled.

גילת הרימה את השלט ונתנה בי מבט מרושע. החלטתי
gilat herima et hashalat venatna bi mabat merusha hekhlateti
Gilat she lifted D.O. the remote control and she gave at me look evil I decided

לשתוק.
lishtok
to be quiet

Gilat picked up the remote control and gave me an evil look. I decided to quiet down.

מיכה הרים את ידו. "נפלה לך חתיכה מהתקרה על הראש?"
mikha herim et yado nafla lekha khatikha mehatikra al harosh
Micha he raised D.O. his hand it fell to you piece of the ceiling on the head

Micha held up his hand. "Did a piece of the ceiling fall on your head?"

"גילת לא הרשתה לי להשתמש שוב במשקולות, אז בחרתי סדרת
gilat lo hirsheta li lehishtamesh shuv bemishkolot az bakharti sidrat
Gilat no she allowed to me to use again with weights so I picked routine of

תרגילים אחרת מהספר."
targilim akheret mehasefer
exercises another from the book

"Gilat wouldn't let me use the hand weights again, so I picked another exercise routine from the book."

"תרגול אירובי שדורש הרמת ברכיים ובעיטות," הוסיפה גילת.
tirgul eirobi shedoresh haramat birka'im uve'itot hosifa gilat
exercise aerobic that required lifting of knees and kicks she added Gilat

"An aerobics exercise that called for knee lifts and kicks," Gilat added.

"זה היה אימון לא רע," אמרתי.
ze haya imun lo ra amarti
this it was exercise not bad I said

"It was a pretty good workout," I said.

"עד שהוא התקרב מדי לטלוויזיה," אמרה גילת.
ad shehu hitkarev midai latelevizya amra gilat
until that he he got close to too to the television she said Gilat

"Until he got too close to the television," said Gilat.

"תפסיקי להפריע," התלוננתי.
tafsiki lehafri'a hitlonanti
you will stop to interrupt I complained

"Quit interrupting," I complained.

"הוא תקע את הרגל ישר לתוך הטלוויזיה," אמרה גילת.
hu taka et haregel yashar letokh hatelevizya amra gilat
he he thrusted D.O. the foot straight into the television she said Gilat

"He put his foot right through the TV," said Gilat.

Now my three college friends were howling. Udi was holding his knees, rocking from side to side. Tears were coming from Nati's eyes.

עכשיו שלושת חבריי מהאוניברסיטה התגלגלו מצחוק. אודי אחז
akhshav shloshet khaverai meha'universita hitgalgelu mitskhok udi akhaz
now three of my friends from the university they rolled from laughter Udi he grabbed

בברכיו והתנודד מצד לצד. דמעות זלגו מעיניו של נתי.
bevirkav vehitnoded mitsad letsad dma'ot zalgu me'einav shel nati
his knees and he swayed from side to side tears they dripped from his eyes of Nati

I fumed in silence. What could I say?

רתחתי בשקט. מה יכולתי לומר?
ratakhti besheket ma yakholti lomar
I boiled in silence what I could to say

"I had to go to the store on Tuesday to get a new TV for today's game. Rafi was too ashamed," Gilat concluded.

"הייתי צריכה ללכת לחנות ביום שלישי לקנות טלוויזיה חדשה
ha'iti tsrikha lalekhet lakhanut beyom shlishi liknot televizya khadasha
I should have to go to the store on Tuesday to buy television new

למשחק של היום. רפי היה נבוך מדי," סיכמה גילת.
lamiskhak shel hayom rafi haya navokh midai sikma gilat
for the game of today Rafi he was embarrassed too she concluded Gilat

It took a few minutes for my friends to get control of themselves.

לקח לחבריי מספר דקות להרגע ולשלוט בעצמם.
lakakh lekhaverai mispar dakot leheraga velishlot be'atsmam
it took for my friends a few minutes to calm down and to control themselves

"You still haven't told me how you hurt your head," Micha asked.

"עדיין לא סיפרת לי איך נפגעת בראש," אמר מיכה.
ada'in lo siparta li eikh nifgata barosh amar mikha
still no you told to me how you were injured on the head he said Micha

"Gilat told me I had to exercise in a spot that was far away from the new television. I moved to the side of the room over there," I pointed to a spot near the fireplace.

"גילת אמרה לי שאני צריך להתאמן בפינה רחוקה מהטלוויזיה
gilat amra li she'ani tsarikh lehitamen befina rekhoka mehatelevizya
Gilat she said to me that I I need to exercise in a corner far from the television

החדשה. עברתי לצד ההוא של החדר," הצבעתי על נקודה ליד
hakhadasha avarti latsad hahu shel hakheder hitsbati al nekuda leyad
the new I moved to the side that one of the room I pointed at spot next to

האח.
ha'akh
the fireplace

"I also picked a different aerobics routine."

"וגם בחרתי סדרת תרגול אירובי אחרת."
vegam bakharti sidrat tirgul eirobi akheret
and also I picked routine of exercise aerobic different

"Jumping jacks," said Gilat.

"קפיצות פישוק," אמרה גילת.
kfitsot pisuk amra gilat
jumping spread she said Gilat

"How did you injure yourself doing jumping jacks?" asked Micha.

"איך נפצעת מקפיצות פישוק?" שאל מיכה.
eikh niftsata mikfitsot pisuk sha'al mikha
how you were injured from jumping spread he asked Micha

"We used to have a pretty, glass light mounted on the ceiling to illuminate that part of the room," said Gilat.

"הייתה לנו מנורה יפה מזכוכית על התקרה, שהאירה את החלק הזה
haita lanu menora yafa mizkhukhit al hatikra shehe'ira et hakhelek haze
we had light pretty from glass on the ceiling that lit up D.O. the part the that

של החדר," אמרה גילת.
shel hakheder amra gilat
of the room she said Gilat

היא הצביעה על חוטי חשמל שהידלדלו להם בעצבות מהתקרה,
hi hitsbi'a al khutei khashmal shehidaldelu lahem be'atsvut mehatikra
she she pointed at wires of electricity that (they) dangled to them sorrowfully from the ceiling

סמוך לאח.
samukh la'akh
near the fireplace

She pointed to two electrical wires that were now dangling forlornly from the ceiling near the fireplace mantle.

"לא נכון," אמר לה מיכה.
lo nakhon amar la mikha
not correct he said to her Micha

"He didn't," Micha said to her.

"הוא צפה בסדרה ההיא עם הערפדים," ענתה גילת.
hu tsafa basidra hahi im ha'arpadim anta gilat
he he watched at the tv show that one with the vampires she replied Gilat

"He was watching that show with the vampires," she replied.

"זאת שמראים בה את החזה של הערפדיות," הוספתי, בתקווה
zot shemarim ba et hakhaze shel ha'arpadiyot hosafti betikva
this that they show in it D.O. the breasts of the vampires I added in hope

להסביר למה פישלתי בפעם השלישית.
lehasbir lama fishalti bapa'am hashlishit
to explain why I screwed up for the time the third

"The one where they show the breasts of the lady vampires," I added, hoping to explain why I had screwed up a third time.

"הוא היה מרותק כל כך לחזה שהוא לא שם לב שהוא קופץ
hu haya merutak kol kakh lakhaze shehu lo sam lev shehu kofets
he he was engrossed so in the breasts that he no he paid attention that he he jumps

קרוב יותר למנורה," אמרה גילת.
karov yoter lamenora amra gilat
close more to the light she said Gilat

"He was so engrossed in the breasts he didn't realize he was jumping closer to the light," said Gilat.

"הוא מחא כפיים בחוזקה והרס את המנורה," סיכם
hu makha kapa'im bekhozka veharas et hamenora sikem
he he clapped hands forcefully and he destroyed D.O. the light fixture he concluded

מיכה.
mikha
Micha

"He clapped his hands together and demolished the fixture," concluded Micha.

"חתיכות גדולות של זכוכית נפלו על הראש שלו," אמרה גילת.
khatikhot gdolot shel zkhukhit naflu al harosh shelo amra gilat
pieces large of glass they fell on the head his she said Gilat

"Large pieces of glass dropped onto his head," said Gilat.

"הדבר הבא שאני זוכר זה שעשו לי עשרה תפרים בבית
hadavar haba she'ani zokher ze she'asu li asara tfarim beveit
the thing next that I I remember this that they did to me ten stitches at house of

החולים," אמרתי.
hakholim amarti
the sick I said

"Next thing I knew, I was getting ten stitches at the hospital," I said.

83

They kept laughing at me through the entire first half of the game. During a time out, Micha said to me: "Seriously, you can't keep trying to exercise in this room. You could break everything."

הם המשיכו לצחוק עליי במהלך כל המחצית הראשונה של המשחק.

hamiskhak shel harishona hamakhatsit kol bemahalakh alai litskhok himshikhu hem
the game of the first the half all during at me to laugh they continued they

באחד מפסקי הזמן אמר לי מיכה: "ברצינות, אתה לא יכול להמשיך

lehamshikh yakhol lo ata birtsinut mikha li amar mipiskei hazman be'ekhad
to continue you can no you seriously Micha to me he said of the time-outs in one

לנסות להתאמן בחדר הזה. אתה יכול לשבור הכל."

hakol lishbor yakhol ata haze bakheder lehitamen lenasot
everything to break you can you the this in the room to exercise to try

"Gilat told me I have to spend my lunch hours with her at the gym. That way she can keep an eye on me and make sure I eat a lot of yogurt."

"גילת אמרה לי שאני צריך ללכת איתה למכון הכושר בהפסקת

behafsakat limekhon hakosher ita lalekhet tsarikh she'ani li amra gilat
in break of to the gym with her to go I have to that I to me she said Gilat

הצוהריים. כך היא תוכל להשגיח עליי ולוודא שאני

she'ani ulevade alai lehashgi'akh tukhal hi kakh hatsohora'im
that I and to make sure for me to watch out she will be able she that way the lunch

אוכל הרבה יוגורט."

yogurt harbe okhel
yogurt a lot I eat

"Excellent plan," everyone said.

"תוכנית מצוינת," אמרו כולם.

kulam amru metsuyenet tokhnit
everyone they said excellent plan

STORY 9

In Good Repair

"אנחנו צריכים לקרוא לשרברב," אמרה לי אשתי גילת.
gilat ishti li amra lishravrav likro tsrikhim anakhnu
Gilat my wife to me she said to a plumber to call we need we

"We need to call a plumber," my wife Gilat said to me.

"למה?"
lama
why

"Why?"

"טוחן האשפה התקלקל."
hitkalkel ha'ashpa tokhen
it stopped working the garbage grinder of

"The garbage disposal is broken."

"שרברבים הם יקרים," עניתי. "אני יכול לקנות טוחן אשפה חדש
khadash ashpa tokhen liknot yakhol ani aniti yekarim hem shravravim
new the garbage grinder of to buy I can I I replied expensive they plumbers

ולהרכיב אותו בעצמי."
be'atsmi oto uleharkiv
myself it and to install

"Plumbers are expensive," I replied. "I can probably buy a new disposal and install it myself."

"רפי, אני חושבת שאתה צריך לתת לבעל מקצוע לעשות את
et la'asot leva'al miktso'a latet tsarikh she'ata khoshevet ani rafi
D.O. to do to a professional to allow you should that you I think I Rafi

העבודה הזאת."
hazot ha'avoda
the this the work

"Rafi, I think you should let a professional do the work."

"אין לך אמון בכישורים הטכניים של בעלך?" שאלתי.
sha'alti ba'alekh shel hatekhniyim bakishurim emun ein lakh
I asked your husband of the technical in the qualifications faith you don't have

"Don't you have faith in your husband's mechanical abilities?" I asked.

"אתה טוב בגיזום הגדר החיה ובכיסוח הדשא," ענתה לי.
li anta hadeshe uvakhisu'akh hagader hakhaya begizum tov ata
to me she replied the grass and mowing the hedge at pruning good you

"You're good at cutting the hedges and mowing the lawn," she replied to me.

"אני יכול לבצע גם עבודות טכניות," התעקשתי.
hitakashti tekhniyot avodot gam levatse'a yakhol ani
I insisted technical works also to perform I can I

"I can do technical work, too," I insisted.

"מה עם עמוד התאורה שהחלפת בגינה?" שאלה.
sha'ala bagina shehekhlafta hate'ura amud im ma
she asked in the garden that you replaced the lighting pole with what

"What about the light pole that you replaced in the front yard?" she asked.

85

"It works fine."

הוא עובד מצוין."
hu / oved / metsuyan
it / it works / excellent

"It leans fifteen centimeters to the left," she said.

הוא נוטה חמישה עשר סנטימטרים שמאלה," אמרה.
hu / note / khamisha asar / sentimetrim / smola / amra
it / it tilts / fifteen / centimeters / to the left / she said

"That way you get more light on the driveway."

כך יש יותר אור על שביל הכניסה."
kakh / yesh / yoter / or / al / shvil / haknisa
that way / there is / more / light / on / path of / the entrance

"And the fuse blows out if we turn on the television while the front light is shining."

והנתיך נשרף אם מדליקים את הטלוויזיה כשהאור בגינה
vehanatikh / nisraf / im / madlikim / et / hatelevizya / ksheha'or / bagina
and the fuse / it was burned / if / we turn on / D.O. / the television / as the light / in the garden

דולק."
dolek
it is turned on

"Blame the electrician who wired the house," I said. "He overloaded the circuit."

תאשימי את החשמלאי שהתקין את החיווט בבית," אמרתי.
ta'ashimi / et / hakhashmalai / shehitkin / et / hakhivut / baba'it / amarti
you will blame / D.O. / the electrician / that he installed / D.O. / the wiring / in the house / I said

הוא יצר עומס יתר על המערכת."
hu / yatsar / omes / yeter / al / hama'arekhet
he / he created / burden / excessive / on / the circuit system

"I still think you should call a plumber."

אני בכל זאת חושבת שצריך להזמין שרברב."
ani / bekhol zot / khoshevet / shetsarikh / lehazmin / shravrav
I / nevertheless / I think / that you should / to call / plumber

I didn't argue with Gilat any further. Secretly, I planned to do the work myself. I would show her how easy it is to fix things around the house.

לא המשכתי בוויכוח עם גילת. תכננתי בחשאי לבצע את העבודה
lo / himshakhti / baviku'akh / im / gilat / tikhnanti / bakhashai / levatse'a / et / ha'avoda
no / I continued / with the argument / with / Gilat / I planned / secretly / to perform / D.O. / the work

בעצמי. אני אראה לה כמה קל לתקן דברים בבית.
be'atsmi / ani / ar'e / la / kama / kal / letaken / dvarim / baba'it
by myself / I / I will show / to her / how / easy / to fix / things / in the house

— 2 —

It's Saturday. The kids are spending the weekend with my parents. Gilat just left to visit some friends from her college days. I will be alone for at least six hours. Time to put my plan into action. I called my next door neighbor Jacob, a retired engineer.

שבת היום. הילדים מבלים את סוף השבוע אצל הוריי. גילת יצאה
shabat / hayom / hayeladim / mevalim / et / sof hashavu'a / etsel / horai / gilat / yatsa
Saturday / today / the kids / they spend / D.O. / the weekend / at / my parents / Gilat / she left

זה עתה לבקר חברות מימי האוניברסיטה. אהיה לבד למשך שש
ze ata / levaker / khaverot / miyemei / ha'universita / ehiye / levad / lemeshekh / shesh
just now / to visit / friends / from days of / the university / I will be / alone / for / six

שעות לפחות. זה הזמן להוציא לפועל את התוכנית שלי. התקשרתי
sha'ot / lefakhot / ze / hazman / lehotsi lapo'al / et / hatokhnit / sheli / hitkasharti
hours / at least / this / the time / to carry out / D.O. / the plan / my / I called

לשכני יעקב, מהנדס בגמלאות.
lishkheni / ya'akov / mehandes / begimla'ot
to my neighbor / Jacob / engineer / retired

86

"תוכל לעזור לי להתקין טוחן אשפה חדש היום?"

hayom	khadash	tokhen ashpa	lehatkin	li	la'azor	tukhal
today	new	garbage disposal	to install	to me	to help	you will be able

"Can you help me put in a new garbage disposal today?"

"ודאי."

vadai
sure

"Sure."

"בוא אלי עכשיו. כבר קניתי טוחן חדש. הוא מוחבא במחסן."

bamakhsan	mukhba	hu	khadash	tokhen	kaniti	kvar	akhshav	elai	bo
in the storeroom	hidden	it	new	grinder	I bought	already	now	to me	come

"Come right over. I already bought a new disposal. It's hidden in the storeroom."

"גילת לא רוצה שאתה תעשה את העבודה הזו, נכון?"

nakhon	hazo	ha'avoda	et	ta'ase	she'ata	rotsa	lo	gilat
correct	the this	the work	D.O.	you will do	that you	she wants	no	Gilat

"Gilat doesn't want you doing this work, does she?"

"למה אתה אומר את זה?"

ze	et	omer	ata	lama
that	D.O.	you say	you	why

"Why do you say that?"

"מכיוון שהיית צריך להסתיר את טוחן האשפה החדש במחסן.

bamakhsan	hakhadash	tokhen ha'ashpa	et	lehastir	sheha'ita tsarikh	mikeivan
in the storeroom	the new	the garbage disposal	D.O.	to hide	that you should have	because

חוץ מזה, אני זוכר את הפעם שגרמת להצפה בחדר

bakhadar	lehatsafa	shegaramta	hapa'am	et	zokher	ani	khuts mize
in the room of	to flooding	that you caused	the time	D.O.	I remember	I	in addition

האמבטיה בקומה השנייה כשניסית להתקין ברז מים קרים חדש

khadash	karim	ma'im	berez	lehatkin	kshenisita	hashniya	bakoma	ha'ambatya
new	cold	water	faucet of	to install	when you tried	the second	on the floor	the bath

בכיור."

bakiyor
in the sink

"Because you had to hide the new disposal in the storeroom. Also, I remember the time you flooded your second floor bathroom when you tried to install a new cold water faucet in the sink."

"זו הייתה תאונה," אמרתי.

amarti	te'una	haita	zo
I said	accident	it was	that

"That was an accident," I said.

"שכחת להבריג את הידית לצינור."

latsinor	hayadit	et	lehavrig	shakhakhta
to the pipe	the handle	D.O.	to screw	you forgot

"You forgot to screw the handle into the pipe."

"זו לא הייתה אשמתי. הילדים הפריעו לי."

li	hifri'u	hayeladim	ashmati	haita	lo	zo
to me	the interrupted	the kids	my fault	it was	no	that

"It wasn't my fault. I was interrupted by the kids."

"כשפתחת את ברז המים הראשי הידית עפה מהצינור בכזו

bekhazo	mehatsinor	afa	hayadit	harashi	hama'im	berez	et	kshepatakhta
in such	from the pipe	it flew off	the handle	the main	the water	valve of	D.O.	when you opened

עוצמה, שהיא נתקעה בתקרה."

batikra	nitke'a	shehi	otsma
in the ceiling	it stuck	that it	intensity

"When you turned the main water valve to the house back on, the handle shot off the pipe so hard it wedged into the ceiling."

"Don't remind me."

"אל תזכיר לי."
al · tazkir · li
don't · you will remind · to me

"Meanwhile, you were in the storeroom and didn't hear the water spraying all over the bathroom floor."

בינתיים, היית במחסן ולא שמעת את המים ניתזים
beinta'im · ha'ita · bamakhsan · velo · shamata · et · hama'im · nitazim
meanwhile · you were · in the storeroom · and no · you heard · D.O. · the water · they were sprayed

על הרצפה באמבטיה."
al · haritspa · ba'ambatya
on · the floor · in the bathroom

"I've put that episode behind me."

"השארתי את הסיפור הזה מאחוריי."
hisharti · et · hasipur · haze · me'akhorai
I left behind · D.O. · the affair · the that · behind me

"The water damage was so bad you had to replace the ceiling above the living room," said Jacob.

"הנזק מהמים היה גדול כל כך שהיה צריך להחליף את התקרה
hanezek · mehama'im · haya · gadol · kol kakh · shehaya tsarikh · lehakhlif · et · hatikra
the damage · from the water · it was · serious · so · that it needed · to replace · D.O. · the ceiling

בחדר המגורים," אמר יעקב.
bakhadar hamegurim · amar · ya'akov
in the living room · he said · Jacob

"Do you want to help me or not?"

"אתה רוצה לעזור לי או לא?"
ata · rotse · la'azor · li · o · lo
you · you want · to help · to me · or · not

"I'll be glad to help. I'm just explaining why I know Gilat doesn't want you to do this job. I'll be right over."

"אשמח לעזור לך. אני רק מסביר איך אני יודע שגילת לא רוצה
esmakh · la'azor · lekha · ani · rak · masbir · eikh · ani · yode'a · shegilat · lo · rotsa
I will be happy · to help · to you · I · just · I explain · how · I · I know · that Gilat · no · she wants

שתעשה את העבודה. אני תיכף מגיע."
sheta'ase · et · ha'avoda · ani · tekhef · magi'a
that you will do · D.O. · the job · I · in a moment · I arrive

---
3

Twenty minutes later, we were in my kitchen laying out our tools. Jacob took the new garbage disposal out of its packaging.

כעבור עשרים דקות היינו במטבח שלי, פורסים בפנינו את
ka'avor · esrim · dakot · ha'inu · bamitbakh · sheli · porsim · befaneinu · et
after · twenty · minutes · we were · in the kitchen · my · we spread out · in front of us · D.O.

כלי העבודה. יעקב הוציא את טוחן האשפה החדש מהאריזה.
klei · ha'avoda · ya'akov · hotsi · et · tokhen ha'ashpa · hakhadash · meha'ariza
tools of · the work · Jacob · he took out · D.O. · the garbage disposal · the new · from its packaging

"First we need to disconnect the old disposal," Jacob said.

"קודם כל אנחנו צריכים לפרק את טוחן האשפה הישן," אמר
kodem kol · anakhnu · tsrikhim · lefarek · et · tokhen ha'ashpa · hayashan · amar
first of all · we · we need · to disconnect · D.O. · the garbage disposal · the old · he said

יעקב.
ya'akov
Jacob

הוא התכופף והכניס את ראשו בארון שמתחת לכיור. כבר
hu hitkofef vehikhnis et rosho ba'aron shemitakhat lakiyor kvar
he he ducked and he inserts D.O. his head in the cabinet that under to the sink already

הוצאנו מהארון את כל בקבוקי הפלסטיק, חומרי הניקוי
hotsenu meha'aron et kol bakbukei haplastik khomrei hanikui
we removed from the cabinet D.O. all bottles of the plastic materials of the cleaning

ושאר הפריטים המאוחסנים בו, כדי שלא יפריעו לנו. יעקב
ush'ar hapritim hame'ukhsanim bo, kedei shelo yafri'u lanu ya'akov
and rest of the items that are stored in it, so that that no they will hinder to us Jacob

בילה מספר דקות כשראשו בתוך הארון, עושה דבר מה.
bila mispar dakot ksherosho betokh ha'aron, ose dvar ma
he spent a few minutes with his head inside the cabinet, he does something

He ducked his head down and stuck it into the cabinet that was under the sink. We already took all the plastic bottles, cleaning supplies, and other assorted items out of the cabinet so they wouldn't be in our way. Jacob spent a few minutes with his head inside the cabinet, doing something or other.

ואז אמר, "בוא תראה את זה."
ve'az amar, "bo tire et ze."
and then he said, come you will check out D.O. this

Then he said, "Come look at this."

הכנסתי את ראשי לתוך הארון.
hikhnasti et roshi letokh ha'aron
I put in D.O. my head into the cabinet

I stuck my head into the cabinet.

"זה צינור הניקוז שפרקתי עכשיו מטוחן האשפה." הוא הצביע
"ze tsinor hanikuz sheperakti akhshav mitokhen ha'ashpa." hu hitsbi'a
this pipe of the drainage that I detached now from the garbage disposal he he pointed at

על צינור פלסטיק לבן שהיה תלוי ליד טוחן האשפה.
al tsinor plastik lavan shehaya talui leyad tokhen ha'ashpa
at pipe plastic white that it was hanging next to the garbage disposal

"This is the drain pipe that I just detached from the disposal." He pointed to a white plastic pipe hanging near the disposal.

"טוחן האשפה מוצמד לתחתית הכיור כאן." הוא הצביע על
"tokhen ha'ashpa mutsmad letakhtit hakiyor kan." hu hitsbi'a al
the garbage disposal it is attached to the bottom of the sink here he he pointed at at

משהו אחר. אביזר מתכתי כלשהו. "שים את המברג שלך
mashehu akher. avizer matakhti kolshehu. "sim et hamavreg shelkha
something different contraption metallic some sort put D.O. the screwdriver your

על הסגר בדיוק במקום שבו הוא מתקפל כלפי מטה,
al haseger bediyuk bamakom shebo hu mitkapel klapei mata
on the latch precisely at the place that in which it it is folded in the direction of down

ואז תן מכות בפטיש כדי לפתוח את הסגר ולשחרר את
ve'az ten makot bapatish kedei lifto'akh et haseger uleshakhrer et
and then give hits with the hammer in order to to open D.O. the latch and to loosen D.O.

טוחן האשפה."
tokhen ha'ashpa
the garbage disposal

"The disposal is latched onto the bottom of the sink right here." He pointed to something different. A metal contraption of some kind. "Put your screwdriver on the latch right where it folds down and then tap it with a hammer to open the latch and loosen the disposal."

עשיתי כדבריו. שום דבר לא קרה.
asiti kidvarav. shum davar lo kara
I did as he said nothing no it happened

I did what he said. Nothing happened.

"The latch seems to be rusted tight," I said.

"הסגר כנראה תקוע בגלל חלודה," אמרתי.
haseger the latch — *kanire* apparently — *taku'a* stuck — *biglal* because of — *khaluda* rust — *amarti* I said

Jacob stood up. It's hard bending down looking into the cabinet.

יעקב נעמד. קשה להתכופף ולהסתכל בארון.
ya'akov Jacob — *ne'emad* he stood up — *kashe* hard — *lehitkofef* to bend down — *ulehistakel* and to look — *ba'aron* in the cabinet

"Tap it harder," he said.

"תן מכות חזקות יותר," אמר.
ten give — *makot* hits — *khazakot* hard — *yoter* more — *amar* he said

I gave the screwdriver a mighty whack. Success! The latch came loose. The disposal fell from the mount ring.

הלמתי בחוזקה במברג. הצלחה! הסגר השתחרר. טוחן האשפה
halamti I struck — *bekhozka* strongly — *bamavreg* with the screwdriver — *hatslakha* success — *haseger* the latch — *hishtakhrer* it came loose — *tokhen ha'ashpa* the garbage disposal

נפל מטבעת התושבת.
nafal it fell — *mitaba'at* from ring of — *hatoshevet* the mount

"What happened?" asked Jacob.

"מה קרה?" שאל יעקב.
ma what — *kara* it happened — *sha'al* he asks — *ya'akov* Jacob

"You won't believe what a big hole a heavy disposal can make when it falls onto the bottom of a kitchen cabinet," I responded.

"לא תאמין איזה חור גדול עושה טוחן אשפה כבד כשהוא נופל
lo no — *ta'amin* you will believe — *eize* what a — *khor* hole — *gadol* big — *ose* it makes — *tokhen ashpa* garbage disposal — *kaved* heavy — *kshehu* when it — *nofel* it falls

על רצפת ארון מטבח," עניתי.
al on — *ritspat* floor of — *aron* cabinet of — *mitbakh* kitchen — *aniti* I responded

"I guess I should have held onto the disposal while you loosened the latch."

"כנראה שהייתי צריך להחזיק את הטוחן כשאתה שחררת את הסגר."
kanire probably — *sheha'iti tsarikh* that I should have — *lehakhzik* to hold — *et* D.O. — *hatokhen* the grinder — *kshe'ata* when you — *shikhrarta* you loosened — *et* D.O. — *haseger* the latch

I stood up so Jacob could look into the cabinet.

נעמדתי כדי שיעקב יוכל להסתכל פנימה לתוך הארון.
ne'emadeti I stood up — *kedei* so that — *sheya'akov* that Jacob — *yukhal* he will be able — *lehistakel* to look — *pnima* inward — *letokh* into — *ha'aron* the cabinet

"That's some hole," he agreed. "It looks like a small cannon ball went through the floor of the cabinet. I have a small piece of plywood at home that we can use to fix that hole. Don't do anything until I get back."

"זה חור רציני," הסכים. "זה נראה כאילו פגז קטן עבר דרך
ze that — *khor* hole — *retsini* serious — *hiskim* he agreed — *ze* that — *nire* it looks — *ke'ilu* as if — *pagaz* cannonball — *katan* small — *avar* it passed — *derekh* through

רצפת הארון. יש לי בבית חתיכה קטנה של דיקט שנוכל
ritspat floor of — *ha'aron* the cabinet — *yesh li* I have — *baba'it* at home — *khatikha* piece — *ktana* small — *shel* of — *dikt* plywood — *shenukhal* that we will be able

להשתמש בה כדי לתקן את החור. אל תעשה כלום עד
lehishtamesh to use — *ba* for it — *kedei* in order to — *letaken* to fix — *et* D.O. — *hakhor* the hole — *al* don't — *ta'ase* you will do — *klum* nothing — *ad* until

שאחזור."
she'ekhzor that I will come back

כשתחזור גילת תגיד מה לדאוג, התחלתי הלך, שיעקב בזמן
kshetakhzor gilat tagid ma lidog hitkhalti halakh sheya'akov bizman
when she will return Gilat she will say what to worry I started he went that Jacob in the time

פתחתי הראש. את לנקות כדי מים לכוס זקוק הייתי הביתה.
patakhti harosh et lenakot kedei ma'im lekhos zakuk ha'iti habaita
I opened the head D.O. to clear in order to water to glass of in need of I was homeward

לאחר הכיור. תוך אל לזרום למים והנחתי הקרים המים ברז את
le'akhar hakiyor tokh el lizrom lama'im vehenakhti hakarim hama'im berez et
after the sink inside to to run to the water and I let the cold the water faucet of D.O.

וישבתי כוס מילאתי וקרים. נעימים היו המים שניות מספר
veyashavti kos mileti vekarim ne'imim hayu hama'im shniyot mispar
and I sat down glass I filled and cold nice they were the water seconds a few

דקות. מספר כעבור חזר יעקב המטבח. לשולחן
dakot mispar ka'avor khazar ya'akov hamitbakh leshulkhan
minutes a few after he came back Jacob the kitchen at table of

While Jacob was gone, I started to worry about what Gilat would say when she got home. I needed a glass of water to clear my head. I turned on the cold water and let it run into the sink. After a few seconds the water was nice and cold. I filled a glass and sat at the kitchen table. Jacob came back a few minutes later.

לקנות תצטרך הזאת. הדיקט את חתיכת למצוא הצלחתי "לא
liknot titstarekh hazot hadikt et khatikhat limtso hitslakhti lo
to buy you will need the that the plywood D.O. the piece of to find I succeeded no

המטבח?" רצפת על גדולה שלולית יש למה, "הי, אמר. בחנות," דיקט
hamitbakh ritspat al gdola shlulit yesh lama hei amar bakhanut dikt
the kitchen floor of on big puddle there is why hey he said at the store plywood

"I couldn't find that piece of plywood. You'll have to buy a piece at the store," he said. "Hey, why is there a big puddle on the kitchen floor?"

שלולית?" "איזו
shlulit eizo
puddle what

"What puddle?"

הזרמת לא "אתה שבידי. המים בכוס הבחין יעקב
hizramta lo ata shebeyadi hama'im bekhos hivkhin ya'akov
you caused to flow no you that is in my hand the water at glass of he noticed Jacob

נכון?" הכיור, לתוך מים
nakhon hakiyor letokh ma'im
correct the sink into water

Jacob saw my glass of water. "You didn't run water into the sink, did you?"

לכיור. שמתחת הארון לתוך הבטנו שנינו
lakiyor shemitakhat ha'aron letokh hibatnu shneinu
to the sink that is under the cabinet into we looked both of us

We both peered into the cabinet under the sink.

יעקב. אמר בלגן, איזה "תראה
ya'akov amar balagan eize tire
Jacob he said mess what a you will look

"Look at this mess," said Jacob.

מחובר." לא הניקוז שצינור "שכחתי
mekhubar lo hanikuz shetsinor shakhakhti
connected not the drainage that pipe of I forgot

"I forgot that the drain pipe was disconnected."

תוך אל מהכיור שזרמו מים של טובים ליטרים כמה כאן "יש
tokh el mehakiyor shezarmu ma'im shel tovim litrim kama kan yesh
inside to from the sink that they flowed water of good liters a few here there is

"There must be a few liters of water that ran out of the sink and into that hole. Now it's leaking out onto the floor."

"החור. עכשיו זה דולף אל הרצפה."
haritspa el dolef ze akhshav hakhor
the floor to it leaks this now the hole

"I'll clean it up."

"אני אנקה את זה."
ze et anake ani
this D.O. I will clean I

"You do that. Then go to the store and buy a small piece of plywood. I'm going home to take a nap. Call me when you are back from the store."

"עשה זאת. אחר כך לך לחנות ותקנה חתיכת דיקט. אני הולך
holekh ani dikt khatikhat vetikne lakhanut lekh akhar kakh zot ase
I go I plywood piece of and you will buy to the store go then that do

הביתה לנוח. תתקשר אלי כשתחזור מהחנות."
mehakhanut kshetakhzor elai titkasher lanu'akh habaita
from the store when you will return to me you will call to rest homeward

——4——

It took me more than an hour to clean up the kitchen and buy a small piece of wood to cover the hole in the cabinet. When I got home, I called Jacob on the phone.

לקח לי יותר משעה לנקות את המטבח ולקנות חתיכה קטנה
ktana khatikha veliknot hamitbakh et lenakot misha'a yoter li lakakh
small piece and to buy the kitchen D.O. to clean than hour more to me it took

של דיקט כדי לכסות את החור בארון. כשחזרתי הביתה
habaita kshekhazarti ba'aron hakhor et lekhasot kedei dikt shel
homeward when I returned in the cabinet the hole D.O. to cover in order to plywood of

התקשרתי ליעקב.
leya'akov hitkasharti
to Jacob I called

"Jacob had to go to our son's house," his wife told me. "They needed someone to watch the baby while they went shopping."

"יעקב היה צריך ללכת לבן שלנו," אמרה לי אשתו. "הם היו צריכים
hayu tsrikhim hem ishto li amra shelanu laben haya tsarikh lalekhet ya'akov
they needed they his wife to me she told our to the son he had to go Jacob

מישהו שישגיח על התינוק כשהם עושים קניות."
kniyot osim kshehem hatinok al sheyashgi'akh mishehu
shopping they do while they the baby over that he will supervise someone

"He was supposed to help me fix something," I whined.

"הוא היה אמור לעזור לי לתקן משהו," התבכיינתי.
hitbakhyanti mashehu letaken li la'azor amur haya hu
I whined something to fix to me to help supposed to he was he

"Grandchildren come first," she said to me. "Anyway, I thought you weren't allowed to fix things in the house any more."

"הנכדים קודמים לכל," אמרה לי. "בכל מקרה, חשבתי
khashavti bekhol mikre li amra lakol kodmim hanekhadim
I thought anyway to me she said to all they take precedence the grandchildren

שאסור לך לתקן עוד דברים בבית."
baba'it dvarim od letaken lekha she'asur
at home things more to fix to you that forbidden

"I'd rather not talk about that."

"אני מעדיף לא לדבר על זה."
ze al ledaber lo ma'adif ani
that about to talk no I prefer I

92

מעל בגג ההוא החור את לסתום כשניסית זוכרת "אני
me'al bagag hahu hakhor et listom kshenisita zokheret ani
above on the roof that one the hole D.O. to seal when you tried I remember I

חדר השינה שלכם. החלקת מהגג ישר על השיחים."
khadar hasheina shelakhem hekhlakta mehagag yashar al hasikhim
the bedroom your you slid from the roof straight onto the bushes

"I remember when you tried to seal that hole on the roof above your bedroom. You slid down the roof and right into the bushes."

"הגג היה הרבה יותר חלקלק משציפיתי."
hagag haya harbe yoter khalaklak mishetsipiti
the roof it was much more slippery than I expected

"The roof was a lot more slippery than I expected."

בגינה לעץ עצמך את לקשור חכם מספיק היית "לפחות
bagina la'ets atsmekha et likshor khakham maspik ha'ita lefakhot
in the garden to the tree yourself D.O. to tie smart enough you were at least

זמן הרבה די העליון מהענף התנדנדת לגג. שטיפסת לפני
zman harbe dei ha'elyon mehe'anaf hitnadnadeta lagag shetipasta lifnei
time much quite the top from the branch you dangled to the roof that you climbed before

עד שהשוטר הציל אותך, לא?"
ad shehashoter hitsil otkha lo
until that the policeman he saved you no

"At least you were smart enough to tie yourself to that tree in the backyard before you climbed onto the roof. Didn't you dangle from the top limb for a while until the police officer saved you?"

"זה היה תרגול טוב עבורו," אמרתי. "אני באמת צריך לנתק עכשיו."
ze haya tirgul tov avuro amarti ani be'emet tsarikh lenatek akhshav
that it was training good for him I said I really I need to hang up now

"It was a good training exercise for him," I said. "I really have to go now."

וגילת איננו יעקב. בעיה לי הייתה עכשיו הטלפון. את ניתקתי
vegilat einenu ya'akov be'aya haita li akhshav hatelefon et nitakti
and Gilat he is not here Jacob problem I had now the telephone D.O. I disconnected

תגיע הביתה בעוד שלוש שעות.
tagi'a habaita be'od shalosh sha'ot
she will arrive homeward in another three hours

I hung up the phone. Now I had a problem. Jacob was gone and Gilat would be home in three hours.

שישבה לכלבה, אמרתי לבד," העבודה את לעשות שאצטרך "נראה
sheyashva lakalba amarti levad ha'avoda et la'asot she'etstarekh nire
who she sat to the dog I said alone the job D.O. to do that I will need it looks

והביטה בי כשמבט מוזר נסוך על פניה.
vehibita bi kshemabat muzar nasukh al paneiha
and she looked at me with a look strange spread over on her face

"Looks like I'll have to do the job myself," I said to the dog, who is sitting there watching me with a funny look on her face.

חיפוש ביפנית. כתובות היו הן ההתקנה. הוראות את בדקתי
khipus beyapanit ktuvot hayu hen hahatkana hora'ot et badakti
search in Japanese written they were they the installation instructions of D.O. I examined

החלה הבהלה. נוספת. הוראות חוברת שאין גילה מהיר
hekhela habehala nosefet hora'ot khoveret she'ein gila mahir
it began the panic additional instructions booklet of that there aren't it revealed quick

להזדחל במעלה בטני.
lehizdakhel bema'ale bitni
to creep up rising in my stomach

I studied the installation instructions. They were written in Japanese. A quick search told me that there was no other instruction book. Panic started to rise in my stomach.

—5—

93

After five minutes of feverish thinking, I concluded that I had only one course of action. Reluctantly, I picked up the phone and dialed another number.

אחרי חמש דקות של חשיבה קדחתנית, הגעתי למסקנה שיש לי
akharei khamesh dakot shel khashiva kadakhtanit, higati lemaskana sheyesh li
after five minutes of thinking feverish I reached to the conclusion that I have

אפשרות אחת בלבד. בחוסר רצון הרמתי את הטלפון וחייגתי למספר
efsharut akhat bilvad. bekhoser ratson heramti et hatelefon vekhiyagti lemispar
possibility one only reluctantly I lifted D.O. the telephone and I dialed to number

אחר.
akher
another

The phone rang once. I dreaded having this conversation. It rang a second time. My self confidence was at its lowest ebb since seventh grade. A third ring sounded in my ear. Maybe nobody was home. Unfortunately, the call was answered.

הטלפון צלצל צלצול אחד. חרדתי מפני השיחה. צלצול
hatelefon tsiltsel tsiltsul ekhad. kharadeti mipnei hasikha. tsiltsul
the telephone it rang ring one I dreaded because of the conversation ring

שני. הביטחון העצמי שלי היה בשפל הנמוך ביותר מאז
sheni. ha'bitakhon ha'atsmi sheli haya bashefel hanamukh beyoter me'az
second the self confidence my it was at the low point the low most since

כיתה ז'. צלצול שלישי נשמע באזני. ייתכן שאין אף אחד
kita za'in. tsiltsul shlishi nishma be'ozni. itakhen she'ein af ekhad
seventh grade ring third it sounded in my ear perhaps that there isn't no one

בבית. לרוע המזל, הצלצול נענה.
baba'it. lero'a hamazal, hatsiltsul na'ana
at home unfortunately the ring it was answered

"Hello," said a voice that had tormented me for years.

"הלו," אמר קול שייסר אותי במשך שנים.
halo, amar kol sheyiser oti bemeshekh shanim.
hello he said voice that it tormented me for years

"Hi Mira. I need a little help."

"היי מירה. אני צריך קצת עזרה."
hai mira ani tsarikh ktsat ezra.
hi Mira I I need a little help

"Rafi, so nice to hear from you," my sister Mira cooed into the phone. "What is the problem?"

"רפי, נחמד מאוד לשמוע ממך," המתה אחותי מירה לתוך הטלפון.
rafi nekhmad me'od lishmo'a mimkha, hamta akhoti mira letokh hatelefon
Rafi nice very to hear from you she cooed my sister Mira into the telephone

"מה הבעיה?"
ma habe'aya
what the problem

I swallowed my pride. "Can you explain over the phone how to install a garbage disposal?"

בלעתי את גאוותי. "תוכלי להסביר לי בטלפון איך להתקין
bala'ti et ga'avti. tukhli lehasbir li batelefon eikh lehatkin
I swallowed D.O. my pride could you to explain to me on the telephone how to install

טוחן אשפה?"
tokhen ashpa
garbage disposal

"When did you decide to be a plumber?"

"מתי החלטת להיות שרברב?"
matai hekhlateta lihiyot shravrav
when you decided to be plumber

"מאז שהשרברבים התחילו לנהוג במכוניות יקרות יותר מהמכונית
me'az *sheshravravim* *hitkhilu* *linhog* *bimkhoniyot* *yekarot* *yoter* *mehamekhonit*
ever since / that plumbers / they started / to drive / with cars / expensive / more / than the car

שלי."
sheli
my

"Ever since plumbers started driving more expensive cars than mine."

"אתה זוכר את הפעם ההיא כשניסית לעזור לי לבנות את
ata *zokher* *et* *hapa'am* *hahi* *kshenisita* *la'azor* *li* *livnot* *et*
you / you remember / D.O. / the time / that one / when you tried / to help / to me / to build / D.O.

מדפי הספרים ההם?" שאלה מירה.
madafei *hasfarim* *hahem* *sha'ala* *mira*
shelves of / the books / those / she asks / Mira

"Do you remember that time you tried to help me build those bookshelves?" Mira asked.

אחותי מבוגרת ממני בשנה. היא תמיד ידעה לבנות ולתקן דברים.
akhoti *mevugeret* *mimeni* *beshana* *hi* *tamid* *yada* *livnot* *uletaken* *dvarim*
my sister / older / than me / by year / she / always / she knew / to build / and to fix / things

כשהיינו בגיל העשרה ניסיתי לעזור לה כמה פעמים.
ksheha'inu *begil* *ha'esre* *nisiti* *la'azor* *la* *kama* *pe'amim*
when we were / at age of / the teenage / I tried / to help / to her / a few / times

My sister is a year older than I am. She has always been able to build and fix things. When we were teenagers I tried to help her a few times.

"אל תזכירי לי," אמרתי.
al *tazkiri* *li* *amarti*
don't / you will remind / to me / I said

"Don't remind me," I said.

"הכית את הבוהן שלך בפטיש בלי הפסקה. היא התנפחה
hiketa *et* *habohen* *shelkha* *befatish* *bli* *hafsaka* *hi* *hitnapkha*
you hit / D.O. / the thumb / your / with hammer / without / stopping / it / it became swollen

כל כך שאמא נאלצה להחזיק בשבילך את המסמרים."
kol kakh *she'ima* *ne'eltsa* *lehakhzik* *bishvilkha* *et* *hamasmerim*
so / that mom / she was forced / to hold / for you / D.O. / the nails

"You kept hitting your thumb with a hammer. It got so swollen that mom had to hold the nails for you."

"היא החזיקה רק מסמר אחד," אמרתי.
hi *hakhzika* *rak* *masmer* *ekhad* *amarti*
she / she held / only / nail / one / I said

"She only held one nail," I said.

"נכון," צחקה מירה. "היא פרשה כשהיכתה גם את הבוהן שלה."
nakhon *tsakhaka* *mira* *hi* *parsha* *kshehiketa* *gam* *et* *habohen* *shela*
correct / she laughed / Mira / she / she quit / when you hit / also / D.O. / the thumb / her

"That's right," Mira laughed. "She quit when you hit her thumb, too."

"אני הרבה יותר טוב עם הפטיש עכשיו," אמרתי. "יכולתי לעשות את
ani *harbe* *yoter* *tov* *im* *hapatish* *akhshav* *amarti* *yakholti* *la'asot* *et*
I / much / more / good / with / the hammer / now / I said / I could / to do / D.O.

העבודה בעצמי אבל הוראות ההתקנה כתובות ביפנית."
ha'avoda *be'atsmi* *aval* *hora'ot* *hahatkana* *ktuvot* *beyapanit*
the job / myself / but / instructions of / the installation / written / in Japanese

"I'm much better with hammers now," I said. "I could probably do the job myself, but the installation instructions are printed in Japanese."

"שים את הטלפון על רמקול," נאנחה אחותי. "אני אדריך אותך
sim *et* *hatelefon* *al* *ramkol* *ne'enkha* *akhoti* *ani* *adrikh* *otkha*
put / D.O. / the telephone / on / speaker / she sighed / my sister / I / I will guide / you

"Put the phone on speaker," my sister sighed. "I'll walk you through the whole thing."

לאורך כל העבודה.״
le'orekh kol ha'avoda
throughout all of the job

— 6 —

Gilat arrived home just as I was putting the tools away.

גילת הגיעה הביתה ממש כשהחזרתי את כלי העבודה למקומם.
gilat higi'a habaita mamash kshehekhzarti et klei ha'avoda limkomam
Gilat she arrived homeward just as I returned D.O. tools of the work to their place

"We have a new garbage disposal," I told her.

״יש לנו טוחן אשפה חדש,״ אמרתי לה.
yesh lanu tokhen ashpa khadash amarti la
we have garbage disposal new I told to her

She went into the kitchen and looked under the sink.

היא ניגשה למטבח והביטה מתחת לכיור.
hi nigsha lamitbakh vehibita mitakhat lakiyor
she she approached to the kitchen and she looked under to the sink

"It really is new," she said. "What plumber did you use?"

״זה באמת חדש,״ אמרה. ״לאיזה שרברב קראת?״
ze be'emet khadash amra le'eize shravrav karata
this truly new she said to what plumber you called

"I did it myself."

״עשיתי את זה בעצמי.״
asiti et ze be'atsmi
I did D.O. it by myself

"No you didn't," my lovely wife said. "Nothing in the kitchen is broken."

״לא נכון,״ אמרה אשתי החביבה. ״שום דבר במטבח לא שבור.״
lo nakhon amra ishti hakhaviva shum davar bamitbakh lo shavur
not correct she said my wife the lovely nothing in the kitchen not broken

"Look in the cabinet again," I told her. "Under the garbage can."

״תסתכלי בארון שוב,״ אמרתי לה. ״מתחת לפח האשפה.״
tistakli ba'aron shuv amarti la mitakhat lefakh ha'ashpa
you will look in the cabinet again I told to her under to can of the garbage

"Look at the size of this hole!" she exclaimed a few seconds later. "You could fit a pumpkin into it."

״איזה חור גדול!״ קראה כעבור מספר שניות. ״אפשר להכניס לתוכו
eize khor gadol kara ka'avor mispar shniyot efshar lehakhnis letokho
what a hole big she shouted after a few seconds it is possible to insert inside it

דלעת.״
dla'at
pumpkin

"I was going to fix it with a piece of plywood, but I didn't have time."

״התכוונתי לתקן אותו עם חתיכת דיקט, אבל לא היה לי זמן.״
hitkavanti letaken oto im khatikhat dikt aval lo haya li zman
I planned to fix it with piece of plywood but no I had time

"If this is the only damage you did, then I'm impressed," said Gilat. "Are you sure you didn't have any help?"

״אם זה הנזק היחיד שגרמת זה מרשים,״ אמרה גילת. ״אתה
im ze hanezek hayakhid shegaramta ze marshim amra gilat ata
if this the damage the only that you caused this impressive she said Gilat you

בטוח שלא קיבלת שום עזרה?״
batu'akh shelo kibalta shum ezra
sure that no you received any help

"יעקב היה כאן בהתחלה אבל הוא היה צריך ללכת."
ya'akov haya kan bahatkhala aval hu haya tsarikh lalekhet
Jacob he was here at the beginning but he he had to to leave

"Jacob was here at the beginning but he had to leave."

"זה מצריך חגיגה. בוא נפתח בקבוק יין."
ze matsrikh khagiga. bo niftakh bakbuk ya'in
this it requires celebration let's we will open bottle of wine

"This calls for a celebration. Let's open a bottle of wine."

היא נטלה בקבוק שרדונה מהמקרר ומזגה שתי כוסות.
hi natla bakbuk shardone mehamekarer umazga shtei kosot
she she took bottle of chardonnay from the refrigerator and she poured two glasses

She took a bottle of chardonnay out of the refrigerator and poured two glasses.

הרמנו לחיים.
heramnu lekha'im
we raised to life

We toasted.

"לחיי התיקונצ׳יק שלי," אמרה גילת בעודנו לוגמים מהשרדונה.
lekhayei hatikunchik sheli amra gilat be'odenu logmim mehashardone
to toast of the handyman my she said Gilat while we we sip from the chardonnay

"A toast to my handyman," said Gilat as we took a sip of the chardonnay.

נשארנו במטבח, שותים יין ומכינים את ארוחת הערב. גילת בישלה.
nisharnu bamitbakh shotim ya'in umekhinim et arukhat ha'erev bishla gilat
we stayed in the kitchen we drink wine and we prepare D.O. the dinner she cooked Gilat

ערכתי את השולחן והכנתי סלט. גילת סיפרה לי על חבריה מהאוניברסיטה.
arakhti et hashulkhan vehekhanti salat. gilat sipra li al khavereiha meha'universita
I set D.O. the table and I prepared salad Gilat she told to me about her friends from the university

We stayed in the kitchen, drinking the wine and preparing dinner. Gilat did the cooking. I set the table and made a salad. Gilat told me all about her college friends.

"הלכנו לקניון ואכלנו סושי לארוחת הצוהריים," אמרה.
halakhnu lakanyon ve'akhalnu sushi le'arukhat hatsohora'im amra
we went to the mall and we ate sushi for lunch she said

"We went to the mall and ate sushi for lunch," she said.

"זה נחמד."
ze nekhmad
that nice

"That's nice."

גילת ואני היינו כבר בכוס היין השלישית כשהתיישבנו לארוחת הערב. הרגשתי מאוד נינוח.
gilat va'ani ha'inu kvar bekhos haya'in hashlishit kshehityashavnu le'arukhat ha'erev. hirgashti me'od nino'akh
Gilat and I we were already on glass of the wine the third when we sat down for dinner I felt very relaxed

Gilat and I were on our third glass of wine by the time we sat down to dinner. I was feeling very relaxed.

"ובכן, דיברת היום עם מישהו מעניין מלבד יעקב?" שאלה גילת.
uv'khen dibarta hayom im mishehu me'anyen milvad ya'akov sha'ala gilat
so you spoke today with someone interesting aside from Jacob she asks Gilat

"So did you talk to anyone interesting today besides Jacob?" she asked.

"התקשרתי לאחותי מירה," ציינתי.
hitkasharti le'akhoti mira tsiyanti
I called to my sister Mira I mentioned

"I called my sister Mira," I mentioned.

"Aha," Gilat said as she pointed a finger at me. "Mira helped you."

"אהה," אמרה גילת כשהיא זוקפת אצבע לעברי. "מירה עזרה לך."

aha	amra	gilat	kshehi	zokefet	etsba	le'evri	mira	azra	lekha
aha	she said	Gilat	as she	she points	finger	toward me	Mira	she helped	to you

"No fair," I complained. "You gave me alcohol to sneak the truth out of me."

"לא הוגן," התלוננתי. "השקית אותי באלכוהול כדי לסחוט

lo	hogen	hitlonanti	hishket	oti	be'alkohol	kedei	liskhot
not	fair	I complained	you gave a drink to	me	with alcohol	in order to	to squeeze

ממני את האמת."

mimeni	et	ha'emet
from me	D.O.	the truth

"I can't help it if you have no tolerance for wine," she giggled.

"זו לא אשמתי שאתה לא יודע לשתות יין," היא גיחכה.

zo	lo	ashmati	she'ata	lo	yode'a	lishtot	ya'in	hi	gikhakha
this	not	my fault	that you	no	you can	to drink	wine	she	she giggled

"You took unfair advantage of me," I complained.

"ניצלת אותי באופן לא הוגן," התלוננתי.

nitsalt	oti	be'ofen	lo	hogen	hitlonanti
you exploited	me	in manner	not	fair	I complained

"You don't have to feel ashamed," Gilat said. "You were smart to ask someone else to help."

"אתה לא צריך להתבייש," אמרה גילת. "זה היה חכם מצדך

ata	lo	tsarikh	lehitbayesh	amra	gilat	ze	haya	khakham	mitsid'kha
you	no	you need	to feel ashamed	she said	Gilat	that	it was	smart	on your part

לבקש עזרה ממישהו."

levakesh	ezra	mimishehu
to ask for	help	from someone

"The installation instructions were written in Japanese."

"הוראות ההתקנה היו כתובות ביפנית."

hora'ot	hahatkana	hayu	ktuvot	beyapanit
instructions of	the installation	they were	written	in Japanese

"Not everyone was born to be an expert with tools and mechanical things," Gilat said. "You have lots of other talents that your sister lacks."

"לא כל אחד נולד להיות מומחה לשימוש בכלי עבודה ודברים

lo	kol ekhad	nolad	lihiyot	mumkhe	leshimush	bikhlei	avoda	udvarim
not	everyone	he was born	to be	expert	to usage	with tools of	work	and things

מכניים," אמרה גילת. "יש לך הרבה כשרונות אחרים שאין לאחותך."

mekhaniyim	amra	gilat	yesh lekha	harbe	kishronot	akherim	she'ein la'akhot'kha
mechanical	she said	Gilat	you have	many	talents	others	that your sister doesn't have

"Like what?"

"כמו מה?"

kmo	ma
like	what

She thought for a minute. "You are really good at rubbing my feet."

היא חשבה לרגע. "אתה באמת טוב בעיסוי הרגליים שלי."

hi	khashva	lerega	ata	be'emet	tov	be'isui	haragla'im	sheli
she	she thought	for a moment	you	really	good	at massage of	the feet	my

"I don't want people to know about that. They might think I'm strange."

"אני לא רוצה שאנשים ידעו על זה. הם עלולים לחשוב שאני

ani	lo	rotse	she'anashim	yadu	al	ze	hem	alulim	lakhshov	she'ani
I	no	I want	that people	they will know	about	that	they	might	to think	that I

מוזר."

muzar
strange

שעושה לי עיסוי ברגליים מאשר בעל שמתקן דברים. אתה לא צריך להרגיש חסר בטחון בגלל שאתה לא יודע לתקן דברים בבית. בוא נשכור אנשים שיעשו את העבודות האלה."

"סודך שמור עמי. זה רק שאני הרבה יותר מאושרת עם בעל
sod'kha shamur imi. ze rak she'ani harbe yoter me'usheret im ba'al
your secret / it is guarded / with me / this / only / that I / much / more / happy / with / husband

שעושה לי עיסוי ברגליים מאשר בעל שמתקן דברים. אתה
she'ose li isui baragla'im me'asher ba'al shemetaken dvarim. ata
who (he) does / for me / massage / on the feet / than / husband / who (he) fixes / things / you

לא צריך להרגיש חסר בטחון בגלל שאתה לא יודע לתקן
lo tsarikh lehargish khasar bitakhon biglal she'ata lo yode'a letaken
no / you need / to feel / lacking of / security / because of / that you / no / you know / to fix

דברים בבית. בוא נשכור אנשים שיעשו את העבודות האלה."
dvarim baba'it bo niskor anashim sheya'asu et ha'avodot ha'ele
things / at home / let's / we will hire / people / who (they) will do / D.O. / the jobs / the those

"זה נשמע כמו תוכנית טובה," אמרתי. "אין לך מושג כמה הייתי
ze nishma kmo tokhnit tova," amarti. "ein lakh musag kama ha'iti
that / it sounds / like / plan / good / I said / you don't have / idea / how / I was

מתוח היום."
matu'akh hayom
tense / today

"Your secret is safe with me. It's just that I'm much happier with a husband who rubs my feet than I would be with a husband who fixes things. You don't have to feel insecure about not being handy around the house. Let's hire people to do that stuff."

"That sounds like a good plan," I said. "You don't know how stressful my day has been."

99

STORY 10

All Inclusive

אכלנו ארוחת ערב עם יוסי ומירה, זוג נחמד מצפת. פגשנו אותם
akhalnu arukhat erev im yosi umira, zug nekhmad mitsfat. pagashnu otam
we ate dinner with Yossi and Mira, couple nice from Safed. we met them

בבר הבריכה מוקדם יותר אחר הצוהריים. היה כל כך כיף איתם
bebar habreikha mukdam yoter akhar hatsohora'im. haya kol kakh kef itam
at the bar the pool early more after the noon. it was so fun with them

שהזמנו אותם להצטרף אלינו לארוחת הערב.
shehizmanu otam lehitstaref eleinu le'arukhat ha'erev.
that we invited them to join to us for the dinner.

We were having dinner with Yossi and Mira, a nice couple from Safed. We had met them at the pool swim up bar earlier in the afternoon. They were such fun people that we asked them to join us for dinner.

"אז מה עשיתם שניכם היום?" שאל יוסי.
"az ma asitem shneikhem hayom?" sha'al yosi.
"so what you did two of you today?" he asks Yossi.

"So what did you two do today?" asked Yossi.

"רפי שתה עשר מרגריטות ונרדם על החוף," אמרה גילת.
"rafi shata eser margaritot venirdam al hakhof," amra gilat.
"Rafi he drank ten margaritas and he fell asleep on the beach," she said Gilat.

"עכשיו יש לו כוויות שמש."
"akhshav yesh lo kviyot shemesh."
"now he has burns of sun."

"Rafi drank ten margaritas and fell asleep on the beach," Gilat said. "Now he has a bad sunburn."

מירה הביטה בי. "אתה נראה ורוד קצת," העירה.
mira hibita bi. "ata nire varod ktsat," he'ira.
Mira she looked at me. "you you seem pink a little," she remarked.

Mira looked at me. "You do look a little pink," she remarked.

"השמש כאן בקנקון ממש חזקה. צריך להיזהר," אמר יוסי.
"hashemesh kan bekankun mamash khazaka. tsarikh lehizaher," amar yosi.
"the sun here in Cancun really powerful. you need to be careful," he said Yossi.

"תשתה כמה מרגריטות נוספות ותרגיש טוב יותר."
"tishte kama margaritot nosafot vetargish tov yoter."
"you will drink a few margaritas additional and you will feel good more."

"The sun here in Cancun is really powerful. You have to be careful," said Yossi. "Have a few more margaritas and you'll feel better."

"המקום הזה ממש נהדר," אמרה מירה. "אנחנו יכולים לאכול ולשתות
"hamakom haze mamash nehedar," amra mira. "anakhnu yekholim le'ekhol velishtot
"the place the this really great," she said Mira. "we we can to eat and to drink

כאוות נפשנו, והכל כלול במחיר. וחוץ מזה, יש להם
ke'avat nafshenu, vehakol kalul bamekhir. vekhuts mize, yesh lahem
as much as we want, and everything included in the price. and outside of this, they have

פעילויות מים נהדרות, קיאקים, שיט בסירות וצלילה בשנורקלים
pe'iluyot ma'im nehedarot, kayakim, sha'it besirot utslila bishnorkelim
activities of water great, kayaks, sailing in boats and diving with snorkels

"This place is so great," Mira said. "We can eat and drink as much as we want, and it's all included in the price. Plus they have great water sports, kayaks, sailboats, and snorkeling right here at the resort."

101

ממש כאן באתר הנופש."
be'atar hanofesh *kan* *mamash*
at the resort / here / exactly

"I hope my mother is doing alright watching the kids," Gilat said.

"אני מקווה שאמא שלי מסתדרת עם הילדים," אמרה גילת.
gilat *amra* *hayeladim* *im* *mistaderet* *sheli* *she'ima* *mekava* *ani*
Gilat / she said / the kids / with / she manages / my / that mother / I hope / I

"She'll be fine," I said.

"היא תסתדר," אמרתי.
amarti *tistader* *hi*
I said / she will manage / she

"What if something happens?"

"מה אם יקרה משהו?"
mashehu *yikre* *im* *ma*
something / it will happen / if / what

"Nothing bad will happen," I said. "But your mother has the telephone number of the hotel. She can always call that number and ask them to find us."

"שום דבר רע לא יקרה," אמרתי. "אבל יש לאמא שלך את מספר
mispar *et* *shelakh* *yesh le'ima* *aval* *amarti* *yikre* *lo* *ra* *shum davar*
number of / D.O. / your / mother has / but / I said / it will happen / no / bad / nothing

הטלפון של המלון. היא תמיד יכולה להתקשר ולבקש שימצאו
sheyimtse'u *ulevakesh* *lehitkasher* *yekhola* *tamid* *hi* *hamalon* *shel* *hatelefon*
that they will find / and to ask / to call / she can / always / she / the hotel / of / the telephone

אותנו."
otanu
us

"The water aerobics was a strenuous workout," Gilat mentioned. "Rafi tried it, but he couldn't keep up the pace."

"האימון האירובי במים היה מתיש," ציינה גילת. "רפי ניסה,
nisa *rafi* *gilat* *tsiyna* *matish* *haya* *bama'im* *ha'eirobi* *ha'imun*
he tried / Rafi / Gilat / she mentioned / exhausting / it was / in the water / the aerobic / the training

אבל הוא לא הצליח לעמוד בקצב."
la'amod baketsev *hitsli'akh* *lo* *hu* *aval*
to keep up / he succeeded / no / he / but

"Was this before or after the heavy drinking?" Yossi asked.

"זה היה לפני או אחרי האלכוהול?" שאל יוסי.
yosi *sha'al* *ha'alkohol* *akharei* *o* *lifnei* *haya* *ze*
Yossi / he asks / the alcohol / after / or / before / it was / this

"Before," I said. "Omar runs the aerobics. He's like an army drill sergeant. I don't know how all those women at the pool could swing their arms and pump their legs for a full hour."

"לפני," אמרתי. "עומר מדריך את האימון האירובי. הוא כמו
kmo *hu* *ha'eirobi* *ha'imun* *et* *madrikh* *omar* *amarti* *lifnei*
like / he / the aerobic / the training / D.O. / he leads / Omar / I said / before

סמל מחלקה בתרגיל צבאי. אני לא מבין איך כל הנשים האלה
ha'ele *hanashim* *kol* *eikh* *mevin* *lo* *ani* *tsva'i* *betargil* *samal makhlaka*
the those / the women / all / how / I understand / no / I / army / in drill / drill sergeant

בבריכה מסוגלות לנפנף בזרועותיהן ולהקפיץ את רגליהן במשך שעה
sha'a *bemeshekh* *ragleihen* *et* *ulehakpits* *bizro'oteihen* *lenafnef* *mesugalot* *babreikha*
hour / for / their legs / D.O. / and to bounce / with their arms / to wave / they are able / at the pool

שלמה."
shlema
whole

"עומר מלמד גם שיעורי סלסה בשעה ארבע בכל יום," אמרה גילת.
gilat amra yom bekhol arba besha'a salsa shi'urei gam melamed omar
Gilat she said day in every four at hour salsa lessons of also he teaches Omar

"הוא נתן לי שיעור כשרפי נחר על החוף."
hakhof al nakhar ksherafi shi'ur li natan hu
the beach on he snored when Rafi lesson to me he gave he

"Omar also gives salsa lessons at four o'clock every day," Gilat said. "He gave me a lesson while Rafi was snoring on the beach."

"לא סיפרת לי שעומר נתן לך שיעור ריקוד," אמרתי. "אני לא
lo sipart li she'omar natan lakh shi'ur rikud amarti ani lo
no you told to me that Omar he gave to you lesson of dance I said I not

בטוח שזה מוצא חן בעיניי."
be'einai khen motse sheze batu'akh
in my eyes grace it finds that this sure

"You didn't tell me that Omar gave you a dance lesson," I said. "I'm not sure I like that."

"ובעיניי לא מוצאת חן הדרך שבה נעצת מבטים בשתי הבחורות
habakhurot bishtei na'atsta mabatim sheba haderekh khen motset lo uve'einai
the girls at two of you stared in which the way grace she finds no and in my eyes

הצעירות בחוטיני בזמן האימון האירובי במים," אמרה גילת.
gilat amra bama'im ha'eirobi ha'imun bizman bakhutini hatse'irot
Gilat she said in the water the aerobic the training of during in g-string the young

"And I don't like the way you were staring at those two young girls in the thong bikinis during the water aerobics," Gilat said.

עצמתי את עיניי ונזכרתי בשתי הנשים היפהפיות שגילת
shegilat hayefefiyot hanashim bishtei venizkarti einai et atsamti
that Gilat the gorgeous the women in two of and I remembered my eyes D.O. I closed

הזכירה. היה להן שיזוף מושלם, כמה קעקועים קלאסיים, וציפורניים
vetsiporna'im klasiyim ka'aku'im kama mushlam shizuf haya lahen hizkira
and fingernails classy tattoos a few perfect suntan they had she mentioned

צבועות בצבע בהיר. די היה במחשבה עליהן כדי להעלים
leha'alim kedei aleihen bamakhshava haya dai bahir betseva tsvu'ot
to hide in order to of them with the thought it was enough bright with color painted

את כאב כוויות השמש למשך שניות אחדות.
akhadot shniyot lemeshekh hashemesh kviyot ke'ev et
a few seconds for the sun burns of pain of D.O.

I closed my eyes and remembered the two gorgeous young women Gilat was talking about. They had perfect tans, a few classy tattoos, and brightly polished fingernails. The thought of them was enough to make the sunburn pain stop for a few seconds.

"היו להן עגילי טבור ממש יפים," נאנחתי.
ne'enakhti yafim mamash tabur agilei hayu lahen
I sighed pretty really belly-button ring of they had

"They had really pretty belly button rings," I sighed.

גילת חבטה בי. "היית צריך להסתכל ממש מקרוב כדי לדעת
lada'at kedei mikarov mamash ha'ita tsarikh lehistakel bi khavta gilat
to know in order to from close up really you must have looked at me she punched Gilat

את זה," אמרה.
amra ze et
she said that D.O.

Gilat punched me. "You must have gotten a real close look to know that," she said.

"אני יודעת לאיזה בחורות אתה מתכוון," קטעה אותה מירה.
mira ota kata mitkaven ata bakhurot le'eize yoda'at ani
Mira her she interrupted you mean you girls of which I know I

"I know the girls you mean," Mira interrupted. "I have shoes older than them."

"יש לי נעליים יותר מבוגרות מהן."

yesh li	na'ala'im	yoter	mevugarot	mehen
I have	shoes	more	old	than them

"Did you notice two guys in cowboy hats standing in the pool the entire afternoon?" asked Yossi.

"שמתם לב לשני הבחורים בכובעי בוקרים שעמדו בבריכה כל

samtem lev	lishnei	habakhurim	bekhova'ei	bokrim	she'amdu	babreikha	kol
you noticed	to the two of	the guys	in hats of	cowboys	that they stood	in the pool	all

אחר הצוהריים?" שאל יוסי.

akhar	hatsohora'im	sha'al	yosi
after	the noon	he asked	Yossi

"They were at the water aerobics," Gilat said. "Drinking beer out of large insulated cups in one hand and doing the exercises with the other. It was so funny."

"הם היו באימון האירובי במים," אמרה גילת. "שתו בירה

hem	hayu	be'imun	ha'eirobi	bama'im	amra	gilat	shatu	bira
they	they were	at training	the aerobic	in the water	she said	Gilat	they drank	beer

מכוסות תרמיות גדולות ביד אחת, ועשו תרגילים ביד

mikosot	termiyot	gdolot	beyad	akhat	ve'asu	targilim	bayad
from cups	insulated	large	in hand	one	and they did	exercises	with the hand

השנייה. זה היה כל כך מצחיק."

hashniya	ze	haya	kol kakh	matskhik
the second	this	it was	so	funny

"Are you going to listen to the band that is playing here tonight?" asked Yossi.

"אתם מתכוונים ללכת לשמוע את הלהקה שתנגן כאן הלילה?"

atem	mitkavnim	lalekhet	lishmo'a	et	halahaka	shetenagen	kan	halaila
you	you intend	to go	to listen	D.O.	the band	that (it) will play	here	tonight

שאל יוסי.

sha'al	yosi
he asks	Yossi

"I think we'll stay in the room and read. My sunburn is killing me. You two have fun," I said.

"אני חושב שנישאר בחדר ונקרא. כוויות השמש הורגות

ani	khoshev	shenisha'er	bakheder	venikra	kviyot	hashemesh	horgot
I	I think	that we will stay	in the room	and we will read	burns of	the sun	it kills

אותי. תהנו שניכם," אמרתי.

oti	tehanu	shneikhem	amarti
me	you will have fun	two of you	I said

— 2 —

We arrived for the manager's cocktail party at five o'clock. Yossi and Mira were already sitting near the bar. We joined them for a few drinks.

"הגענו למסיבת הקוקטייל של המנהל בחמש בערב. יוסי

higanu	limsibat	hakoktel	shel	hamenahel	bekhamesh	ba'erev	yosi
we arrived	to party of	the cocktail	of	the manager of	at five	in the evening	Yossi

ומירה כבר ישבו ליד הבר. הצטרפנו אליהם לכמה משקאות.

umira	kvar	yashvu	leyad	habar	hitstarafnu	aleihem	lekhama	mashka'ot
and Mira	already	they sat	near	the bar	we joined	to them	for a few	drinks

"You don't look too good," I said to Yossi.

"אתה לא נראה טוב במיוחד," אמרתי ליוסי.

ata	lo	nire	tov	bimyukhad	amarti	leyosi
you	no	you appear	good	especially	I said	to Yossi

"He met some Irish guys at the karaoke bar last night," said Mira. "They drank shots and sang songs un-

"הוא פגש כמה בחורים אירים בבר הקריוקי אתמול בלילה," אמרה

hu	pagash	kama	bakhurim	irim	bebar	hakaryoki	etmol	balaila	amra
he	he met	a few	guys	Irish	at bar	the karaoke	yesterday	at the night	she said

מירה. "הם שתו שוטים ושרו שירים עד חצות."

mira — *hem* — *shatu* — *shotim* — *vesharu* — *shirim* — *ad* — *khatsot*

Mira — they — they drank — shots — and they sang — songs — until — midnight

til midnight."

"והיינו צריכים לקום ממש מוקדם היום לצלילה בשונית," הוסיף

veha'inu tsrikhim — *lakum* — *mamash* — *mukdam* — *hayom* — *letslila* — *bashunit* — *hosif*

and we had to — to wake up — really — early — today — for scuba diving — at the reef — he added

יוסי.

yosi

Yossi

"And we had to get up really early for a dive out at the reef today," Yossi added.

"האלכוהול, הצלילה, וטלטולי הסירה במים עשו את

ha'alkohol — *hatslila* — *vetiltulei* — *hasira* — *bama'im* — *asu* — *et*

the alcohol — the scuba diving — and the movement of — the boat — on the water — they made — D.O.

יוסי ממש חולה," אמרה מירה.

yosi — *mamash* — *khole* — *amra* — *mira*

Yossi — really — sick — she said — Mira

"The alcohol, the diving, and the boat bouncing up and down on the water made Yossi very ill," Mira said.

"הם בטח עדיין מנקים את הסירה," אמר יוסי.

hem — *betakh* — *ada'in* — *menakim* — *et* — *hasira* — *amar* — *yosi*

they — probably — still — they clean — D.O. — the boat — he said — Yossi

"They're probably still cleaning up the boat," Yossi said.

"רב החובל אסר עלינו לעלות על הסירה שלו ליתר השבוע,"

rav hakhovel — *asar* — *aleinu* — *la'alot* — *al* — *hasira* — *shelo* — *leyeter* — *hashavu'a*

the captain — he banned — on us — to get into — on — the boat — his — for rest of — the week

התלוננה מירה. "עכשיו לא נוכל לצלול יותר."

hitlonena — *mira* — *akhshav* — *lo* — *nukhal* — *litslol* — *yoter*

she complained — Mira — now — no — we will be able — to dive — more

"The captain banned us from his boat for the rest of the week," Mira complained. "Now we can't go diving anymore."

"לא יכולת להוציא את הראש מחוץ לסירה?" שאלתי.

lo — *yakholta* — *lehotsi* — *et* — *harosh* — *mikhuts* — *lasira* — *sha'alti*

no — you could — to take out — D.O. — the head — out of — of the boat — I asked

"Couldn't you hang your head over the side?" I asked.

"ניסיתי, אבל לא הספקתי."

nisiti — *aval* — *lo* — *hispakti*

I tried — but — no — I managed on time

"I tried to, but I didn't make it."

"אז מה אתה שותה עכשיו?" שאלה גילת.

az — *ma* — *ata* — *shote* — *akhshav* — *sha'ala* — *gilat*

so — what — you — you drink — now — she asked — Gilat

"So what are you drinking now?" Gilat asked.

"רק בירה. אני מקווה שעוד אלכוהול ירגיע את הבטן שלי."

rak — *bira* — *ani* — *mekave* — *she'od* — *alkohol* — *yargi'a* — *et* — *habeten* — *sheli*

just — beer — I — I hope — that more — alcohol — it will calm — D.O. — the stomach — my

"Just a beer. I'm hoping more alcohol will settle my stomach."

"מה אתם עשיתם היום?" שאלה מירה.

ma — *atem* — *asitem* — *hayom* — *sha'ala* — *mira*

what — you — you did — today — she asked — Mira

"What did you guys do today?" asked Mira.

"רפי למד איך להכניס את המכונית השכורה להילוך אחורי," אמרה

rafi — *lamad* — *eikh* — *lahakhnis* — *et* — *hamekhonit* — *haskhura* — *lehilukh akhori* — *amra*

Rafi — he learned — how — to put in — D.O. — the car — the rented — into reverse — she said

"Rafi learned how to put our rental car into reverse gear," Gilat said proudly.

105

גילת בגאווה.
gilat bega'ava
Gilat with pride

Yossi and Mira looked at me a little strangely.

יוסי ומירה הביטו בי במבט מוזר מעט.
yosi umira hibitu bi bemabat muzar me'at
Yossi and Mira they looked at at me with look strange a little

"We drove to Tulum to see the ruins," I said. "On the way we stopped at a convenience store and I parked the car with the front facing the store. When we tried to leave I couldn't put the car into reverse."

"נסענו לטולום לראות את העתיקות," אמרתי. "בדרך עצרנו
nasanu letulum lirot et ha'atikot, amarti. baderekh atsarnu
we drove to Tulum to see D.O. the ruins I said on the way we stopped

במינימרקט והחניתי את המכונית כשהחזית בכיוון החנות.
beminimarket vehekhneiti et hamekhonit kshehakhazit bekhivun hakhanut
at minimarket and I parked D.O. the car with the front in direction of the store

כשניסינו לנסוע משם לא הצלחתי להכניס להילוך אחורי."
kshenisinu linso'a misham lo hitslakhti lehakhnis lehilukh akhori
when we tried to drive from there no I succeeded to put in to reverse

"Why not?"

"למה לא?"
lama lo
why not

"I didn't know how. The shift knob showed me where reverse was located but the stick wouldn't move into that position."

"לא ידעתי איך. כתוב על ידית ההילוכים איפה נמצא ההילוך האחורי,
lo yadati eikh. katuv al yadit hahilukhim eifo nimtsa hahilukh ha'akhori
no I knew how written on the stick shift where it is located the reverse

אבל הידית לא עברה לשם."
aval hayadit lo avra lesham
but the knob no it moved to there

"We paid a nice young man to show us," Gilat said.

"שילמנו לבחור צעיר ונחמד כדי שיראה לנו," אמרה גילת.
shilamnu levakhur tsa'ir venekhmad kedei sheyare lanu, amra gilat
we paid to young man young and nice in order to he will show to us she said Gilat

"Ten pesos for showing us how to work the gears and thirty pesos for not laughing at me," I said.

"עשרה פסו כדי שיראה לנו איך להפעיל את ההילוכים
asara peso kedei sheyare lanu eikh lehafil et hahilukhim
ten peso in order to that he will show to us how to use D.O. the gears

ושלושים פסו כדי שלא יצחק עליי," אמרתי.
ushloshim peso kedei shelo yitskhak alai, amarti
and thirty peso so that that no he will laugh at me I said

"Haven't you ever driven a manual transmission before?" Mira asked.

"אף פעם לא נהגת במכונית עם מוט הילוכים ידני?" שאלה מירה.
af pa'am lo nahagta bimkhonit im mot hilukhim yedani? sha'ala mira
never no you drove in car with stick shift manual she asked Mira

"Yes, but this car had a little ring at the bottom of the shift knob. I had to pull up the ring to engage reverse gear," I said.

"כן, אבל למכונית הזאת הייתה טבעת קטנה בחלק התחתון של
ken, aval lamekhonit hazot haita taba'at ktana bakhelek hatakhton shel
yes but this car had ring little on the part the lower of

מוט ההילוכים. הייתי צריך למשוך את הטבעת מעלה כדי להכניס
mot hahilukhim. ha'iti tsarikh limshokh et hataba'at mala kedei lehakhnis
the stick shift I had to to pull D.O. the ring upwards in order to to put in

לְהִילּוּךְ אֲחוֹרִי,״ אָמַרְתִּי.
amarti *lehilukh akhori*
I said / to reverse

״זֶה טְרִיק חָדָשׁ,״ אָמַר יוֹסִי.
yosi *amar* *khadash* *trik* *ze*
Yossi / he said / new / trick / that
"That's a new trick," Yossi said.

״אַתֶּם מִתְכַּוְּנִים לָלֶכֶת לַאֲרוּחַת הָעֶרֶב בַּמִּזְנוֹן?״ שָׁאֲלָה גִּילַת אֶת מִירָה.
mira *et* *gilat* *sha'ala* *bamiznon* *le'arukhat ha'erev* *lalekhet* *mitkavnim* *atem*
Mira / D.O. / Gilat / she asked / at the buffet / to the dinner / to go / you intend / you
"Are you going to dinner at the buffet tonight?" Gilat asked Mira.

״הֶחְלַטְנוּ לְהַזְמִין שֵׁרוּת חֲדָרִים, לְמִקְרֶה שֶׁיּוֹסִי יֶחֱלֶה שׁוּב.
shuv *yekhele* *sheyosi* *lemikre* *khadarim* *sherut* *lehazmin* *hekhlatnu*
again / he will become ill / that Yossi / in case / rooms / service of / to order / we decided
"We decided to order room service, in case Yossi gets ill again. We'll probably see you tomorrow sometime."

בֶּטַח נִרְאֶה אֶתְכֶם שׁוּב מָתַישֶׁהוּ מָחָר.״
makhar *mataishehu* *shuv* *etkhem* *nire* *betakh*
tomorrow / sometime / again / you / we will see / probably

3

״מָה עָבַר לְךָ בָּרֹאשׁ?״ צָעֲקָה גִּילַת.
gilat *tsa'aka* *barosh* *lekha* *avar* *ma*
Gilat / she yelled / in the head / to you / it passed / what
"What were you thinking?" Gilat yelled.

״זוֹ לֹא הָיְתָה אַשְׁמָתִי,״ אָמַרְתִּי.
amarti *ashmati* *haita* *lo* *zo*
I said / my fault / it was / no / this
"It wasn't my fault," I said.

״אַתָּה אֲפִילוּ לֹא יוֹדֵעַ לְהַשִּׁיט סִירַת צַעֲצוּעַ בָּאַמְבַּטְיָה. לָמָּה שְׁתִיקַח
shetikakh *lama* *ba'ambatya* *tsa'atsu'a* *sirat* *lehashit* *yode'a* *lo* *afilu* *ata*
that you took / why / in the bathtub / toy / boat of / to sail / you know / no / even / you
"You don't even know how to sail a toy boat in our tub. Why would you take out one of the resort sailboats into a choppy ocean?"

אַחַת מֵהַסִּירוֹת שֶׁל אֲתַר הַנֹּפֶשׁ לְתוֹךְ אוֹקְיָנוּס גָּלִי?״
gali *okyanos* *letokh* *atar hanofesh* *shel* *mehasirot* *akhat*
choppy / ocean / into / the resort / of / of the boats / one

״זֶה נִרְאָה כָּל כָּךְ קַל. נִרְאָה שֶׁכָּל הָאוֹרְחִים הָאֲחֵרִים הִצְלִיחוּ
hitslikhu *ha'akherim* *ha'orkhim* *shekol* *nira* *kal* *kol kakh* *nira* *ze*
they succeeded / the others / the guests / that all / it seemed / easy / so / it looked / this
"It looked so easy. All the other guests seemed to be able to handle the sailboats."

לְהִסְתַּדֵּר עִם הַסִּירוֹת.״
hasirot *im* *lehistader*
the boats / with / to manage themselves

״אֲבָל אַתָּה הָרַסְתָּ אֵיכְשֶׁהוּ אֶת הַסִּירָה.״
hasira *et* *eikhshehu* *harasta* *ata* *aval*
the boat / D.O. / somehow / you wrecked / you / but
"But you somehow wrecked your boat."

״הַצֶּוֶת בַּדּוּכָן סְפּוֹרְט הַמַּיִם הָיָה מְאוֹד נֶחְמָד. אַף אֶחָד לֹא צָעַק
tsa'ak *lo* *af ekhad* *nekhmad* *me'od* *haya* *hama'im* *sport* *bedukhan* *hatsevet*
he yelled / no / nobody / nice / very / he was / the water / sport of / at the counter / the staff
"The staff working at the water sports counter were very nice. Nobody screamed at me. How come you are so angry?"

עליי. איך זה שאת כל כך כועסת?"
ko'eset kol kakh eikh ze she'at alai
angry so how come you at me

"Because we have to pay the resort for a new sail."

"כי אנחנו צריכים לשלם לאתר הנופש עבור מפרש חדש."
khadash mifras avur le'atar hanofesh leshalem tsrikhim anakhnu ki
new sail for to the resort to pay we need we because

"Can't they just sew up the hole in the sail?"

"הם לא יכולים פשוט לתפור את החור במפרש?"
bamifras hakhor et litpor pashut yekholim lo hem
in the sail the hole D.O. to sew simply they can no they

"That hole was bigger than our rental car."

"החור היה גדול יותר מהמכונית השכורה שלנו."
shelanu haskhura mehamekhonit yoter gadol haya hakhor
our the rental than the car more big it was the hole

Gilat was walking down the beach a few hours earlier when she came upon my poor sailboat, laying flat in the water. I was standing on the jetty, watching the water sports employees unhook the sail from the mast. The sail was impaled on a large pole embedded in the rocks on the jetty. The two girls with the polished nails, tattoos, and tiny bathing suits were standing next to me. Gilat figured correctly that I had taken the ladies on a pleasure ride that ended badly. She has been mad at me ever since.

גילת הלכה לאורך החוף שעות אחדות קודם לכן כשנתקלה
kshenitkela kodem lakhen akhadot sha'ot hakhof le'orekh halkha gilat
when she encountered previously a few hours the beach along she walked Gilat

בסירה המסכנה שלי, מוטלת אופקית על המים. אני עמדתי על
al amadeti ani hama'im al ofkit mutelet sheli hamiskena basira
on I stood I the water on horizontally strewn my the poor with the boat

הרציף, צופה בעובדי ספורט המים משחררים את המפרש מהתורן.
mehatoren hamifras et meshakhrerim hama'im sport be'ovdei tsofe haretsif
from the mast the sail D.O. they release the water sport of at employees of I watch the jetty

עמוד גדול חדר דרך המפרש. העמוד היה מקובע לסלעים על הרציף.
haretsif al lasla'im mekuba haya ha'amud hamifras khadar derekh gadol amud
the jetty on to the rocks fixed it was the pole the sail it impaled large pole

שתי הבחורות עם הלכה על ציפורניהן, הקעקועים ובגדי הים
uvigdei hayam haka'aku'im tsiporneihen al halaka im habakhurot shtei
and the bathing suits the tattoos their fingernails on the nail polish with the girls two of

הזעירים עמדו בסמוך אליי. גילת ניחשה נכון, שלקחתי את
et shelakakhti nakhon nikhasha gilat elai besamukh amdu haze'irim
D.O. that I took correctly she guessed Gilat to me beside they stood the tiny

הגברות לשיט תענוגות שהסתיים באופן גרוע. היא כעסה עליי
alai ka'asa hi garu'a be'ofen shehistayem lesha'it ta'anugot hagvarot
with me she is angry she bad in way that ended for pleasure cruise the ladies

מאותו רגע ואילך.
me'oto rega va'elakh
from that moment on

She smacked me in the back of the head. "Why did you tell the water sports staff that you were an expert sailor?"

היא חבטה בי בעורף. "למה אמרת לצוות ספורט המים
hama'im sport letsevet amarta lama ba'oref bi khavta hi
the water sport of to the staff of you told why on the nape at me she smacked she

שאתה שייט מומחה?"
mumkhe shayat she'ata
expert sailor that you

"רציתי להרשים את הבחורות," הודיתי.

"I wanted to impress the girls," I admitted.

"ולמה הפלגת עם שתי בנות שהן צעירות מכדי להצביע בבחירות במקום עם אשתך?"

"And why were you sailing with two girls who are too young to vote, instead of with your wife?"

"לא היית מסכימה להפליג אלא אם היינו מבקשים מאחד מחברי הצוות לעזור לי להשיט את הסירה," רטנתי.

"You wouldn't have gone unless we asked one of the staff members to help me sail the boat," I muttered.

"ברור. אני מניחה שהיית זקוק לעזרה, לא?"

"Duh. I guess you needed the help, didn't you."

למרבה המזל ישבנו בבר הראשי בתוך אתר הנופש. בעוד שתי דקות עמד להתחיל שיעור. עמדנו ללמוד כיצד להכין מרטיני.

Luckily we were sitting at the main bar inside the resort. In two minutes a class was starting. We were going to learn how to make martinis.

"בואי נשכח מהעבר," אמרתי לגילת. "אני כבר לא יכול לחכות ללמוד איך להכין מרטיני."

"Let's forget about the past," I said to Gilat. "I can't wait to learn how to make martinis."

היא חבטה בעורפי פעם נוספת, למזל. אבל לא חזק כמו החבטה הקודמת, כך שפירשתי זאת שהיא כבר איננה כועסת כל כך. קיוויתי שאחרי שתשתה כמה כוסות מרטיני היא תשכח מכל העניין.

She smacked me in the back of the head one more time for good luck. But not as hard as the last smack, which I interpreted to mean that she was not as angry. I hoped that after she had a few martinis, she would forget about this whole episode.

All the seats at the bar were filled. At four o'clock, Omar appeared next to Luciano, our favorite bartender.

עומר הופיע ארבע בשעה. תפוסים היו הבר על המקומות כל
omar hofi'a arba besha'a tfusim hayu habar al hamkomot kol
Omar he appeared four at hour taken they were the bar at the seats all

ליד לוצ׳יאנו, הברמן החביב עלינו.
leyad luchi'ano habarmen hekhaviv aleinu
next to Luciano the bartender the favorite on us

"Is everyone ready to learn about martinis?" he yelled.

"כולם מוכנים ללמוד על מרטיני?" צעק.
kulam mukhanim lilmod al martini tsa'ak
everyone they are ready to learn about martini he yelled

"Yes!" we all yelled back.

"כן!" צעקנו כולנו בחזרה.
ken tsa'aknu kulanu bakhazara
yes we yelled all of us back

He walked down the length of the bar. When he saw Gilat, he picked up her hand and kissed her knuckles.

הוא צעד לאורך הבר. כשראה את גילת, נטל את ידה
hu tsa'ad le'orekh habar kshera'a et gilat natal et yada
he he walked along the bar when he saw D.O. Gilat he grasped D.O. her hand

ונשק את פרקי אצבעותיה.
venashak et pirkei estbe'oteiha
and he kissed D.O. her knuckles

"Are all aerobics instructors this friendly?" I asked.

"כל מדריכי האירובי כאלה ידידותיים?" שאלתי.
kol madrikhei ha'eirobi ka'ele yedidutiyim sha'alti
all instructors of the aerobics this friendly I asked

"It was a kiss of pity. He heard about the hopeless man I married."

"זו היתה נשיקה מתוך רחמים. הוא שמע על הגבר חסר התקווה
zo haita neshika mitokh rakhamim hu shama al hagever khasar hatikva
this it was kiss out of pity he he heard about the man the hopeless

שנישאתי לו."
sheniseti lo
that I am married to him

"Let's focus on the martinis," I said.

"בואי נתמקד במרטיני," אמרתי.
bo'i nitmaked bamartini amarti
let's we will focus on on the martini I said

We learned how to make more martinis than I knew existed. Omar did not kiss Gilat's hand again. I think he saw me glowering at him.

למדנו איך להכין יותר סוגי מרטיני ממה שידעתי שיש.
lamadnu eikh lehakhin yoter sugei martini mima sheyadati sheyesh
we learned how to prepare more types of martini than what that I knew that there are

עומר לא נישק שוב את ידה של גילת. אני חושב שהוא הבחין
omar lo nishek shuv et yada shel gilat ani khoshev shehu hivkhin
Omar no he kissed again D.O. her hand of Gilat I I think that he he noticed

במבט הזועף שנעצתי בו.
bamabat hazo'ef shena'atsti bo
at the look the angry that I affixed on him

"בוא נחתור בקיאק לאתר הנופש הסמוך," אמר לי יוסי.
bo *nakhtor* *bekayak* *le'atar hanofesh* *hasamukh* *amar* *li* *yosi*
let's / we will paddle / in kayak / to the resort / the adjacent / he said / to me / Yossi

"Let's paddle in a kayak down to the next resort," Yossi said to me.

"אני נהנה לשבת כאן, מול הים ולשתות פינה קולדה," אמרתי. "למה
ani *nehene* *lashevet* *kan*, *mul* *hayam* *velishtot* *pina kolada*, *amarti*. *lama*
I / I enjoy / to sit / here / facing / the sea / and to drink / pina colada / I said / what

שארצה להזיע?"
she'ertse *lehazi'a*?
that I will want / to sweat

"I like sitting here by the ocean sipping this piña colada," I said. "Why would I want to work up a sweat?"

"שמעתי שבגדים הם בגדר רשות באתר הנופש ההוא. נוכל
shamati *shebgadim* *hem* *begeder reshut* *be'atar hanofesh* *hahu*. *nukhal*
I heard / that clothes / they / optional / at the resort / that one / we will be able

להסתכל על כל האנשים הערומים."
lehistakel *al* *kol* *ha'anashim* *ha'arumim*.
to check out / at / all / the people / the naked

"I heard that clothing is optional at that resort. We can check out all the naked people."

"מי אמר לך?"
mi *amar* *lekha*?
who / he told / to you

"Who told you?"

"הבחורים עם כובעי הקאובוי," אמר יוסי.
habakhurim *im* *kova'ei* *hakauboi*, *amar* *yosi*.
the guys / with / hats of / the cowboy / he said / Yossi

"The guys with the cowboy hats," Yossi said.

"הם לא יצאו מהבריכה כבר ארבעה ימים. איך הם יודעים?"
hem *lo* *yatsu* *mehabreikha* *kvar* *arba'a* *yamim*. *eikh* *hem* *yodim*?
they / no / they got out / of the pool / already / four / days / how / they / they know

"They haven't gotten out of the pool in four days. How would they know?"

"הנשים שלהם הן סוכנות נסיעות. הן יודעות הכל על האזור
hanashim *shelahem* *hen* *sokhnot* *nesi'ot*. *hen* *yodot* *hakol* *al* *ha'ezor*
the wives / their / they / agents of / travels / they / they know / everything / about / the area

הזה."
haze.
the this

"Their wives are travel agents. They know everything about this area."

"אי אפשר פשוט ללכת על החוף?"
i efshar *pashut* *lalekhet* *al* *hakhof*?
impossible / simply / to walk / on / the beach

"Can't we just walk down the beach?"

"יש גדר גדולה שחוסמת את הדרך," אמר יוסי.
yesh *gader* *gdola* *shekhosemet* *et* *haderekh*, *amar* *yosi*.
there is / fence / big / that (it) blocks / D.O. / the way / he said / Yossi

"There is a big fence blocking the way," Yossi said.

הנחתי את המשקה שלי. "קצת כושר לא יזיק לי."
henakhti *et* *hamashke* *sheli*. *ktsat* *kosher* *lo* *yazik* *li*.
I put down / D.O. / the drink / my / a little / fitness / no / it will hurt / to me

I put my drink down. "A little exercise wouldn't hurt me."

עשר דקות מאוחר יותר יוסי ואני חתרנו בקיאקים שלנו במרץ
eser *dakot* *me'ukhar* *yoter* *yosi* *va'ani* *khatarnu* *bakayakim* *shelanu* *bemerets*
ten / minutes / late / more / Yossi / and I / we paddled / in the kayaks / our / vigorously

Ten minutes later Yossi and I were paddling our kayaks furiously toward the next resort. When we got there, we had a major disappointment.

111

לכיוון אתר הנופש הסמוך. כשהגענו לשם, ציפתה לנו
lekhivun — in direction of; *atar hanofesh* — the resort; *hasamukh* — the adjacent; *kshehiganu* — when we arrived; *lesham* — to there; *tsipta* — it awaited; *lanu* — for us

אכזבה מרה.
akhzava — disappointment; *mara* — bitter

"They have a big screen set up in front of the naked part of the beach," Yossi said.

"יש להם מסך גדול מול חוף הנודיסטים," אמר יוסי.
yesh lahem — they have; *masakh* — screen; *gadol* — big; *mul* — in front of; *khof* — beach; *hanudistim* — the nudists; *amar* — he said; *yosi* — Yossi

"No fair. I busted a gut paddling against the wind to get down here and now I can't see any skin," I added.

"לא הוגן. קרעתי את עצמי בחתירה נגד כיוון הרוח כדי
lo — not; *hogen* — fair; *karati* — I tore; *et* — D.O.; *atsmi* — myself; *bakhatira* — with paddling; *neged* — against; *kivun* — direction of; *haru'akh* — the wind; *kedei* — in order to

להגיע לכאן, ועכשיו אני לא יכול לראות אף פיסת עור," הוספתי.
lehagi'a — to get to; *lekhan* — to here; *ve'akhshav* — and now; *ani* — I; *lo* — no; *yakhol* — I can; *lirot* — to see; *af* — any; *pisat* — piece of; *or* — skin; *hosafti* — I added

We sat in the water, thirty meters from shore, bobbing up and down in our kayaks.

ישבנו במים, שלושים מטר מהחוף, מתנודדים מעלה ומטה
yashavnu — we sat; *bama'im* — in the water; *shloshim* — thirty; *meter* — meter; *mehakhof* — from the beach; *mitnodedim* — we sway; *mala* — up; *vamata* — and down

בקיאקים שלנו.
bakayakim — in the kayaks; *shelanu* — our

"Let's land the kayaks," I suggested.

"בוא נרד לחוף," הצעתי.
bo — let's; *nered* — we will go down; *lakhof* — to the beach; *hitsati* — I suggested

Yossi hesitated.

יוסי היסס.
yosi — Yossi; *hises* — he hesitated

"I'm not sure I want to get naked," he said.

"אני לא בטוח שאני רוצה להתפשט," אמר.
ani — I; *lo* — not; *batu'akh* — sure; *she'ani* — that I; *rotse* — I want; *lehitpashet* — to get undressed; *amar* — he said

"Not everyone at the resort is naked. The people in front of the screen are wearing bathing suits."

"לא כולם באתר עירומים. האנשים שלפני המסך לובשים
lo — not; *kulam* — everyone; *ba'atar* — at the resort; *eiromim* — naked; *ha'anashim* — the people; *shelifnei* — that in front of; *hamasakh* — the screen; *lovshim* — they wear

בגדי ים."
bigdei yam — bathing suits

I could see Yossi thinking things over.

יכולתי לראות שיוסי חוכך בדעתו.
yakholti — I was able; *lirot* — to see; *sheyosi* — that Yossi; *khokhekh beda'ato* — he has his doubts

"There's a double kayak pulled up on the beach over by those chairs," I said. "We can pull ours right next to that one."

"יש קיאק כפול על החוף ליד הכיסאות ההם," אמרתי. "נוכל
yesh — there is; *kayak* — kayak; *kaful* — double; *al* — on; *hakhof* — the beach; *leyad* — next to; *hakisot* — the chairs; *hahem* — those; *amarti* — I said; *nukhal* — we will be able to

112

לגרור את שלנו ממש לידו."
ligror et shelanu mamash leyado
to pull D.O. ours right next to it

"הקיאק הזה הוא מאתר הנופש שלנו," אמר יוסי. "יש לו אותו סימן
hakayak haze hu me'atar hanofesh shelanu, amar yosi. yesh lo oto siman
the kayak the that it from the resort our he said Yossi it has same marking

ואותו צבע."
ve'oto tseva
and same color

"That kayak is from our resort," Yossi said. "It has the same markings and color."

"אתה רואה, אנחנו לא היחידים שחשבו על הרעיון הזה. יהיה
ata ro'e anakhnu lo hayekhidim shekhashvu al hara'ayon haze. ihiye
you you see we not the only who (they) thought about the idea the this it will be

בסדר. בוא נעשה את זה."
beseder. bo na'ase et ze
fine let's we will do D.O. it

"You see, we're not the only ones with this idea. It will be fine. Let's do it."

לקח ליוסי חמש דקות נוספות לאזור אומץ לעגון את הקיאק שלו.
lakakh leyosi khamesh dakot nosafot le'ezor omets la'agon et hakayak shelo
it took for Yossi five minutes additional to build courage to anchor D.O. the kayak his

It took five more minutes for Yossi to get brave enough to land his kayak.

"חבל שלא שתיתי עוד כמה משקאות," אמר תוך שגררנו את
khaval shelo shatiti od kama mashka'ot, amar tokh shegararnu et
too bad that no I drank another few drinks he said while that we pulled D.O.

הקיאקים שלנו אל מחוץ למים.
hakayakim shelanu el mikhuts lama'im
the kayaks our to out of of the water

"I wish I'd had a few more drinks," he said as we pulled our kayaks out of the water.

"אז, נוריד את בגדי הים או שנשאיר אותם?" שאלתי.
az, norid et bigdei hayam o shenashir otam? sha'alti
so we will remove D.O. bathing suits or we will keep them I asked

"So, do we take off our suits or leave them on?" I asked.

לאחר דיון קצר החלטנו להישאר בבגדי הים שלנו. התהלכנו
le'akhar diyun katsar hekhlatnu lehisha'er bevigdei hayam shelanu. hit'halakhnu
after discussion short we decided to stay in the bathing suits our we walked around

בנחת אל מאחורי המסך שהוצב על החוף. היו שם עשרה
benakhat el me'akhorei hamasakh shehutsav al hakhof. hayu sham asara
unhurriedly to behind the screen that is placed on the beach there was there ten

או חמישה עשר קשישים וקשישות, שרועים על כיסאות נוח. אחדים
o khamisha asar kshishim ukshishot, sru'im al kisot no'akh. akhadim
or fifteen old men and old women they are lying on deck chairs some

מהם לבשו בגדי ים, אולם רובם היו עירומים לחלוטין.
mehem lavshu bigdei yam, ulam rubam hayu eiromim lakhalutin
of them they wore bathing suits however most of them they were naked completely

After some debate, we decided to leave our suits on. We sauntered behind the screen that had been set up on the beach. There were ten or fifteen old men and old ladies lying on chaise lounges. Some had bathing suits, but most were completely naked.

"תראה את כל הקמטים על האנשים האלה," לחש יוסי.
tire et kol hakmatim al ha'anashim ha'ele, lakhash yosi
you will look D.O. all the wrinkles on the people the those he whispered Yossi

"Look at all the wrinkles on those people," Yossi whispered.

113

Older people do not look very sexy when they are naked. I made a mental note to wear lots of clothes when I turned seventy.

אנשים	קשישים	לא	נראים	סקסיים	במיוחד	בעירום.	הבטחתי	לעצמי
anashim	kshishim	lo	nirim	seksiyim	bimyukhad	be'eirom	hivtakhti	le'atsmi
people	senior	no	they look	sexy	especially	nude	I promised	to myself

ללבוש	הרבה	בגדים	כשאגיע	לגיל	שבעים.
lilbosh	harbe	bgadim	kshe'agi'a	legil	shivim
to wear	a lot	clothes	when I will reach	to age	seventy

"Let's try the hot tub," I said.

"בוא	ננסה	את	הג׳קוזי",	אמרתי.
bo	nenase	et	hajakuzi	amarti
let's	we will try	D.O.	the hot tub	I said

We walked over to a large hot tub that was located just off the beach. There were at least twenty people already in the tub, talking and relaxing. They all looked fairly wrinkle free. Most of them were naked. I noticed a few exceptional looking women.

הלכנו	אל	עבר	ג׳קוזי	גדול	שניצב	סמוך	לחוף.	לפחות
halakhnu	el	ever	jakuzi	gadol	shenitsav	samukh	lakhof	lefakhot
we walked	to	direction	hot tub	large	that is positioned	close to	to the beach	at least

עשרים	אנשים	כבר	היו	בג׳קוזי,	מפטפטים	ונחים.	כולם
esrim	anashim	kvar	hayu	bajakuzi	mefatpetim	venakhim	kulam
twenty	people	already	they were	in the hot tub	they chat	and they relax	everyone

נראו	נטולי	קמטים	למדי.	רובם	היו	עירומים.	הבחנתי	בנשים
niru	netulei	kmatim	lemadai	rubam	hayu	eiromim	hivkhanti	benashim
they look	devoid of	wrinkles	quite	most of them	they were	naked	I noticed	at women

אחדות	בעלות	מראה	יוצא דופן.
akhadot	ba'alot	mare	yotse dofen
some	having	appearance	exceptional

"This is going to be so good," I said as we casually entered the water and sat down.

"זה	עומד	להיות	כל כך	טוב,"	אמרתי	תוך	שאנחנו	נכנסים	כבדרך אגב
ze	omed	lihiyot	kol kakh	tov	amarti	tokh	she'anakhnu	nikhnasim	kivederekh agav
this	it is going to be		so	good	I said	as	that we	we enter	casually

למים	ומתיישבים.
lama'im	umityashvim
into the water	and we sit down

As I started to check out our fellow bathers, Yossi started poking me on the shoulder.

כשהתחלתי	לבחון	את	הרוחצים	האחרים,	החל	יוסי	לגעת	בכתפי.
kshehitkhalti	livkhon	et	harokhatsim	ha'akherim	hekhel	yosi	laga'at	bikhtefi
when I started	to examine	D.O.	the bathers	the others	he started	Yossi	to poke	on my shoulder

"What?" I said, as I looked over at him.

"מה?"	אמרתי,	מתבונן	בו.
ma	amarti	mitbonen	bo
what	I said	I look at	at him

He was staring at two bare chested women sitting in the sun about three meters from the hot tub. I followed his eyes and took a big gulp of air. Gilat and Mira were holding Mai Tai's and staring back at us.

מבטו	היה	נעוץ	בשתי	נשים	חשופות	חזה	שישבו	בשמש,	כשלושה
mabato	haya	na'uts	bishtei	nashim	khasufot	khaze	sheyashvu	bashemesh	kishlosha
his gaze	it was	affixed	on two	women	bare	chest	that (they) sat	in the sun	about three

מטרים	מהג׳קוזי.	עקבתי	אחר	מבטו	ונשימתי נעתקה.	גילת	ומירה
metrim	mehajakuzi	akavti	akhar	mabato	uneshimati ne'etka	gilat	umira
meters	from the hot tub	I followed	after	his gaze	and it took my breath away	Gilat	and Mira

ישבו	שם,	אוחזות	בקוקטייל	מאי טאי	ולוטשות בנו מבט	בחזרה.
yashvu	sham	okhazot	bekokteil	mai tai	velotshot banu mabat	bakhazara
they sat	there	they hold	at cocktail	Mai Tai	and they stare at us	back

5

114

"אתה כזה סוטה," אמרה לי גילת כשהמטוס המריא משדה התעופה של קנקון.

ata kaze sote amra li gilat kshehamatos himri misde hate'ufa shel kankun
you such pervert she said to me Gilat as the plane it took off from the airport of Cancun

"You are such a pervert," Gilat said to me as our plane took off from the Cancun airport.

"רק רגע, גם את היית שם. בלי חלק עליון, אם יורשה לי להוסיף."

rak rega gam at ha'it sham bli khelek elyon im yurshe li lehosif
just moment also you you were there without part upper if it will be allowed to me to add

"Wait a minute. You were there, too. With no top on, I might add."

"הלכתי לשם כדי להשתזף. אתה סתם רצית לראות בחורות עירומות."

halakhti lesham kedei lehishtazef ata stam ratsita lirot bakhurot eiromot
I went to there in order to to sunbathe you just you wanted to see girls naked

"I went there to work on my tan. You just wanted to see naked girls."

"אתמול חשבת שזה די מצחיק."

etmol khashavt sheze dei matskhik
yesterday you thought that this quite funny

"Yesterday you thought it was pretty funny."

היא צחקקה ונשקה ללחיי. "אני סתם מקניטה אותך."

hi tsikhkeka venashka lelekhyi ani stam maknita otkha
she she giggled and she kissed to my cheek I just I tease you

She giggled and kissed my cheek. "I'm just teasing you."

"לא היה אכפת לך שיוסי יראה את החזה שלך?" שאלתי.

lo haya ikhpat lakh sheyosi yire et hakhaze shelakh sha'alti
no it bothered you that Yossi he will see D.O. the chest your I asked

"You didn't mind Yossi seeing your chest?" I asked.

"לא ממש. איבדתי את הביישנות כשהנקתי את הילדים."

lo mamash ibadeti et habaishanut kshehenakti et hayeladim
not really I lost D.O. the shyness when I breastfed D.O. the kids

"Not really. I lost my shyness when I was breastfeeding the kids."

"מירה נראתה נחמד מאוד בלי חלק עליון," אמרתי.

mira nirata nekhmad me'od bli khelek elyon amarti
Mira she looked nice very without part upper I said

"Mira looked very nice without her bikini top," I said.

גילת צחקה וחבטה בזרועי. אשתי היכתה אותי במהלך השבוע

gilat tsakhaka vekhavta bizro'i ishti hikta oti bemahalakh hashavu'a
Gilat she laughed and she punched at my arm my wife she hit me during the week

הזה יותר מאשר במהלך כל שנות נישואינו.

haze yoter ma'asher bemahalakh kol shnot nisu'einu
the this more than during all years of our marriage

Gilat laughed and punched me in the arm. My wife had hit me more times this week than the entire rest of our married life.

נשענתי לאחור בכסאי והבטתי מהחלון. חצי האי יוקטן החל

nishanti le'akhor bekhisi vehibateti mehakhalon khatsi ha'i yukatan hekhel
I leaned back in my chair I looked from the window the peninsula Yucatan it began

I sat back in my seat and looked out the window. The Yucatan Peninsula receded from my view as the plane headed out over the Gulf of Mexico.

115

להיעלם מעיניי כשהמטוס פנה לכיוון מפרץ מקסיקו.
lehe'alem me'einai kshehamatos pana lekhivun mifrats <u>mek</u>siko
to disappear from my eyes as the airplane it turned in direction gulf of Mexico

"It was a pretty good vacation, despite all the crazy things that happened," I said.

"זו הייתה חופשה מוצלחת, למרות כל הדברים המטורפים שקרו,"
zo haita khufsha mutslakhat lamrot kol hadvarim hametorafim shekaru
it it was vacation good despite all the things the crazy that (they) happened

אמרתי.
<u>a</u>marti
I said

Murder Mystery in L.A.

"זה רעיון גרוע," אני צועק אל תוך אוזנו של נתי.
nati shel ozno tokh el tso'ek ani garu'a ra'ayon ze
Nati of his ear inside to I yell I bad idea this

"This is a bad idea," I yell into Nati's ear.

"לשתות בבר?" הוא שואל.
sho'el hu bebar lishtot
he asks he in bar to drink

"Drinking in a bar?" he asks.

"לא אכפת לי לשתות בבר," אני אומר לו. "רק לא הבר הזה."
haze habar lo rak lo omer ani bebar lishtot ikhpat li lo
the this the bar not just to him I tell I in bar to drink I mind no

"I don't mind drinking in a bar," I tell him. "Just not this bar."

אודי חוזר עם שתי בירות וכוס יין עבורי.
avuri ya'in vekhos birot shtei im khozer udi
for me wine and glass of beers two of with he comes back Udi

Udi comes back with two beers and a glass of wine for me.

"יש הרבה אנשים עם פרוסה גדולה של גבינה מפלסטיק על הראש,"
harosh al miplastik gvina shel gdola prusa im anashim harbe yesh
the head on of plastic cheese of big slice with people a lot of there are

"There are a lot of people with big plastic slices of cheese on their heads," he yells.

הוא צועק.
tso'ek hu
he yells he

להקה של מתבגרים על הבמה מקימה רעש חזק ממה שעור התוף
she'or hatof mima khazak mekima ra'ash habama al mitbagrim shel lahaka
that eardrum than what powerful it makes noise the stage on teenagers of band

שלי יכול לסבול. אני חש מסוחרר מעט בגלל הצלילים. קשה
kashe hatslilim biglal me'at mesukhrar khash ani lisbol yakhol sheli
hard the sounds on account of slightly dizzy I feel I to tolerate it can my

A band of teenagers on stage is making more noise than my eardrums can handle. I feel slightly dizzy with the sound. It's hard to hear anyone talking.

לשמוע מישהו מדבר.
medaber mishehu lishmo'a
he talks anyone to hear

"זו הסיבה שאני לא רוצה לשתות בבר הזה," אני משיב בצעקה.
bitse'aka meshiv ani haze babar lishtot rotse lo she'ani hasiba zo
yelling I reply I the this in the bar to drink I want no that I the reason this

"That's why I don't want to drink in this bar," I yell back. "Let's find a neutral site."

"בואו נמצא מקום ניטרלי."
neitrali makom nimtsa bo'u
neutral place we will find let's

עשרים דקות מאוחר יותר אנחנו הולכים באוויר הלילה החם של
shel hakham halaila be'avir holkhim anakhnu yoter me'ukhar dakot esrim
of the warm the night in air we walk we more late minutes twenty

Twenty minutes later we walk through the warm night air of California. We are trying to find a bar that isn't packed with people from the state of Wisconsin.

קליפורניה. אנחנו מנסים למצוא בר שאיננו עמוס באנשים ממדינת
kalifornya / anakhnu / menasim / limtso / bar / she'einenu / amus / be'anashim / mimedinat
California / we / we try / to find / bar / that (it) isn't / packed / with people / from state of

ויסקונסין.
wiskonsin
Wisconsin

"Why do they always wear those fake plastic cheese wedges on their heads before a big football game?" I ask.

"למה הם תמיד חובשים את משולשי גבינת הפלסטיק
lama / hem / tamid / khovshim / et / meshulashei / gvinat / haplastik
why / they / always / they wear on their head / D.O. / triangles of / cheese of / the plastic

המזויפים האלה על הראש לפני כל משחק פוטבול חשוב?" אני
hamezuyafim / ha'ele / al / harosh / lifnei / kol / miskhak / futbol / khashuv / ani
the fake / the those / on / the head / before / every / game of / football / important / I

שואל.
sho'el
I ask

"What?" Nati and Udi say. Our ears are still ringing from the loud noises the band was making.

"מה?" אומרים נתי ואודי. אוזנינו עדיין מצלצלות מהרעש החזק
ma / omrim / nati / ve'udi / ozneinu / ada'in / metsaltselot / mehara'ash / hakhazak
what / they say / Nati / and Udi / our ears / still / they ring / from the noise / the loud

שהקימה הלהקה.
shehekima / halahaka
that they made / the band

"I said I'm too old to listen to bad rock and roll anymore," I yell at them.

"אמרתי שאני זקן מכדי להאזין לרוקנ'רול גרוע," אני צועק אליהם.
amarti / she'ani / zaken / mikhdei / leha'azin / lerokenrol / garu'a / ani / tso'ek / eleihem
I said / that I / old / too / to listen / to rock and roll / bad / I / I yell / to them

The three of us are vacationing with our wives in Los Angeles for a week. The kids are home with their grandparents. Tonight, the ladies were too tired to go out after dinner. Nati, Udi, and I decided to hit the bars and have some fun. We didn't realize that the University of Wisconsin football team is playing the University of California tomorrow. Half the state of Wisconsin has invaded Los Angeles for the game. Everywhere we look, we see people with milky white skin and plastic cheese slices on their heads.

שלושתינו נמצאים בחופשה בת שבוע בלוס אנג'לס עם הנשים. הילדים
shloshteinu / nimtsa'im / bekhufsha / bat shavu'a / belos anjeles / im / hanashim / hayeladim
three of us / we are found / on vacation / week-long / in Los Angeles / with / the wives / the kids

בבית עם סבא וסבתא. הערב הנשים היו עייפות מדי
baba'it / im / saba / vesavta / ha'erev / hanashim / hayu / ayefot / midai
at the home / with / grandpa / and grandma / tonight / the wives / they were / tired / too

מכדי לצאת אחרי ארוחת הערב. נתי, אודי, ואני החלטנו לצאת
mikhdei / latset / akharei / arukhat ha'erev / nati / udi / va'ani / hekhlatnu / latset
than / to go out / after / the dinner / Nati / Udi / and I / we decided / to go out

ולבלות קצת בברים. לא ידענו שנבחרת הפוטבול של
ulevalot / ktsat / babarim / lo / yadanu / shenivkheret / hafutbol / shel
and to have a good time / a little / at the bars / no / we knew / that varsity team / the football / of

אוניברסיטת ויסקונסין משחקת נגד אוניברסיטת קליפורניה מחר.
universitat / wiskonsin / mesakheket / neged / universitat / kalifornya / makhar
university of / Wisconsin / they play / against / university of / California / tomorrow

חצי ממדינת ויסקונסין פלש ללוס אנג'לס לקראת המשחק. בכל
khatsi / mimedinat / wiskonsin / palash / lelos anjeles / likrat / hamiskhak / bekhol
half / of state of / Wisconsin / it invaded / to Los Angeles / leading up to / the game / in every

מקום שאליו אנו מסבים את מבטנו אנחנו רואים אנשים בעלי עור
makom / she'elav / anu / mesevim / et / mabatenu / anakhnu / ro'im / anashim / ba'alei / or
place / that to which / we / we turn / D.O. / our gaze / we / we see / people / having / skin

לבנבן בגוון חלבי ופרוסת גבינת פלסטיק לראשם.
levanban begavan khalavi ufrusat gvinat plastik lerosham
pale white in shade milky and pieces of cheese of plastic to their head

"אין להם הרבה שמש בויסקונסין, נכון?" שואל אודי.
ein lahem harbe shemesh bewiskonsin nakhon sho'el udi
they don't have much sun in Wisconsin correct he asks Udi

"They don't get a lot of sun in Wisconsin, do they?" Udi asks.

"אני חושב שהעור שלהם בהיר כל כך בגלל שהמתיישבים הראשונים
ani khoshev sheha'or shelahem bahir kol kakh biglal shehamityashvim harishonim
I I think that the skin their pale so because of that the settlers the first ones

היו ויקינגים," אומר נתי. "תראו את הגודל של האנשים האלה."
hayu vikingim omer nati tiru et hagodel shel ha'anashim ha'ele
they were vikings he says Nati you will look D.O. the size of the people the these

"I think their skin is so pale because the original settlers were Vikings," Nati says. "Look at the size of these people."

אכן, נראה שגובהו ומשקלו הממוצעים של תושב ויסקונסין
akhen nira shegovho umishkalo hamemutsa'im shel toshav wiskonsin
indeed it seemed that his height and his weight the average of resident of Wisconsin

הם כפולים מגובהו ומשקלו של אדם רגיל מלוס אנג'לס.
hem kfulim migovho umishkalo shel adam ragil milos anjeles
they double of his height and his weight of person typical from Los Angeles

Indeed, it seemed like the average height and weight of a person from Wisconsin is double that of the typical person from Los Angeles.

"הבר האחרון היה מטורף," אומר אודי. "הייתי בשרותי הגברים
habar ha'akharon haya metoraf omer udi ha'iti besherutei hagvarim
the bar the last it was crazy he says Udi I was in restroom of the men

ושני אוהדי ויסקונסין החזיקו בחור עם חולצה של אוניברסיטת
ushnei ohadei wiskonsin hekhziku bakhur im khultsa shel universitat
and two of supporters of Wisconsin they held guy with shirt of university of

קליפורניה. הם טבלו את ראשו באסלה שוב ושוב ושרו."
kalifornya hem tavlu et rosho ba'asla shuv vashuv vesharu
California they they dunked D.O. his head in the toilet again and again and they sang

"That last bar was crazy," Udi says. "I was in the men's room and two Wisconsin supporters were holding a guy with a University of California shirt. They kept dunking his head in the toilet and singing."

"אוהדי ספורט הם מטורפים," אני אומר להם. "הנה בר שנראה שקט
ohadei sport hem metorafim ani omer lahem hine bar shenire shaket
fans of sport they crazy I I tell to them here is bar that it seems quiet

למדי."
lemadai
pretty

"Sports fans are crazy," I tell them. "Here's a bar that seems pretty quiet."

אנחנו פוסעים אל תוך מקום שאורותיו מעומעמים. חמישה אנשים
anakhnu posim el tokh makom she'orotav me'umamim khamisha anashim
we we walk to inside place that its lights dim five people

יושבים על הבר, מדברים בקולות שקטים. שאר המקום ריק.
yoshvim al habar medabrim bekolot shketim sh'ar hamakom reik
they sit down at the bar they talk with voices quiet rest of the place empty

We walk into a dimly lit place. Five people sit at the bar talking in low tones. The rest of the place is empty.

אנחנו מתיישבים בבר ומזמינים סיבוב משקאות. "המקום הזה
anakhnu mityashvim babar umazminim sivuv mashka'ot hamakom haze
we we sit down at the bar and we order round of drinks the place the this

We sit at the bar and order a round of drinks. "This place is much less stressful," I say.

119

הרבה פחות מלחיץ,″ אני אומר.
omer	ani	malkhits	pakhot	harbe
I say	I	stressful	less	much

We talk about our next day's activities. The wives want to go to the Los Angeles Museum of Art. We want to go to the La Brea tar pits.

אנחנו דנים בפעילויות הצפויות למחר. הנשים רוצות ללכת
anakhnu	danim	bape'iluyot	hatsfuyot	lemakhar	hanashim	rotsot	lalekhet
we discuss	about the activities	the expected	for tomorrow	the wives	they want	to go

למוזיאון לוס אנג׳לס לאומנות. אנחנו רוצים לראות את אתר בורות
lemuzei'on	los anjeles	le'omanut	anakhnu	rotsim	lirot	et	atar	borot
to museum of	Los Angeles	of art	we	we want	to see	D.O.	site of	pits of

הזפת הטבעית בלה-בריאה.
hazefet	hativit	bela-bre'a
the tar	the natural	in La Brea

I notice a puddle on the floor near where we are sitting.

אני מבחין בשלולית על הרצפה סמוך למקום שבו אנחנו יושבים.
ani	mavkhin	bishlulit	al	haritspa	samukh	lamakom	shebo	anakhnu	yoshvim
I	I notice	at puddle	on	the floor	near	to the place	that in it	we	we sit

"You've got something on the floor," I tell the bartender.

″יש לכם משהו על הרצפה,″ אני אומר לברמן.
yesh lakhem	mashehu	al	haritspa	ani	omer	labarmen
you have	something	on	the floor	I	I tell	to the bartender

"Don't worry, it's dry," he says.

″אל תדאג, זה יבש,″ הוא אומר.
al	tidag	ze	yavesh	hu	omer
don't	you will worry	this	dry	he	he says

"What is it?" I ask.

″מה זה?″ אני שואל.
ma	ze	ani	sho'el
what	this	I	I ask

"Blood. Some guy got shot here an hour ago. He was sitting on your stool."

″דם. איזה בחור נורה כאן לפני שעה. הוא ישב על הכיסא שלך.″
dam	eize	bakhur	nora	kan	lifnei	sha'a	hu	yashav	al	hakise	shelkha
blood	some	guy	he was shot	here	ago	hour	he	he sat	on	the chair	your

"That explains why the place is so quiet," Nati says.

″זה מסביר למה המקום שקט כל כך,″ אומר נתי.
ze	masbir	lama	hamakom	sheket	kol kakh	omer	nati
that	it explains	why	the place	quiet	so	he says	Nati

"What are the odds there will be another gunfight here tonight?" Udi asks.

″מה הסיכוי שיהיה כאן קרב יריות נוסף הלילה?″ שואל אודי.
ma	hasikui	she'ihiye	kan	krav	yeriyot	nosaf	halaila	sho'el	udi
what	the chance	that it will be	here	fight of	shooting	another	tonight	he asks	Udi

"Probably zero. We should stay," I say.

″ככל הנראה אפס. כדאי לנו להישאר,″ אני אומר.
kekhol hanire	efes	kedai	lanu	lehisha'er	ani	omer
probably	zero	it is worthwhile	for us	to stay	I	I say

A few minutes later someone taps on my shoulder. I look around and see a gorgeous woman. She hands me a package.

מספר דקות לאחר מכן מישהו טופח קלות בכתפי. אני מביט מסביב
mispar	dakot	le'akhar miken	mishehu	tofe'akh	kalot	bikhtefi	ani	mabit	misaviv
a few	minutes	later	someone	he taps	lightly	on my shoulder	I	I look	around

ורואה אישה יפהפייה. היא מגישה לי חבילה.
vero'e	isha	yafefiya	hi	magisha	li	khavila
and I see	woman	gorgeous	she	she hands	to me	package

והולכת, היא אומרת, "הנה הכסף ופרטים על המטרה שלך,"
veholekhet omeret hi shelkha hamatara al ufratim hakesef hine
and she walks she says she your the target about and details the money here is

לדרכה.
ledarka
on her way

"Here is your money and the information about your target," she says, and she walks away.

שהיא עד להגיב מכדי הזה הנהדר האישה ממראה מופתע אני
shehi ad lehagiv mikhdei haze hanehedar ha'isha mimare mufta ani
that she until to react to the this the lovely the woman from the sight of surprised I

כמעט יוצאת.
kimat yotset
almost she goes outside

I am too amazed by the sight of this beautiful woman to react until she is almost out the door.

"הי," אני צועק, "על מה את מדברת?"
hei ani tso'ek al ma at medaberet
hey I I yell about what you you talk

"Hey," I yell, "what are you talking about?"

אני פותח את המעטפה. היא מלאה בשטרות של מאה דולר.
ani pote'akh et hama'atafa hi mele'a bishtarot shel me'a dolar
I I open D.O. the envelope it full with bills of hundred dollar

I open the envelope. It's stuffed with hundred dollar bills.

"תראו את זה, חבר'ה. אנחנו יכולים לשתות בחינם כל הלילה."
tiru et ze khevre anakhnu yekholim lishtot bekhinam kol halaila
you will look D.O. this guys we we can to drink free all tonight

"Look at this, guys. We can drink free all night."

אנחנו מוציאים את הכסף. בנוסף, יש שם תצלומים של אדם
anakhnu motsi'im et hakesef benosaf yesh sham tatslumim shel adam
we we take out D.O. the money in addition there are there pictures of person

בעל מראה מרושע שצלקת מעטרת את לחיו, ותדפיס מחשב
ba'al mare merusha shetsaleket me'ateret et lekhyo vetadpis makhshev
having appearance wicked that a scar it adorns D.O. his cheek and printout of computer

הכולל את פרטיו האישיים של הבחור.
hakolel et pratav ha'ishiyim shel habakhur
that includes D.O. his details the personal of the guy

We pull out the money. In addition, there are pictures of some nasty looking person with a scar on his cheek and a printout with personal information about the guy.

"מה זה?" שואל נתי.
ma ze sho'el nati
what this he asks Nati

"What is this?" Nati asks.

ואז, המשטרה פורצת דרך הדלת.
ve'az hamishtara poretset derekh hadelet
and then the police she bursts into through the door

And then, the police burst through the door.

— 2 —

"הייתי בטוח למדי שאתם לא רוצחים שכירים כשהתחלתם לבכות,"
ha'iti batu'akh lemadai she'atem lo rotskhim skhirim kshehitkhaltem livkot
I was sure pretty that you not hit men when you started to cry

"I was pretty sure you guys weren't professional hit men when you started crying," the detective tells us.

121

אומר לנו הבלש.
habalash *lanu* *omer*
the detective to us he tells

"So why did it take four hours and five thousand dollars worth of lawyer fees before you let us go?" Nati asks.

"אז למה לקח ארבע שעות וחמשת אלפים דולר שכר טרחת עורך דין
orekh din *skhar tirkhat* *dolar* *vakhameshet alafim* *sha'ot* *arba* *lakakh* *lama* *az*
lawyer fees of dollar and five thousand hours four it took why so

עד ששחררת אותנו?" שואל נתי.
nati *sho'el* *otanu* *sheshikhrarta* *ad*
Nati he asks us that you released until

We are retrieving our personal effects, belts, and shoelaces at the front desk of some maximum security police facility near Hollywood.

אנחנו אוספים את חפצינו האישיים, חגורות ושרוכי נעליים בדלפק
bedelpek *na'ala'im* *usrokhei* *khagorot* *ha'ishiyim* *khafatseinu* *et* *osfim* *anakhnu*
at desk shoes and shoelaces of belts the personal our objects D.O. we gather we

הקבלה במתקן משטרה שמור כלשהו סמוך להוליווד.
leholiwud *samukh* *kolshehu* *shamur* *mishtara* *bemitkan* *hakabala*
Hollywood close to some secure police at facility of the reception

"The District Attorney was at a party. He wouldn't sign any release papers until it was over."

"התובע המחוזי היה במסיבה. הוא לא הסכים לחתום על
al *lakhtom* *hiskim* *lo* *hu* *bemesiba* *haya* *hamkhozi* *hatove'a*
on to sign he consented no he at party he was the district the prosecutor

מסמכי השחרור לפני שהמסיבה נגמרה."
nigmera *shehamesiba* *lifnei* *hashikhrur* *mismakhei*
it was over that the party before the release documents of

"What's his address?" I ask. "I'd like to send him a Christmas present."

"מה הכתובת שלו?" אני שואל. "אני רוצה לשלוח לו מתנה
matana *lo* *lishlo'akh* *rotse* *ani* *sho'el* *ani* *shelo* *haktovet* *ma*
gift to him to send I want I I ask I his the address what

לחג המולד."
lekhag hamolad
for Christmas

"Don't get smart," the cop at the front desk says. "We could have kept you all night."

"אל תתחכם," אומר השוטר בדלפק הקבלה. "יכולנו להשאיר
lehashir *yakholnu* *hakabala* *bedelpek* *hashoter* *omer* *titkhakem* *al*
to keep we could the reception at desk of the cop he says you will be a wise aleck don't

אתכם כאן כל הלילה."
halaila *kol* *kan* *etkhem*
the night all here you

"We just got tired of hearing you scream that the other inmates scared you," the detective says.

"פשוט נמאס לנו לשמוע אתכם צורחים שהעצורים האחרים
ha'akherim *sheha'atsurim* *tsorkhim* *etkhem* *lishmo'a* *nimas lanu* *pashut*
the others that the detainees you scream you to hear we were fed up simply

מפחידים אתכם," אומר הבלש.
habalash *omer* *etkhem* *mafkhidim*
the detective he says you they scare

"You put us in a holding cell with two drug dealers, a crazy biker, and a guy who just bit someone's ear off," Udi says.

"הכנסתם אותנו לתא מעצר עם שני סוחרי סמים, אופנוען מטורף
metoraf *ofano'an* *samim* *sokharei* *shnei* *im* *ma'atsar* *leta* *otanu* *hikhnastem*
crazy biker drugs dealers of two of with detention in cell us you put

ובחור שזה עתה קטע אוזן של מישהי בנשיכה," אומר אודי.

and guy that right now he amputated ear of someone with a bite," he says Udi.

"אין לנו מגורים מיוחדים לחנונים מישראל," אומר השוטר בדלפק. "לפחות לא זרקו אתכם לתא עם המטורפים האלה עם הגבינה על הראש."

"We don't have special accommodations for nerds from Israel," the desk cop says. "At least we didn't throw you into the cell with those crazy people with cheese on their heads."

"כשאתה מציג את זה כך, היה לנו מזל," אני אומר לשוטרים.

"When you put it that way, we were lucky," I tell the cops.

"מה עם הכסף?" אני שואל.

"What about the money?" I ask.

"הוא לא שלכם. הוא נועד לרוצח השכיר האמיתי."

"That's not yours. It was intended for the real hit man."

"הוא בטח היה הבחור שנורה לפני שהגענו לבר," אומר אודי.

"He must have been the guy who was shot before we arrived at the bar," Udi says.

"אם הסוכנים החשאיים שלכם שמו מארב על הבר, איך זה שלא ידעתם על היריות שהיו שם קודם?" שואל נתי.

"If your undercover agents had the bar staked out, why didn't you know about the earlier shooting?" asks Nati.

"לא היה לנו מארב על הבר. עקבנו אחרי האישה. ואף אחד לא דיווח על היריות קודם. תשאלנו את הברמן במשך שעתיים עד שהודה שפשוט השליך את הבחור למכל האשפה."

"We didn't have the bar staked out. We were following the woman. And nobody reported the earlier shooting. We questioned the bartender for two hours before he admitted that he just threw the guy into a dumpster."

"What kinds of people live in this town?" I ask. "Someone gets shot in front of them and they continue drinking while the bartender throws the body in a dumpster and washes the floor."

"איזה מין אנשים גרים בעיר הזאת?" אני שואל. "מישהו נורה
eize min anashim garim ba'ir hazot sho'el ani nora mishehu
what kind of people they live in the city the this I ask I someone he was shot

ממש לנגד עיניהם והם ממשיכים לשתות בזמן שהברמן
mamash leneged eineihem vehem mamshikhim lishtot bizman shehabarmen
precisely in front of their eyes and they they continue to drink while that the bartender

משליך את הגופה למיכל האשפה ושוטף את הרצפה."
mashlikh et hagufa lemeikhal ha'ashpa veshotef et haritspa
he throws D.O. the body into container of the garbage and he washes D.O. the floor

"They were probably unemployed actors," the detective says.

"הם היו מן הסתם שחקנים מובטלים," אומר הבלש.
hem hayu min hastam sakhkanim muvtalim omer habalash
they they were probably actors unemployed he says the detective

"And what about the woman you followed?"

"ומה לגבי האישה שעקבתם אחריה?"
uma legabei ha'isha she'akavtem akhareiha
and what about the woman that you followed after her

"We lost her when the police charged into the bar."

"איבדנו אותה כשהמשטרה נכנסה לבר."
ibadnu ota kshehamishtara nikhnesa labar
we lost her when the police she entered into the bar

"Great," I say.

"נפלא," אני אומר.
nifla ani omer
wonderful I I say

We leave the police station and try to get a taxi. It's four thirty in the morning, so we don't have much luck. As we wait in the street, I get another tap on my shoulder. The gorgeous woman again.

אנחנו עוזבים את תחנת המשטרה ומנסים להשיג מונית. השעה ארבע
anakhnu ozvim et takhanat hamishtara umenasim lehasig monit hasha'a arba
we we leave D.O. station of the police and we try to obtain taxi the hour four

וחצי בבוקר, כך שלא היה לנו הרבה מזל. בעוד אנחנו ממתינים
vakhetsi baboker kakh shelo haya lanu harbe mazal be'od anakhnu mamtinim
and half in the morning so that no we had much luck as we we wait

ברחוב, אני חש בנקישה נוספת בכתפי. שוב האישה היפהפייה.
barkhov ani khash binkisha nosefet bikhtefi shuv ha'isha hayefefiya
on the street I I feel with tapping another on my shoulder again the woman the gorgeous

This time I have the presence of mind to grab her. She sticks a small gun in my face and I let go.

הפעם יש לי מספיק תושייה לתפוס אותה. היא תוקעת אקדח קטן
hapa'am yesh li maspik tushiya litpos ota hi toka'at ekdakh katan
this time I have enough quick-wittedness to grab her she she thrusts gun small

בפניי ואני משחרר את אחיזתי.
befanai va'ani meshakhrer et akhizati
at my face and I I release D.O. my grasp

"Big Sam says you have to give the money back by noon, or you're toast," she says.

"סם הגדול אומר שאתם צריכים להחזיר את הכסף עד הצוהריים, או
sem hagadol omer she'atem tsrikhim lehakhzir et hakesef ad hatsohora'im o
Sam the big he says that you you need to return D.O. the money by the noon or

שתהיו בצרה צרורה," היא אומרת.
shetihiyu betsara tsrura hi omeret
that you will be in deep trouble she she says

124

שלושתנו לוטשים בה מבט. היא נסוגה אל תוך מכונית שהמתינה
shloshteinu lotshim ba mabat hi nasoga el tokh mekhonit shehimtina
three of us we stare at her she she retreats to inside car that it waited

לה והפליגה משם.
la vehifliga misham
for her and it departed from there

The three of us stare at her. She backs into a waiting car and it drives off.

"אנחנו באמת בצרות עכשיו," אומר אודי.
anakhnu be'emet betsarot akhshav omer udi
we really in trouble now he says Udi

"We are really in trouble now," Udi says.

שעתיים מאוחר יותר אנחנו עוזבים את תחנת המשטרה בפעם השנייה.
sha'ata'im me'ukhar yoter anakhnu ozvim et takhanat hamishtara bapa'am hashniya
two hours late more we we leave D.O. station of the police for time the second

Two hours later we leave the police station for the second time.

"אני לא מאמין שהם לא מאמינים לנו," אני אומר.
ani lo ma'amin shehem lo ma'aminim lanu ani omer
I no I believe that they no they believe to us I I say

"I can't believe they don't believe us," I say.

"אני לא מאמין שבחורה איימה עלינו באקדח ממש בחזית
ani lo ma'amin shebakhura iyma aleinu be'ekdakh mamash bekhazit
I no I believe that lady she threatened on us with gun precisely in front of

התחנה שלהם ואף אחד לא ראה," אומר אודי.
hatakhana shelahem ve'af ekhad lo ra'a omer udi
the station their and nobody no he saw he says Udi

"I can't believe a lady pulled a gun on us right in front of their station and nobody saw it," Udi says.

"זה מזכיר לי סרט רע במיוחד," אומר נתי.
ze mazkir li seret ra bimyukhad omer nati
this it reminds to me movie bad especially he says Nati

"This reminds me of a really bad movie," Nati says.

"אתם חושבים שסם הגדול הזה יעשה לנו צרות?" שואל אודי.
atem khoshvim shesem hagadol haze ya'ase lanu tsarot sho'el udi
you you think that Sam the big the this he will make for us troubles he asks Udi

"Do you think this Big Sam guy is going to give us trouble?" Udi asks.

"פשוט נסביר שהבחורה נתנה את הכסף לאנשים הלא
pashut nasbir shehabakhura natna et hakesef la'anashim halo
simply we will explain that the young lady she gave D.O. the money to the people the not

"We'll just explain that the girl gave the money to the wrong people. It's her fault," I say.

נכונים. זו אשמתה," אני אומר.
nekhonim zo ashmata ani omer
correct this her fault I I say

המזל היחידי שלנו הוא שבשעה שש וחצי בבוקר יש שוב
hamazal hayekhidi shelanu hu shebesha'a shesh vakhetsi baboker yesh shuv
the luck the only our it that at hour six and half in the morning there are again

Our only good luck is that taxis are back on the street at six thirty in the morning. As a sleepy driver takes us back to our hotel, we make a pact not to tell our wives anything. I sneak into my hotel room just as Gilat wakes up from a refreshing night's sleep.

מוניות בכבישים. בזמן שנהג ישנוני אחד מסיע אותנו בחזרה למלון
moniyot bakvishim bizman shenahag yashnuni ekhad masi'a otanu bakhazara lamalon
taxis on the streets when a driver sleepy one he drives us back to the hotel

שלנו, אנחנו מסכימים שלא לספר לנשים דבר. אני חומק אל חדר
shelanu anakhnu maskimim shelo lesaper lanashim davar ani khomek el khadar
our we we agree that not to tell to the wives thing I I sneak to room of

125

המלון ממש כשגילת מתעוררת משנת לילה מרעננת.
mera'anenet laila mishnat mitoreret kshegilat mamash hamalon
refreshing night from sleep of she wakes up when Gilat precisely the hotel

"Did you have a good time, Rafi?" she asks.

"נהנית, רפי?" היא שואלת.
sho'elet hi rafi neheneta
she asks she Rafi did you have fun

"You have no idea."

"אין לך מושג כמה."
kama musag ein lakh
how much idea you don't have

———————————— 3 ————————————

I am too tired to argue with Gilat about what sights to see, which is why I find myself standing next to her a few hours later, viewing three hundred year old paintings. Udi and Nati and their wives are with us.

אני עייף מכדי להתווכח עם גילת על האתרים שנראה, וזו
vezo shenire ha'atarim al gilat im lehitvake'akh mikhdei ayef ani
and this that we will see the sites about Gilat with to argue too tired I

הסיבה שאני מוצא את עצמי עומד לצידה שעות אחדות מאוחר יותר,
yoter me'ukhar akhadot sha'ot letsida omed atsmi et motse she'ani hasiba
more late a few hours beside her I stand myself D.O. I find that I the reason

מביט בציורים בני שלוש מאות שנה. אודי, נתי והנשים שלהם
shelahem vehanashim nati udi shana me'ot shlosh bnei betsiyurim mabit
their and the wives Nati Udi year hundred three aged at paintings I look

נמצאים איתנו.
itanu nimtsa'im
with us they are (located)

"Isn't this art museum so much nicer than those tar pits?" Gilat asks me.

"מוזיאון האמנות הזה הרבה יותר נחמד מבורות הזפת, לא?" גילת
gilat lo hazefet miborot nekhmad yoter harbe haze ha'omanut muzei'on
Gilat no the tar than pits of nice more much the this the art museum of

שואלת אותי.
oti sho'elet
me she asks

I barely mumble a response. I'm having a hard enough time keeping my eyes open, much less talk. I notice that Udi and Nati are having similar problems.

אני בקושי ממלמל תשובה. מספיק קשה לי לשמור על עיניי פקוחות,
pkukhot einai lishmor al li kashe maspik tshuva memalmel bekoshi ani
open my eyes to keep for me hard enough response I mumble barely I

שלא לדבר על להוציא מילה. אני מבחין כי אודי ונתי חווים
khovim venati udi ki mavkhin ani mila lehotsi shelo ledaber al
they experience and Nati Udi that I notice I word to utter not to mention

בעיות דומות.
domot be'ayot
similar problems

The ladies decide that we should eat our lunch at the museum.

הנשים מחליטות שאנחנו צריכים לאכול את ארוחת הצוהריים
arukhat hatsohora'im et le'ekhol tsrikhim she'anakhnu makhlitot hanashim
the lunch D.O. to eat we should that we they decide the ladies

במוזיאון.
bamuzei'on
at the museum

"תראו, יש להם תפריט צמחוני במזנון," אומרת אשתו של נתי.
tiru yesh lahem tafrit tsimkhoni bamiznon omeret ishto shel nati
you will look / they have / menu / vegetarian / in the cafeteria / she says / his wife / of / Nati

"Look, they have a vegetarian menu in the cafeteria," Nati's wife says.

"אתם כל כך שקטים היום," אומרת אשתו של אודי בעודנו אוכלים את
atem kol kakh shketim hayom omeret ishto shel udi be'odenu okhlim et
you / so / quiet / today / she says / his wife / of / Udi / while we / we eat / D.O.

בורגר הטופו שלנו. "מה עשיתם בחוץ כל כך מאוחר, בכל אופן?"
burger hatofu shelanu ma asitem bakhuts kol kakh me'ukhar bekhol ofen
burger of / the tofu / our / what / you did / outside / so / late / anyway

"You are so quiet today," Udi's wife says as we eat our tofu burgers. "What were you doing out so late, anyway?"

"עשינו חיים," אני ממלמל.
asinu khayim ani memalmel
we were having a good time / I / I murmur

"Having fun," I murmur.

"זו כוס הקפה השלישית שלך," אשתו של נתי אומרת לו. "לא
zo kos hakafe hashlishit shelkha ishto shel nati omeret lo lo
that / cup of / the coffee / the third / your / his wife / of / Nati / she says / to him / no

תצליח לישון הלילה."
tatsli'akh lishon halaila
you will succeed / to sleep / tonight

"That's your third cup of coffee," Nati's wife tells him. "You'll never sleep tonight."

"אני רק מנסה לצלוח את היום," הוא אומר.
ani rak menase litslo'akh et hayom hu omer
I / just / I try / to get through / D.O. / the day / he / he says

"I'm just trying to get through the day," he says.

אחרי ארוחת הצוהריים, אנחנו אומרים לנשים שעלינו לגשת
akharei arukhat hatsohora'im anakhnu omrim lanashim she'aleinu lageshet
after / the lunch / we / we tell / to the wives / that we have to / to approach

לשירותים.
lasherutim
to the restrooms

After lunch, we tell the wives we have to visit the restroom.

"ניפגש בתערוכת כלי החרס מהמזרח התיכון," אומרת גילת.
nipagesh beta'arukhat klei hakheres mehamizrakh hatikhon omeret gilat
we will meet / in exhibition of / pottery / from the Middle East / she says / Gilat

"Meet us in the Middle Eastern pottery exhibit," Gilat says.

אנחנו מתיזים מים על פנינו בניסיון להישאר ערים.
anakhnu matizim ma'im al paneinu benisayon lehisha'er erim
we / we splash / water / on / our faces / in effort / to stay / awake

We splash water on our faces in an effort to keep awake.

לפני שאנו פונים לעזוב, נכנסים שני גברים בעלי חזות מרושעת
lifnei she'anu ponim la'azov nikhnasim shnei gvarim ba'alei khazut merusha'at
before / that we / we turn / to leave / they enter / two of / men / having / appearance / evil

וחוסמים את דרכנו.
vekhosmim et darkenu
and they block / D.O. / our way

Before we can leave, two nasty looking men walk in and block our exit.

"איפה הכסף?" אומר הגבוה ביניהם.
eifo hakesef omer hagavoha beineihem
where / the money / he says / the tall / among them

"Where's the money?" the taller one says.

"The police took it as evidence," I whine. "They wouldn't give it back to us."

"המשטרה לקחה אותו כראיה," אני מייבב. "הם לא היו מוכנים
hamishtara lak'kha oto kiraya ani meyabev hem lo hayu mukhanim
the police she took it as evidence I whine they not they were prepared

להחזיר לנו אותו."
lehakhzir lanu oto
to return to us it

"Big Sam is not going to like this," he says.

"סם הגדול לא יאהב את זה," הוא אומר.
sem hagadol lo yohav et ze hu omer
Sam the big no he will like D.O. this he he says

"The guy who was supposed to get the money was shot an hour before we got to the bar," Nati says. "That woman made a mistake and gave Big Sam's money to the wrong people."

"הבחור שהיה אמור לקבל את הכסף נורה שעה לפני
habakhur shehaya amur lekabel et hakesef nora sha'a lifnei
the guy that he was supposed to get D.O. the money he was shot hour before

שהגענו לבר," אומר נתי. "האישה הזאת טעתה ונתנה
shehiganu labar omer nati ha'isha hazot ta'ata venatna
that we arrived to the bar he says Nati the woman the that she made a mistake and she gave

את הכסף של סם הגדול לאנשים הלא נכונים."
et hakesef shel sem hagadol la'anashim halo nekhonim
D.O. the money of Sam the big to people the not correct

"Why would a professional hit man allow himself to be gunned down while he was waiting for his money?" sneers the smaller man.

"למה שרוצח שכיר יאפשר למישהו לירות בו כשהוא מחכה
lama sherotse'akh sakhir ye'afsher lemishehu lirot bo kshehu mekhake
why would a hit man he will allow to someone to shoot at him while he he waits

לכסף שלו?" מגחך הנמוך מבין השניים.
lakesef shelo megakhekh hanamukh mibein hashna'im
for the money his he sneers the short from among the two

"Apparently, things like this happen in Los Angeles all the time," Udi responds.

"ככל הנראה דברים כאלה קורים בלוס אנג'לס כל הזמן," עונה
kekhol hanire dvarim ka'ele korim belos anjeles kol hazman one
apparently things like these they happen in Los Angeles all the time he responds

אודי.
udi
Udi

"You're lucky she gave the money to the wrong guy," I tell them. "The police were tailing her. If they had grabbed the real hit man he would have told them all about Big Sam. On the other hand, we know nothing about Big Sam, so things worked out pretty good for him."

"יש לכם מזל שהיא נתנה את הכסף לבחור הלא נכון," אני
yesh lakhem mazal shehi natna et hakesef labakhur halo nakhon ani
you have luck that she she gave D.O. the money to the guy the not correct I

אומר להם. "המשטרה עקבה אחריה. אם היו תופסים את
omer lahem hamishtara akva akhareiha im hayu tofsim et
I tell to them the police she followed after her if they were they grab D.O.

הרוצח השכיר האמיתי הוא היה מספר להם על סם הגדול.
harotse'akh hasakhir ha'amiti hu haya mesaper lahem al sem hagadol
the hit man the real he he was he tells to them about Sam the big

מצד שני, אנחנו לא יודעים כלום על סם הגדול, כך שהכל
mitsad sheni anakhnu lo yodim klum al sem hagadol kakh shehakol
on the other hand we no we know nothing about Sam the big so that everything

הסתדר על הצד הטוב ביותר בשבילו."
histader al hatsad hatov beyoter bishvilo
it worked out for the best for him

"כדאי שאתקשר לסם הגדול," אומר הבחור הגבוה. "אתם
kedai she'etkasher lesem hagadol omer habakhur hagavoha atem
(it is) worthwhile that I will call to Sam the big he says the fellow the tall you

תישארו כאן."
tisha'aru kan
you will stay here

"I better call Big Sam," the taller fellow says. "You stay right here."

הוא יוצא להתקשר, בעוד שותפו נשאר איתנו בשירותים. אנחנו
hu yotse lehitkasher be'od shutafo nishar itanu basherutim anakhnu
he he goes out to call while his partner he stays with us in the restroom we

מנצלים את ההזדמנות לשבת בשלושה תאים נפרדים ולנוח
menatslim et hahizdamnut lashevet bishlosha ta'im nifradim velanu'akh
we take advantage of D.O. the opportunity to sit in three stalls separate and to rest

מעט.
me'at
a little

He goes outside to make a call while his partner stays in the bathroom with us. We take the opportunity to sit in three separate stalls and get some rest.

לאחר חמש דקות חוזר הבחור הגבוה.
le'akhar khamesh dakot khozer habakhur hagavoha
after five minutes he comes back the guy the tall

After five minutes, the tall guy comes back in.

"אתם בואו איתנו. סם הגדול רוצה לראות אתכם."
atem bo'u itanu sem hagadol rotse lirot etkhem
you come with us Sam the big he wants to see you

"You guys come with us. Big Sam wants to see you."

אנחנו מהססים, אבל שני הגברים מראים לנו את האקדחים
anakhnu mehasesim aval shnei hagvarim marim lanu et ha'ekdakhim
we we hesitate but two of the men they show to us D.O. the guns

שבנרתיקי הכתף שלהם, כך שאנחנו יוצאים איתם מחדר
shebenartikei hakatef shelahem kakh she'anakhnu yotsim itam mekhadar
that in the holsters of the shoulder their so that we we leave with them from room of

השירותים.
hasherutim
the restroom

We are hesitant to leave, but the two of them show us the guns in their shoulder holsters, so we leave the bathroom with them.

ארבעה קשישים ממתינים בתור להיכנס לשירותים.
arba'a kshishim mamtinim bator lehikanes lasherutim
four old people they wait in the line to enter into the bathroom

Four senior citizens are lined up waiting to get into the bathroom.

"הגיע הזמן שתסיימו לנקות את המקום," אומר אחד מהם.
higi'a hazman shetesaimu lenakot et hamakom omer ekhad mehem
it's about time that you will finish to clean D.O. the place he says one of them

"אוטובוס הסיור שלנו עומד לצאת ואנחנו נאלצים לחכות
otobus hasiyur shelanu omed latset ve'anakhnu ne'elatsim lekhakot
bus of the tour our it is about to to leave and we we are forced to wait

עשר דקות לשירותים. זה לא בסדר."
eser dakot lasherutim ze lo beseder
ten minutes for the bathroom this not okay

"It's about time you guys finished cleaning the place," one of them says. "Our tour bus is about to leave and we have to wait ten minutes for the bathroom. It's not right."

129

"Who said we were cleaning?" I ask.

"מי אמר שאנחנו מנקים?" אני שואל.

sho'el	ani	menakim	she'anakhnu	amar	mi
I ask	I	we clean	that we	he said	who

"The tall guy," another senior answers.

"הבחור הגבוה," עונה קשיש אחר.

akher	kashish	one	hagavoha	habakhur
another	senior	he answers	the tall	the guy

"He lied to you," Nati yells.

"הוא שיקר לך," צועק נתי.

nati	tso'ek	lekha	shiker	hu
Nati	he yells	to you	he lied	he

Suddenly, the four seniors with full bladders attack Big Sam's men.

לפתע תוקפים ארבעת הקשישים בעלי השלפוחיות המלאות את אנשיו

anashav	et	hamele'ot	hashalpukhiyot	ba'alei	hakshishim	arba'at	tokfim	lefeta
his men	D.O.	the full	the bladders	having	the seniors	four of	they attack	suddenly

של סם הגדול.

hagadol	sem	shel
the big	Sam	of

"I don't know what tour these guys are with, but they all know judo," says Nati.

"אין לי מושג באיזה סיור הם משתתפים, אבל הם כולם יודעים

yodim	kulam	hem	aval	mishtatfim	hem	siyur	be'eize	musag	ein li
they know	all of them	them	but	they participate	they	tour	on what	idea	I don't have

ג'ודו," אומר נתי.

nati	omer	judo
Nati	he says	judo

"Remind me to be nice to older people from now on," Udi tells me as we watch the guy with a walker grab Big Sam's shorter gunman in a choke hold.

"תזכיר לי להיות נחמד לקשישים מעכשיו והלאה," אומר לי

li	omer	ve'hala	me'akhshav	likshishim	nekhmad	lihiyot	li	tazkir
to me	he tells	and onward	from now	to seniors	nice	to be	to me	you will remind

אודי תוך שאנו צופים בבחור בהליכון תופס את הנמוך בין שני

shnei	bein	hanamukh	et	tofes	behalikhon	babakhur	tsofim	tokh she'anu	udi
two of	between	the short	D.O.	he grabs	with walker	at the guy	we watch	as we	Udi

אנשיו של סם הגדול בתפיסת חנק.

khenek	bitfisat	hagadol	sem	shel	anashav
choking	with hold of	the big	Sam	of	his men

Within two minutes, the bad guys are unconscious and handcuffed.

בתוך שתי דקות, הרעים מחוסרי הכרה וכבולים באזיקים.

be'azikim	ukhvulim	hakara	mekhusarei	hara'im	dakot	shtei	betokh
with handcuffs	and handcuffed	consciousness	lacking of	the bad (guys)	minutes	two of	within

--- 4 ---

Today our wives are visiting Pasadena. Udi, Nati, and I sleep until about eleven and have lunch with our police detective acquaintance.

היום הנשים שלנו מבקרות בפסדינה. אודי, נתי ואני ישנים עד השעה

hasha'a	ad	yeshenim	va'ani	nati	udi	bepasadina	mevakrot	shelanu	hanashim	hayom
the hour	until	we sleep	and I	Nati	Udi	in Pasadena	they visit	our	the wives	today

אחת עשרה בערך וסועדים ארוחת צוהריים עם מכרנו בלש

balash	makarenu	im	arukhat tsohora'im	veso'adim	be'erekh	akhat esre
detective of	our acquaintance	with	lunch	and we eat	about	eleven

המשטרה.

hamishtara
the police

"לא ידענו שעקבתם אחרינו אתמול," אומר נתי.
nati omer etmol akhareinu she'akavtem yadanu lo
Nati he says yesterday after us that you followed we knew no

"We didn't know you were following us yesterday," Nati says.

"גם אנשיו של סם הגדול לא ידעו. לכן היה קל כל כך לעצור
la'atsor kol kakh kal haya lakhen yadu lo hagadol sem shel anashav gam
to arrest so easy it was therefore they knew no the big Sam of his men also

אותם מחוץ לחדר השירותים."
hasherutim mikhuts lakhadar otam
the bathroom outside of room of them

"Neither did Big Sam's men. That's why it was so easy to arrest them outside the bathroom."

"היה לאנשיכם מסווה מצוין," אני אומר.
omer ani metsuyan masve haya le'ansheikhem
I say I excellent disguise your men had

"Your men had good disguises," I say.

"למעשה, פשוט נעזרנו בכמה חבר'ה שקרובים לפרישה," הוא
hu lifrisha shekrovim khevre bekhama ne'ezarnu pashut lema'ase
he to retirement who are close guys by a few we were helped simply actually

אומר.
omer
he says

"Actually, we just used some of the guys who are near retirement," he says.

"אז מה עם סם הגדול?" מתעניין אודי.
udi mitanyen hagadol sem ma im az
Udi he takes an interest the big Sam what about so

"So what about Big Sam?" Udi asks interestedly.

"התובע המחוזי עשה עסקה עם אחד מאנשיו של סם. הוא אמר לנו
lanu amar hu sem shel me'anashav ekhad im iska asa hamekhozi hatove'a
to us he told he Sam of of his men one with deal he made the district prosecutor

איפה מתחבא סם הגדול והודה שסם הוציא חוזה על אחד
ekhad al khoze hotsi shesem vehoda hagadol sem mitkhabe eifo
one on contract he took out that Sam and he admitted the big Sam he hides where

ממתחריו. עצרנו את סם הבוקר, עם האישה שנתנה לכם
lakhem shenatna ha'isha im haboker sem et atsarnu mimitkharav
to you who (she) gave the woman with this morning Sam D.O. we arrested of his competitors

את הכסף."
hakesef et
the money D.O.

"The District Attorney made a deal with one of Sam's men. He told us where Big Sam was hiding and admitted that Sam had put a contract on one of his competitors. We arrested Sam this morning, along with the woman who gave you the money."

"איזו הקלה," אני אומר. "עכשיו נוכל לסיים את החופשה שלנו
shelanu hakhufsha et lesayem nukhal akhshav omer ani hakala eizo
our the vacation D.O. to finish we will be able now I say I relief what a

בלי שהנשים שלנו יצפו במישהו חונק אותנו או דורס
dores o otanu khonek bemishehu itspu shelanu shehanashim bli
he runs over or us he strangles at someone they will watch our that the wives without

אותנו בבולדוזר."
bebuldozer otanu
with bulldozer us

"That's a relief," I say. "Now we can finish our vacation without our wives seeing us get strangled or run over by a bulldozer."

"Just promise that you take your next vacation in some other place," the detective says.

רק	תבטיחו	שבחופשה	הבאה	שלכם	תצאו	למקום	אחר,
rak	tavṭikhu	shebakhufsha	haba'a	shelakhem	titsu	lemakom	akher
just	you will promise	that on the vacation	the next	your	you will go out	to a place	another

אומר	הבלש.
omer	habalash
he says	the detective

"Maybe we'll try Wisconsin," Nati says. "The people seem normal enough."

אולי	ננסה	את	ויסקונסין,"	אומר	נתי.	"האנשים	שם	נראים	נורמלים
ulai	nenase	et	wiskonsin	omer	nati	ha'anashim	sham	nirim	normalim
maybe	we will try	D.O.	Wisconsin	he says	nati	the people	there	they seem	normal

למדי."
lemadai
quite

STORY 12

Mommy and Me

"אתה חייב לעצור אותה, מר לוי."
ata khayav la'atsor ota mar levi
you / you have to / to stop / her / Mr. / Levi

"You have to stop her, Mr. Levi."

"מה בדיוק אמא שלי עושה?"
ma bediyuk ima sheli osa
what / exactly / mom / my / she does

"What is my mother doing, exactly?"

"עדנה מספרת לכולם בכפר הגמלאים שהיא נקשרה לשולחן
edna mesaperet lekhulam bikhfar hagimla'im shehi nikshera lashulkhan
Edna / she tells / to everyone / in village of / the pensioners / that she / she was strapped / to table

למשך שעתיים ולא הורשתה ללכת לשירותים."
lemeshekh sha'ata'im velo hursheta lalekhet lasherutim
for / two hours / and no / she was allowed / to go / to the bathroom

"Edna is telling everyone in her retirement community that she was strapped to a table for two hours and wasn't allowed to go to the bathroom."

נשמע כאילו ד"ר נחמה אנגל, רופאת השיניים שלי, כרסמה תוך
nishma ke'ilu doktor nekhama engel rofat hashina'im sheli kirsema tokh
it sounds / as if / doctor / Nechama / Engel / dentist / my / she gnawed / while

דיבור בטלפון. אולי חרקה בשיניה. התפתיתי לומר לה
dibur batelefon ulai kharka beshineiha hitpateiti lomar la
talking / on the telephone / maybe / she ground / with her teeth / I was tempted / to tell / to her

שפעולות כאלה אינן בריאות לשיניים, אבל היא מן הסתם כבר
shepe'ulot ka'ele einan bri'ot lashina'im aval hi min hastam kvar
that actions / like these / they are not / healthy / for the teeth / but / she / probably / already

ידעה זאת.
yada zot
she knew / that

It sounded like Dr. Nechama Engel, my dentist, was gnawing on the phone as she was speaking. Maybe she was grinding her teeth. I was tempted to tell her that these actions are bad for the teeth, but she probably knew that already.

במקום זאת אמרתי, "היא לא נקשרה לשולחן. היא ישבה בכיסא
bimkom zot amarti hi lo nikshera lashulkhan hi yashva bekhise
instead of / this / I said / she / no / she was strapped / to table / she / she sat / in chair of

רופא השיניים שלך. אפשרת לה לקום אחרי שעה כדי לגשת
rofe hashina'im shelakh ifshart la lakum akharei sha'a kedei lageshet
the dentist / your / you let / to her / to get up / after / hour / in order to / to approach

לשירותים."
lasherutim
to the bathroom

Instead I said, "She wasn't strapped to a table. She was sitting in your dental chair. You let her get up after an hour to go to the bathroom."

"אני יודעת. אבל עדנה מספרת לשכניה שעיניתי אותה. ארבעה
ani yoda'at aval edna mesaperet lishkheneiha she'initi ota arba'a
I / I know / but / Edna / she tells / to her neighbors / that I tortured / her / four

"I know. But Edna is telling her neighbors that I tortured her. Four people from the retirement village have already called to cancel their appointments. One lady said she heard I didn't even have a license."

התור	את	לבטל	התקשרו	כבר	הגמלאים	מכפר	אנשים
hator	*et*	*levatel*	*hitkashru*	*kvar*	*hagimla'im*	*mikfar*	*anashim*
the appointment	D.O.	to cancel	they called	already	the pensioners	from village of	people

רישיון."	אפילו	לי	שאין	ששמעה	אמרה	אחת	גברת	שלהם.
rishayon	*afilu*	*she'ein li*		*sheshama*	*amra*	*akhat*	*gveret*	*shelahem*
license	even	that I don't have		that she heard	she said	one	lady	their

Dr. Engel sounded desperate. Half of her patients lived in my mother's community. If they believed the things my mother was saying, Dr. Engel would lose a lot of business.

בקהילה	התגוררו	מלקוחותיה	מחצית	נואשת.	נשמעה	אנגל	ד"ר
bakehila	*hitgoreru*	*milakokhoteiha*	*makhatsit*	*no'eshet*	*nishme'a*	*engel*	*doktor*
in the community	they lived	of her patients	half	desperate	she sounded	Engel	doctor

ד"ר	אמי,	שמספרת	לדברים	יאמינו	אם	אמי.	חיה	שבה
doktor	*imi*	*shemesaperet*	*ladvarim*	*ya'aminu*	*im*	*imi*	*khaya*	*sheba*
doctor	my mother	that she says	of the things	they will believe	if	my mother	she lives	that in it

מעבודתה.	ניכר	חלק	תפסיד	אנגל
me'avodata	*nikar*	*khelek*	*tafsid*	*engel*
of her business	substantial	part	she will lose	Engel

Edna Levi, my mother, is eighty-eight years old. She doesn't suffer from any diseases. She walks without a cane. Her mind is still sharp. She has a few minor medical problems, but she is in great physical shape for her age.

סובלת	איננה	היא	ושמונה.	שמונים	בת	היא	אמי,	לוי,	עדנה
sovelet	*einena*	*hi*	*ushmone*	*shmonim*	*bat*	*hi*	*imi*	*levi*	*edna*
she suffers	she does not	she	and eight	eighty	aged	she	my mother	Levi	Edna

יש לה	חד.	עדיין	מוחה	מקל.	ללא	הולכת	היא	כלשהן.	ממחלות
yesh la	*khad*	*ada'in*	*mokha*	*makel*	*lelo*	*holekhet*	*hi*	*kolshehen*	*mimakhalot*
she has	sharp	still	her mind	cane	without	she walks	she	any	from diseases

לגילה.	מעולה	גופני	במצב	היא	אולם	אחדות,	קלות	רפואיות	בעיות
legila	*me'ule*	*gufani*	*bematsav*	*hi*	*ulam*	*akhadot*	*kalot*	*refu'iyot*	*be'ayot*
for her age	great	physical	in shape	she	but	a few	minor	medical	problems

Unfortunately, mom is unhappy with her life. She believes that if she is not happy, then nobody should be happy. Therefore, she goes out of her way to make everyone else's life miserable. Now it was Dr. Engel's turn to feel the wrath of Edna.

היא	שאם	מאמינה	היא	בחייה.	מאושרת	איננה	אמא	המזל,	לרוע
hi	*she'im*	*ma'amina*	*hi*	*bekhayeiha*	*me'usheret*	*einena*	*ima*	*hamazal*	*lero'a*
she	that if	she believes	she	with her life	happy	she is not	mom		unfortunately

היא	לכן,	מאושר.	להיות	צריך	לא	אחד,	אף	מאושרת,	איננה
hi	*lakhen*	*me'ushar*	*lihiyot*	*tsarikh*	*lo*	*ekhad*	*af*	*me'usheret*	*einena*
she	therefore	happy	to be	he needs	no	nobody		happy	she is not

הסובבים	כל	של	חייהם	את	לאמלל	כדי	מגדרה	יוצאת
hasovevim	*kol*	*shel*	*khayeihem*	*et*	*le'amlel*	*kedei*	*migidra*	*yotset*
the people around	all	of	their lives	D.O.	to make miserable	in order to		she goes out of her way

של	זעמה	בחמת	לחוש	אנגל	ד"ר	של	תורה	זה	היה	עכשיו.	אותה
shel	*za'ama*	*bekhamat*	*lakhush*	*engel*	*doktor*	*shel*	*tora*	*ze*	*haya*	*akhshav*	*ota*
of	at the wrath		to feel	Engel	doctor	of	her turn	that	it was	now	her

עדנה.
edna
Edna

"I'll call mom right now," I said.

אמרתי.	מיד,"	לאמא	אתקשר	"אני
amarti	*miyad*	*le'ima*	*etkasher*	*ani*
I said	right now	to mom	I will call	I

"I already tried. Her telephone line is busy. Could you drive over there and talk with her? Please."

ולדבר	לשם	לנסוע	תוכל	תפוס.	שלה	הטלפון	ניסיתי.	"כבר
uledaber	*lesham*	*linso'a*	*tukhal*	*tafus*	*shela*	*hatelefon*	*nisiti*	*kvar*
and to talk	to there	to drive	you will be able	busy	her	the telephone	I tried	already

אִתָּה ? בבקשה."
bevakasha ita
please with her

סגרתי את הטלפון הסלולרי שלי ונכנסתי למכוניתי. בעודי נוסע את
et nose'a be'odi limkhoniti venikhnasti sheli haselulari hatelefon et sagarti
D.O. I drive as I into my car and I got into my the cellular the phone D.O. I shut

שלושת הקילומטרים אל דירתה של אמי, יכולתי לחוש באשמה
ba'ashma lakhush yakholti imi shel dirata el hakilometrim shloshet
in the guilt to feel I could my mother of her apartment to the kilometers three of

ההולכת וממלאת אותי. בעייתה הגדולה של ד"ר אנגל הייתה באשמתי.
be'ashmati haita engel doktor shel hagdola be'ayata oti umemalet haholekhet
at my fault it was Engel doctor of the big her problem me and it fills it goes

I shut my cell phone and jumped into my car. As I drove the three kilometers to my mother's apartment, I could feel the guilt descending on me. It was my fault that Dr. Engel was having this big problem.

שבועות אחדים קודם לכן החלו שיניה של אמי לכאוב. היא לא
lo hi likhov imi shel shineiha hekhelu kodem lakhen akhadim shavu'ot
no she to hurt my mom of her teeth they started previously a few weeks

ביקרה אצל רופא השיניים כבר שנים.
shanim kvar rofe hashina'im etsel bikra
years in the dentist at she visited

A few weeks ago, mom's teeth started giving her a lot of pain. She hadn't seen a dentist in years.

"למה להוציא כסף על השיניים שלי, אני אמות בתוך כמה שנים,"
shanim kama betokh amut ani sheli hashina'im al kesef lehotsi lama
years a few within I will die I my the teeth on money to spend why

נהגה לומר לי.
li lomar nahaga
to me to tell she used to

"Why spend money on my teeth, I'll be dead in a few years," she kept telling me.

התעקשתי שתלך לראות את רופאת השיניים שלי, ד"ר אנגל.
engel doktor sheli rofat hashina'im et lirot shetelekh hitakashti
Engel doctor my the dentist D.O. to see that she will go I insisted

I insisted that she go to see my dentist, Dr. Engel.

"אני אלך, אבל בלי צילומי רנטגן," אמרה אמא.
ima amra tsilumei rentgen bli aval elekh ani
mom she said x-rays without but I will go I

"I'll go, but no x-rays," mom said.

"ד"ר אנגל צריכה לבצע צילומי רנטגן כדי שתוכל לראות אם
im lirot shetukhal kedei tsilumei rentgen levatse'a tsrikha engel doktor
if to see that she will be able so that x-rays to perform she needs Engel doctor

יש בעיות נסתרות," אמרתי לה.
la amarti nistarot be'ayot yesh
to her I said hidden problems there are

"Dr. Engel has to take x-rays so she can see if there are any hidden problems," I told her.

"כמה יעלו צילומי הרנטגן?" שאלה.
sha'ala tsilumei harentgen ya'alu kama
she asks the x-rays they will cost how much

"How much will the x-rays cost?" she asked.

"זה לא משנה. את זקוקה להם."
lahem zkuka at meshane lo ze
to them in need of you it matters no that

"It doesn't matter. You need them."

135

"I can't afford x-rays."

"אני לא יכולה להרשות לעצמי צילומי רנטגן."
tsilumei *rentgen* — leharshot le'atsmi — yekhola — lo — ani
x-rays — to afford — I can — no — I

"You've got plenty of money."

"יש לך הרבה כסף."
kesef — harbe — yesh lakh
money — plenty — you have

"You don't know how much money I have," Mom said.

"אתה לא יודע כמה כסף יש לי," אמרה אמא.
ima — amra — yesh li — *kesef* — *kama* — yode'a — lo — ata
mom — she said — I have — money — how much — you know — no — you

"I know all about your finances. I pay your bills."

"אני יודע הכל אודות הכספים שלך. אני משלם את החשבונות
hakheshbonot — et — meshalem — ani — shelakh — haksafim — al odot — hakol — yode'a — ani
the bills — D.O. — I pay — I — your — the finances — about — all — I know — I

שלך."
shelakh
your

Mom tried a new argument.

אמא ניסתה טיעון חדש.
khadash — ti'un — nista — ima
new — argument — she tried — mom

"I need the money in case I have to go into a nursing home."

"אני צריכה את הכסף למקרה שאצטרך לעבור למוסד סיעודי."
lemosad si'udi — la'avor — she'etstarekh — lemikre — hakesef — et — tsrikha — ani
to nursing home — to move — that I will need — in case — the money — D.O. — I need — I

"You also need to be able to chew your food without pain," I told her.

"את גם צריכה להיות מסוגלת ללעוס את האוכל שלך ללא כאבים,"
ke'evim — lelo — shelakh — ha'okhel — et — lilos — mesugelet — lihiyot — tsrikha — gam — at
pains — without — your — the food — D.O. — to chew — able — to be — you need — also — you

אמרתי לה.
la — amarti
to her — I told

Eventually, I dragged mom to see Dr. Engel. She needed a root canal and a cap on one of her front teeth. Three other teeth had cavities that needed to be fixed.

לבסוף גררתי את אמא לד"ר אנגל. היא נזקקה לטיפול שורש
shoresh — letipul — nizkeka — hi — engel — ledoktor — ima — et — gararti — levasof
root — for treatment of — she needed — she — Engel — to doctor — mom — D.O. — I dragged — eventually

ולכתר באחת משיניה הקדמיות. בשלוש שיניים אחרות היו
hayu — akherot — shina'im — beshalosh — hakidmiyot — mishineiha — be'akhat — ulekheter
there were — others — teeth — in three — the front — of her teeth — on one — and for a crown

חורים שהיה צורך לסתום.
listom — tsorekh — shehaya — khorim
to seal — need — that there was — cavities

Two days ago, Dr. Engel did the root canal and put a temporary cap on mom's front tooth. The whole process took two hours. Mom needed to go back twice more before a permanent cap was in place.

לפני יומיים עשתה ד"ר אנגל את טיפול השורש והתאימה לאמא
le'ima — vehitima — hashoresh — tipul — et — engel — doktor — asta — yoma'im — lifnei
for mom — and she fitted — the root — treatment of — D.O. — Engel — doctor — she did — two days — ago

כתר זמני על השן הקדמית. התהליך כולו ארך שעתיים. אמא
ima — sha'ata'im — arakh — kulo — hatahalikh — hakidmit — hashen — al — zmani — keter
mom — two hours — it took — all of it — the process — the front — the tooth — on — temporary — cap

שיורכב עד נוספות פגישות לשתי לחזור צריכה הייתה
sheyurkav · ad · nosafot · pgishot · lishtei · lakhzor · haita tsrikha
that it will be put together · until · additional · appointments · for two of · to go back · she had to

הקבוע. הכתר
hakavu'a · haketer
the permanent · the cap

מטופליה. את מענה אנגל שד"ר לאנשים מספרת אמא עכשיו
metupaleiha · et · me'ana · engel · shedoktor · le'anashim · mesaperet · ima · akhshav
her patients · D.O. · she tortures · Engel · that doctor · to people · she tells · mom · now

Now mom was telling people that Dr. Engel tortures her patients. If I hadn't dragged mom to my dentist, this problem never would have happened. Yes, I felt a lot of guilt.

לא הזו הבעיה שלי, השיניים לרופאת אמא את גורר הייתי לא אם
lo · hazo · habe'aya · sheli · lerofat hashina'im · ima · et · ha'iti gorer · lo · im
no · the this · the problem · my · to the dentist · mom · D.O. · I had dragged · not · if

רבה. אשמה חשתי כן, מתעוררת. הייתה
raba · ashma · khashti · ken · haita mitoreret
a lot · guilt · I felt · yes · it would have arisen

— 2 —

בטלפון. דיברה היא אמא, של לדירתה כשנכנסתי
batelefon · dibra · hi · ima · shel · ledirata · kshenikhnasti
on the telephone · she spoke · she · mom · of · into her apartment · as I entered

As I walked into Mom's apartment, she was on the phone.

שעתיים. למשך לשולחן אותי קשרה היא לך, אומרת "אני
sha'ata'im · lemeshekh · lashulkhan · oti · kashra · hi · lakh · omeret · ani
two hours · for · to the table · me · she strapped · she · to you · I tell · I

"I'm telling you, she strapped me to a table for two hours. Imagine what it did to my back. I still can't move my legs properly," Mom was telling someone.

יכולה לא עדיין אני שלי. לגב עשה זה מה לך תארי
yekhola · lo · ada'in · ani · sheli · lagav · asa · ze · ma · lakh · ta'ari
I can · no · still · I · my · to the back · it did · this · what · to you · you will imagine

למישהי. אמא סיפרה שצריך," כמו רגליי את להזיז
lemishehi · ima · sipra · shetsarikh · kmo · raglai · et · lehaziz
to someone · mom · she told · that I should · like · my legs · D.O. · to move

צעקתי." אמא, הטלפון את "נתקי
tsa'akti · ima · hatelefon · et · natki
I yelled · mom · the telephone · D.O. · hang up

"Hang up the phone, mom," I yelled.

קולי. למשמע מעט קפצה היא
koli · lemishma · me'at · kaftsa · hi
my voice · to the sound of · a little · she jumped · she

She jumped a little at the sound of my voice.

"תודה השפופרת. לתוך אמרה לבקר," הגיע בדיוק שלי "הבן
toda · hashfoferet · letokh · amra · levaker · higi'a · bediyuk · sheli · haben
thanks · the receiver · into · she said · to visit · he arrived · just · my · the son

"My son just arrived for a visit," she said into the phone. "Thanks for calling."

שהתקשרת."
shehitkashart
that you called

שפופרת את מניחה שהיא תוך אמרה משכנותיי," אחת הייתה "זו
shfoferet · et · menikha · tokh shehi · amra · mishkhenotai · akhat · haita · zo
receiver of · D.O. · she sets down · as she · she said · of my neighbors · one · she was · that

"That was one of my neighbors," she said as she put her phone back onto its stand. "She wanted to know all about

137

my cap."

הטלפון על כנה. "היא רצתה לדעת הכל על הכתר שלי."
hatelefon *al* *kana* *hi* *ratsta* *lada'at* *hakol* *al* *haketer* *sheli*
the telephone on its stand she she wanted to know everything about the cap my

"Why are you telling people that the dentist made you lie on a table?"

"למה את מספרת לאנשים שרופאת השיניים הכריחה אותך לשכב על
lama *at* *mesaperet* *le'anashim* *sherofat hashina'im* *hikhrikha* *otakh* *lishkav* *al*
why you you tell to people that the dentist she forced you to lie down on

שולחן?"
shulkhan
table

"That's what she did. My back is killing me."

"זה מה שהיא עשתה. הגב שלי הורג אותי."
ze *ma* *shehi* *asta* *hagav* *sheli* *horeg* *oti*
that what that she she did the back my it kills me

"You were sitting in a dental chair. She just had it tilted backwards."

"ישבת בכיסא של רופא שיניים. היא רק היטתה אותו לאחור."
yashavt *bekhise* *shel* *rofe shina'im* *hi* *rak* *hiteta* *oto* *le'akhor*
you sat in chair of dentist she just she tilted it backward

"How do you know?" Mom asked with annoyance.

"איך אתה יודע?" שאלה אמא, כעוסה.
eikh *ata* *yode'a* *sha'ala* *ima* *ke'usa*
how you you know she asks mom annoyed

"I was there. Remember I drove you to the dentist's office and stayed for the whole visit?"

"הייתי שם. זוכרת שהסעתי אותך למרפאת השיניים ונשארתי שם
ha'iti *sham* *zokheret* *shehisati* *otakh* *lemirpa'at* *hashina'im* *venisharti* *sham*
I was there you remember that I drove you to the clinic of the teeth and I stayed there

במהלך הביקור כולו?"
bemahalakh *habikur* *kulo*
during the visit whole

She scrunched up her face, trying to remember. Mom is very short. When she does that thing with her face, she looks like Yoda's older sister. Her curly white hair is cut short. Every eighty year old woman I have ever seen has short, curly hair. Maybe it's a rule.

היא העוותה את פניה בניסיון להיזכר. אמא נמוכה מאוד. כשהיא
hi *he'evta* *et* *paneiha* *benisayon* *lehizakher* *ima* *nemukha* *me'od* *kshehi*
she she distorted D.O. her face trying to remember mom short very when she

עושה העוויה כזו בפניה, היא נראית כאילו היא אחותו הגדולה
osa *ha'avaya* *kazo* *befaneiha* *hi* *niret* *ke'ilu* *hi* *akhoto* *hagdola*
she does the distorting like that with her face she she looks like she his sister the older

של יודה. שיערה המתולתל והלבן גזור בתספורת קצרה. כל הנשים
shel *yoda* *sei'ara* *hametultal* *vehalavan* *gazur* *betisporet* *ktsara* *kol* *hanashim*
of Yoda her hair the curly and the white cut with haircut short all the women

בנות השמונים שראיתי מעודי הן בעלות שיער קצר ומתולתל. אולי זה
bnot *hashmonim* *shera'iti me'odi* *hen* *ba'alot* *sei'ar* *katsar* *umetultal* *ulai* *ze*
aged the eighty that I ever saw they having hair short and curly maybe this

מין חוק כזה.
min *khok* *kaze*
sort of rule like this

Mom also wears large glasses that turn purple in the sunlight. They hide most of her features. When she's out-side, all you see is the white curly hair and a purple face. It's quite interest-

אמא גם מרכיבה משקפיים גדולים, שצבעם הופך סגול באור
ima *gam* *markiva* *mishkafa'im* *gdolim* *shetsivam* *hofekh* *sagol* *be'or*
mom also she wears glasses large whose color it becomes purple in the light of

כל, בחוץ היא כאשר פניה. תווי רוב את מסתירים הם השמש.
kol bakhuts hi ka'asher tavei paneiha rov et mastirim hem hashemesh
all outside she when her facial features most D.O. they hide they the sun

זה סגולות. ופנים המתולתל הלבן השיער הוא לראות שניתן
ze sgulot ufanim hametultal halavan hasei'ar hu lirot shenitan
this purple and face the curly the white the hair is to see that it is possible

למדי. מעניין
lemadai me'anyen
quite interesting

ing.

היית לא", אמרה. לבסוף אחדות. שניות במשך מהרהרת בה צפיתי
ha'ita lo amra levasof akhadot shniyot bemeshekh meharheret ba tsafiti
you were no she said finally a few seconds for she ponders at her I watched

שם."
sham
there

I watched her think for a few seconds. Finally she said, "You weren't there."

לך אפשרה אנגל ודוקטור ר"וד עיניים. שולחן היה לא ".היית כן"
lakh ifshera engel vedoktor inuyim shulkhan haya lo ha'iti ken
to you she allowed Engel and doctor tortures table of there was not I was yes

שעה." אחרי לשירותים ללכת
sha'a akharei lasherutim lalekhet
hour after to the bathroom to go

"Yes I was. There was no torture table. And Dr. Engel let you go to the bathroom after an hour."

שעתיים." במשך הזה לדבר קשורה אותי השאירה היא נכון. לא"
sha'atayim bemeshekh haze ladavar kshura oti hishira hi nakhon lo
two hours for the that to the thing strapped me she kept she correct not

"No she didn't. She kept me strapped to that thing for two hours."

לשירותים." ללכת לך עזרתי אני"
lasherutim lalekhet lakh azarti ani
to the bathroom to walk to you I helped I

"I helped you walk to the bathroom."

שלי." החזה על גדולה בטון פיסת הניחה היא"
sheli hekhaze al gdola beton pisat henikha hi
my the chest on big concrete piece of she placed she

"She put a big piece of concrete on my chest."

הרנטגן." קרני מפני עלייך להגן כדי עופרת. סינר היה זה"
karnei harentgen mipnei alaikh lehagen kedei oferet sinar haya ze
x-rays from on you to protect in order to lead vest of it was that

"That was a lead vest. To protect you from the x-rays."

עליה. שחולקים שונאת היא התכרכמו. אמא של פניה
aleiha shekholkim sonet hi hitkarkemu ima shel paneiha
with her that (people) disagree she hates she it became yellow mom of her face

Mom got a sour look. She hates it when anyone disagrees with her.

אותך, עינתה אינתה אנגל ר"שד לאנשים לספר להפסיק חייבת את"
otakh inta engel shedoktor le'anashim lesaper lehafsik khayevet at
you she tortured Engel that doctor to people to tell to stop you must you

שלהם." התורים את מבטלים הם" המשכתי.
shelahem hatorim et mevatlim hem himshakhti
their the appointments D.O. they cancel they I continued

"You have to stop telling people that Dr. Engel tortured you," I continued. "They have been canceling their appointments."

139

"I only told three or four people."

"סיפרתי רק לשלושה או ארבעה אנשים."

siparti	rak	lishlosha	o	arba'a	anashim
I told	only	to three	or	four	people

"Bad news travels fast in your retirement village. By tomorrow even the mayor will hear your story if you don't call everyone back and tell them you exaggerated."

"חדשות רעות מתפשטות מהר בכפר הגמלאים שלך. עד מחר

khadashot	ra'ot	mitpashtot	maher	bikhfar	hagimla'im	shelakh	ad	makhar
news	bad	they spread	fast	in village of	the pensioners	your	by	tomorrow

אפילו ראש העיר ישמע את הסיפור שלך אם לא תתקשרי לכולם

afilu	rosh ha'ir	yishma	et	hasipur	shelakh	im	lo	titkashri	lekhulam
even	the mayor	he will hear	D.O.	the story	your	if	no	you will call	to everyone

שוב ותאמרי להם שהגזמת."

shuv	vetomri	lahem	shehigzamt
again	and you will tell	to them	that you exaggerated

Mom changed the topic. "The dentist better not send me a big bill."

אמא שינתה את הנושא. "כדאי מאוד שרופאת השיניים לא תשלח

ima	shinta	et	hanose	kedai me'od	sherofat hashina'im	lo	tishlakh
mom	she changed	D.O.	the topic	she'd better	that the dentist	not	she will send

לי חשבון מנופח."

li	kheshbon	menupakh
to me	bill	inflated

"She already gave you a printout of what everything would cost."

"היא כבר נתנה לך תדפיס של עלות הטיפול כולו."

hi	kvar	natna	lakh	tadpis	shel	alut	hatipul	kulo
she	already	she gave	to you	printout	of	cost of	the treatment	whole

"Why is she making me go back next week? I already have my new tooth."

"למה היא מכריחה אותי לחזור בשבוע הבא? כבר יש לי שן

lama	hi	makhrikha	oti	lakhzor	bashavu'a	haba	kvar	yesh li	shen
why	she	she forces	me	to go back	at the week	next	already	I have	tooth

חדשה."

khadasha
new

"That's a temporary tooth. You have to go back a few more times until the permanent cap is in place. She told you that."

"זו שן זמנית. תצטרכי לחזור עוד כמה פעמים עד

zo	shen	zmanit	titstarkhi	lakhzor	od	kama	pe'amim	ad
that	tooth	temporary	you will have to	to go back	another	a few	times	until

שיורכב הכתר הקבוע. היא אמרה לך את זה."

sheyurkav	haketer	hakavu'a	hi	amra	lakh	et	ze
that it will be assembled	the cap	the permanent	she	she told	to you	D.O.	that

"No she didn't. She just wants more money!"

"לא נכון. היא סתם רוצה עוד כסף!"

lo	nakhon	hi	stam	rotsa	od	kesef
not	correct	she	just	she wants	more	money

"I was there when she told you."

"אני הייתי שם כשהיא אמרה לך."

ani	ha'iti	sham	kshehi	amra	lakh
I	I was	there	when she	she told	to you

"Next time, I want Odelia to take me."

"בפעם הבאה, אני רוצה שאודליה תיקח אותי."

bapa'am	haba'a	ani	rotsa	she'odelya	tikakh	oti
at the time	next	I	I want	that Odelia	she will take	me

140

אני ללכת לרופא השיניים. אותך ששכנע זה הייתי אני לא
ani · lerofe hashina'im · lalekhet · otakh · sheshikhne'a · ze · ha'iti · ani · lo
I · to the dentist · to go · you · who (he) convinced · the one · I was · I · no

אקח אותך לשם.
ekakh · otakh · lesham
I will take · you · to there

> "No. I was the one who convinced you to go to the dentist. I will take you to your appointments."

עליה. החביב הביטוי היה זה לי. אמרה רע, בן היית תמיד
aleiha · hakhaviv · habitui · haya · ze · li · amra · ra · ben · ha'ita · tamid
for her · the favorite · the expression · it was · this · to me · she told · bad · son · you were · always

> "You were always a bad son," she told me. This was her favorite expression.

לכל מתקשרת היא בעוד כשעה אמא של בדירתה נשארתי
lekhol · mitkasheret · hi · be'od · kesha'a · ima · shel · bedirata · nisharti
to all · she calls · she · while · about hour · mom · of · at her apartment · I stayed

אודות על בסיפורה שהגזימה להם ומספרת מכריה
al odot · besipura · shehigzima · lahem · umesaperet · makareiha
about · with her story · that she exaggerated · to them · and she tells · her acquaintances

רופאת השיניים.
rofat hashina'im
the dentist

> I stayed at mom's apartment for about an hour while she called all of her acquaintances and told them that she had exaggerated her story about the dentist.

3

משפחה? קרובת היא האם אודליה. בעניין תוהים בוודאי אתם
krovat mishpakha · hi · ha'im · odelya · be'inyan · tohim · bevadai · atem
relative · she · is it that · Odelia · in the matter of · you wonder · probably · you

וחמש. שבעים בת אנרגיה פצצת היא אודליה לא. סוציאלית? עובדת
vekhamesh · shivim · bat · energya · ptsa'tsat · hi · odelya · lo · sotsyalit · ovedet
and five · seventy · aged · energy · bomb of · she · Odelia · no · social · worker

> You are probably wondering about Odelia. Is she a relative? A social worker? No. Odelia is a seventy-five year old bundle of energy.

בשליחויות העיר ברחבי בהתרוצצות זמנה מרבית את מבלה היא
bishlikhuyot · ha'ir · berakhavei · behitrotsetsut · zmana · marbit · et · mevala · hi
with errands · the city · all over · with running around · her time · most · D.O. · she spends · she

שבו הגמלאים בכפר המתגוררים יותר הקשישים האנשים עבור
shebo · hagimla'im · bikhfar · hamitgorerim · yoter · hakshishim · ha'anashim · avur
that in it · the pensioners · in village of · that live · more · the old (people) · the people · for

מסיעה היא דעתך. על שיעלה מה כל תעשה היא אמי. מתגוררת
masi'a · hi · sheya'ale al da'atkha · kol ma · ta'ase · hi · imi · mitgoreret
she drives · she · that you may think of · everything that · she will do · she · my mom · she lives

מזון מצרכי קונה היא חולים. ובתי מרפאות לחנויות, הקשישים את
mitsrakhei mazon · kona · hi · uvatei kholim · mirpa'ot · lekhanuyot · hakshishim · et
groceries · she buys · she · and hospitals · medical clinics · to stores · the seniors · D.O.

ואז בעצמם. קניות לערוך יכולים שאינם אנשים עבור
ve'az · be'atsmam · kniyot · la'arokh · yekholim · she'einam · anashim · avur
and then · by themselves · shopping · to handle · they are able · who they are not · people · for

אפונה שימורי קופסת שהביאה כך על לתלונותיהם מקשיבה היא
afuna · kufsat shimurei · shehevi'a · al kakh · litlunoteihem · makshiva · hi
peas · can of · that she brought · about it · to their complaints · she listens · she

> She spends most of her time running around town doing errands for the older people who live in my mother's retirement community. You name it, she does it. She drives the senior citizens to stores, doctor offices, and hospitals. She buys groceries for the people who can't shop for themselves. Then she listens to them complain that she brought the wrong size can of peas and the bananas are too expensive.

בגודל הלא נכון ועל כך שהבננות יקרות מדי.
bagodel *halo* *nakhon* *ve'al kakh* *shehabananot* *yekarot* *midai*
of the size | the not | correct | and about it | that the bananas | expensive | too

Sometimes Odelia even brings a sick person's clothes to her house and washes them.

לעתים אודליה אף לוקחת את בגדיהם של אנשים חולים לביתה
le'itim *odelya* *af* *lokakhat* *et* *bigdeihem* *shel* *anashim* *kholim* *leveita*
sometimes | Odelia | even | she takes | D.O. | their clothes | of | people | sick | to her house

ומכבסת אותם.
umekhabeset *otam*
and she washes | them

Odelia doesn't get a lot of thanks for all her good work. Especially from people like my mother, who seem to think they are entitled to these acts of kindness. Just last week I had this conversation with mom.

אודליה איננה מקבלת הרבה תודות על כל עבודתה הברוכה. במיוחד
odelya *einena* *mekabelet* *harbe* *todot* *al* *kol* *avodata* *habrukha* *bimyukhad*
Odelia | she does not | she gets | much | thanks | for | all | her work | the blessed | especially

מאנשים כמו אמי, שנראה כי הם סבורים שהמחוות הנדיבות
me'anashim *kmo* *imi* *shenire* *ki* *hem* *svurim* *shehamekhvot* *hanedivot*
from people | like | my mom | that it seems | that | they | they feel | that the gestures | the generous

הללו מגיעות להם. רק בשבוע שעבר שוחחתי על כך עם אמא.
halalu *magi'ot lahem* *rak* *bashavu'a* *she'avar* *sokhakhti* *al kakh* *im* *ima*
these | they deserve them | just | in week | that it passed | I conversed | about it | with | mom

"Odelia came to visit this morning. She screwed up my whole day."

"אודליה באה לבקר הבוקר. היא הרסה לי את כל היום."
odelya *ba'a* *levaker* *haboker* *hi* *harsa* *li* *et* *kol* *hayom*
Odelia | she came | to visit | this morning | she | she ruined | for me | D.O. | whole | the day

"How did she do that?"

"איך היא עשתה זאת?"
eikh *hi* *asta* *zot*
how | she | she did | that

"She sat there for an hour talking to me," Mom said.

"היא ישבה שם שעה ודיברה איתי," אמרה אמא.
hi *yashva* *sham* *sha'a* *vedibra* *iti* *amra* *ima*
she | she sat | there | hour | and she spoke | with me | she said | mom

"It's good you had a visitor. Hardly anyone ever comes to your apartment."

"זה טוב שהייתה לך אורחת. כמעט אף אחד לא מגיע לבקר בדירה
ze *tov* *shehaita lakh* *orakhat* *kimat* *af ekhad* *lo* *magi'a* *levaker* *badira*
that | good | that you had | guest | hardly | nobody | no | he comes | to visit | at the apartment

שלך."
shelakh
your

"She never listens to me."

"היא אף פעם לא מקשיבה לי."
hi *af pa'am* *lo* *makshiva* *li*
she | never | no | she listens | to me

"Why do you say that?"

"למה את אומרת זאת?"
lama *at* *omeret* *zot*
why | you | you say | that

"I mentioned the heart attack I had last Sunday, and she told me it was nothing. How does she know?"

"הזכרתי את התקף הלב שהיה לי ביום ראשון האחרון, והיא אמרה
hizkarti *et* *hetkef halev* *shehaya li* *beyom rishon* *ha'akharon* *vehi* *amra*
I mentioned | D.O. | the heart attack | that I had | on Sunday | the last | and she | she said

142

שזה שום דבר. איך היא יודעת?"
yoda'at hi eikh shum davar sheze
she knows she how nothing that this

"היא אחות מוסמכת, אמא."
ima musmekhet akhot hi
mom certified nurse she

"She's a registered nurse, mom."

"אז מה? היא לא רופאה."
rofa lo hi ma az
doctor not she what so

"So what? She's not a doctor."

"אפילו אני יודע שלא היה לך התקף לב. את זוכרת שהתקשרת
shehitkashart zokheret at hetkef lev haya lakh shelo yode'a ani afilu
that you called you remember you heart attack you had that no I know I even

אליי ביום ראשון אחר הצהריים וסיפרת לי על התסמינים שלך?"
shelakh hatasminim al li vesipart akhar hatsohora'im beyom rishon elai
your the symptoms about to me and you told afternoon on Sunday to me

"Even I know you didn't have a heart attack. Remember you called me Sunday afternoon and told me your symptoms?"

"כן."
ken
yes

"Yes."

"עצירות וכאב בטן אינם תסמינים של התקף לב."
hetkef lev shel tasminim einam beten ukhe'ev atsirut
heart attack of symptoms they are not stomach and ache of constipation

"Constipation and stomach ache are not the symptoms of a heart attack."

"זה היה יותר מזה. היו לי גם כאבים בחזה."
bakhaze ke'evim gam hayu li mize yoter haya ze
in the chest pains also I had than that more it was it

"It was more than that. I had chest pains, too."

"את ממציאה את זה. שאלתי אותך על כאבים בחזה כשהתקשרת
kshehitkashart bakhaze ke'evim al otakh sha'alti ze et mamtsi'a at
when you called in the chest pains about you I asked that D.O. you make up you

אליי ואמרת שהחזה שלך בסדר."
beseder shelakh shehekhaze ve'amart elai
fine your that the chest and you said to me

"You're making that up. I asked you about chest pains when you called me and you said that your chest was fine."

"ובכן, היא בכל זאת לא צריכה להגיד לי שהבריאות שלי טובה.
tova sheli shehabri'ut li lehagid tsrikha lo bekhol zot hi uv'khen
good my that the health to me to tell she should no nevertheless she well then

היא לא יודעת על כל הכאבים והמכאובים שלי."
sheli vehamakhovim hake'evim kol al yoda'at lo hi
my and the aches the pains all about she knows no she

"Well, she still shouldn't tell me that I have good health. She doesn't know all my aches and pains."

"היא כן יודעת," אמרתי. "היא לוקחת אותך לרופא ויושבת
veyoshevet larofe otakh lokakhat hi amarti yoda'at ken hi
and she sits to the doctor you she takes she I said she knows yes she

בחדר הבדיקה איתך."
itakh habdika bakhadar
with you the examination in the room of

"Yes she does," I said. "She's takes you to the doctor and sits in the examining room with you."

143

"She talks so much to the doctor that he charges extra money for the visit. I keep telling her not to say anything to him, but she won't listen."

היא מדברת עם הרופא כל כך הרבה, שהוא גובה עוד כסף עבור
avur kesef od gove shehu harbe kol kakh harofe im medaberet hi
for money more he bills that he much so the doctor with she talks she

הביקור. אני תמיד אומרת לה לא להגיד לו כלום, אבל היא לא
lo hi aval klum lo lehagid lo la omeret tamid ani habikur
no she but anything to him to say not to her I tell always I the visit

מקשיבה."
makshiva
she listens

"That's because when you go to the doctor, you forget to tell him all your medical problems, so Odelia has to tell him."

זה בגלל שכשאת הולכת לרופא, את שוכחת לספר לו על כל
kol al lo lesaper shokhakhat at larofe holekhet shekshe'at biglal ze
all about to him to tell you forget you to the doctor you go that when you because that

הבעיות הרפואיות שלך, אז אודליה צריכה לספר לו."
lo lesaper tsrikha odelya az shelakh harefu'iyot habe'ayot
to him to tell she needs Odelia so your the medical the problems

"Well then, she should pay for the extra time that he charges me."

אם כך, היא צריכה לשלם עבור הזמן הנוסף שהוא גובה ממני."
mimeni gove shehu hanosaf hazman avur leshalem tsrikha hi im kakh
from me he bills that he the extra the time for to pay she should she that being the case

"Mom, Odelia is the nicest person in the world. Don't ask her to pay for part of your doctor visit. She might be offended."

אמא, אודליה היא האדם הנחמד ביותר בעולם. אל תבקשי
tevakshi al ba'olam beyoter hanekhmad ha'adam hi odelya ima
you will ask don't in the word most the nice the person she Odelia mom

ממנה לשלם חלק ממחיר ביקור הרופא שלך. היא עלולה להיפגע."
lehipaga alula hi shelakh harofe bikur mimekhir khelek leshalem mimena
to be offended likely she your the doctor visit of of price of part to pay from her

"Maybe I'll ask her to start doing my wash," she continued.

אולי אבקש ממנה להתחיל לכבס עבורי," המשיכה.
himshikha avuri lekhabes lehatkhil mimena avakesh ulai
she continued for me to wash (clothes) to start from her I will ask maybe

Mom really resented that Odelia had never offered to do her wash. She felt snubbed.

אמא באמת כעסה על כך שאודליה מעולם לא הציעה לכבס
lekhabes hitsi'a me'olam lo she'odelya al kakh ka'asa be'emet ima
to wash (clothes) she offered never that Odelia about it she was angry really mom

עבורה. היא הרגישה שנוהגים בה בזלזול.
shenohagim ba bezilzul hirgisha hi avura
that they handle her with disrespect she felt she for her

"She only does the wash for people who are really sick. You're not really sick. You can wheel your cart to the laundry room and do your own wash," I said.

היא מכבסת רק עבור אנשים שחולים באמת. את לא באמת
be'emet lo at be'emet shekholim anashim avur rak mekhabeset hi
really not you really that (are) sick people for only she washes she

חולה. את יכולה לדחוף את העגלה שלך לחדר הכביסה ולכבס
ulekhabes hakvisa lakhadar shelakh ha'agala et lidkhof yekhola at khola
and to wash the laundry to the room of your the cart D.O. to push you can you sick

בעצמך," אמרתי.
amarti be'atsmekh
I said by yourself

"אני למעשה נכה. אין לך מושג כמה הברכיים שלי כואבות."

"I'm practically disabled. You don't know how much pain I have in my knees."

"הברכיים שלך בסדר גמור," אמרתי לה.

"Your knees are totally fine," I said to her.

"תמיד היית בן רע!" אמרה אמא.

"You were always a bad son!" she said.

שוב. הביטוי החביב עליה.

There it was again. Her favorite expression.

— 4 —

לאחר ששה שבועות ...

Six weeks later ...

ערב שבת הוא זמן האחווה הגברית. זה מה שעשיתי. שיחקתי פוקר עם שכניי אשר, בני וגבי. בילינו ביחד נינוחים, שותים בירה ומשוחחים.

Friday night is male bonding time. That's what I was doing. Playing poker with my neighbors Asher, Benni, and Gabbi. We were hanging out, relaxing, drinking beer, and talking.

החיים היו לחוצים למדי עבורי ועבור אמי. נדרשו ארבע פגישות נוספות אצל רופאת השיניים במהלך ארבעה שבועות עד שהותקן לה כתר קבוע ובוצעו שלוש סתימות חדשות בשלוש שיניים אחרות. עשרים ושמונה ימים של האזנה לתלונותיה על עבודתה הגרועה של רופאת השיניים ועל מה שכל זה היה צפוי לעלות. לפחות היא לא התקשרה לאנשים בעיר והאשימה

Life has been pretty stressful for me and my mom. It took four more dental visits over a period of four weeks before mom had a permanent cap on her bad tooth and new fillings in three other teeth. Twenty-eight days of listening to her complain about what a bad job the dentist was doing and how much the whole thing was going to cost. At least she wasn't calling any other people in town and accusing Dr. Engel of practicing voodoo.

145

את ד״ר אנגל בעריכת טקסי וודו.
et doktor engel be'arikhat tiksei vudu
D.O. doctor Engel of conducting ceremony of voodoo

"How's your mom doing?" my buddy Gabbi asked.

"מה שלום אמך?" שאל חברי גבי.
ma shlom imkha sha'al khaveri gabi
how is your mom he asks my buddy Gabbi

"She keeps telling me she wants to live at my house," I said.

"היא ממשיכה להגיד לי שהיא רוצה לגור אצלי בבית,"
hi mamshikha lehagid li shehi rotsa lagur etsli baba'it
she she continues to tell to me that she she wants to live at my place at the home

אמרתי.
amarti
I said

"Somebody please deal the cards," Benni said. "I feel lucky."

"שמישהו יחלק את הקלפים, בבקשה," אמר בני. "אני מרגיש
shemishehu yekhalek et haklafim bevakasha amar beni ani margish
would somebody he will deal D.O. cards please he said Benni I I feel

בר מזל."
bar mazal
lucky

"Are you actually considering letting your mother live in your house?" Gabbi asked.

"אתה באמת שוקל לאפשר לאמא שלך לגור אתך בבית?"
ata be'emet shokel le'afsher le'ima shelkha lagur itkha baba'it
you really you consider to allow to mother your to live with you at the house

שאל גבי.
sha'al gabi
he asked Gabbi

I shook my head from side to side. "No way. My marriage can't take the strain. Plus, she would drive me crazy. I tell her that every time she brings up the subject."

הנדתי בראשי מצד לצד. "אין סיכוי. הנישואים שלי לא
henadeti beroshi mitsad letsad ein sikui hanisu'im sheli lo
I shook with my head from side to side there isn't chance the marriage my no

יעמדו בכך. חוץ מזה, היא תשגע אותי. אני אומר לה את
ya'amdu bekhakh khuts mize hi teshage'a oti ani omer la et
they will be able to take it besides she she will drive me crazy I I tell to her D.O.

זה בכל פעם שהיא מעלה את הנושא."
ze bekhol pa'am shehi ma'ala et hanose
that every time that she she raises D.O. the subject

"I didn't know your mother was so difficult," said Gabbi.

"לא ידעתי שאמך קשה כל כך," אמר גבי.
lo yadati she'imkha kasha kol kakh amar gabi
no I knew that your mother difficult so he said Gabbi

"That's because you're new in town," said Asher.

"זה בגלל שאתה חדש בעיר," אמר אשר.
ze biglal she'ata khadash ba'ir amar asher
that because that you new in the town he said Asher

"There are lots of people who have Edna stories," Gabbi said. "She's a real pain."

"יש הרבה אנשים שיש להם סיפורי עדנה," אמר גבי. "היא באמת
yesh harbe anashim sheyesh lahem sipurei edna amar gabi hi be'emet
there are a lot people who (they) have stories of Edna he said Gabbi she really

צרה."
tsara
trouble

"אתה זוכר את המסיבה ההיא אצל קובי בקיץ שעבר?"
ata zokher et hamesiba hahi etsel kobi bakaits she'avar
you — you remember — D.O. — the party — that one — at — Kobi — in the summer — last

צחק בני. "עדנה התחילה לצעוק עלינו שאכלנו כל כך הרבה."
tsakhak beni. edna hitkhila litsok aleinu she'akhalnu kol kakh harbe
he laughed — Benni — Edna — she started — to yell — at us — that we ate — so — much

"Remember that party at Kobi's house last summer?" laughed Benni. "Edna started yelling at us for eating so much."

"היא רצתה לקחת את השאריות הביתה," הוסיף אשר. "היא אילצה
hi ratsta lakakhat et hashe'eriyot habaita, hosif asher. hi iltsa
she — she wanted — to take — D.O. — the leftovers — homeward — he added — Asher — she — she forced

את אשתי להחזיר סלט תפוחי אדמה בחזרה לקערה."
et ishti lehakhzir salat tapukhei adama bakhazara lake'ara
D.O. — my wife — to return — salad of — potatoes — back — in the bowl

"She wanted to take the leftovers home," added Asher. "She made my wife put some potato salad back in the bowl."

"אתה ודאי חש אשמה כשאתה אומר לה שהיא לא יכולה לבוא
ata vadai khash ashma kshe'ata omer la shehi lo yekhola lavo
you — for sure — you feel — guilt — when you — you tell — to her — that she — no — she can — to come

לגור איתך," אמר גבי וגרף את הקופה.
lagur itkha, amar gabi vegaraf et hakupa
to live — with you — he said — Gabbi — and he raked in — D.O. — the jackpot

"You must have so much guilt, telling her she can't live with you," Gabbi said as he raked in a pot.

"אני חש אשמה כבר שנים. שום דבר שאני עושה אינו מספיק טוב
ani khash ashma kvar shanim. shum davar she'ani ose eino maspik tov
I — I feel — guilt — for — years — nothing — that I — I do — it isn't — enough — good

עבורה. אם אני מתקשר חמש פעמים בשבוע, היא מתלוננת שאשתי
avura. im ani mitkasher khamesh pe'amim beshavu'a, hi mitlonenet she'ishti
for her — if — I — I call — five — times — in a week — she — she complains — that my wife

גילת לא מתקשרת. אם אני מבקר פעמיים בשבוע, היא מספרת לי
gilat lo mitkasheret. im ani mevaker pa'ama'im beshavu'a, hi mesaperet li
Gilat — no — she calls — if — I — I visit — twice — in a week — she — she tells — to me

שילדיהם של השכנים מבקרים בכל יום."
sheyaldeihem shel hashkhenim mevakrim bekhol yom
that their kids — of — the neighbors — they visit — every — day

"I've had guilt for years. Nothing I do is good enough for her. If I call five times a week, she complains that my wife Gilat doesn't call. If I visit twice a week, she tells me that her neighbors' kids see them every day."

"איך היא יודעת מה עושים ילדיהם של אנשים אחרים?" שאל בני.
eikh hi yoda'at ma osim yaldeihem shel anashim akherim? sha'al beni
how — she — she knows — what — they do — their kids — of — people — other — he asked — Benni

"How would she know about what other people's kids do?" asked Benni.

"כולם בכפר הגמלאים משקרים זה לזה על כמה יפה
kulam bikhfar hagimla'im meshakrim ze laze al kama yafe
everyone — in the village of — the pensioners — they lie — to each other — about — how much — well

ילדיהם מטפלים בהם. הם גם מתרברבים בנכדיהם
yaldeihem metaplim bahem. hem gam mitravrevim binkhadeihem
their children — they take care — of them — they — also — they brag — about their grandchildren

"Everyone in the retirement village lies to each other about how well their children take care of them. They also brag about their genius grandchildren," I said. "It's a competition to see who has the best relatives."

הגאונים," אמרתי. "זו תחרות - למי יש את הקרובים הטובים
hage'onim amarti zo takharut lemi yesh et hakrovim hatovim
the genius I said this competition of who has D.O. the relatives the good

ביותר."
beyoter
most

"Enough talking," Gabbi interrupted. "Deal the cards."

"די עם הדיבורים," קטע אותי גבי. "חלק את הקלפים."
dai im hadiburim kata oti gabi khalek et haklafim
enough with the talking he interrupted me Gabbi deal D.O. the cards

I dealt another hand. I looked at my cards. Two kings. Maybe I'd win a pot for once.

חילקתי סיבוב נוסף. הסתכלתי בקלפים שלי. שני מלכים. אולי אזכה
khilakti sivuv nosaf histakalti baklafim sheli shnei melakhim ulai ezke
I dealt round another I looked at the cards my two of kings maybe I will win

בקופה פעם אחת.
bakupa pa'am akhat
at the jackpot time one

I actually won that hand by drawing a third king. Still, at the end of the night, I returned home with less money in my wallet. I never win at poker.

בעצם זכיתי ביד הזאת בכך ששלפתי מלך שלישי. ועדיין, בסוף
be'etsem zakhiti bayad hazot bekhakh sheshalafti melekh shlishi va'ada'in besof
actually I won at hand the that by drawing king third and still at end of

הערב, חזרתי הביתה עם פחות כסף בארנקי. אני אף פעם לא
ha'erev khazarti habaita im pakhot kesef be'arnaki ani af pa'am lo
the evening I returned homeward with less money in my wallet I never no

מנצח בפוקר.
menatse'akh bepoker
I win in poker

5

Two weeks later ...

כעבור שבועיים ...
ka'avor shvu'a'im
after two weeks

"You know that Edna cut the flowers in the parking lot."

"אתה יודע שעדנה גזרה את הפרחים במגרש החנייה."
ata yode'a she'edna gazra et haprakhim bemigrash hakhanaya
you you know that Edna she cut D.O. the flowers in the lot of the parking

I was listening to Maggie, the director of the retirement community, complain about my mother.

הקשבתי למגי, מנהלת כפר הגמלאים, מתלוננת על אמי.
hikshavti lemagi menahelet kfar hagimla'im mitlonenet al imi
I listened to Maggie manager of village of the pensioners she complains about my mother

"How could she do that?" I asked. "Mom can't bend over without falling on her face. Anyway, she says she wasn't there."

"איך היא יכלה לעשות זאת?" שאלתי. "אמא לא יכולה להתכופף
eikh hi yakhla la'asot zot sha'alti ima lo yekhola lehitkofef
how she she was able to do that I asked mom no she can to bend over

מבלי ליפול על הפנים. בכל אופן, היא אומרת שלא הייתה שם."
mibli lipol al hapanim bekhol ofen hi omeret shelo haita sham
without to fall on the face anyway she she says that no she was there

148

היא הסתדרה איכשהו. יש שמונה עדים. הם בדיוק יצאו
hi histadra eikhshehu. yesh shmona edim. hem bediyuk yatsu
she she managed somehow. there are eight witnesses. they just they came out

ממשחק הבינגו השבועי כשהיא הניחה את הפרחים בתוך קופסת
mimiskhak habingo hashvu'i kshehi henikha et haprakhim betokh kufsat
from game of the bingo the weekly as she she placed D.O. the flowers in box of

קרטון. לפחות היא גזרה רק את הפרחים ליד שפת המדרכה."
karton. lefakhot hi gazra rak et haprakhim leyad sfat hamidrakha.
cardboard at least she she cut only D.O. the flowers next to curb of the sidewalk

"She managed somehow. There are eight witnesses. They were just coming out of the weekly Bingo game as she was putting the flowers into a cardboard box. At least she cut only the flowers right next to the curb."

"לא נוכל להעמיד פנים שהיא עזרה למועדון הגינון
lo nukhal leha'amid panim shehi azra lemo'adon haginun
no we will be able to pretend that she she helped to club of the gardening

בגיזום כמה צמחים?" שאלתי.
begizum kama tsmakhim? sha'alti.
with pruning a few plants I asked

"Can't we pretend she was helping the garden club by pruning some of the plants?" I asked.

"אני לא חושבת שמועדון הגינון יתמוך בתירוץ כזה. הנשיאה
ani lo khoshevet shemo'adon haginun yitmokh beteiruts kaze. hanesi'a
I not I think that club of the gardening it will support with excuse like that the president

שלהם התעלפה כשראתה את הנזק הבוקר. היינו צריכים להזמין
shelahem hitalfa kshera'ata et hanezek haboker. ha'inu tsrikhim lehazmin
their she fainted when she saw D.O. the damage this morning we had to to order

אמבולנס."
ambulans.
ambulance

"I don't think the garden club is going to support that excuse. Their president fainted when she saw the damage this morning. We had to call an ambulance."

"לפחות הדירה של אמא מקושטת יפה. את צריכה לראות את
lefakhot hadira shel ima mekushetet yafe. at tsrikha lirot et
at least the apartment of mom it is decorated nicely you you should to see D.O.

סידור הפרחים שהיא הכינה," אמרתי.
sidur haprakhim shehi hekhina, amarti.
arrangement of the flowers that she she made I said

"At least mom's apartment is decorated nicely. You should see the floral arrangements she made," I said.

"לעדנה גם הייתה תאונה במטבח בשבוע שעבר," המשיכה מגי.
le'edna gam haita te'una bamitbakh bashavu'a she'avar, himshikha magi.
Edna also had accident in the kitchen in the week that (it) passed she continued Maggie

"Edna also had an accident in the kitchen last week," Maggie continued.

"היא רק שכחה לכבות את האש מתחת למחבת. אני באמת
hi rak shakhekha lekhabot et ha'esh mitakhat lamakhvat. ani be'emet
she just she forgot to turn off D.O. the fire under to the frying pan I really

מצטער על כך שמכבי האש הגיעו."
mitsta'er al kakh shemekhabei ha'esh higi'u.
I am sorry about it that the fire department they arrived

"She just forgot to turn the fire off under her frying pan. I'm really sorry about the fire department showing up."

"היא נעשית סכנה לקהילה," אמרה מגי.
hi na'aseit sakana lakehila, amra magi.
she she becomes danger to the community she said Maggie

"She's becoming a danger to the community," Maggie said.

"Nobody was hurt. Please give mom another chance."

אף אחד לא נפגע. בבקשה תני לאמא הזדמנות נוספת."
nosefet hizdamnut le'ima tni bevakasha nifga lo af ekhad
another chance to mom give please he was injured no nobody

She sighed and rubbed her forehead. It must be tough running a place filled with old people.

היא נאנחה ושפשפה את מצחה. זו בוודאי משימה קשה לנהל
lenahel kasha mesima bevadai zo mitskha et veshifshefa ne'enkha hi
to manage tough task certainly this her forehead D.O. and she rubbed she sighed she

מקום מלא קשישים.
kshishim male makom
old people full place

"OK, Mr. Levi. But I insist that your mother stop cooking. She can have dinner in our main dining room every night. It only costs twenty-five shekels, and the food is very good."

"או קיי, מר לוי. אבל אני מתעקשת שאמך תפסיק לבשל. היא
hi levashel tafsik she'imkha mitakeshet ani aval levi mar o kei
she to cook she will stop that your mother I insist I but Levi mister okay

יכולה לאכול בחדר האוכל הראשי שלנו בכל ערב. זה עולה רק
rak ole ze erev bekhol shelanu harashi bakhadar ha'okhel le'ekhol yekhola
only it costs this evening in every our the main in the dining room to eat she can

עשרים וחמישה שקלים והאוכל מצוין."
metsuyan veha'okhel shkalim vakhamisha esrim
excellent and the food shekels and five twenty

"No more cooking or cutting flowers," I promised.

"לא עוד בישולים או קטיפת פרחים", הבטחתי.
hivtakhti prakhim ktifat o bishulim od lo
I promised flowers picking of or cooking more no

— 6 —

I headed to mom's apartment and told her about my meeting with Maggie.

שמתי פעמיי אל דירתה של אמא וסיפרתי לה על פגישתי עם
im pgishati al la vesiparti ima shel dirata el samti pe'amai
with my meeting about to her and I told mom of her apartment to I headed

מגי.
magi
Maggie

"She doesn't like me," Mom said. "Ever since I whacked her puppy with Rachel's cane."

"היא אינה מחבבת אותי", אמרה אמא. "מאז שהחטפתי לכלבלב
laklavlav shehekhtafti me'az ima amra oti mekhabevet eina hi
to the puppy that I whacked ever since mom she said me she likes she does not she

שלה עם המקל של רחל."
rakhel shel hamakel im shela
Rachel of the cane with her

"Please don't tell me that you hurt her cute little dog," I said.

"בבקשה אל תגידי לי שפגעת בכלב הקטן והחמוד שלה",
shela vehekhamud hakatan bakelev shepagat li tagidi al bevakasha
her and the cute the little at the dog that you hurt to me you will tell don't please

אמרתי.
amarti
I said

"I just wanted it to stop yapping. It was a love tap."

"רק רציתי להפסיק את הנביחות. החטפתי לו מאהבה."
me'ahava lo hekhtafti hanevikhot et lehafsik ratsiti rak
out of love to him I whacked the barking D.O. to stop I wanted just

"הִיא רָאֲתָה אוֹתְךָ עוֹשָׂה זֹאת?"
zot osa otakh ra'ata hi
this you do you she saw she

"Did she see you do it?"

"לֹא, הֶאֱשַׁמְתִּי אֶת רָחֵל. זֶה הַמַּקֵּל שֶׁלָּהּ."
shela hamakel ze rakhel et he'eshamti lo
her the cane this Rachel D.O. I blamed no

"No. I blamed Rachel. It's her cane."

"אָז הִכְנַסְתָּ אֶת רָחֵל לְצָרָה."
letsara rakhel et hikhnast az
to trouble Rachel D.O. you got into so

"So you got Rachel in trouble."

"מָגִי לֹא הֶאֱמִינָה לִי. הִיא אָמְרָה שֶׁרָחֵל חַלָּשָׁה מִכְּדֵי לְהָנִיף אֶת
et lehanif mikhdei khalasha sherakhel amra hi li he'emina lo magi
D.O. to swing too weak that Rachel she said she to me she believed no maggie

הַמַּקֵּל. הָיָה לָנוּ וִיכּוּחַ גָּדוֹל."
gadol viku'akh haya lanu hamakel
big argument we had the cane

"Maggie didn't believe me. She said Rachel is too weak to swing her cane. We had a big argument."

"בּוֹאִי נִשְׁכַּח אֶת רָחֵל וְהַכֶּלֶב. הִבְטַחְתִּי לְמָגִי שֶׁתֹּאכְלִי אֶת
et shetokhli lemagi hivtakhti vehakelev rakhel et nishkakh bo'i
D.O. that you will eat to Maggie I promised and the dog Rachel D.O. we will forget let's

אֲרוּחַת הָעֶרֶב בַּחֶדֶר הָאֹכֶל כָּל עֶרֶב. זֶה אוֹמֵר שֶׁאֵין יוֹתֵר
yoter she'ein omer ze erev kol ha'okhel bakhadar arukhat ha'erev
more that there isn't it means it evening every the dining in the room of the dinner

בִּשּׁוּלִים. אָסוּר גַּם לִקְטוֹף פְּרָחִים אוֹ שִׂיחִים. אֵין גְּדִיעַת עֵצִים."
etsim gdi'at ein sikhim o prakhim liktof gam asur bishulim
trees chopping of there isn't bushes or flowers to pick also forbidden cooking

"Let's forget Rachel and the dog. I promised Maggie you would eat dinner at the hall each night. That means no more cooking. No cutting up the flowers or the bushes either. No chopping down trees."

"אַל תִּהְיֶה כָּזֶה טִיפֵּשׁ. אֵין לִי בִּכְלָל גַּרְזֶן. הֵי, אֲנִי לֹא יְכוֹלָה
yekhola lo ani hei garzen bikhlal ein li tipesh kaze tihiye al
I can no I hey axe at all I don't have silly such you will be don't

לְהַרְשׁוֹת לְעַצְמִי אֲרוּחָה בְּעֶשְׂרִים וַחֲמִשָּׁה שְׁקָלִים כָּל עֶרֶב. אֲנִי עֲנִיָּה."
aniya ani erev kol shkalim vakhamisha be'esrim arukha leharshot le'atsmi
poor I evening every shekels and five for twenty meal to afford

"Don't be so silly. I don't even own an axe. Hey, I can't afford twenty-five shekels every night for dinner. I'm poor."

בַּחֲמֵשׁ הַדַּקּוֹת הַבָּאוֹת נִהַלְנוּ וִיכּוּחַ סוֹעֵר. אִמָּא הִסְכִּימָה לְבַסּוֹף
levasof hiskima ima so'er viku'akh nihalnu haba'ot hadakot bekhamesh
eventually she agreed mom heated discussion we conducted next the minutes for five

לַתְּנָאִיָּה שֶׁל מָגִי, אֲבָל הָיִיתִי צָרִיךְ לְהַבְטִיחַ לְשַׁלֵּם עֲבוּר אֲרוּחוֹתֶיהָ
arukhoteiha avur leshalem lehavti'akh ha'iti tsarikh aval magi shel litna'eiha
her meals for to pay to promise I had to but Maggie of to her terms

בַּחֶדֶר הָאֹכֶל. הָעֻבְדָּה שֶׁלֹּא הָיִיתִי צָרִיךְ לִדְאוֹג שֶׁאִמָּא תִּשְׂרוֹף אֶת
et tisrof she'ima lidog ha'iti tsarikh shelo ha'uvda bakhadar ha'okhel
D.O. she will burn that mom to worry I had to that no the fact in the dining room

בִּנְיַן הַדִּירוֹת שֶׁבּוֹ הִתְגּוֹרְרָה הָיְתָה שָׁוָה עֶשְׂרִים וַחֲמִשָּׁה שְׁקָלִים
shkalim esrim vakhamisha shava haita hitgorera shebo hadirot binyan
shekels twenty five worth it was she lived that in it the apartments building of

We had a heated discussion for the next five minutes. Mom eventually agreed to Maggie's terms, but I had to promise to pay for her meals at the hall. It was worth twenty-five shekels a night so I didn't have to worry about mom burning down her apartment building.

151

לערב.
le'erev
per evening

Mom looked at a list that was sitting on her kitchen table. She frequently made lists of things to complain about.

אמא הביטה ברשימה שהייתה מונחת על שולחן המטבח שלה.
ima *hibita* *bareshima* *shehaita* *munakhat* *al* *shulkhan* *hamitbakh* *shela*
mom she looked at list that (it) was placed on table of the kitchen her

לעתים קרובות הכינה רשימת תלונות.
le'itim krovot *hekhina* *reshimat* *tlunot*
often she prepared list of complaints

"You never take me anyplace."

"אתה אף פעם לא לוקח אותי לשום מקום."
ata *af pa'am* *lo* *loke'akh* *oti* *leshum* *makom*
you never no you take me to any place

I thought for a minute.

חשבתי לרגע.
khashavti *lerega*
I thought for a moment

"Why don't we go to the movies?"

"מדוע איננו הולכים לקולנוע?"
madu'a *einenu* *holkhim* *lakolno'a*
why we don't we go to the movie theater

"That last movie we went to was disgusting. You should be ashamed of yourself."

"הסרט האחרון שהלכנו אליו היה מגעיל. אתה צריך להתבייש
haseret *ha'akharon* *shehalakhnu* *elav* *haya* *magil* *ata* *tsarikh* *lehitbayesh*
the movie the last that we went to it it was disgusting you you should to be ashamed

בעצמך."
be'atsmekha
of yourself

"It's not my fault they say bad words in movies," I answered.

"זו אינה אשמתי שיש מילים גסות בסרטים," עניתי.
zo *eina* *ashmati* *sheyesh* *milim* *gasot* *bisratim* *aniti*
this it is not my fault that there are words bad in movies I answered

"Let's go to the park. We can sit on a bench and watch the birds."

"בואי נלך לפארק. נוכל לשבת על ספסל ולצפות בציפורים."
bo'i *nelekh* *lapark* *nukhal* *lashevet* *al* *safsal* *velitspot* *batsiporim*
let's we will go to the park we will be able to sit on bench and to watch at the birds

"Okay, that sounds good."

"בסדר, זה נשמע טוב."
beseder *ze* *nishma* *tov*
okay that it sounds good

It took her ten minutes to get ready, have a couple sips of water, and use the bathroom just in case. We drove to a local park. It wasn't a long walk from the parking lot to a bench that was shaded by trees. Mom needed to hold on to me the whole time.

לקח לה עשר דקות להתכונן, ללגום שתי לגימות מים, ולהיכנס
lakakh *la* *eser* *dakot* *lehitkonen* *lilgom* *shtei* *legimot* *ma'im* *ulehikanes*
it took for her ten minutes to prepare herself to sip two of sips of water and to go into

לשירותים שיהיה על כל מקרה. נסענו לפארק מקומי. מרחק
lasherutim *she'ihiye* *al kol mikre* *nasanu* *lepark* *mekomi* *merkhak*
to the bathroom that (it) will be just in case we drove to a park local distance of

ההליכה ממגרש החנייה עד לספסל שהיה מוצל על ידי עצים לא
hahalikha *mimigrash hakhanaya* *ad* *lesafsal* *shehaya* *mutsal* *al yedei* *etsim* *lo*
the walk from the parking lot to to bench that (it) was shaded by trees no

היה גדול. אמא היתה צריכה להחזיק בי לכל אורך הדרך.
lekhol orekh haderekh — *lehakhzik bi* — *haita tsrikha* — *ima* — *gadol* — *haya*
for the whole way — to hold on to me — she had to — mom — long — it was

מהספסל יכולנו לראות אגם קטן. לצד האגם היה ממוקם
memukam — *haya* — *ha'agam* — *letsad* — *katan* — *agam* — *lirot* — *yakholnu* — *mehasafsal*
located — it was — the pond — next to — little — pond — to see — we were able — from the bench

מגרש משחקים. ילד קטן רדף אחרי ברווזים ליד המים.
hama'im — *leyad* — *barvazim* — *akharei* — *radaf* — *katan* — *yeled* — *migrash miskhakim*
the water — near — ducks — after — he chased — little — kid — playground

We could see a little pond from the bench. Next to the pond was a playground. A little kid was chasing ducks near the water.

"זה נחמד," אמרתי.
amarti — *nekhmad* — *ze*
I said — nice — this

"This is nice," I said.

"למי אכפת מברווזים?" אמרה אמא. "הביטוח הרפואי שלי לא שילם
shilem — *lo* — *sheli* — *harefu'i* — *habitu'akh* — *ima* — *amra* — *mibarvazim* — *lemi ikhpat*
it paid — no — my — the medical — the insurance — mom — she said — about ducks — who cares

עבור הביקור האחרון שלי אצל הרופא."
harofe — *etsel* — *sheli* — *ha'akharon* — *habikur* — *avur*
the doctor — at — my — the last — the visit — for

"Who cares about ducks?" Mom said. "My health insurance hasn't paid for my last doctor visit."

נאנחתי. "דיברנו על זה מספר פעמים," הזכרתי לה. "הביטוח הרפואי
harefu'i — *habitu'akh* — *la* — *hizkarti* — *pe'amim* — *mispar* — *ze* — *al* — *dibarnu* — *ne'enakhti*
the medical — the insurance — to her — I reminded — times — a few — this — about — we talked — I sighed

שלך שלח לך הצהרה שאומרת כי דמי הביקור נכללים
nikhlalim — *habikur* — *dmei* — *ki* — *she'omeret* — *hats'hara* — *lakh* — *shalakh* — *shelakh*
they are included — the visit — fees of — that — that (it) says — statement — to you — it sent — your

בהשתתפות העצמית."
bahishtatfut ha'atsmit
in the deductible

I sighed. "We talked about this a few times," I reminded her. "Your insurance sent you a statement that said the cost of the visit was applied to your deductible."

"מה זה השתתפות עצמית?"
hishtatfut atsmit — *ze* — *ma*
deductible — this — what

"What's a deductible?"

"הסברתי לך שלוש פעמים על השתתפות עצמית. מדוע אינך
einekh — *madu'a* — *hishtatfut atsmit* — *al* — *pe'amim* — *shalosh* — *lakh* — *hisbarti*
you do not — why — deductible — about — times — three — to you — I explained

כותבת את זה?"
ze — *et* — *kotevet*
this — D.O. — you write

"I've told you three times about deductibles. Why don't you write it down?"

"מעולם לא דיברת איתי על השתתפות עצמית. מה עם רופא
rofe — *ma im* — *hishtatfut atsmit* — *al* — *iti* — *dibarta* — *me'olam lo*
doctor of — what about — deductible — about — with me — you spoke — never

העיניים שלי? הוא שלח לי חשבון על תשעים וחמישה שקלים.
shkalim — *vakhamisha* — *tishim* — *al* — *kheshbon* — *li* — *shalakh* — *hu* — *sheli* — *ha'eina'im*
shekels — and five — ninety — for — bill — to me — he sent — he — my — the eyes

"You never told me about deductibles. What about my eye doctor? He just sent me a bill for ninety-five shekels. He's a thief."

153

הוא גנב."
hu ganav
he thief

"He gave you a complete checkup," I told her.

"הוא עשה לך בדיקה כללית מקיפה," אמרתי לה.
hu asa lakh bdika klalit makifa, amarti la
he he did for you checkup general comprehensive I said to her

"Some young girl did everything. She's probably just a nurse. I'm not paying."

"איזו בחורה צעירה עשתה הכל. היא כנראה רק אחות. אני לא
eizo bakhura tse'ira asta hakol. hi kanire rak akhot. ani lo
some girl young she did everything she probably just nurse I no

משלמת."
meshalemet
I pay

"Odelia told me he did most of the work and the girl took notes," I said.

"אודליה אמרה לי שהוא עשה את רוב העבודה והבחורה רק רשמה
odelya amra li shehu asa et rov ha'avoda vehabakhura rak rashma
Odelia she told to me that he he did D.O. most the work and the girl only she wrote

הערות," אמרתי.
he'arot, amarti
notes I said

"The doctor was eating a bagel. He just watched. I'll sue him."

"הרופא אכל בייגל'ה. הוא רק הסתכל. אני אתבע אותו."
harofe akhal beigale. hu rak histakel. ani etba oto
the doctor he ate bagel he just he watched I I will sue him

My eye started to twitch. Heat started rising to my face. I took a few deep breaths. Miraculously, I was able to calm myself, even though she kept complaining about her doctors. After ten minutes she ran out of things to complain about.

העין שלי התחילה לרעוד. חום החל להציף את פניי. לקחתי מספר
ha'ain sheli hitkhila lirod. khom hekhel lehatsif et panai. lakakhti mispar
the eye my it started to twitch heat it began to flood D.O. my face I took a few

נשימות עמוקות. באורח נס הצלחתי להרגיע את עצמי, למרות שהיא
neshimot amukot. be'orakh nes hitslakhti lehargi'a et atsmi, lamrot shehi
breaths deep miraculously I succeeded to calm D.O. myself even though that she

המשיכה להתלונן על רופאיה. אחרי עשר דקות נגמרו לה הנושאים
himshikha lehitlonen al rofeiha. akharei eser dakot nigmeru la hanosim
she continued to complain about her doctors after ten minutes she ran out of the topics

להתלונן עליהם.
lehitlonen aleihem
to complain about them

We spent another hour sitting on the bench, enjoying the sun and talking about life.

בילינו עוד שעה בישיבה על הספסל, נהנים מהשמש ומשוחחים
bilinu od sha'a biyshiva al hasafsal, nehenim mehashemesh umesokhakhim
we spent another hour by sitting on the bench we enjoy of the sun and we talk

על החיים.
al hakhayim
about the life

7

"הייתי ילד טוב, אז למה אמא שלי מנסה כל כך לאמלל אותי?"
oti — le'amlel — kol kakh — menasa — sheli — ima — lama — az — tov — yeled — ha'iti
me — to make miserable — so — she tries — my — mom — why — so — good — child — I was

"I was a good child, so why is my mother trying so hard to make me miserable?"

"היא איננה זוכרת איזה ילד נהדר היית," אמר ד"ר רוזנברג.
rozenberg — doktor — amar — ha'ita — nehedar — yeled — eize — zokheret — einena — hi
Rosenberg — doctor — he said — you were — wonderful — child — what — she remembers — she does not — she

"She doesn't remember what a wonderful child you were," Dr. Rosenberg said.

ד"ר רוזנברג הוא הפסיכיאטר שלי. אני נפגש איתו כל שבוע. הוא
hu — shavu'a — kol — ito — nifgash — ani — sheli — hapsikhiyater — hu — rozenberg — doktor
he — week — every — with him — I meet — I — my — the psychiatrist — he — Rosenberg — doctor

עוזר לי להתמודד עם הבעיות שיש לי עם אמי.
imi — im — sheyesh li — habe'ayot — im — lehitmoded — li — ozer
my mother — with — that I have — the problems — with — to deal — to me — he helps

Dr. Rosenberg is my psychiatrist. I meet with him every week. He's been helping me deal with the problems I have with my mother.

"לפחות לא השלכתי אותה לאגם," אמרתי.
amarti — la'agam — ota — hishlakhti — lo — lefakhot
I said — into the pond — her — I threw — no — at least

"At least I didn't throw her into the pond," I said.

"זה מוכיח שאתה ילד נהדר," הוא אמר.
amar — hu — nehedar — yeled — she'ata — mokhi'akh — ze
he said — he — wonderful — child — that you — it proves — that

"That proves you are a wonderful child," he said.

"היא סתם אשה מרושעת, נכון?".
nakhon — merusha'at — isha — stam — hi
right — mean — woman — just — she

"She's just a mean person, isn't she?"

"כבר עברנו על זה. היא איננה מאושרת בחייה והיא מוציאה
motsi'a — vehi — bekhayeiha — me'usheret — einena — hi — ze — al — avarnu — kvar
she takes out — and she — with her life — happy — she is not — she — this — about — we went over — already

את זה על כל מי שמתקרב אליה."
eleiha — shemitkarev — mi — kol — al — ze — et
to her — who comes near — who — all — on — this — D.O.

"We've gone over this before. She's unhappy with her life and takes it out on anyone who comes near her."

"היא לעולם לא תשתנה," אמרתי.
amarti — tishtane — le'olam lo — hi
I said — she will change — never — she

"She'll never change," I said.

"זו הסיבה שאתה לומד להתמודד איתה."
ita — lehitmoded — lomed — she'ata — hasiba — zo
with her — to cope — you learn — that you — the reason — this

"This is why you are learning how to cope with her."

"היא עדיין משגעת אותי."
oti — meshaga'at — ada'in — hi
me — she drives crazy — still — she

"She still drives me crazy."

"כן, אבל אתה מתמודד טוב יותר. לפני שנה לא יכולת לישון
lishon — yakholta — lo — shana — lifnei — yoter — tov — mitmoded — ata — aval — ken
to sleep — you were able — no — year — ago — more — good — you handle — you — but — yes

בלילה אחרי ביקור אצלה. אתמול קיבלת את כל הצער שהסבה
sheheseva — hatsa'ar — kol — et — kibalta — etmol — etsla — bikur — akharei — balaila
that she caused — the grief — all — D.O. — you took — yesterday — at her place — visit — after — at the night

"Yes, but you are handling it better. A year ago you couldn't sleep at night after you visited her. Yesterday you took all of the grief she gave you without pulling your hair out. Afterwards, you had a pleasant time with her. That shows major progress."

לך בלי שמרטת את שערותיך. אחר כך בילית איתה
lekha *bli* *shemarateta* *et* *sei'aroteikha*. *akhar kakh* *bilita* *ita*
to you — without — that you pulled out — D.O. — your hairs — afterwards — you had a good time — with her

זמן בנעימים. זה מראה על התקדמות ניכרת."
zman *bane'imim*. *ze* *mare* *al* *hitkadmut* *nikeret*
time — pleasantly — this — it shows — about — progress — substantial

"Yeah, we had a pretty nice time after she stopped complaining to me about doctors."

"כן, נהנינו למדי אחרי שהפסיקה לבכות לי על ענייני
ken, *neheneinu* *lemadai* *akharei* *shehifsika* *livkot* *li* *al* *inyanei*
yes — we had fun — quite — after — that she stopped — to complain — to me — about — matters of

רופאים."
rofim
doctors

"What did you talk about?"

"על מה דיברתם?"
al *ma* *dibartem*
about — what — you talked

"Nice things. The size and shape of her bowel movements that morning. The excess mucus that builds up in her nose. The lady next door who goes to the free weekly lunches at her retirement community and shovels as much extra food as possible into her purse."

"על דברים נחמדים. על הגודל והצורה של היציאה שלה
al *dvarim* *nekhmadim*. *al* *hagodel* *vehatsura* *shel* *hayetsi'a* *shela*
about — things — nice — about — the size — and the shape — of — the bowel movement — her

באותו בוקר. עודפי הליחה המצטברים באפה. השכנה ממול
be'oto *boker*. *odfei* *haleikha* *hamitstabrim* *be'apa*. *hashkhena* *mimul*
at same — morning — excess of — the mucus — that accumulate — in her nose — the neighbor — next door

שהולכת לארוחת הצהריים השבועית המוגשת בחינם בכפר
sheholekhet *le'arukhat* *hatsohora'im* *hashvu'it* *hamugeshet* *bekhinam* *bikhfar*
who goes — to meal of — the noon — the weekly — that is served — free of charge — in village of

הגמלאים שלה ודוחפת לתיקה כמה שיותר אוכל."
hagimla'im *shela* *vedokhefet* *letika* *kama sheyoter* *okhel*
the pensioners — her — and she shoves — into her purse — as much as — food

"Wasn't that fun?" said Dr. Rosenberg.

"זה לא היה משעשע?" אמר ד"ר רוזנברג.
ze *lo* *haya* *mesha'ashe'a*? *amar* *doktor* *rozenberg*
this — no — it was — amusing — he said — doctor — Rosenberg

———8———

"You're making progress because you didn't strangle your mother at the park and didn't get drunk when you came home?" Gilat asked.

"אתה מתקדם בטיפול מכיוון שלא חנקת את אמך
ata *mitkadem* *batipul* *mikeivan* *shelo* *khanakta* *et* *imkha*
you — you make progress — with the treatment — because — that no — you strangled — D.O. — your mother

בפארק ולא השתכרת כשחזרת הביתה?" שאלה גילת.
bapark *velo* *hishtakarta* *kshekhazarta* *habaita*? *sha'ala* *gilat*
at the park — and no — you got drunk — when you returned — homeward — she asked — Gilat

"That's what Dr. Rosenberg said."

"זה מה שד"ר רוזנברג אמר."
ze *ma* *shedoktor* *rozenberg* *amar*
that — what — that doctor — Rosenberg — he said

"This is a cause for celebration. Let's invite your mom over for dinner."

"זו סיבה לחגוג. בוא נזמין את אמא שלך לארוחת ערב."
zo *siba* *lakhgog*. *bo* *nazmin* *et* *ima* *shelkha* *le'arukhat erev*
this — reason — to celebrate — let's — we will invite — D.O. — mom — your — for dinner

"לא הלילה."
halaila lo
tonight not

"Not tonight."

"היא יודעת שאתה נפגש עם פסיכיאטר מכיוון שהיא כה מרושעת
hi yoda'at she'ata nifgash im psikhiyater mikeivan shehi ko merusha'at
she she knows that you you meet with psychiatrist because that she so malicious
אליך?"
eleikha
towards you

"Does she know that you are seeing a psychiatrist because she's so malicious toward you?"

"איזו טובה תצמח מכך שאספר לה? היא חושבת שהיא נחמדה
eizo tova titsmakh mikakh she'asaper la hi khoshevet shehi nekhmada
what good it will develop from it that I will tell to her she she thinks that she nice
לכולם."
lekhulam
to everyone

"What good would it do to tell her? She thinks she's nice to everyone."

"אז מה אתה מתכוון לעשות?"
az ma ata mitkaven la'asot
so what you you intend to do

"So what are you going to do?"

"מה שעשיתי עד עכשיו. אבלה איתה זמן, אקשיב לתלונותיה,
ma she'asiti ad akhshav avale ita zman akshiv litlunoteiha
what that I did until now I will spend time with her time I will listen to her complaints
אנסה לשפר מעט את חייה האומללים, ואתגבר על הדחף
anase leshaper me'at et khayeiha ha'umlalim ve'etgaber al hadakhaf
I will try to improve a little D.O. her life the miserable and I will resist on the urge
לקבור אותה בחיים."
likbor ota bakhayim
to bury her alive

"What I've been doing. Spend time with her, listen to her complaints, try to make her unhappy life a little better, resist the urge to bury her alive."

"אתה עדיין זקוק לפגישות עם הפסיכיאטר?"
ata ada'in zakuk lapgishot im hapsikhiyater
you still in need of to the sessions with the psychiatrist

"Do you still need to see the psychiatrist?"

"כנראה שיהיה עלי לפגוש אותו כל שבוע עד מותה."
kanire she'ihiye alai lifgosh oto kol shavu'a ad mota
probably I will have to to meet him every week until her death

"I'll probably have to meet with him every week until she is dead."

"היא תחיה עוד עשרים שנה!"
hi tikhye od esrim shana
she she will live another twenty year

"She'll live for another twenty years!"

"אני מקווה. תוכלי לסבול אותי עד אז?" אמרתי.
ani mekave tukhli lisbol oti ad az amarti
I I hope will you be able to tolerate me until them I said

"I hope so. Can you tolerate me until then?" I said.

גילת התחלחלה.
gilat hitkhalkhela
Gilat she shuddered

Gilat shuddered.

Story 12

"I guess you're worth it," she said.

אני מניחה שאתה שווה את זה," אמרה."

ani	menikha	she'ata	shave	et	ze	amra
I	I guess	that you	worth	D.O.	this	she said

STORY 13

Evolution

"אני מאמין באלוהים, אבל אני לא חושב שהוא מעורב מדי בחיי
ani ma'amin be'elohim aval ani lo khoshev shehu me'orav midai bekhayei
I believe / in god / but / I / no / I think / that he / involved / too / in the lives of

היום יום שלנו. הוא ברא את העולם והתניע עניינים לפני כמה
hayom yom shelanu hu bara et ha'olam vehitni'a inyanim lifnei kama
the daily / our / he / he created / D.O. / the universe / and he started / matters / ago / a few

מיליארד שנים. ואז הוא נשען לאחור להתבונן."
milyard shanim ve'az hu nishan le'akhor lehitbonen
billion / years / and then / he / he leaned / backward / to watch

"I believe in God but I don't think he gets too involved in our daily lives. He created the universe and set things in motion a few billion years ago. And then he sat back to watch."

אני מהרהר מספר שניות, ואז ממשיך.
ani meharher mispar shniyot ve'az mamshikh
I / I ponder / a few / seconds / and then / I continue

I think for a few seconds and then continue.

"האבולוציה היא דרכו של אלוהים לשמור על הסדר בעולם.
ha'evolutsya hi darko shel elohim lishmor al haseder ba'olam
the evolution / it / his way / of / god / to maintain / about / the order / in the world

אם משהו מתחיל להשתבש, האבולוציה מוצאת תשובה. לפעמים זה
im mashehu matkhil lehishtabesh ha'evolutsya motset tshuva lifamim ze
if / something / it starts / to be disrupted / the evolution / it finds / answer / sometimes / this

לוקח מאה או שתיים, אבל בסופו של דבר האבולוציה מסייעת לעולם
loke'akh me'a o shta'im aval besofo shel davar ha'evolutsya mesaya'at la'olam
it takes / century / or / two / but / in the end / the evolution / it helps / to the world

לפתור את בעיותיו."
liftor et be'ayotav
to solve / D.O. / its problems

"Evolution is God's way of keeping order in the world. If something starts to go wrong, evolution finds an answer. Sometimes it takes a century or two, but eventually evolution helps the world solve its problems."

אני מביט בבחור שאתו אני משוחח. הוא לא נראה מתעניין.
ani mabit babakhur she'ito ani mesokhe'akh hu lo nire mitanyen
I / I look / at the guy / that with him / I / I talk with / he / no / he seems / he takes an interest

I look at the guy I am talking to. He doesn't seem interested.

"לפני מאות שנים," אני ממשיך, "אנשים דאגו מפני מוות ממגיפות.
lifnei me'ot shanim ani mamshikh anashim da'agu mipnei mavet mimagefot
ago / hundreds / years / I / I continue / people / they worried / from / death / from plague

עוד לפני כן, בני האדם לא עיכלו חלב של בעלי חיים. ואז
od lifnei khen bnei ha'adam lo iklu khalav shel ba'alei khayim ve'az
still / before that / the humans / no / they digested / milk / of / animals / and then

האבולוציה נכנסה לתמונה. הגנטיקה שלנו השתנתה צעד אחר צעד.
ha'evolutsya nikhnesa latmuna hagenetika shelanu hishtanta tsa'ad akhar tsa'ad
the evolution / it entered / to the picture / the genetics / our / it changed / bit by bit

"Centuries ago," I continue, "people worried about dying from plague. Even longer ago, humans couldn't digest animals milk. Then evolution stepped into the picture. Our genetics changed bit by bit. In addition, new technologies have boosted our evolutionary response. Eventually, we will be more resistant to diseases that are killing us today. These are great examples of how evolution creates solutions to problems."

בנוסף, טכנולוגיות חדשות המריצו את התגובה האבולוציונית שלנו.
benosaf *tekhnologyot* *khadashot* *himritsu* *et* *hatguva* *ha'evulotsyonit* *shelanu*
in addition new technologies they boosted D.O. the response the evolutionary our

לימים אנחנו נפתח עמידות לרבות מהמחלות שקוטלות אותנו
leyamim *anakhnu* *nefate'akh* *amidut* *lerabot* *mehamakhalot* *shekotlot* *otanu*
eventually we we will develop resistance to many of the diseases that they kill us

היום. אלו הן דוגמאות מצוינות לאופן שבו אבולוציה יוצרת
hayom *elu* *hen* *dugma'ot* *metsuyanot* *la'ofen* *shebo* *evolutsya* *yotseret*
today these they examples excellent to the way that in it evolution it creates

פתרונות לבעיות."
pitronot *live'ayot*
solutions to problems

The man is still unresponsive.

האיש עדיין איננו מגיב.
ha'ish *ada'in* *eineno* *megiv*
the man still he is not he responds

"I know what you are thinking," I tell him. "Deadly diseases are not a good example, because now humans are dying of AIDS, malaria, and cholera. But I am sure that evolution will figure out how to combat these diseases, too."

"אני יודע מה אתה חושב," אני אומר לו. "מחלות קטלניות אינן
ani *yode'a* *ma* *ata* *khoshev*, *ani* *omer* *lo*. "*makhalot* *katlaniyot* *einan*
I I know what you you think I say to him diseases deadly they are not

דוגמא טובה, מכיוון שבני אדם מתים בימינו מאיידס, מלריה, וכולרה.
dugma *tova*, *mikeivan* *shebnei adam* *metim* *beyameinu* *mi'eids*, *malarya* *vekholera*.
example good because that humans they die in our days from AIDS malaria and cholera

אבל אני בטוח שהאבולוציה תמצא תשובה איך להילחם גם במחלות
aval *ani* *batu'akh* *sheha'evolutsya* *timtsa* *tshuva* *eikh* *lehilakhem* *gam* *bamakhalot*
but I sure that the evolution it will find answer how to combat also at the diseases

הללו."
halalu
these

I pull a bottle of water out of my jacket pocket and take a few sips.

אני שולף בקבוק מים מכיס המעיל ולוגם לגימות אחדות.
ani *sholef* *bakbuk* *ma'im* *mikis* *hame'il* *velogem* *legimot* *akhadot*.
I I pull out bottle of water from the pocket of the coat and I sip sips a few

"Here's another example of evolution solving a problem," I say to the man. "You are a parasite who causes misery and suffering for other people. Evolution developed a cure. That would be me!"

"הנה דוגמה נוספת לפתרון בעיה על ידי האבולוציה," אני אומר
hine *dugma* *nosefet* *lefitron* *be'aya* *al yedei* *ha'evolutsya*," *ani* *omer*
here example additional to solution of problem by the evolution I I say

לאיש. "אתה טפיל הגורם מצוקה וסבל לאנשים אחרים.
la'ish. "*ata* *tapil* *hagorem* *metsuka* *vesevel* *le'anashim* *akherim*.
to the man you parasite that (it) causes trouble and suffering for people other

האבולוציה פיתחה מרפא. זה אני!"
ha'evolutsya *pitkha* *marpe* *ze* *ani*!"
the evolution it developed cure that I

I realize that I'm wasting my time. After all, this guy doesn't care about my theory of the universe. He's got three bullet holes in his heart!

אני מבין שאני מבזבז את זמני. אחרי הכל, לבחור לא אכפת
ani *mevin* *she'ani* *mevazbez* *et* *zmani*. *akharei hakol*, *labakhur lo ikhpat*
I I understand that I I waste D.O. my time after all the guy doesn't care

מהתאוריה שלי על אודות היקום. יש לו שלושה נקבי כדורים
mehate'orya *sheli* *al odot* *hayekum*. *yesh lo* *shlosha* *nikvei* *kadurim*
about the theory my about the universe he has three holes of bullets

Evolution

בלבו !
belibo
in his heart

— 2 —

ימים אחדים קודם לכן ...
yamim akhadim kodem lakhen
days a few previously

A few days earlier ...

אני נשען לאחור בכיסא המסתובב ומביט החוצה מחלון
ani nishan le'akhor bakise hamistovev umabit hakhutsa mikhalon
I lean backward in the chair the revolving and I look outside from the window of

המשרד. זהו בוקר סתווי יפה. הכל שלו ורגוע.
hamisrad. zehu boker stavi yafe. hakol shalev veragu'a.
the office this is morning autumnal beautiful everything peaceful and quiet

I lean back in my swivel chair and look out of the office window. It's a pretty autumn morning. Everything is peaceful and quiet.

ואז אני שומע פסיעות כבדות במסדרון. הדלת נפתחת וגבר גדול
ve'az ani shome'a psiyot kvedot bamisderon. hadelet niftakhat vegever gadol
and then I I hear steps heavy in the corridor the door it is opened and man large

בעל מבנה מרובע פוסע פנימה. הוא מביט בי כאילו הייתי צורת
ba'al mivne meruba pose'a pnima. hu mabit bi ke'ilu ha'iti tsurat
owner of shape of square he walks inside he looks at me like I was form of

חיים נחותה שהוא עומד לבצע בה ניתוח מחקרי.
khayim nekhuta shehu omed levatse'a ba nitu'akh mekhkari.
life lower that he he is about to to perform on it dissection of research

Then I hear heavy footsteps in the hall. The door opens and a large, square man walks in. He looks at me like I am a lower life form that he is about to dissect.

"תרצה להגיש בקשה לפוליסת ביטוח חיים?" אני שואל אותו.
tirtse lehagish bakasha lepolisat bitu'akh khayim?" ani sho'el oto.
you will want to submit request for policy of insurance of life I ask him

"אם אתה בריא ואינך מעשן תוכל לקבל כיסוי של מיליון
"im ata bari ve'einkha me'ashen tukhal lekabel kisui shel milyon
if you healthy and you are not smoker you could to receive coverage of million

שקלים לפחות. אני יכול להשיג לך פרמיות מצוינות."
shkalim lefakhot. ani yakhol lehasig lekha premyot metsuyanot."
shekels at least I I can to obtain for you premiums excellent

"Would you like to apply for a life insurance policy?" I ask him. "If you are in good health and don't smoke you can qualify for at least a million shekels in coverage. I can get you great rates."

מבטו נודד מהרהיטים היקרים שלי לתמונות המהודרות שעל
mabato noded meharahitim hayekarim sheli latmunot hamehudarot she'al
his gaze it wanders from the furnishings the expensive my to the pictures the fancy that on

הקיר.
hakir.
the wall

His gaze wanders from my expensive furniture to the fancy pictures on the wall.

"משרד נחמד," הוא אומר.
misrad nekhmad," hu omer.
office nice he he says

"Nice office," he says.

"נכון. יש לי מכונת קפה חדשה. תרצה קפה נטול? מאיפה
"nakhon. yesh li mekhonat kafe khadasha. tirtse kafe natul? me'eifo
correct I have machine of coffee new you will want coffee lacking from where

"Yes it is. I have a new coffee maker. You want some decaf? Where did you get all those scars and that crooked

161

Story 13

nose? If you work in a hazardous profession, you have to disclose that on the application."

קיבלת את כל הצלקות האלה ואת האף המעוקם? אם אתה
kibalta et kol hatsalakot ha'ele ve'et ha'af hame'ukam? im ata
you received D.O. all the scars the those and D.O. the nose the crooked if you

עובד במקצוע מסוכן, אתה צריך להצהיר על כך בטופס הבקשה."
oved bemiktso'a mesukan, ata tsarikh lehats'hir al kakh batofes habakasha
you work in profession hazardous you need you to declare about it on the form the request

"Stop talking about life insurance," he says to me.

"תפסיק לדבר על ביטוח חיים," הוא אומר לי.
tafsik ledaber al bitu'akh khayim, hu omer li
stop to talk about insurance of life he he says to me

"I can't place the accent," I mention. "Russia? The Balkans, maybe?"

"אני לא מצליח לזהות את המבטא," אני מציין. "רוסיה? הבלקן
ani lo matsli'akh lezahot et hamivta, ani metsayen. rusya? habalkan
I no I succeed to identify D.O. the accent I mention Russia the Balkans

אולי?"
ulai
maybe

"I am from Ramat Gan."

"אני מרמת גן."
ani meramat gan
I from Ramat Gan

He puts his hand into his pocket, brings out a small picture, and puts it on my desk. I look at it and see a young woman, maybe twenty-four or twenty-five years old.

הוא מכניס את ידו לכיסו, מוציא תצלום קטן ומניח
hu makhnis et yado lekhiso, motsi tatslum katan umani'akh
he he inserts D.O. his hand to his pocket he takes out photograph small and he places

אותו על שולחני. אני מביט בתצלום, ורואה אישה צעירה, בת
oto al shulkhani. ani mabit batatslum, vero'e isha tse'ira, bat
it on my table I look at the photograph and I see woman young aged

עשרים וארבע או עשרים וחמש.
esrim ve'arba o esrim vekhamesh
twenty four or twenty five

"She is very pretty, your daughter, yes?" he asks.

"היא יפה מאוד, הבת שלך, נכון?" הוא שואל.
hi yafa me'od, habat shelkha, nakhon? hu sho'el
she pretty very the daughter your correct he he asks

I realize that this is a serious visit. We stare at each other for a few seconds.

אני מבין שזהו ביקור רציני. אנחנו בוהים זה בזה למשך
ani mevin shezehu bikur retsini. anakhnu bohim ze baze lemeshekh
I I understand that this is visit serious we we stare at one another for

שניות אחדות.
shniyot akhadot
seconds a few

"You are not talking so much now, are you?" he asks. "That is because you love your daughter and do not want to see anything happen to her."

"אתה לא מדבר כל כך הרבה עכשיו, נכון?" הוא שואל. "זה מפני
ata lo medaber kol kakh harbe akhshav, nakhon? hu sho'el. ze mipnei
you no you talk so much now correct he he asks this because

שאתה אוהב את הבת שלך ואתה לא רוצה שיקרה לה
she'ata ohev et habat shelkha ve'ata lo rotse sheyikre la
that you you love D.O. the daughter your and you no you want that it will happen to her

משהו."
mashehu
something

"אתה מאיים עליי?" אני שואל.
ata me'ayem alai ani sho'el
you you threaten at me I I ask

"Are you threatening me?" I ask.

"לא. אני אומר שתעשה הכל כדי להגן על הבת
lo ani omer sheta'ase hakol kedei lehagen al habat
no I I say that you will do everything in order to to protect regarding the daughter

"No. I am saying you would do anything to protect your daughter."

שלך."
shelkha
your

הוא מושיט לי פיסת נייר. כתוב בה: "תתכונן. יומיים. שטרות
hu moshit li pisat niyar. katuv ba: titkonen. yoma'im shtarot
he he hands to me piece of paper written on it prepare yourself two days bills

He gives me a piece of paper. On it is written: "Be ready. Two days. Small unmarked bills."

קטנים לא מסומנים."
ktanim lo mesumanim
small not marked

על הפתק מצוין גם סכום כסף גדול. הוא קם ויוצא.
al hapetek metsuyan gam skhum kesef gadol. hu kam veyotse
on the note it is indicated also sum of money large he he gets up and he walks out

There is also a large amount of money written on the note. Then he gets up and walks out.

3

איש בתחנת המשטרה העירונית לא מוכן להקשיב לבעיה שלי.
ish betakhanat hamishtara ha'ironit lo mukhan lehakshiv labe'aya sheli
person in the station of the police the municipal not ready to listen to the problem my

אין להם משאבים לטיפול בפשעים מסוג זה. לפחות הם נחמדים
ein lahem mashabim letipul bifsha'im misug ze. lefakhot hem nekhmadim
they don't have resources for handling for crimes of type this at least they nice

מספיק כדי לתת לי את מספר הטלפון של מטה מחוז
maspik kedei latet li et mispar hatelefon shel mate makhoz
enough in order to to give to me D.O. number of the telephone of headquarters of district

Nobody in my town police department wants to hear about my problem. They don't have the resources to deal with this type of crime. At least they are nice enough to give me the phone number for the Central District Headquarters.

מרכז.
merkaz
central

לאחר מכן אני מדבר עם מישהו, שמעביר אותי למישהו אחר,
le'akhar miken ani medaber im mishehu, shema'avir oti lemishehu akher,
then I I talk with someone who (he) transfers me to someone different

שמעביר אותי לבלש הסמל אלברט זוהר. הוא עובד
shema'avir oti labalash hasamal albert zohar. hu oved
who (he) transfers me to the detective the sergeant Albert Zohar he he works

ביחידה המטפלת במקרי סחיטה. אני מספר לו את סיפורי. כשאני
biyekhida hametapelet bemikrei skhita. ani mesaper lo et sipuri. kshe'ani
in unit that (it) deals with cases of extortion I I tell to him D.O. my story when I

Then I talk to someone who switches me to someone else, who switches me to Detective Sergeant Albert Zohar. He works in a division that handles extortion cases. I tell him my story. When I am done, I ask him a few questions.

163

מסיים, אני שואל אותו מספר שאלות.
she'elot mispar oto sho'el ani mesayem
questions a few him I ask I I finish

"Do you have someone who will investigate?" I ask.

יש לך מישהו שיחקור?" אני שואל.
sho'el ani sheyakh'kor mishehu yesh lekha
I ask I who (he) will investigate someone you have

"Absolutely."

"בהחלט.
behekhlet
absolutely

"I've heard that there were at least three other insurance men like me who have been victims of extortion in the last six months. Is your department investigating those cases?"

"שמעתי שהיו לפחות שלושה סוכני ביטוח נוספים כמוני
kamoni nosafim bitu'akh sokhnei shlosha lefakhot shehayu shamati
like me additional insurance agents of three at least that there were I heard

שהיו קורבן לסחיטה בשישת החודשים האחרונים. המחלקה
hamakhlaka ha'akharonim hakhodashim besheshet liskhita korban shehayu
the department the last the months in the six of to extortion victim that (they) were

שלך חוקרת את המקרים הללו?"
halalu hamikrim et khokeret shelkha
those the cases D.O. it investigates your

"Yes."

"כן.
ken
yes

"How come you haven't arrested anyone yet?"

"איך זה שעדיין לא עצרתם אף אחד?"
af ekhad atsartem lo she'ada'in ze eikh
no one you detained no that yet this how

"We have a number of strong leads."

"יש לנו מספר כיווני חקירה רציניים."
retsiniyim khakira kivunei mispar yesh lanu
serious investigation directions of number of we have

"Weren't two of the victims shot to death?" I ask.

"אבל שניים מהקורבנות נורו למוות, לא?" אני שואל.
sho'el ani lo lemavet noru mehakorbanot shna'im aval
I ask I no to death they were shot of the victims two but

"Yes," he says.

"כן," הוא אומר.
omer hu ken
he says he yes

"And wasn't the wife of the third victim killed with the same gun?"

"ואשתו של הקורבן השלישי נרצחה באותו אקדח, לא?"
lo ekdakh be'oto nirtsekha hashlishi hakorban shel ve'ishto
no gun with same she was murdered the third the victim of and his wife

"Yes. All of this was reported by the media."

"כן. כל זה דווח בתקשורת."
batikshoret duvakh ze kol ken
by the media it was reported this all yes

"Why don't you have any suspects?"

"למה אין לכם חשודים?"
khashudim ein lakhem lama
suspects you don't have why

אני לא יכול לדון בחקירה שעדיין מתנהלת."
ani lo yakhol ladun bekhakira she'ada'in mitnahelet
I no I can to discuss about investigation that still it is being conducted

"I can't talk about an ongoing investigation."

"סמל זוהר, אני חושש שהעבריינים האלה חכמים יותר מהמשטרה."
samal zohar, ani khoshesh sheha'avaryanim ha'ele khakhamim yoter mehamishtara
sergeant Zohar I I am worried that the criminals the these smart more than the police

"Sergeant Zohar, I'm worried that these criminals are smarter than the police."

"אני לא יכול להגיב."
ani lo yakhol lehagiv
I no I can to comment

"I can't comment."

"אולי עדיף שאשלם להם את הסכום שביקשו. אני יכול להרשות לעצמי."
ulai adif she'ashalem lahem et haskhum shebiksu. ani yakhol leharshot le'atsmi.
maybe preferable that I will pay to them D.O. the sum that they demanded. I can to be able to afford

"Maybe I should pay them what they want. I can afford it."

"שני אנשים שילמו. הם נרצחו בידי הכנופייה בכל זאת."
shnei anashim shilmu. hem nirtsekhu biydei haknufiya bekhol zot.
two of people they paid. they they were murdered by the hands of the gang nevertheless

"Two people paid. They were killed by the gang anyway."

"אולי הם נרצחו בגלל שהחליטו לשתף פעולה עם המשטרה והעבריינים גילו את זה."
ulai hem nirtsekhu biglal shehekhlitu leshatef pe'ula im hamishtara veha'avaryanim gilu et ze.
maybe they they were murdered because of that they decided to share activity with the police and the criminals they found out D.O. this

"Maybe they were killed because they decided to cooperate with the police and the criminals found out."

"גם על זה אני לא יכול להגיב."
gam al ze ani lo yakhol lehagiv.
also about that I no I can to comment

"I can't comment about that either."

"אתה לא עוזר. כל פעם שאני אומר משהו חשוב אתה אומר לי שאתה לא יכול להגיב."
ata lo ozer. kol pa'am she'ani omer mashehu khashuv ata omer li she'ata lo yakhol lehagiv.
you no you help. every time that I I say something important you you tell to me that you no you can to comment

"You aren't helping. Every time I say something important you tell me that you can't comment."

"המחלקה שלי עובדת מסביב לשעון כדי למצוא את הכנופייה הזאת. תוכל לעזור לנו בכך שתשתף איתי פעולה. אני
hamakhlaka sheli ovedet misaviv lasha'on kedei limtso et haknufiya hazot. tukhal la'azor lanu bekhakh sheteshatef iti pe'ula. ani
the department my it works around to the clock in order to to find D.O. the gang the this. you will be able to help to us in that that you will share with me activity. I

"My department is working around the clock to find this gang. You can help us by working with me. Can I come to your office and look for fingerprints?"

165

יכול לבוא למשרד שלך ולחפש טביעות אצבע?"
yakhol lavo lamisrad shelkha ulekhapes tvi'ot *etsba*
I can to come to the office your and to look for fingerprints

"He wore gloves," I say.

"הוא לבש כפפות," אני אומר.
hu lavash kfafot ani omer
he he wore gloves I I say

"Well, at least meet with me and make a formal complaint."

"אז לפחות תיפגש איתי ותגיש תלונה רשמית."
az lefakhot tipagesh iti vetagish tluna rishmit
then at least you will meet with me and you will submit complaint official

"I'm not sure I want to do that. Three people are dead and you don't appear to be making any progress."

"אני לא בטוח שאני רוצה לעשות את זה. שלושה אנשים מתים ולא
ani lo batu'akh she'ani rotse la'asot et ze shlosha anashim metim velo
I not sure that I I want to do D.O. that three people they died and no

נראה שאתם מתקדמים."
nire she'atem mitkadmim
it seems that you you progress

"Then why did you call?"

"אז למה התקשרת?"
az lama hitkasharta
then why you called

"That's a good question. Let me think about my situation and get back to you."

"זו שאלה טובה. תן לי לחשוב על המצב ולחזור אליך."
zo she'ela tova ten li lakhshov al hamatsav velakhzor eleikha
this question good let to me to think about the situation and to get back to you

Five minutes after my conversation with Sergeant Zohar, I call Michael Hershko. He is the insurance agent whose wife was murdered five months ago. I ask him to meet me for lunch the next day.

חמש דקות לאחר שיחתי עם סמל זוהר, אני מתקשר למיכאל
khamesh dakot le'akhar sikhati im samal zohar ani mitkasher lemikha'el
five minutes after my conversation with sergeant Zohar I call to Michael

הרשקו. הוא סוכן הביטוח שאשתו נרצחה לפני חמישה
hershko hu sokhen habitu'akh she'ishto nirtsekha lifnei khamisha
Hershko he agent of the insurance who his wife she was murdered ago five

חודשים. אני מבקש ממנו להיפגש איתי לארוחת צוהריים למחרת.
khodashim ani mevakesh mimenu lehipagesh iti le'arukhat tsohora'im lemokhorat
months I I ask of him to meet with me for meal of noon the following day

— 4 —

Michael Hershko looks terrible. His face is gaunt, his beard is ragged. He has trouble focusing on the menu.

מיכאל הרשקו נראה נורא. פניו כחושים, זקנו מוזנח. הוא
mikha'el hershko nire nora panav k'khushim zkano muznakh hu
Michael Hershko he looks terrible his face gaunt his beard neglected he

מתקשה להתרכז בתפריט.
mitkashe lehitrakez batafrit
he finds it difficult to focus on on the menu

"The medication makes it hard for me to do things," he says. "I'm sleepy all the time."

"התרופה מקשה עליי לעשות דברים," הוא אומר. "אני מנומנם
hatrufa maksha alai la'asot dvarim hu omer ani menumnam
the medication it makes difficult for me to do things he he says I I sleepy

166

כל הזמן."
kol hazman
all the time

אנחנו מדברים על כמה עצוב הוא מאז שאשתו נרצחה. לאחר
anakhnu medabrim al kama atsuv hu me'az she'ishto nirtsekha le'akhar
we talk about how sad he since that his wife she was murdered after

מספר דקות אני משנה את הנושא ומספר לו שאותה קבוצת
mispar dakot ani meshane et hanose umesaper lo she'ota kvutsat
a few minutes I change D.O. the topic and I tell to him that the same group of

עבריינים מאיימת על בתי.
avaryanim me'ayemet al biti
criminals she threatens on my daughter

We talk about how sad he has been since his wife was killed. I change the subject after a few minutes and explain that the same group of criminals is threatening my daughter.

"כדאי לי לערב את המשטרה?" אני שואל.
kedai li le'arev et hamishtara ani sho'el
it is worthwhile to me to involve D.O. the police I I ask

"Should I get the police involved?" I ask.

"לא. תשלם להם."
lo teshalem lahem
no you will pay to them

"No. Pay them."

"לשלם לנצח?"
leshalem lanetsakh
to pay forever

"Pay forever?"

"הם אמרו לי שיעזבו אותי בשקט אחרי שאשלם במשך
hem amru li sheya'azvu oti besheket akharei she'ashalem bemeshekh
they they told to me that they will leave me in silence after that I will pay for duration

"They told me they would leave me alone after I paid for one year," he says.

שנה," הוא אומר.
shana hu omer
year he he says

"האמנת להם?"
he'emanta lahem
you believed to them

"Did you believe them?"

"לא. אז הלכתי למשטרה."
lo az halakhti lamishtara
no so I went to the police

"No. So I went to the police."

"למה אשתך נרצחה?" אני שואל.
lama ishtekha nirtsekha ani sho'el
why your wife she was murdered I I ask

"Why was your wife murdered?" I ask.

"איכשהו, העבריינים ידעו שאני עובד עם המשטרה."
eikhshehu ha'avaryanim yadu she'ani oved im hamishtara
somehow the criminals they knew that I I work with the police

"Somehow, the criminals knew I was working with the police."

"איך הם ידעו?"
eikh hem yadu
how they they knew

"How did they know that?"

167

"My next payment was supposed to be made at a gas station on the highway. A few detectives followed me. They wore regular clothes so they would blend in with the people at the gas station. The criminals must have seen them, because nobody showed up to take the money."

התשלום	הבא	שלי	היה	אמור	להימסר	בתחנת	דלק	על
hatashlum	haba	sheli	haya	amur	lehimaser	betakhanat	delek	al
the payment	next	my	it was	supposed to	to be delivered	at station of	gas	on

הכביש	המהיר.	כמה	בלשים	עקבו	אחריי.	הם	לבשו	בגדים
hakvish	hamahir	kama	balashim	akvu	akharai	hem	lavshu	bgadim
the highway		a few	detectives	they followed	after me	they	they wore	clothes

אזרחיים	כדי	להשתלב	בין	האנשים	בתחנת	הדלק.	העבריינים
ezrakhiyim	kedei	lehishtalev	bein	ha'anashim	betakhanat	hadelek	ha'avaryanim
civilian	in order to	to blend in	among	the people	at the station	the gas	the criminals

בוודאי	ראו	אותם,	כי	אף אחד	לא	הופיע	לקחת	את הכסף."
bevadai	ra'u	otam	ki	af ekhad	lo	hofi'a	lakakhat	et hakesef
surely	they saw	them	because	no one	no	he showed up	to take	D.O. the money

He waits a moment, takes a few sips of coffee.

הוא	ממתין	רגע,	לוגם	לגימות	אחדות	מהקפה.
hu	mamtin	rega	logem	legimot	akhadot	mehakafe
he	he waits	moment	he sips	sips	a few	of the coffee

"A few days later my wife was shot at close range. It was a professional hit."

כמה	ימים	אחר כך	אשתי	נורתה	מטווח	קצר.	זה	היה	רצח
kama	yamim	akhar kakh	ishti	norta	mitvakh	katsar	ze	haya	retsakh
a few	days	later	my wife	she was shot	from range	short	this	it was	murder

מקצועי."
miktso'i
professional

He starts to cry.

הוא	מתחיל	לבכות.
hu	matkhil	livkot
he	he starts	to cry

"She would still be alive if I had not gone to the police."

"היא	עדיין	הייתה	בחיים	אם	לא	הייתי	הולך	למשטרה."
hi	ada'in	haita	bakhayim	im	lo	ha'iti	holekh	lamishtara
she	still	she would be	alive	if	not	I had gone		to the police

After our gloomy lunch I drive him back to his house.

אחרי	ארוחת	הצוהריים	העגומה	שלנו	אני	מסיע	אותו	בחזרה	לביתו.
akharei	arukhat	hatsohora'im	ha'aguma	shelanu	ani	masi'a	oto	bakhazara	leveito
after	meal of	the noon	the sad	our	I	I drive	him	back to	to his house

"I don't go to the office any more," he tells me. "I'm too depressed to work."

"אני	לא	הולך	יותר	למשרד,"	הוא	אומר	לי.	"אני	יותר מידי	מדוכא
ani	lo	holekh	yoter	lamisrad	hu	omer	li	ani	yoter midai	meduka
I	no	I go	more	to the office	he	he tells	to me	I	too much	depressed

מכדי	לעבוד."
mikhdei	la'avod
for	to work

"You should take a job with a big agency," I tell him. "Most places would love to have a successful salesman like you working with them. Plus, it will do you good to be with people."

"אתה	צריך	לקחת	משרה	בסוכנות	גדולה,"	אני	אומר	לו.	"רוב
ata	tsarikh	lakakhat	misra	besokhnut	gdola	ani	omer	lo	rov
you	you should	to take	job	at agency	big	I	I tell	to him	most

המקומות	ישמחו	לקבל	לעבודה	סוכן	מכירות	מצליח	כמוך.
hamekomot	yismekhu	lekabel	le'avoda	sokhen	mekhirot	matsli'akh	kamokha
the places	they will be happy	to have	for employment	agent of	sales	successful	like you

חוץ מזה, יעשה לך טוב להיות עם אנשים."
khuts mize ya'ase lekha tov lihiyot im anashim
in addition — it will be — for you — good — to be — with — people

הוא מושך בכתפיו בתבוסה.
hu moshekh bikhtefav bitvusa
he — he shrugs — in defeat
He gives me a defeated shrug.

"לפחות תיפגש עם יועץ אבל מקצועי," אני אומר.
lefakhot tipagesh im yo'ets evel miktso'i ani omer
at least — you will meet — with — counselor of — grief — professional — I — I say
"At least meet with a professional grief counselor," I say.

אני עוצר בחניית הבית.
ani otser bekhaniyat haba'it
I — I stop — in parking of — the house
I pull the car into his driveway.

הוא יוצא מהמכונית, מנופף נפנוף קטן לשלום וגורר רגליו
hu yotse mehamkhonit menofef nifnuf katan leshalom vegorer raglav
he — he gets out — from the car — he waves — waving — little — for goodbye — and he drags — his feet
בדרכו אל ביתו. אני חוזר למשרד ומנמנם. עליי להיות רענן
bedarko el beito ani khozer lamisrad umenamnem alai lihiyot ra'anan
on his way — to — his house — I — I return — to the office — and I nap — I have to — to be — refreshed
לקראת משחק הפוקר.
likrat miskhak hapoker
in preparation for — game of — the poker
He gets out of the car, gives me a little wave, and shuffles into his home. I go back to my office and take a nap. I have to be fresh for the poker game.

—5—

אני מביט סביב השולחן בשחקנים האחרים. מיקי, סוחר הסמים, יושב
ani mabit sviv hashulkhan basakhkanim ha'akherim miki sokher hasamim yoshev
I — I look — around — the table — at the players — the others — Micky — dealer of — the drugs — he sits
לימיני. נודף ממנו ריח של ג'ל לשיער ואפטר שייב. חברתו
liymini nodef mimenu rei'akh shel jel lesei'ar ve'after sheiv khaverto
to my right — it dissipates — from him — smell — of — gel — for the hair — and aftershave — his girlfriend
עומדת מאחוריו, רוכנת ונושקת לאוזנו. אני מתקשה להביט
omedet me'akhorav rokhenet venosheket le'ozno ani mitkashe lehabit
she stands — behind him — she bends forward — and she kisses — to his ear — I — I find it difficult — to look
בקלפים שלי.
beklafim sheli
at cards — my
I look around the table at the other players. Micky, the drug dealer, sits on my right. He smells like hair gel and aftershave. His girlfriend stands behind him, leaning down and kissing his ear. I have a hard time looking at my cards.

גיא, רואה חשבון, יושב מולי. חליפתו מקומטת, עניבתו מעוקמת
gai ro'e kheshbon yoshev muli khalifato mekumetet anivato me'ukemet
Guy — accountant — he sits — opposite me — his suit — wrinkled — his tie — crooked
ושני הכפתורים העליונים בחולצתו פתוחים. בקבוק הוויסקי שלו
ushnei hakaftorim ha'elyonim bekhultsato ptukhim bakbuk hawiski shelo
and two of — buttons — the top — on his shirt — open — bottle — the whiskey — his
כבר ריק בחציו, ועדיין לא שיחקנו יותר משעה.
kvar reik bekhetsi'o ve'ada'in lo sikhaknu yoter misha'a
already — empty — in half of it — and still — no — we played — more — than hour
Guy, an accountant, sits across from me. His suit is wrinkled, his tie is crooked and the top two buttons on his shirt are open. His bottle of whiskey is already half empty and we haven't played for more than an hour.

169

"Hard day at the office, Guy?" I ask him.

"יום קשה במשרד, גיא?" אני שואל אותו.

yom	kashe	bamisrad	gai	ani	sho'el	oto
day	hard	at the office	Guy	I	I ask	him

"Some government lawyers are making my life very difficult," he answers.

"כמה עורכי דין מפרקליטות המדינה עושים לי חיים קשים,"

kama	orkhei din	mipraklitut	hamdina	osim	li	khayim	kashim
a few	lawyers	from attorney's office of	the state	they make	for me	life	hard

הוא עונה.

hu	one
he	he answers

Boris, the fourth member of our group, is on my left. Boris lends money to people who cannot get loans from banks. He charges very high interest rates. If his clients don't pay the loans back on time, his assistant breaks their legs.

בוריס, החבר הרביעי בקבוצה, יושב לשמאלי. בוריס מלווה כסף

boris	hakhaver	harevi'i	bakvutsa	yoshev	lismoli	boris	malve	kesef
Boris	the member	the fourth	in the group	he sits	to my left	Boris	he lends	money

לאנשים שאינם יכולים לקבל הלוואה בבנק. הוא גובה ריביות

le'anashim	she'einam	yekholim	lekabel	halva'a	bebank	hu	gove	ribiyot
to people	that are not	they are able	to get	loan	at bank	he	he charges	interest

גבוהות מאוד. אם לקוחותיו אינם משלמים את החזרי ההלוואה

gvohot	me'od	im	lakokhotav	einam	meshalmim	et	hakhzerei	hahalva'a
high	very	if	his clients	they are not	they pay	D.O.	repayments of	the loan

במועד, העוזר שלו שובר להם את הרגליים.

bamo'ed	ha'ozer	shelo	shover	lahem	et	haragla'im
on time	the assistant	his	he breaks	for them	D.O.	the legs

Boris's assistant sits in the corner watching a big screen television. Some sort of show about home makeovers.

עוזרו של בוריס יושב בפינה, צופה בטלוויזיה במסך גדול.

ozro	shel	boris	yoshev	bapina	tsofe	batelevizya	bemasakh	gadol
his assistant	of	Boris	he sits	in the corner	he watches	at the television	on screen	big

תוכנית עיצוב בתים כלשהי.

tokhnit	itsuv	batim	kolshehi
program of	design of	houses	of some sort

Why does a guy who beats on people for a living enjoy those silly reality shows? There is no accounting for taste.

מדוע בחור המכה אנשים למחייתו נהנה מתוכניות הריאליטי

madu'a	bakhur	hamake	anashim	lemikhyato	nehene	mitokhniyot	harei'aliti
why	guy	that (he) beats	people	for his living	he enjoys	of programs of	the reality

המטופשות האלה? על טעם ועל ריח אין להתווכח.

hametupashot	ha'ele	al	ta'am	ve'al	rei'akh	ein	lehitvake'akh
the stupid	the those	about	taste	and about	smell	there isn't	to debate

We are playing poker in a room of a volunteer fire station in Holon. The fire chief deals the cards for us and takes a five percent commission from every pot. Judging by the nice furniture in the firehouse, that commission has brought a lot of money into the firehouse over the years. I wonder how much the fire chief keeps for himself.

אנחנו משחקים פוקר בחדר בתחנת כיבוי האש למתנדבים בחולון.

anakhnu	masakhakim	poker	bekheder	betakhanat kibui ha'esh	lemitnadvim	bekholon
we	we play	poker	in room	in the fire station	for volunteers	in Holon

מפקד התחנה מחלק עבורנו את הקלפים, ולוקח חמישה

mefaked	hatakhana	mekhalek	avurenu	et	haklafim	veloke'akh	khamisha
commander of	the station	he deals	for us	D.O.	the cards	and he takes	five

אחוזים עמלה מכל קופה. אם לשפוט על פי הריהוט הנחמד

akhuzim	amla	mikol	kupa	im	lishpot	al pi	harihut	hanekhmad
percent	commission	from every	(jack)pot	if	to judge	according to	the furniture	the nice

בתחנת הכיבוי, העמלה הזו הכניסה לתחנה כסף רב

betakhanat	hakibui	ha'amla	hazo	hikhnisa	latakhana	kesef	rav
in station of	the extinguishing	the commission	the that	it brought in	to the station	money	much

במהלך השנים. מעניין כמה שומר מפקד התחנה לעצמו.
bemahalakh hashanim me'anyen kama shomer mefaked hatakhana le'atsmo
over the course of / the years / interesting / how much / he keeps / commander of / the station / for himself

שותפתי, איילה, יושבת על ספה בסמוך לטלוויזיה. היא קוראת
shutafti ayala yoshevet al sapa besamukh latelevizya hi koret
my partner / Ayala / she sits / on / couch / in proximity to / to the television / she / she reads

ספר מאת סטיבן הוקינג. משהו על הכוכבים וכוכבי הלכת.
sefer me'et stiven hoking mashehu al hakokhavim vekhokhvei halekhet
book / by / Steven / Hawking / something / about / the stars / and the planets

> My associate, Ayala, sits on a couch near the television. She is reading a book by Stephen Hawking. Something about the stars and planets.

גיא מעיף מבטים לעבר איילה ללא הרף. מיקי היה מציץ גם הוא,
gai me'if mabatim le'ever ayala lelo heref miki haya metsits gam hu
Guy / he glances / toward / Ayala / continuously / Micky / he would / to glance / also / he

אלא שהחברה שלו חסמה את שדה ראייתו. בוריס אינו
ela shehakhavera shelo khasma et sde re'iyato boris eino
except / that the girlfriend / his / she blocked / D.O. / field of / his vision / Boris / he doesn't

מביט. נדמה שהוא מרוכז ביד שקיבל. מפקד תחנת הכיבוי
mabit nidme shehu merukaz bayad shekibel mefaked takhanat hakibui
he looks / it seems / that he / focused / on the hand / that he received / commander of / the fire station

ממקד את מבטו בקלפים ובכסף.
memaked et mabato baklafim uvakesef
he focuses / D.O. / his gaze / on the cards / and on the money

> Guy keeps glancing over at Ayala. Micky would look too, except his girlfriend was blocking his view. Boris doesn't look. He appears focused on his hand. The fire chief keeps his eyes on the cards and the money.

איילה נמוכה ממני בכחמישה סנטימטרים, כלומר גובהה מטר
ayala nemukha mimeni bekhekhamisha sentimetrim klomar govha meter
Ayala / short / than me / by about five / centimeters / meaning / her height / meter

ושמונים. היא בעלת שיער חום באורך בינוני. מצחה
ushmonim hi ba'alat sei'ar khum be'orekh beinoni mitskha
and eighty / she / possessor of / hair / brown / in length / medium / her forehead

מתקמט מעט כאשר היא מתרכזת בספרה. היא לובשת
mitkamet me'at ka'asher hi mitrakezet besifra hi loveshet
it becomes wrinkled / a little / when / she / she concentrates / at her book / she / she wears

אימונית נוחה, ללא איפור או תכשיטים.
imunit nokha lelo ipur o takhshitim
track suit / comfortable / without / makeup / or / jewelry

> Ayala is maybe five centimeters shorter than me, which puts her at about one meter eighty. She has medium length brown hair. Her forehead wrinkles slightly as she concentrates on the book she is reading. She wears a comfortable track suit, but no makeup or jewelry.

"היא לא חברה שלך," אומר בוריס. "למה אתה מביא אותה?"
hi lo khavera shelkha omer boris lama ata mevi ota
she / not / girlfriend / your / he says / Boris / why / you / you bring / her

> "She's not your girlfriend," Boris says. "Why do you bring her?"

"למזל," אני אומר לו. "אני צריך הרבה מזל הלילה. בוא נקווה
lemazal ani omer lo ani tsarikh harbe mazal halaila bo nekave
for luck / I / I say / to him / I / I need / a lot / luck / tonight / let's / we will hope

שארוויח הרבה כסף."
she'arvi'akh harbe kesef
that I will gain / a lot / money

> "For luck," I tell him. "I need lots of luck tonight. Let's hope I win big money."

171

"Let's hope you don't," says Boris.

"בוא נקווה שלא," אומר בוריס.
bo nekave shelo omer boris
let's we will hope that no he says Boris

"How's your wife doing, Guy?" I ask.

"מה שלום אשתך, גיא?" אני שואל.
ma shlom ishtekha gai ani sho'el
what is well being of your wife Guy I I ask

"Fine."

"בסדר."
beseder
fine

Guy's wife is the daughter of a well known gangster from Tel Aviv. His father-in-law is called Arye the Ax. Guy does all the financial work for Arye's businesses.

אשתו של גיא היא בתו של עבריין ידוע מתל אביב. חמו
ishto shel gai hi bito shel avaryan yadu'a mitel aviv khamo
his wife of Guy she his daughter of criminal famous from Tel Aviv his father-in-law

נקרא אריה הגרזן. גיא עושה את כל עבודת הכספים עבור עסקיו
nikra arye hagarzen gai ose et kol avodat haksafim avur asakav
he is named Arye the ax Guy he does D.O. all work of the finance for his business

של אריה.
shel arye
of Arye

"Anyone watch the game last Monday?" I ask.

"מישהו ראה את המשחק ביום שני האחרון?" אני שואל.
mishehu ra'a et hamiskhak beyom sheni ha'akharon ani sho'el
someone he saw D.O. the game on Monday the last I I ask

I'm answered with a few grunts and curses. This is not a friendly group.

אני נענה במספר נהמות וקללות. זו איננה קבוצה ידידותית.
ani ne'ana bemispar nehamot uklalot zo einena kvutsa yedidutit
I I am answered with a few grunts and curses this it isn't group friendly

Micky gently pushes his girlfriend away. "Meytal, I can't think with you hanging all over me. Go watch TV."

מיקי מזיז מעליו את חברתו בעדינות. "מיטל, אני לא יכול
miki meziz me'alav et khaverto be'adinut meital ani lo yakhol
Micky he nudges off of him D.O. his girlfriend gently Meytal I no I can

לחשוב כשאת תלויה מעליי. לכי תראי טלוויזיה."
lakhshov kshe'at tluya me'alai lekhi tiri televizya
to think when you hanging on top of me go watch television

She glides away and sits next to Ayala.

היא מחליקה לדרכה ומתיישבת לצד איילה.
hi makhlika ledarka umityashevet letsad ayala
she she glides to her way and she sits down beside Ayala

"Any of you guys ever have dealings with the police?" I ask them.

"למישהו מכם היה פעם עסק עם המשטרה?" אני שואל.
lemishehu mikem haya pa'am esek im hamishtara ani sho'el
to someone of you he was occasion dealing with the police I I ask

"Who hasn't?" asks Boris.

"למי לא?" שואל בוריס.
lemi lo sho'el boris
to who not he asks Boris

"I have something going on right now," I tell them. "Do you know if any of the top people are willing to do favors for guys like us?"

"יש לי איזה עניין עכשיו," אני אומר להם. "אתם יודעים אם מישהו
yesh li eize inyan akhshav ani omer lahem atem yodim im mishehu
I have some issue now I I tell to them you you know if someone

בצמרת יהיה מוכן לעשות טובות לאנשים כמונו?"
batsameret *ihiye* *mukhan* *la'asot* *tovot* *le'anashim* *kamonu*
at the top / he will be / ready / to do / favors / for people / like us

אנחנו משחקים קלפים דקות אחדות.
anakhnu *mesakhakim* *klafim* *dakot* *akhadot*
we / we play / cards / minutes / several

We play cards for a few more minutes.

"אם המחיר נכון, תוכל לשכנע מישהו לעשות משהו," אומר
omer *mashehu* *la'asot* *mishehu* *leshakhne'a* *tukhal* *nakhon* *hamekhir* *im*
he says / something / to do / someone / to convince / you will be able / right / the price / if

"If the price is right, you can convince someone to do something," Boris says.

בוריס.
boris
Boris

"מי?"
mi
who

"Who?"

"תלוי מה אתה רוצה."
talui *ma* *ata* *rotse*
depends / what / you / you want

"It depends on what you want."

"אני רוצה להפסיק חקירה," אני אומר.
ani *rotse* *lehafsik* *khakira* *ani* *omer*
I / I want / to stop / investigation / I / I say

"I want to stop an investigation," I say.

"אולי יש לי שם. תן לי את הסלולרי שלך."
ulai *yesh li* *shem* *ten* *li* *et* *haselulari* *shelkha*
perhaps / I have / name / give / to me / D.O. / the cellphone / your

"I might have a name. Give me your cell phone number."

אני כותב את מספר הטלפון על פיסת נייר ומחליק אותה אליו.
ani *kotev* *et* *mispar* *hatelefon* *al* *pisat* *niyar* *umakhlik* *ota* *elav*
I / I write / D.O. / number / the telephone / on / piece of / paper / and I slip / it / to him

I write my phone number on a piece of paper and slide it over to him.

"תן לי כמה ימים," הוא אומר.
ten *li* *kama* *yamim* *hu* *omer*
give / to me / a few / days / he / he says

"Give me a few days," he says.

"אני חייב לך," אני אומר לו.
ani *khayav* *lekha* *ani* *omer* *lo*
I / I owe / to you / I / I tell / to him

"I owe you," I tell him.

גיא זורק את קלפיו על השולחן ופורש. גם אני. בוריס ומיקי
gai *zorek* *et* *klafav* *al* *hashulkhan* *uforesh* *gam* *ani* *boris* *umiki*
Guy / he throws / D.O. / his cards / on / the table / and he quits / also / I / Boris / and Micky

מושכים קלפים אחדים.
moshkhim *klafim* *akhadim*
they draw / cards / some

Guy throws his cards on the table and folds. I do, too. Boris and Micky draw some cards.

"מישהו רוצה בירה?" אני שואל.
mishehu *rotse* *bira* *ani* *sho'el*
anyone / he wants / beer / I / I ask

"Anyone want a beer?" I ask.

Micky gives me a nod. I walk to the refrigerator and get two bottles of beer. When I get back to the table, Micky is raking in the chips.

מיקי מהנהן לעברי. אני צועד לכיוון המקרר ולוקח שני
miki mehanhen le'evri ani tso'ed lekhivun hamekarer veloke'akh shnei
Micky he nods toward me I walk to direction of the refrigerator and I take two of

בקבוקי בירה. כשאני שב לשולחן, מיקי גורף את הז׳יטונים.
bakbukei bira kshe'ani shav lashulkhan miki goref et hajitonim
bottles of beer when I I sit to the table Micky he sweeps away D.O. the chips

"The cards are cold tonight," says Boris.

"הקלפים קרים הערב," אומר בוריס.
haklafim karim ha'erev omer boris
the cards cold tonight he says Boris

The fire chief deals a new hand. We start talking about basketball. Four hours later, I decide to call it a night.

מפקד התחנה מחלק יד נוספת. אנחנו מתחילים לשוחח על
mefaked hatakhana mekhalek yad nosefet anakhnu matkhilim lesokhe'akh al
commander of the station he deals hand additional we we start to talk about

כדורסל. ארבע שעות מאוחר יותר, אני מחליט לסיים את הערב.
kadursal arba sha'ot me'ukhar yoter ani makhlit lesayem et ha'erev
basketball four hours late more I I decide to finish D.O. the night

"You've won a lot of money," Guy says as Ayala and I turn to leave. "Stick around so we can get some of it back."

"הרווחת הרבה כסף," אומר גיא כשאיילה ואני פונים לצאת. "תישאר
hirvakhta harbe kesef omer gai kshe'ayala va'ani ponim latset tisha'er
you earned a lot money he says Guy when Ayala and I we turn to leave you will stay

בסביבה, כדי שנוכל לקבל חלק ממנו בחזרה."
basviva kedei shenukhal lekabel khelek mimenu bakhazara
in the surroundings so that that we will be able to get part of it back

"Thanks, Guy, but I need the money right now for something else."

"תודה, גיא, אבל אני צריך את הכסף עכשיו למשהו אחר."
toda gai aval ani tsarikh et hakesef akhshav lemashehu akher
thanks Guy but I I need D.O. the money now for something else

"Right. That thing about the ongoing police investigation," he says.

"כן. העניין עם חקירת המשטרה," הוא אומר.
ken ha'inyan im khakirat hamishtara hu omer
yes the issue with investigation of the police he he says

We walk out of the firehouse and down the street to our car. On our way we pass by a long, tall hedge. I search in my pocket for the car remote.

אנחנו יוצאים מתחנת הכיבוי וצועדים במורד הרחוב לכיוון
anakhnu yotsim mitakhanat hakibui vetso'adim bemorad harekhov lekhivun
we we exit from the fire station and we walk down the street to direction of

המכונית. בדרכנו אנחנו חולפים על פני גדר חיה ארוכה וגבוהה.
hamkhonit bedarkenu anakhnu kholfim al pnei gader khaya aruka ugvoha
the car on our way we we pass by hedge long and tall

אני מחפש בכיסי את שלט המכונית.
ani mekhapes bekhisi et shalat hamkhonit
I I search for in my pocket D.O. remote of the car

Suddenly, Ayala spins on her left foot. She smashes her right foot into the face of a big guy who appeared from behind the hedge. He drops the club he is holding and falls backwards onto his butt.

לפתע, איילה מסתובבת על רגלה השמאלית. היא מטיחה את רגלה
lefeta ayala mistovevet al ragla hasmalit hi metikha et ragla
suddenly Ayala she turns around on her foot the left she she slams D.O. her foot

הימנית בפניו של בחור גדול, שהופיע מאחורי הגדר החיה. הוא
hayemanit befanav shel bakhur gadol shehofi'a me'akhorei hagader hakhaya hu
the right in his face of guy big who appeared behind the hedge he

174

שומט את האלה שבידיו ונופל לאחור על ישבנו.
shomet et ha'ala shebeyadav venofel le'akhor al yashvano
he drops D.O. the club that is in his hand and he falls backward on his butt

I lean against the car, as two other men spring out of the darkness. One holds a small bat. The other has a knife. They are young - maybe 19 or 20 years old. A little shorter than me, but they probably weigh fifteen kilograms more than me.

אני נשען על המכונית כששני גברים נוספים מזנקים מתוך החשכה.
ani nishan al hamkhonit ksheshnei gvarim nosafim mezankim mitokh hakhashekha
I lean on the car when two of men additional they leap out of the darkness

אחד מהם אוחז במחבט קטן. האחר אוחז בידיו סכין. הם
ekhad mehem okhez bemakhbet katan. ha'akher okhez beyadav sakin. hem
one of them he grasps at bat small. the other he grasps in his hand knife. they

צעירים - אולי בני 19 או 20. מעט נמוכים ממני, אבל שוקלים
tse'irim ulai bnei tsha esre o esrim me'at nemukhim mimeni aval shoklim
young maybe age of nineteen or twenty a little short than me but they weigh

כחמישה עשר קילוגרם יותר ממני.
kekhamisha asar kilogram yoter mimeni
about fifteen kilogram more than me

איילה ניצבת בפניה אליהם. ברכיה כפופות מעט. אמות ידיה
ayala nitsevet befaneiha aleihem. birkeiha kfufot me'at. amot yadeiha
Ayala she stands at her face towards them. her knees bent a little. her forearms

Ayala stands facing them. Her knees are slightly bent. The forearms are up and the elbows are in. Her fists are loosely clenched. The left foot is forward, and the right toes are pointing to the side. Both heels are off the ground. This is the traditional Muay Thai fighting stance.

מורמות ומרפקיה צמודים לגופה. אגרופיה קמוצים ברפיון. רגלה
muramot umarpekeiha tsmudim legufa. egrofeiha kmutsim berifyon. ragla
raised and her elbows next to to her body. her fists closed loosely. her foot

השמאלית מושטת קדימה ואצבעות רגלה הימנית פונות הצידה.
hasmalit mushetet kadima ve'etsba'ot ragla hayemanit ponot hatsida.
the left extended forward and her toes the right they face aside

שני העקבים מורמים מהרצפה. זוהי עמידת קרב המואי-תאי
shnei ha'akevim muramim meharitspa. zohi amidat krav hamui-tai
two of the heels raised from the ground. this is standing of combat of the muay thai

המסורתית.
hamasortit.
the traditional

שני הבחורים הקשוחים מביטים בחברם היושב על הקרקע. ידיו
shnei habakhurim hakshukhim mabitim bekhaveram hayoshev al hakarka. yadav
two of the guys the tough they look at their friend that (he) sits on the ground. his hands

The two tough guys look at their friend sitting on the ground. He has his hands up to his face. Blood is spurting out between his fingers.

מורמות אל פניו. דם ניגר מבין אצבעותיו.
muramot el panav. dam nigar mibein etsbe'otav.
raised to his face. blood it flows from between his fingers

הם מהססים ואיילה תוקפת. הבחור האוחז במחבט מנסה להניפו.
hem mehasesim ve'ayala tokefet. habakhur ha'okhez bamakhbet menase lehanifo.
they they hesitate and Ayala she attacks. the guy that (he) grasps at the bat he tries to raise it

They hesitate and Ayala attacks. The guy holding the bat tries to swing it. Too late.

מאוחר מדי.
me'ukhar midai.
late too

מרפקה של איילה מרסק את אפו ורגלה השמאלית שומטת את
marpeka shel ayala merasek et afo veragla hasmalit shometet et
her elbow of Ayala it smashes D.O. his nose and her leg the left it knocks down D.O.

Ayala's elbow smashes his nose and her left leg sweeps his feet out from under him before the bat moves five centimeters.

רגליו מתחתיו לפני שהמחבט נע יותר מחמישה סנטימטרים.
raglav mitakhtav lifnei shehamakhbet na yoter mekhamisha sentimetrim
his legs from beneath him before that the bat it moves more than five centimeters

As he falls, she dances clear of a knife thrust from the second man. He stabs too hard and winds up off balance. Ayala closes in before he can recover.

בעודו נופל, היא חומקת בצעדי ריקוד מסכינו המונפת של
be'odo nofel hi khomeket bitsa'adei rikud misakino hamunefet shel
as he falls she she slips away with steps of dance from his knife the raised of

הבחור האחר. הוא הולם חזק מדי ומאבד את שיווי משקלו. לפני
habakhur ha'akher hu holem khazak midi ume'abed et shivui mishkalo lifnei
the man the other he he strikes hard too and he loses D.O. his balance before

שהוא מספיק להתאושש, איילה סוגרת עליו.
shehu maspik lehitoshesh ayala sogeret alav
that he enough to recover Ayala she closes in on him

She knees him in the kidney and punches the side of his jaw with a hard jab. His body buckles from the force of the strike.

היא נותנת לו ברכייה בכליות ומכה בצד הלסת שלו
hi notenet lo birkiya baklayot umaka betsad haleset shelo
she she gives to him knee-kick in the kidneys and she punches in side of the jaw his

בעוצמה. גופו קורס מעוצמת המכה.
be'otsma gufo kores me'otsmat hamaka
with strength his body it collapses from strength of the strike

As he falls, she dances over to the guy with the bat and stomps his testicles. He whimpers and passes out.

בעודו נופל, היא מרקדת אל עבר הבחור עם המחבט ודורכת
be'odo nofel hi merakedet el ever habakhur im hamakhbet vedorekhet
as he falls she she dances to direction of the guy with the bat and she steps on

על אשכיו. הוא מייבב ומאבד את הכרתו.
al ashakhav hu meyabev ume'abed et hakarato
on his testicles he he wails and he passes out

Then she shuffles back to the guy with the knife who is now on the ground. She kicks him in the head. He drops the knife and lays still.

היא חומקת בחזרה לבחור עם הסכין, השרוע כעת על הקרקע. היא
hi khomeket bakhazara labakhur im hasakin hasru'a ka'et al hakarka hi
she she escapes back to the guy with the knife that lies now on the ground she

בועטת בראשו. הוא שומט את הסכין ושוכב ללא תזוזה.
bo'etet berosho hu shomet et hasakin veshokhev lelo t'zuza
she kicks at his head he he drops D.O. the knife and he lies down without movement

By this time, our first assailant has pulled himself back onto his feet. He fumbles with a gun that is stuck in his pants pocket. His hands are slippery with the blood from his nose and mouth, which makes it hard for him to grab the gun.

בשלב זה, התוקף הראשון שלנו גרר עצמו בחזרה למצב
beshalav ze hatokef harishon shelanu garar atsmo bakhazara lematsav
at stage this the attacker the first our he dragged himself back to situation of

עמידה. הוא ממשש אקדח התחוב בכיס מכנסיו. ידיו חלקלקות
amida hu memashesh ekdakh hatakhuv bekhis mikhnasav yadav khalaklakot
standing he he gropes gun the inserted in pocket of his pants his hands slippery

מהדם הניגר מאפו ומפיו, דבר המקשה עליו
mehadam hanigar me'apo umipiv davar hamakshe alav
from the blood that flows from his nose and from his mouth a thing which makes difficult on him

לאחוז באקדח.
le'ekhoz ba'ekdakh
to grab at the gun

אני חובט בצד ראשו ללא מאמץ עם אלה שאני מחזיק בכיסי.
ani khovet betsad rosho lelo ma'amats im ala she'ani makhzik bekhisi
I / I strike / on side / his head / without / strain / with / club / that I / I store / in my pocket

הוא מתמוטט חזרה אל המדרכה.
hu mitmotet khazara el hamidrakha
he / he collapses / returning / to / the pavement

I casually swat him on the side of the head with a little club that I keep in my pocket. He crumbles back onto the pavement.

"אתה צריך נרתיק כתף," אני אומר לבחור מחוסר ההכרה. "יותר
ata tsarikh nartik katef, ani omer labakhur mekhusar hahakara. yoter
you / you need / holster of / shoulder / I / I tell / to the guy / lacking of / consciousness / more

קל לשלוף את האקדח."
kal lishlof et ha'ekdakh.
easy / to pull out / D.O. / the gun

"You need a shoulder holster," I tell the unconscious man. "Makes it easier to pull out the gun."

"הוא לא יכול לשמוע אותך," אומרת איילה.
hu lo yakhol lishmo'a otkha, omeret ayala.
he / no / he can / to hear / you / she says / Ayala

"He can't hear you," Ayala says.

נשימתה אפילו אינה כבדה. שנינו נכנסים למכוניתי ונוסעים משם.
neshimata afilu eina kveda. shneinu nikhnasim limkhoniti venosim misham.
her breathing / even / it isn't / heavy / two of us / we enter / into my car / and we drive / from there

She isn't even breathing hard. The two of us get into my car and drive off.

"איך הם ידעו על משחק הפוקר?" היא שואלת.
eikh hem yadu al miskhak hapoker? hi sho'elet.
how / they / they knew / about / game of / the poker / she / she asks

"How did they know about the poker game?" she asks.

"אולי הם חברים בקבוצת המתנדבים של מכבי האש," אני אומר.
ulai hem khavarim bikvutsat hamitnadvim shel mekhabei ha'esh, ani omer.
maybe / they / members / in the group of / the volunteers / of / the fire department / I / I say

"Maybe they are members of the volunteer fire department," I say.

— 6 —

האיש מרמת גן, בעל המבטא המצחיק מתקשר אליי למחרת
ha'ish meramat gan, ba'al hamivta hamatskhik mitkasher elai lemokhorat
the man / from Ramat Gan / owner of / the accent / the funny / he calls / to me / the following day

בבוקר. בטלפון הנייד שלי! איך הוא השיג את המספר?
baboker. batelefon hanayad sheli! eikh hu hisig et hamispar?
in the morning / on telephone / the mobile / my / how / he / he obtained / D.O. / the number

The man from Ramat Gan with the funny accent calls me the next morning. On my cell phone! How did he get that number?

"תביא את המתנה שלי לחניה של פארק רמת גן בשעה
tavi et hamatana sheli lakhanaya shel park ramat gan besha'a
you will bring / D.O. / the gift / my / to the parking lot / of / park of / Ramat Gan / at o'clock

שתיים," הוא אומר.
shta'im, hu omer.
two / he / he says

"You will bring my gift to the Ramat Gan Park parking lot at two o'clock," he says.

"לא," אני עונה.
lo, ani one.
no / I / I answer

"No," I answer.

177

There is a pause on the line.

יש הפסקה על הקו.
hakav al hafsaka yesh
the line on pause there is

"You don't have the gift?" he asks.

"אין לך את המתנה?" הוא שואל.
sho'el hu hamatana et ein lekha
he asks he the gift D.O. you don't have

"I have it, but I'm not driving all the way down there to meet you."

"היא אצלי, אבל אני לא נוסע את כל הדרך עד לשם כדי
kedei lesham ad haderekh kol et nose'a lo ani aval etsli hi
in order to to there as far as the way all D.O. I drive not I but in my possession it

לפגוש אותך."
otkha lifgosh
you to meet

"I'm not joking. You must do what I say."

"אני לא צוחק. אתה חייב לעשות מה שאני אומר לך."
lekha omer she'ani ma la'asot khayav ata tsokhek lo ani
to you I say that I what to do you must you I joke not I

"If you want your money, I'll give it to you at a place that I pick."

"אם אתה רוצה את הכסף שלך, אני אתן לך אותו במקום שאני
she'ani bemakom oto lekha eten ani shelkha hakesef et rotse ata im
that I at place it to you I will give I your the money D.O. you want you if

אבחר."
evkhar
I will pick

He thinks for a few seconds.

הוא מהרהר שניות אחדות.
akhadot shniyot meharher hu
a few seconds he ponders he

"If the police are there, I will know. I am very careful."

"אם המשטרה תהיה שם, אני אדע. אני מאוד זהיר."
zahir me'od ani eda ani sham tihiye hamishtara im
careful very I I will know I there she will be the police if

"Don't worry," I tell him, "no police will be there."

"אל תדאג," אני אומר לו, "שום משטרה לא תהיה שם."
sham tihiye lo mishtara shum lo omer ani tidag al
there she will be no police no to him I tell I you will worry don't

After twenty seconds of silence he says, "Okay, where do you want to bring the gift?"

כעבור עשרים שניות של שתיקה הוא אומר, "או קיי, לאן אתה רוצה
rotse ata le'an o kei omer hu shtika shel shniyot esrim ka'avor
you want you to where okay he says he silence of seconds twenty after

להביא את המתנה?"
hamatana et lehavi
the gift D.O. to bring

"I'll meet you at track 5 in the Ajami train station. The one in Jaffa, not the Hagana Station. That's a nice public place."

"אני אפגוש אותך ברציף 5 בתחנת הרכבת בעג'מי. התחנה
hatakhana be'ajami harakevet betakhanat khamesh beratsif otkha efgosh ani
the station at Ajami the train at station of five at platform you I will meet I

ביפו, לא תחנת ההגנה. זה מקום ציבורי נחמד."
nekhmad tsiburi makom ze hahagana takahnat lo beyafo
nice public place that the Hagana station of not in Jaffa

"אתה דואג שאני אעשה לך משהו?"
mashehu lekha e'ese she'ani do'eg ata
something to you I will do that I you worry you

"Are you worried that I will do something to you?"

"אני רוצה שיהיו עדים."
edim sheyihiyu rotse ani
witnesses that there will be I want I

"I want to have witnesses."

"תזכור," הוא אומר לי, "אם המשטרה תופיע, אני אדע."
eda ani tofi'a hamishtara im li omer hu tizkor
I will know I it will show up the police if to me he says he you will remember

"Remember," he tells me, "if the police show up, I will know."

"אני מבין," אני אומר.
omer ani mevin ani
I say I I understand I

"I understand," I say.

"דרך אגב, אתה מקבל המחאות?"
hamkha'ot mekabel ata derekh agav
checks you accept you by the way

"By the way, do you accept checks?"

הוא לא מגחך אפילו.
afilu megakhekh lo hu
even he chuckles no he

He doesn't even chuckle.

שעות אחדות מאוחר יותר אני עומד ברציף 5, קורא עיתון.
iton kore khamesh beratsif omed ani yoter me'ukhar akhadot sha'ot
newspaper I read five at platform I stand I more later a few hours

רכבת עוצרת, ועשרה נוסעים יורדים ממנה. הרכבת רועמת הלאה
hala ro'emet harakevet mimena yordim nosim ve'asara otseret rakevet
onward it thunders the train from it they get off passengers and ten it stops train

לכיוון לוד. איש לא שם לב אליי. ידידי החדש צועד
tso'ed hakhadash yadidi elai sam lev lo ish lod lekhivun
he walks the new my friend to me he paid attention no man Lod in the direction of

לאורך הרציף ונעמד מולי.
muli vene'emad haratsif le'orekh
in front of me and he stops (standing) the platform along the length of

A few hours later I am standing on track 5 reading a newspaper. A train stops and ten people get off. Then the train rumbles onward toward Lod. Nobody pays any attention to me. My new friend walks down the platform and stands in front of me.

"איפה המתנה שלי?" הוא שואל.
sho'el hu sheli hamatana eifo
he asks he my the gift where

"Where is my gift?" he asks.

זו שאלה טובה, מאחר שאיני נושא מזוודה או תיק.
tik o mizvada nose she'eini me'akhar tova she'ela zo
bag or suitcase I carry that I am not since good question this

This is a good question, since I don't have a suitcase or backpack with me.

"היא כאן קרוב," אני אומר. "לפני שאני מביא אותה, נוכל לעשות
la'asot nukhal ota mevi she'ani lifnei omer ani karov kan hi
to make we will be able it I bring that I before I say I nearby here it

עסקה?"
iska
deal

"It's nearby," I say. "Before I get it, can we make some kind of deal?"

He looks amused.

הוא נראה משועשע.
hu	nire	meshu'asha
he	he looks	amused

"Take off your jacket," he says.

"תוריד את הז'קט," הוא אומר.
torid	et	ha'zhaket	hu	omer
you will take off	D.O.	the jacket	he	he says

After I do this he pats his hands around my chest, stomach, back, and thighs. After a few minutes, he stops.

לאחר שאני עושה כדבריו הוא טופח בידיו סביב חזי, בטני,
le'akhar	she'ani	ose	kidvarav	hu	tofe'akh	beyadav	sviv	khazi	bitni
after	that I	I do	as he said	he	he pats	with his hands	around	my chest	my stomach

גבי וירכיי. כעבור דקות אחדות הוא עוצר.
gabi	viyrekhai	ka'avor	dakot	akhadot	hu	otser
my back	and my thighs	after	minutes	a few	he	he stops

"You are not wearing any electronic devices. We can talk. The deal is that you must pay me every month."

"אין עליך שום ציוד אלקטרוני. אנחנו יכולים לדבר. העסקה היא
ein	aleikha	shum	tsiyud	elektroni	anakhnu	yekholim	ledaber	ha'iska	hi
there isn't	on you	any	equipment	electronic	we	we can	to talk	the deal	it

שאתה חייב לשלם לי כל חודש."
she'ata	khayav	leshalem	li	kol	khodesh
that you	you must	to pay	to me	every	month

"That's a lot of money," I say. "Can we call your boss and negotiate something different?"

"זה הרבה כסף," אני אומר. "נוכל להתקשר לבוס שלך ולדון
ze	harbe	kesef	ani	omer	nukhal	lehitkasher	lebos	shelkha	veladun
that	a lot	money	I	I say	we will be able	to call	to boss	your	and to discuss

בסידור אחר?"
besidur	akher
in arrangement	another

"The boss doesn't make deals."

"הבוס לא עושה עסקאות."
habos	lo	ose	iska'ot
the boss	no	he makes	deals

"Is there a way I could pay a percentage of my earnings? Some months I don't make as much as others."

"יש אפשרות שאשלם אחוזים מהרווחים שלי? יש חודשים
yesh	efsharut	she'ashalem	akhuzim	meharevakhim	sheli	yesh	khodashim
there is	possibility	that I will pay	percentages	of the earnings	my	there are	months

שאני מרוויח פחות."
she'ani	marvi'akh	pakhot
that I	I earn	less

"No more talking. Take me to the money," he responds.

"מספיק לדבר. קח אותי לכסף," הוא עונה.
maspik	ledaber	kakh	oti	lakesef	hu	one
enough	to talk	take	me	to the money	he	he responds

The guy seems determined, so I lead him to the back of track 5 and down a stairway. Halfway down the stairs a backpack lays on the floor. An electric box is attached to the wall about two meters above the steps. As he looks at the backpack, I grab a gun from the top of the electric box and shoot him

הבחור נראה נחוש, אז אני מוביל אותו אל מאחורי רציף 5
habakhur	nire	nakhush	az	ani	movil	oto	el	me'akhorei	ratsif	khamesh
the guy	he seems	determined	so	I	I lead	him	to	behind	platform	five

ובמורד גרם מדרגות. במחצית הדרך במורד המדרגות מונח תרמיל גב
uvemorad	gerem madregot	bemakhatsit	haderekh	bemorad	hamadregot	munakh	tarmil gav
and down	staircase	at half of	the way	down	the stairs	is placed	backpack

על הרצפה. קופסת חשמל מחוברת לקיר כשני מטרים מעל
me'al metrim kishnei lakir mekhuberet khashmal kufsat haritspa al
above — meters — about two of — to the wall — it is attached — electricity — box of — the floor — on

המדרגות. בעוד הוא מביט בתרמיל הגב, אני נוטל את האקדח המונח
hamunakh ha'ekdakh et notel ani betarmil hagav mabit hu be'od hamadregot
that is placed — the gun — D.O. — I take — I — at the backpack — he looks — he — as — the steps

על קופסת החשמל ויורה בו שלוש פעמים בליבו.
belibo pe'amim shalosh bo veyore hakhashmal kufsat al
in his heart — times — three — at him — and I shoot — the electricity — box of — on

"היית צריך לקחת את ביטוח החיים ההוא," אני אומר לגופתו.
legufato omer ani hahu hakhayim bitu'akh et lakakhat ha'ita tsarikh
to his corpse — I say — I — that one — the life — insurance of — D.O. — to take — you should have

three times in the heart.

"You should have taken that life insurance policy," I say to his corpse.

7

האקדח מצויד במשתיק קול, כך שאיש אינו ממהר במורד
bemorad memaher eino she'ish kakh bemashtik kol metsuyad ha'ekdakh
down — he hurries — he is not — that person — this way — with a silencer — it is equipped — the gun

המדרגות לראות מה קרה. אני מתקשר במהירות ללאה.
lele'a bimhirut mitkasher ani kara ma lirot hamadregot
to Leah — quickly — I call — I — it happened — what — to see — the stairs

The gun is silenced, so nobody rushes down the stairs to see what happened. I make a quick call to Leah.

"זה נעשה," אני אומר לה.
la omer ani na'asa ze
to her — I tell — I — it is done — this

"It's done," I tell her.

עשרים שניות מאוחר יותר אני שומע צלצול מתכתי. חברי הצוות
hatsevet khavrei matakhti tsiltsul shome'a ani yoter me'ukhar shniyot esrim
the team — members of — metallic — sound — I hear — I — more — late — seconds — twenty

שלי סוגרים את הדלתות בראש גרם המדרגות ובתחתיתו בשרשראות.
besharshera'ot uvetakhtito gerem hamadregot berosh hadlatot et sogrim sheli
with chains — and at bottom of it — the staircase — at top of — the doors — D.O. — they shut — my

זה מעניק לי זמן לחקור. אני בודק את כיסיו. כלום. אני פושט
poshet ani klum kisav et bodek ani lakh'kor zman li ma'anik ze
I take off — I — nothing — his pockets — D.O. — I check — I — to investigate — time — to me — it provides — this

את בגדיו ומחפש כתובות קעקע או צלקות. כלום.
klum tsalakot o ktovot ka'aka umekhapes bgadav et
nothing — scars — or — tattoos — and I look for — his clothes — D.O.

Twenty seconds later I hear clanging sounds. Members of my team are chaining shut the doors at the top and the bottom of the stairway. This gives me time to investigate. I check his pockets. Nothing. I take his clothes off and look for tattoos or scars. Nothing.

בעודי עוסק בחיפוש, אני מסביר לו את תיאוריית האבולוציה
ha'evolutsya te'oryat et lo masbir ani bekhipus osek be'odi
the evolution — theory of — D.O. — to him — I explain — I — with searching — I deal with — as I

שלי. אתם זוכרים את המונולוג מתחילת הסיפור, לא?
lo hasipur mitkhilat hamonolog et zokhrim atem sheli
no — the story — from beginning of — the monologue — D.O. — you remember — you — my

While I do these things, I explain my theory of evolution to him. You remember that monologue from the beginning of this story, don't you?

אני קוצץ את אצבעותיו ומניח אותן בשקית ניילון. נוכל
nukhal nailon besakit otan umani'akh etsbe'otav et kotsets ani
we will be able — nylon — in a small bag — them — and I place — his fingers — D.O. — I chop — I

I chop off his fingers and put them in a plastic baggie. We can get prints and DNA from the fingers, and they are a lot easier to carry than the whole body.

להשיג טביעות ודנ"א מהאצבעות, וקל הרבה יותר לשאת אותן
lehasig tvi'ot ve-DNA meha'etsba'ot, vekal harbe yoter laset otan
to obtain prints and DNA from the fingers, and easy much more to carry them

מאשר את הגופה כולה.
me'asher et hagufa kula.
than D.O. the body whole

I walk down the stairs and knock on the closed door at the bottom. Adina unlocks a chain and opens the door. She chains the door shut again and we head to her car. With any luck, the body won't be discovered for a few weeks. After all, this is Ajami.

אני צועד במורד גרם המדרגות ונוקש על הדלת הסגורה שבתחתיתו.
ani tso'ed bemorad gerem hamadregot venokesh al hadelet hasgura shebetakhtito.
I walk down the staircase and I knock on the door the closed that at bottom of it.

עדינה פותחת מנעול שרשרת ופותחת את הדלת לרווחה. היא סוגרת
adina potakhat manul sharsheret ufotakhat et hadelet lirvakha. hi sogeret
Adina she opens lock of chain and she opens D.O. the door wide open. she she shuts

את הדלת בשרשרת שוב ואנחנו פונים אל הרכב. עם מעט מזל,
et hadelet besharsheret shuv ve'anakhnu ponim el harekhev. im me'at mazal,
D.O. the door with chain again and we we turn to the car. with a little luck,

הגופה לא תתגלה במשך מספר שבועות. אחרי הכל, זו עג'מי.
hagufa lo titgale bemeshekh mispar shavu'ot. akharei hakol, zo ajami.
the body no it will be discovered during a few weeks. after all, this Ajami.

---8---

Adina drives us away from the train station. She's wearing a business suit. Her ponytail has been replaced with a more mature hairstyle.

עדינה מסיעה אותנו הרחק מתחנת הרכבת. היא לובשת חליפת
adina masi'a otanu harkhek mitakhanat harakevet. hi loveshet khalifat
Adina she drives us far away from station of the train. she she wears suit of

עסקים. הקוקו שלה הוחלף בתסרוקת בוגרת יותר.
asakim. hakuku shela hukhlaf betisroket bogeret yoter.
businesses. the ponytail her it is replaced with hairstyle mature more.

"Why are you wearing that suit?" I ask her.

"למה את לובשת את החליפה הזאת?" אני שואל אותה.
"lama at loveshet et hakhalifa hazot?" ani sho'el ota.
why you you wear D.O. the suit the that?" I I ask her.

"I'm blending in with the commuters," she answers.

"אני מתערה בין הנוסעים," היא עונה.
"ani mitara bein hanos'im," hi ona.
I blend in among the riders," she she answers.

"Drop me off at the insurance office. I've got an appointment at four thirty. You can take the fingers back to headquarters. Take the gun too. Tell Leah to get rid of it."

"תורידי אותי בסוכנות הביטוח. יש לי פגישה בארבע וחצי.
"toridi oti basokhnut habitu'akh. yesh li pgisha be'arba vakhetsi.
you will drop off me at the agency of the insurance. I have appointment at four and half.

את יכולה לקחת את האצבעות בחזרה למפקדה. קחי גם את
at yekhola lakakhat et ha'etsba'ot bakhazara lamifkada. k'khi gam et
you you can to take D.O. the fingers back to the headquarters. take also D.O.

האקדח. תגידי ללאה להיפטר ממנו."
ha'ekdakh. tagidi lele'a lehipater mimeno."
the gun. you will tell to Leah to get rid of of it."

"Did you mind fog the guy in the stairwell?"

"ערפלת את הבחור במדרגות?"
"irpalta et habakhur bamadregot?"
you fogged D.O. the guy on the stairs?"

"ערפלתי אותו כשהיינו על הרציף. למה את חושבת שהוא הסכים
irpalti oto ksheha'inu al haratsif. lama at koshevet shehu hiskim
I fogged | him | when we were | on | the platform | why | you | you think | that he | he agreed

לבוא איתי?"
lavo iti
to come | with me

"I did it while we were on the platform. Why do you think he was willing to follow me?"

"וזה הפך את הירייה בו לקלה."
veze hafakh et hayeriya bo lekala
and that | it made | D.O. | the shooting | at him | to easy

"And that made it easy for you to shoot him."

"ודאי. נתתי לו דחיפה מנטלית להסתכל על תרמיל הגב. הוא אפילו
vadai. natati lo dkhifa mentalit lehistakel al tarmil hagav. hu afilu
for sure | I gave | to him | push | mental | to look | at | the backpack | he | even

לא שם לב שאני לוקח את האקדח. אבל יכולתי ככל הנראה לעשות
lo sam lev she'ani loke'akh et ha'ekdakh. aval yakholti kekhol hanire la'asot
no | he noticed | that I | I take | D.O. | the gun | but | I could | probably | to do

זאת בלי לערפל אותו."
zot bli le'arpel oto
this | without | to fog | him

"Sure. I gave him a mental push to look at the backpack. He didn't even notice me grab the gun. But I probably could have done it without fogging him."

"אני יודעת כמה אתה מהיר," היא אומרת.
ani yoda'at kama ata mahir, hi omeret
I | I know | how | you | fast | she | she says

"I know how fast you are," she says.

"לא הפכתי איטי יותר בגיל העמידה," אני מזכיר לה.
lo hafakhti iti yoter begil ha'amida, ani mazkir la
no | I became | slow | more | with middle age | I | I remind | to her

"I haven't slowed down with middle age," I remind her.

"מישהו במצב רוח רע."
mishehu bematsav ru'akh ra
somebody | in mood | bad

"Somebody is in a bad mood."

"אני פשוט שונא לירות באנשים."
ani pashut sone lirot be'anashim
I | simply | I hate | to shoot | at people

"I just hate shooting people."

"אבל אתה עושה את זה בכל זאת."
aval ata ose et ze bekhol zot
but | you | you do | D.O. | it | nevertheless

"But you still do it."

"אני סוכן השטח, זוכרת? מישהו צריך לעשות את העבודה
ani sokhen hashetekh, zokheret? mishehu tsarikh la'asot et ha'avoda
I | agent of | the field | you remember | somebody | he needs | to do | D.O. | the work

הקשה."
hakasha
the hard

"I'm the field agent, remember? Somebody has to do the hard work."

"תזכיר לי שוב למה כולם חושבים שאתה סוכן ביטוח אמיתי,"
tazkir li shuv lama kulam khoshvim she'ata sokhen bitu'akh amiti,
you will remind | to me | again | why | everyone | they think | that you | agent of | insurance | real

"Remind me again why everyone thinks you're a real insurance agent," she says.

183

היא אומרת.

omeret hi
she says she

"My special ability can manifest in a few different ways. I can fog a person's mind so that they don't know what is happening. I can change their memories of recent events. I can persuade them to do simple things like look at a backpack or drop a gun. And I can make them believe I am someone else."

"היכולת המיוחדת שלי יכולה להתבטא בכמה צורות. אני יכול לערפל

le'arpel yakhol ani tsurot bekhama lehitbate yekhola sheli hameyukhedet hayekholet
to fog I can I ways in a few to manifest it can my the special the ability

את מוחו של אדם כך שלא ידע מה קורה. אני יכול

yakhol ani kore ma yada shelo kakh adam shel mokho et
I can I it happens what he knew that no in this manner person of his brain D.O.

לשנות את זכרונותיו לגבי אירועים. אני יכול לשכנע אותו לעשות

la'asot oto leshakhne'a yakhol ani eru'im legabei zikhronotav et leshanot
to do him to persuade I can I events about his memories D.O. to change

דברים פשוטים, כמו להביט בתרמיל גב או לשמוט אקדח. ואני יכול

yakhol va'ani ekdakh lishmot o betarmil gav lehabit kmo pshutim dvarim
I can and I gun to drop or in a backpack to look like simple things

לגרום לו להאמין שאני מישהו אחר."

akher mishehu she'ani leha'amin lo ligrom
else someone that I to believe to him to cause

"Can you hypnotize a whole room?" she asks.

"אתה יכול להפנט חדר שלם?" היא שואלת.

sho'elet hi shalem kheder lehapnet yakhol ata
she asks she whole room to hypnotize you can you

"It's not hypnosis. I don't even know how to describe my talent, but it only works on individuals and small groups."

"זו לא היפנוזה. אני אפילו לא יודע איך לתאר את הכישרון שלי,

sheli hakisharon et leta'er eikh yode'a lo afilu ani hipnoza lo zo
my the talent D.O. to describe how I know no even I hypnosis not this

אבל הוא עובד רק על אנשים בודדים וקבוצות קטנות."

ktanot ukvutsot bodedim anashim al rak oved hu aval
small and groups isolated people on only it works it but

"Where is the person you've been impersonating?" Adina asks.

"איפה האדם שהתחזית לו?" שואלת עדינה.

adina sho'elet lo shehitkhazeita ha'adam eifo
Adina she asks to him that you impersonated the person where

"I sent him and his daughter on a nice trip to Spain for a few weeks. They were happy to go when I explained to him that our top analyst thought he would be the next target."

"שלחתי אותו ואת בתו לטיול נחמד בספרד למספר שבועות.

shavu'ot lemispar bisfarad nekhmad letiyul bito ve'et oto shalakhti
weeks for a few in Spain nice for a trip his daughter and D.O. him I sent

הם שמחו לנסוע כשהסברתי לו שהאנליסט הראשי שלנו

shelanu harashi sheha'analist lo kshehisbarti linso'a samkhu hem
our the head that the analyst to him when I explained to travel they were happy they

סבור שהוא עומד להיות המטרה הבאה."

haba'a hamatara lihiyot omed shehu savur
the next the target to be he was about to that he he thinks

"Who is your top analyst?"

"מי האנליסט הראשי שלכם?"

shelakhem harashi ha'analist mi
your the head the analyst who

"רונן."
ronen
Ronen

"Ronen."

"לא אני?"
ani *lo*
I not

"Not me?"

"את האנליסטית הבכירה הראשית."
harashit *habkhira* *ha'analistit* *at*
the head the senior the analyst you

"You are the top senior analyst."

"יופי," היא אומרת.
omeret *hi* *yofi*
she says she great

"Good," she says.

יש רגע שקט בעוד אני מתבונן בהתפעלות באזור היפהפה של
shel *hayefefe* *ba'ezor* *behitpa'alut* *mitbonen* *ani* *be'od* *shaket* *rega* *yesh*
of the gorgeous at the area in wonder I observe I as quiet moment of there is

מרכז שכונת עג'מי.
ajami *shkhunat* *merkaz*
Ajami neighborhood of center of

There is a minute of quiet as I admire beautiful downtown Ajami.

"אני מקווה שאתה לא באמת מוכר פוליסות ביטוח," אומרת עדינה.
adina *omeret* *bitu'akh* *polisot* *mokher* *be'emet* *lo* *she'ata* *mekava* *ani*
Adina she says insurance policies of you sell really not that you I hope I

"I hope you are not actually selling insurance policies," Adina says.

"עדיין לא מכרתי אף אחת. אנשים לא מאמינים לי כשאני מסביר את
et *masbir* *kshe'ani* *li* *ma'aminim* *lo* *anashim* *af akhat* *makharti* *lo* *ada'in*
D.O. I explain when I to me they believe no people not one I sold not still

יתרונות ביטוח החיים. כנראה שאין לי פרצוף אמין."
amin *partsuf* *she'ein li* *kanire* *hakhayim* *bitu'akh* *yitronot*
trustworthy face that I don't have apparently the life insurance of advantages of

"I haven't sold one yet. People don't believe me when I explain the benefits of life insurance. Apparently I don't have an honest face."

יש רגע נוסף של שקט כשאנחנו משתלבים בנתיבי איילון.
ayalon *bintivei* *mishtalvim* *kshe'anakhnu* *sheket* *shel* *nosaf* *rega* *yesh*
Ayalon in the routes of we merge when we silence of additional moment there is

There is another minute of silence as we merge onto the Ayalon Highway.

"את שואלת הרבה שאלות היום," אני אומר לעדינה.
le'adina *omer* *ani* *hayom* *she'elot* *harbe* *sho'elet* *at*
to Adina I tell I today questions a lot you ask you

"You are asking a lot of questions today," I tell Adina.

"אני מתאמנת על כישורי השיחה שלי."
sheli *hasikha* *kishurei* *al* *mitamenet* *ani*
my the conversation skills of on I practice I

"I'm practicing my conversation skills."

"את מתכננת להיות עורכת דין?"
orekhet din *lihiyot* *metakhnenet* *at*
lawyer to become you plan you

"Are you planning to become a lawyer?"

"לא, אני רק מנסה להיות חברה טובה יותר בצוות."
batsevet *yoter* *tova* *khavera* *lihiyot* *menasa* *rak* *ani* *lo*
in the team more good member to be I try just I no

"No, I'm just trying to be a better member of the team."

185

"Did Leah say anything to you?"

"לאה אמרה לך משהו?"
mashehu lakh amra le'a
something to you she said Leah

"She mentioned that I need to work on my people skills."

"היא ציינה שאני צריכה לעבוד על יחסי האנוש שלי."
hi tsiyna she'ani tsrikha la'avod al yakhasei ha'enosh sheli
she she mentioned that I I need to work on the interpersonal relations my

"Because you threw that monitor at Ronen?"

"בגלל שזרקת את המסך ההוא על רונן?"
biglal shezarakt et hamasakh hahu al ronen
because of that you threw D.O. the monitor that one at Ronen

"He is so annoying sometimes."

"הוא כל כך מעצבן לפעמים."
hu kol kakh me'atsben lifamim
he so annoying sometimes

I chuckle.

אני מגחך.
ani megakhekh
I I chuckle

"Who do you think the dead guy worked for?" she asks.

"עבור מי עבד הבחור המת לדעתך?" היא שואלת.
avur mi avad habakhur hamet leda'atekha hi sho'elet
for who he worked the guy the dead to your opinion she she asks

"Ronen is pretty sure it's someone very high up in the Central District Headquarters."

"רונן בטוח למדי שזה מישהו בכיר מאוד במטה מחוז מרכז."
ronen batu'akh lemadai sheze mishehu bakhir me'od bemate makhoz merkaz
Ronen sure reasonably that it someone senior very at headquarters of district of center

"And you believe him?"

"ואתה מאמין לו?"
ve'ata ma'amin lo
and you you believe him

"He's never been wrong with any of his other predictions. One of the guys I play poker with is going to send me a few names to look into."

"הוא מעולם לא טעה באף אחת מהתחזיות שלו. אחד
hu me'olam lo ta'a be'af akhat mehatakhaziyot shelo ekhad
he never he was wrong at not even one of the predictions his one

מהבחורים שאני משחק איתם פוקר ישלח לי כמה שמות
mehabakhurim she'ani mesakhek itam poker yishlakh li kama shemot
of the guys that I I play with them poker he will send to me a few names

לבדיקה."
livdika
for examination

"Why do those gangsters let you play poker with them?"

"למה העבריינים האלו נותנים לך לשחק איתם פוקר?"
lama ha'avaryanim ha'elu notnim lekha lesakhek itam poker
why the criminals the those they let to you to play with them poker

"I used to do a lot of freelance work. Sometimes I did jobs for criminals. They know my reputation."

"נהגתי לעשות הרבה עבודות עצמאיות. מדי פעם עשיתי עבודות עבור
nahagti la'asot harbe avodot atsmaiyot midei pa'am asiti avodot avur
I used to to do a lot jobs freelance sometimes I did jobs for

186

עבריינים. הם מכירים את המוניטין שלי."
avaryanim hem makirim et hamonitin sheli
criminals they they know D.O. the reputation my

"אם אתה יכול לערפל את מוחם של אנשים, איך זה שאתה לא
im ata yakhol le'arpel et mokham shel anashim, eikh ze she'ata lo
if you you can to fog D.O. their brains of people how this that you no

מרוויח ערמות של כסף בכל פעם שאתה משחק פוקר?"
marvi'akh aremot shel kesef bekhol pa'am she'ata mesakhek poker
you earn piles of money every time that you you play poker

"Since you can mind fog people, how come you don't win big piles of money every time you play poker?"

"אני לא רוצה."
ani lo rotse
I no I want

"I don't want to."

"למה לא?"
lama lo
why not

"Why not?"

"אני משחק עם החבר'ה האלה כדי לאסוף מידע, לא כדי
ani mesakhek im hakhevre ha'ele kedei le'esof meida, lo kedei
I I play with the guys the those in order to to collect information not in order to

להרוויח כסף. זו הסיבה שאני משחק במקומות שונים, עם קבוצות
leharvi'akh kesef. zo hasiba she'ani mesakhek bimkomot shonim, im kvutsot
to win/earn money this the reason that I I play in places different with groups

שונות של אנשים. בדרך כלל אני מנסה להרוויח קצת או להפסיד קצת.
shonot shel anashim. bederekh klal ani menase leharvi'akh ktsat o lehafsid ktsat
different of people usually I I try to earn a little or to lose a little

מה שאני לא רוצה לעשות זה למשוך אליי תשומת לב רבה בכך
ma she'ani lo rotse la'asot ze limshokh elai tsumat lev raba bekhakh
what that I no I want to do this to attract toward me attention a lot such

שאנצח כל הזמן."
she'anatse'akh kol hazman
that I will win all the time

"I play poker with those guys to collect information, not to win money. That's why I play in different locations with different groups of people. I usually try to win a little bit or lose a little bit. The thing I don't want to do is call a lot of attention to myself by winning all the time."

"הרווחת הרבה כסף אתמול בלילה."
hirvakhta harbe kesef etmol balaila
you earned a lot money yesterday in the night

"You won a lot of money yesterday night."

"נסחפתי. ניסיתי להרשים את הבחורה שהייתה שם."
niskhafti. nisiti leharshim et habakhura shehaita sham
I got carried away I tried to impress D.O. the young woman that (she) was there

"I got carried away. I was trying to impress this girl who was there."

"איילה?"
ayala
Ayala

"Ayala?"

"מישהי אחרת. היא הייתה חתיכה."
mishehi akheret. hi haita khatikha
someone else she she was attractive

"Someone else. She was hot."

187

"Too much information!" Adina yells at me.

"יותר מדי מידע!" מרימה עליי עדינה את קולה.

kola	et	adina	alai	merima	meida	yoter midai
her voice	D.O.	Adina	at me	she raises	information	too much

The car becomes quiet again. Adina practices her tailgating and lane changing skills. A few drivers honk at us.

המכונית הופכת שוב שקטה. עדינה מתרגלת את כישורי המעקב

hama'akav	kishurei	et	metargelet	adina	shketa	shuv	hofekhet	hamkhonit
the tracking	qualifications of	D.O.	she practices	Adina	quiet	again	it becomes	the car

והחלפת המסלולים שלה. נהגים אחדים צופרים לעברנו.

le'evrenu	tsofrim	akhadim	nahagim	shela	hamaslulim	vehakhlafat
toward us	they honk	a few	drivers	her	the lanes	and changing of

---

"Wave your gun at them," she tells me.

"תנפנף באקדח שלך מולם," היא אומרת לי.

li	omeret	hi	mulam	shelkha	ba'ekdakh	tenafnef
to me	she tells	she	in front of them	your	with the gun	you will wave

---

"This is Jaffa. They probably have bigger guns."

"זו יפו. בטח יש להם אקדחים גדולים יותר."

yoter	gdolim	ekdakhim	yesh lahem	betakh	yafo	zo
more	big	guns	they have	surely	Jaffa	this

"Did you tell the corpse your theory about evolution?" she asks.

"סיפרת לגופה את התאוריה שלך על האבולוציה?" היא שואלת.

sho'elet	hi	ha'evolutsya	al	shelkha	hate'orya	et	lagufa	siparta
she asks	she	the evolution	about	your	the theory	D.O.	to the corpse	you told

---

"I explained my theory to him while I was searching his clothing."

"הסברתי לו את התאוריה שלי בזמן שערכתי חיפוש בבגדיו."

bivgadav	khipus	she'arakhti	bizman	sheli	hate'orya	et	lo	hisbarti
his clothing	searching	that I conducted	while	my	the theory	D.O.	to him	I explained

---

"Don't you think it's a little strange to talk to dead people?" she asks.

"אתה לא חושב שזה מוזר קצת לדבר לאנשים מתים?" היא שואלת.

sho'elet	hi	metim	le'anashim	ledaber	ktsat	muzar	sheze	khoshev	lo	ata
she asks	she	dead	to people	to talk	a little	strange	that it	you think	no	you

---

"Everyone who visits a cemetery talks to dead people," I say.

"כל מי שמבקר בבית קברות מדבר לאנשים מתים," אני אומר.

omer	ani	metim	le'anashim	medaber	beveit kvarot	shemevaker	kol mi
I say	I	dead	to people	he talks	in a cemetery	who (he) visits	anyone

---

"That's different. They aren't explaining their view of the universe. Anyway, we didn't get our special powers from evolution."

"זה שונה. הם לא מסבירים את דעותיהם על היקום. בכל אופן,

bekhol ofen	hayekum	al	de'oteihem	et	masbirim	lo	hem	shone	ze
anyway	the universe	about	their opinions	D.O.	they explain	no	they	different	that

לא קיבלנו את הכוחות המיוחדים שלנו מהאבולוציה."

meha'evolutsya	shelanu	hameyukhadim	hakokhot	et	kibalnu	lo
from the evolution	our	the special	the powers	D.O.	we received	no

---

"Then how did we get these strange talents?"

"אז איך קיבלנו את הכישרונות המוזרים האלה?"

ha'ele	hamuzarim	hakishronot	et	kibalnu	eikh	az
the these	the strange	the talents	D.O.	we received	how	then

"Aliens from outer space added their DNA to human chromosomes back in the stone age. Every few generations after that, something unusual pops out - like us."

"חוצנים מהחלל החיצון הוסיפו את הדנ"א שלהם לכרומוזומים

likhromozomim	shelahem	ha-DNA	et	hosifu	mehakhalal hakhitson	khotsanim
to chromosomes of	their	the DNA	D.O.	they added	from outer space	aliens

אנושיים בתקופת האבן. בכל כמה דורות מאז צץ משהו

mashehu	tsats	me'az	dorot	kama	bekhol	ha'even	bitkufat	enoshiyim
something	it pops up	since	generations	few	in every	the stone	in age of	human

ייחודי - כמונו."
yikhudi — *kamonu*
unique — like us

"זה טיפשי," אני אומר.
ze tipshi, ani omer
that silly, I I say

"That's silly," I say.

"לא טיפשי כמו האמונה שלך באלוהים שאיננו קיים."
lo tipshi kmo ha'emuna shelkha be'elohim she'einenu kayam
not silly like the faith your in god that he is not existent

"Not as silly as you believing in a god who doesn't exist."

"אני לא מאמין שאני עובד עם אתאיסטית," אני קורא. "שאר החבר'ה
ani lo ma'amin she'ani oved im ate'istit, ani kore. sh'ar hakhevre
I no I believe that I I work with atheist, I I shout. rest of the buddies

בחוליה' ישמעו על זה."
bakhulya yishme'u al ze
in the squad they will hear about this

"I can't believe I work with an atheist," I exclaim. "The rest of "The Squad" will hear about this."

"אף אחד לא הסכים לקרוא לצוות שלנו 'החוליה'," היא אומרת.
af ekhad lo hiskim likro latsevet shelanu hakhulya, hi omeret
nobody no they agreed to call to the team our The Squad, she she says

"Nobody agreed to call our team 'The Squad'," she says.

"אף אחד גם לא התנגד."
af ekhad gam lo hitnaged
nobody also no he opposed

"Nobody disagreed either."

"לא רצינו לפגוע ברגשותיך. זה שם אידיוטי."
lo ratsinu lifgo'a berigshoteikha. ze shem idiyoti
no we wanted to hurt at your feelings. this name stupid

"We didn't want to hurt your feelings. It's a stupid name."

"אני אוהב אותו. אולי נוכל להזמין ז'קטים עם כיתוב 'החוליה'
ani ohev oto. ulai nukhal lehazmin zhaketim im kituv hakhulya
I I like it. maybe we will be able to order jackets with text The Squad

על הגב."
al hagav
on the back

"I like it. Maybe we can order jackets with 'The Squad' written on the back."

"אני חושבת שאנחנו צריכים לערוך הצבעה על השם," היא אומרת.
ani khoshevet she'anakhnu tsrikhim la'arokh hatsba'a al hashem, hi omeret
I I think that we we should to arrange voting on the name, she she says

"I think we should vote on the name," she says.

"נראה."
nire
we will see

"We'll see."

באותו לילה מצלצל הטלפון הנייד. אני עונה ושומע קול נוסף
be'oto laila metsaltsel hatelefon hanayad. ani one veshome'a kol nosaf
in same night it rings the phone the mobile. I I answer and I hear voice additional

That night the cell phone rings. I answer and hear another voice with a strange accent.

בעל מבטא מוזר.
ba'al *mivta* *muzar*
owner of accent strange

"Where is he?"

"איפה הוא?"
eifo *hu*
where he

"Who is this?"

"מי זה?"
mi *ze*
who this

"Don't act stupid. I'll ask again - where is he?"

"אל תהיה טיפש. אני אשאל שוב - איפה הוא?"
al *tihiye* *tipesh* *ani* *eshal* *shuv* - *eifo* *hu*
don't you will be stupid I I will ask again where he

"Are you talking about the guy I was supposed to meet today at track 5?" I ask.

"אתה מדבר על הבחור שהייתי אמור לפגוש היום ברציף 5?"
ata *medaber* *al* *habakhur* *sheha'iti* *amur* *lifgosh* *hayom* *beratsif* *khamesh*
you you talk about the guy that I was supposed to meet today at platform five

אני שואל.
ani *sho'el*
I I ask

"Stop wasting time. Answer the question."

"תפסיק לבזבז זמן. תענה על השאלה."
tafsik *levazbez* *zman* *ta'ane* *al* *hashe'ela*
you will stop to waste time you will answer regarding the question

"I don't know," I say. "I spent half an hour at a train station in Ajami, praying I wouldn't get mugged by some commuter, and your man never showed."

"אני לא יודע," אני אומר. "בזבזתי חצי שעה בתחנת הרכבת בעג'מי,
ani *lo* *yode'a,* *ani* *omer.* *bizbazti* *khatsi* *sha'a* *betakhanat* *harakevet* *be'ajami,*
I not I know I I say I wasted half of hour at station of the train in Ajami

מתפלל שלא ישדדו אותי, והאיש שלך לא הופיע."
mitpalel *shelo* *yishdedu* *oti,* *veha'ish* *shelkha* *lo* *hofi'a*
I pray that no they will rob me and the man your no he showed up

"He was there. What happened to him?"

"הוא היה שם. מה קרה לו?"
hu *haya* *sham.* *ma* *kara* *lo*
he he was there what it happened to him

"I don't know."

"אני לא יודע."
ani *lo* *yode'a*
I no I know

This went on for a few minutes. He kept claiming that I did something and I kept telling him that I did nothing. I was lying, but the guy on the phone didn't know that. Finally he decided I was telling the truth. After all, who would believe that someone with my sunny personality could shoot somebody in the heart and chop off his fingers?

השיחה ממשיכה כך למשך מספר דקות. הוא ממשיך לטעון
hasikha *mamshikha* *kakh* *lemeshekh* *mispar* *dakot.* *hu* *mamshikh* *liton*
the conversation it continues like this for a few minutes he continues to claim

שעשיתי משהו ואני ממשיך לומר לו שלא עשיתי כלום. אני משקר,
she'asiti *mashehu* *va'ani* *mamshikh* *lomar* *lo* *shelo* *asiti* *klum.* *ani* *meshaker,*
that I did something and I I continue to tell to him that no I did nothing I lie I

אבל הבחור בטלפון לא ידע את זה. לבסוף, הוא מחליט שאני
aval *habakhur* *batelefon* *lo* *yada* *et* *ze.* *levasof,* *hu* *makhlit* *she'ani*
but the guy on the phone no he knew D.O. this finally he he decides that I

190

אומר אמת. אחרי הכל, מי יאמין שמישהו בעל אישיות עליזה

omer / *emet* / *akharei* / *hakol* / *mi* / *ya'amin* / *shemishehu* / *ba'al* / *ishiyut* / *aliza*

I tell / truth / after / all / who / he will believe / that someone / owner of / personality / jolly

כשלי יכול לירות במישהו בליבו ולקצוץ את אצבעותיו?

kesheli / *yakhol* / *lirot* / *bemishehu* / *belibo* / *veliktsots* / *et* / *etsbe'otav*

like mine / he can / to shoot / at someone / in his heart / and to chop off / D.O. / his fingers

"אני אחזור אליך," הוא אומר.

ani / *ekhzor* / *eleikha* / *hu* / *omer*

I / I will get back / to you / he / he says

"I'll get back to you," he says.

"אני שומע את זה מהרבה בנות," אני אומר כשהוא מנתק את

ani / *shome'a* / *et* / *ze* / *meharbe* / *banot* / *ani* / *omer* / *kshehu* / *menatek* / *et*

I / I hear / D.O. / that / from a lot / girls / I / say / as he / he disconnects / D.O.

השיחה.

hasikha

the call

"I hear that from a lot of girls," I say, as he disconnects the call.

למחרת, אני קורא בעיתון שהבחור שיריתי בו כבר נמצא.

lemokhorat / *ani* / *kore* / *ba'iton* / *shehabakhur* / *sheyariti* / *bo* / *kvar* / *nimtsa*

the next day / I / I read / in the newspaper / that the guy / that I shot / at him / already / he was found

איש תחזוקה חרוץ כלשהו ניסר את השרשרת שסגרה את הדלת

ish takhzuka / *kharuts* / *kolshehu* / *niser* / *et* / *hasharsheret* / *shesagra* / *et* / *hadelet*

janitor / industrious / some / he sawed / D.O. / the chain / that it closed / D.O. / the door

וגילה את הגופה.

vegila / *et* / *hagufa*

and he discovered / D.O. / the body

The next day, I read in the newspaper that the man I shot has already been found. Some industrious janitor sawed off the chain that kept the door closed and discovered the body.

הכתבה מרמזת שזה היה רצח של המאפיה. אני חושב להתקשר

hakatava / *meramezet* / *sheze* / *haya* / *retsakh* / *shel* / *hamafya* / *ani* / *khoshev* / *lehitkasher*

the article / it suggests / that this / it was / murder / of / the mafia / I / I think / to call

לכתבת ולתקן את סיפורה, אבל מחליט שלא. היא לא תאמין

lakatevet / *uletaken* / *et* / *sipura* / *aval* / *makhlit* / *shelo* / *hi* / *lo* / *ta'amin*

to the reporter / and to correct / D.O. / her story / but / I decide / that no / she / no / she will believe

לי.

li

to me

The story suggests that this murder is a mob execution. I think about calling the reporter to correct her story, but decide against it. She wouldn't believe me.

מאוחר יותר באותו יום אני פוסע למזנון מקומי לארוחת צוהריים

me'ukhar / *yoter* / *be'oto* / *yom* / *ani* / *pose'a* / *lemiznon* / *mekomi* / *le'arukhat tsohora'im*

late / more / in the same / day / I / I amble / to diner / local / for lunch

לפריטים העצמאות. מלחמת ברוח מעוצב המזנון נחמדה.

lepritim / *ha'atsma'ut* / *milkhemet* / *beru'akh* / *me'utsav* / *hamiznon* / *nekhmada*

to items / the independence / war of / in spirit of / it is designed / the diner / nice

בתפריט יש שמות חמודים.

batafrit / *yesh* / *shemot* / *khamudim*

on the menu / there are / names / cute

Later that day I amble over to a local diner for a nice lunch. The diner is decorated with a War of Independence theme. The items on the menu all have cute names.

A ninety year old waitress dressed like Paula Ben-Gurion comes over to take my order.

מלצרית בת תשעים, לבושה כמו פולה בן-גוריון, ניגשת לקחת
meltsarit bat tishim levusha kmo pola ben-guryon nigeshet lakakhat
waitress aged ninety dressed like Paula Ben-Gurion she approaches to take

ממני הזמנה.
mimeni hazmana
from me order

"What is today's special?" I ask.

"מה מנת היום?" אני שואל.
ma mnat hayom ani sho'el
what dish of the day I I ask

"Onion soup and lamb sausage."

"מרק בצל ונקניק טלה."
marak batsal venaknik tale
soup of onion and sausage of lamb

"Is it good?"

"זה טעים?"
ze ta'im
this tasty

"How should I know? I don't eat here."

"איך אני יכולה לדעת? אני לא אוכלת כאן."
eikh ani yekhola lada'at ani lo okhelet kan
how I I can to know I no I eat here

"Why not?"

"למה לא?"
lama lo
why not

"I have to watch my cholesterol."

"אני צריכה לשמור על הכולסטרול."
ani tsrikha lishmor al hakolesterol
I I need to watch out for the cholesterol

"Do you still serve breakfast?"

"אתם עדיין מגישים ארוחת בוקר?"
atem ada'in magishim arukhat boker
you still you serve breakfast

"No breakfast after eleven o'clock. It says so right on the menu."

"אין ארוחת בוקר אחרי אחת עשרה. כתוב על התפריט."
ein arukhat boker akharei akhat esre katuv al hatafrit
there isn't breakfast after eleven written on the menu

"I'm thinking about the tuna salad. Is it fresh?"

"אני חושב על סלט הטונה. הוא טרי?"
ani khoshev al salat hatuna hu tari
I I think about salad of the tuna it fresh

"Are you going to order something today, or are you here to take a survey?"

"אתה מתכוון להזמין משהו היום, או שאתה כאן כדי לערוך
ata mitkaven lehazmin mashehu hayom o she'ata kan kedei la'arokh
you you intend to order something today or that you here in order to to conduct

מחקר?"
mekh'kar
research

"I thought you would enjoy some conversation," I tell her. "After all, the place isn't very busy."

חשבתי שתהני מקצת שיחה," אני אומר לה. "אחרי הכל,
khashavti shetehani miktsat sikha ani omer la akharei hakol
I thought that you will enjoy of a little conversation I I tell to her after all

המקום לא ממש עמוס."

hamakom	lo	mamash	amus
the place	not	very	busy

"טוב, הרגליים שלי כואבות," היא אומרת לי, "אז תמהר

tov	haragla'im	sheli	ko'avot	hi	omeret	li	az	temaher
well	the legs	my	they hurt	she	she tells	to me	so	you will hurry

ותזמין."

vetazmin
and you will order

"Well, my feet hurt," she tells me, "so hurry up and order."

"אני אקח המבורגר וקוקה-קולה."

ani	ekakh	hamburger	vekoka kola
I	I will take	hamburger	and Coca-Cola

"I'll take a hamburger and a Coca-Cola."

המלצרית רושמת את ההזמנה בפנקסה והולכת לדרכה. עשר דקות

hameltsarit	roshemet	et	hahazmana	befinkasa	veholekhet	ledarka	eser	dakot
the waitress	she writes	D.O.	the order	in her notepad	and she walks	to her way	ten	minutes

מאוחר יותר מתיישב בחור מכוער על הדלפק לצדי. זה מוזר, מכיוון

me'ukhar	yoter	mityashev	bakhur	mekho'ar	al	hadelpek	letsidi	ze	muzar	mikeivan
late	more	he sits	guy	ugly	at	the counter	beside me	this	strange	since

שיש שרפרפים פנויים רבים. בדרך כלל אנשים ביפו לא רוצים

sheyesh	shrafrafim	pnuyim	rabim	bederekh klal	anashim	beyafo	lo	rotsim
that there are	stools	empty	many	usually	people	in Jaffa	no	they want

לשבת זה ליד זה אלא אם אין להם ברירה.

lashevet	ze leyad ze	ela im	ein lahem	breira
to sit	side by side	unless	they don't have	choice

The waitress writes my order onto her notepad and walks away. Ten minutes later an ugly guy sits next to me at the counter. This is unusual, since there are plenty of empty stools. People in Jaffa don't normally want to sit right next to each other if they can avoid it.

"בשבוע הבא אתה משלם כפול," הוא אומר לי. "אני אגיע למשרד

beshavu'a	haba	ata	meshalem	kaful	hu	omer	li	ani	agi'a	lamisrad
for week	next	you	you pay	double	he	he says	to me	I	I will come	to the office

שלך ביום שלישי. בלי שינויי מקום."

shelkha	beyom shlishi	bli	shinuyei	makom
your	on Tuesday	no	changes of	location

"Next week you pay double," he says to me. "I will be at your office on Tuesday. No changes in location."

ואז הוא עוזב. אני מדבר אל תוך סיכה בז'קט שלי.

ve'az	hu	ozev	ani	medaber	el	tokh	sika	ba'zhaket	sheli
and then	he	he leaves	I	I talk	to	inside	pin	on the jacket	my

Then he leaves. I talk into a pin on my jacket.

"הוא בדרכו החוצה. שיער חום, מטר שמונים וחמש, שוקל

hu	bedarko	hakhutsa	sei'ar	khum	meter	shmonim vekhamesh	shokel
he	on his way	outside	hair	brown	meter	eighty-five	he weighs

כתשעים וחמישה קילו. הוא לובש מעיל כהה וג׳ינס. נראה כאילו

ketishim vekhamisha	kilo	hu	lovesh	me'il	kehe	vejins	nire	ke'ilu
about ninety-five	kilogram	he	he wears	coat	dark	and jeans	he looks	like

הלך מכות עם רכבת והפסיד."

halakh makot	im	rakevet	vehifsid
he fought	with	train	and he lost

"He's on his way out. Brown hair, one meter eighty-five, weighs about ninety-five kilos. He is wearing a dark jacket and jeans. Looks like he lost a fight with a train."

Story 13

I have a small receiver in my ear so I can hear the person on the other end. A private investigator who has been following me since yesterday.

באוזני מותקן מקלט קטן, כך שאני יכול לשמוע את האדם
be'ozni mutkan maklet katan, kakh she'ani yakhol lishmo'a et ha'adam
in my ear / installed / receiver / small / so / that I / I can / to hear / D.O. / the person

שבצדו השני של הקו. חוקרת פרטית שעוקבת אחריי מאז
shebetsido hasheni shel hakav. khokeret pratit she'okevet akharai me'az
that's on the other end / of / the line / investigator / private / that she follows / after me / since

אתמול.
etmol
yesterday

"I've got him," the private investigator reports. "I'll call you later and tell you where he ends up."

"מצאתי אותו," מדווחת החוקרת הפרטית. "אני אתקשר אליך מאוחר
"matsati oto," medavakhat hakhokeret hapratit. "ani etkasher eleikha me'ukhar
I found / him / she reports / the investigator / the private / I / I will call / to you / late

יותר לדווח לך לאן הוא הולך."
yoter ledave'akh lekha le'an hu holekh.
more / to report / to you / to where / he / he goes

Just then the waitress brings my hamburger. It is delicious. I leave her a nice tip when I leave.

בדיוק אז מביאה המלצרית את ההמבורגר שלי. הוא טעים. כשאני
bediyuk az mevi'a hameltsarit et hahamburger sheli. hu ta'im. kshe'ani
precisely / then / she brings / the waitress / D.O. / the hamburger / my / it / delicious / when I

עוזב אני משאיר לה תשר נאה.
ozev ani mashir la tesher na'e.
I leave / I / I leave behind / to her / tip / substantial

The rest of my day is uneventful. I read a few manuals about how to sell dental insurance to people who don't want it. I play a few games on the office computer. Then I do a crossword puzzle. Next I take a nap. Finally, I go online to read gossip about Hollywood celebrities. There are thousands of websites devoted to this.

המשך היום נטול התרחשויות מיוחדות. אני קורא מדריכים אחדים
hemshekh hayom natul hitrakhashuyot meyukhadot. ani kore madrikhim akhadim
the rest of / the day / devoid / events / special / I / I read / manuals / a few

העוסקים במכירת ביטוח שיניים לאנשים שאינם מעוניינים בו.
ha'oskim bimkhirat bitu'akh shina'im le'anashim she'einam me'unyanim bo.
that deal with / with the sale of / insurance of / dental / to people / that are not / interested / in it

אני משחק קצת במחשב במשרד. אני פותר תשבץ. לאחר מכן
ani mesakhek ktsat bamakhshev bamisrad. ani poter tashbets. le'akhar miken
I / I play / a little / with the computer / in the office / I / I solve / crossword puzzle / afterward

אני מנמנם. לבסוף, אני גולש באינטרנט וקורא רכילות על אודות
ani menamnem. levasof, ani golesh ba'internet vekore rekhilut al odot
I / I nap / finally / I / I browse / on the internet / and I read / gossip / about

כוכבי הוליווד. ישנם אלפי אתרים שמוקדשים לנושא.
kokhvei holivud. yeshnam alfei atarim shemukdashim lanose.
stars of / Hollywood / there are / thousands of / sites / that are dedicated / to the topic

At six thirty the private investigator calls back.

בשעה שש וחצי מתקשרת החוקרת הפרטית.
besha'a shesh vakhetsi mitkasheret hakhokeret hapratit.
at hour / six / and half / she calls / the investigator / the private

"The guy went to an old apartment building in Holon, picked up his laundry, and did some wash at a nearby laundromat."

"הבחור הלך לבניין דירות ישן בחולון, אסף את הכביסה
"habakhur halakh levinyan dirot yashan bekholon, asaf et hakvisa
the guy / he went / to building / apartments / old / in Holon / he gathered / D.O. / the laundry

שלו וכיבס אותה במכבסה אוטומטית ליד הבניין."
shelo vekhibes ota bemikhbasa otomatit leyad habinyan.
his / and he laundered / it / at laundromat / automatic / near / the building

"שמת לב אם היו ארנבונים על אחת מהפיג׳מות שהוא כיבס?"
samt lev im hayu arnevonim al akhat mehapijamot shehu kibes
you noticed if there were bunnies on one of the pajamas that he he laundered

"Did you notice if any of the pajamas he washed had bunnies on them?"

"ארנבונים?"
arnevonim
bunnies

"Bunnies?"

"כן. גורי ארנבים. אני אוהב פיג׳מות עם ארנבונים."
ken gurei arnavim ani ohev pijamot im arnevonim
yes pups of rabbits I I love pajamas with bunnies

"Yeah. Baby rabbits. I love pajamas with bunnies."

"לא התקרבתי כל כך."
lo hitkaravti kol kakh
no I got close so

"I didn't get that close."

"את אמורה לשים לב לדברים כאלה. אני מתכוון לשלוח מכתב תלונה לאחראי שלך."
at amura lasim lev ledvarim ka'ele ani mitkaven lishlo'akh mikhtav tluna la'akhra'i shelakh
you supposed to to notice to things like these I I plan to send letter of complaint to the supervisor your

"You are supposed to notice these things. I plan to send a complaint letter to your supervisor."

"חיים, אין לי אחראי."
kha'im ein li akhra'i
Haim I don't have supervisor

"Haim, I don't have a supervisor."

"שכחתי. איפה הבחור עכשיו?"
shakhakhti eifo habakhur akhshav
I forgot where the guy now

"I forgot. Where is the guy now?"

"שותה במסעדה בראשון."
shote be'misada berishon
he drinks at restaurant in Rishon LeTsiyon

"Drinking at a restaurant in Rishon."

"תני לי את הכתובת. אהיה שם בתוך חצי שעה."
tni li et haktovet ehiye sham betokh khatsi sha'a
give to me D.O. the address I will be there in half hour

"Give me the address. I'll be there in half an hour."

"אתה צריך הוראות הגעה?"
ata tsarikh hora'ot haga'a
you you need instructions of arrival

"Do you need directions?"

"ברור שלא. יש לי ג׳י.פי.אס."
barur shelo yesh li jipi'es
of course that not I have GPS

"Of course not. I have GPS."

כשאני מגיע למסעדה אני מזהה את האיש שלי יושב בקצה הבר. אני מתיישב במושב שלצידו. הוא מביט בי. אני מחייך.
kshe'ani magi'a lamisada ani mezahe et ha'ish sheli yoshev biktse habar ani mityashev bamoshav sheletsido hu mabit bi ani mekhayekh
when I I arrive to the restaurant I I recognize D.O. the man my he sits at the end of the bar I I sit down in the seat that is beside him he he looks at me I I smile

When I get to the restaurant I spot my man sitting at the end of the bar. I take the seat next to him. He looks at me. I smile. He doesn't recognize me. As I mentioned earlier, my special ability allows me to control what people see and hear.

הוא איננו מזהה אותי. כפי שציינתי קודם, היכולת המיוחדת
hu eineno mezahe oti. kfi shetsiyanti kodem, hayekholet hameyukhedet
he / he doesn't / he recognizes / me / as / that I mentioned / before / the ability / the special

שלי מאפשרת לי לשלוט במה שאנשים רואים ושומעים.
sheli me'afsheret li lishlot bema she'anashim ro'im veshomim.
my / it allows / to me / to control / in what / that people / they see / and they hear

"Aren't those GPS systems amazing?" I ask the guy.

מערכות הניווט האלה מדהימות, לא?" אני שואל את הבחור.
ma'arakhot hanivut ha'ele madhimot, lo?" ani sho'el et habakhur.
systems of / the navigation / the those / amazing / no / I ask / I / D.O. / the guy

"Leave me alone," he mutters.

"עזוב אותי בשקט," הוא רוטן.
azov oti besheket," hu roten.
leave / me / in quiet / he / he grumbles

"My GPS has a British voice. I like to pretend I'm driving with Winston Churchill."

"לג'י.פי.אס שלי יש קול בריטי. אני אוהב לדמיין שאני נוסע עם וינסטון
lejipi'es sheli yesh kol briti. ani ohev ledamyen she'ani nose'a im vinston
my GPS has / voice / British / I / I like / to imagine / that I / I drive / with / Winston

צ'רצ'יל."
tchertchil."
Churchill

"If you talk to me again I will punch you."

"אם תדבר איתי שוב אני אחטיף לך."
im tedaber iti shuv ani akhtif lekha."
if / you will talk / with me / again / I / I will punch / to you

At this point, I hit him with a full blast of my mental fog.

בשלב זה אני מכה בו במלוא כוחו של הערפול המוחי שלי.
beshalav ze ani make bo bimlo kokho shel ha'irpul hamokhi sheli.
at stage / this / I / I hit / at him / with fullness of / its strength / of / the fog / the mental / my

"Why don't you finish that drink and we'll take a ride," I say to him.

"למה שלא תסיים את המשקה הזה ונצא לנסיעה," אני
lama shelo tesayem et hamashke haze venetse linsi'a," ani
why / that no / you will finish / D.O. / the drink / the that / and we will leave / for ride / I

אומר לו.
omer lo.
I say / to him

He gulps the rest of his beer and follows me outside to my car.

הוא גומע את שארית הבירה שלו ויוצא אחריי החוצה אל
hu gome'a et she'erit habira shelo veyotse akharai hakhutsa el
he / he swallows / D.O. / remainder of / the beer / his / and goes out / after me / outside / to

מכוניתי.
mekhoniti.
my car

"Get in and relax," I tell him. "I'll drive."

"היכנס והירגע," אני אומר לו. "אני אנהג."
hikanes veheraga," ani omer lo. "ani enhag."
get in / and relax / I / I tell / to him / I / I will drive

I handcuff the gentleman to the passenger side door and call Leah. We agree to meet at a deserted construction site near Bat Yam. Twenty min-

אני קושר את האדון באזיקים לדלת בצד הנוסע
ani kosher et ha'adon be'azikim ladelet betsad hanose'a
I / I tie / D.O. / the gentleman / with handcuffs / to the door / on the side of / the passenger

ומתקשר ללאה. אנחנו מחליטים להיפגש באתר בנייה נטוש סמוך
umitkasher lele'a anakhnu makhlitim lehipagesh be'atar bniya natush samukh
and I call / to Leah / we / we decide / to meet / at site of / construction / deserted / adjacent

לבת ים עשרים דקות לאחר מכן ראשו של הבחור צלול, אבל ידיו
levat yam esrim dakot le'akhar miken rosho shel habakhur tsalul, aval yadav
to Bat Yam / twenty / minutes / afterward / his head / of / the guy / clear / but / his hands

ורגליו קשורות.
veraglav kshurot
and his feet / tied

utes later, the guy's head is clear, but his hands and feet are tied.

לאה משוחחת איתו. ללאה יש יכולת מעניינת. היא מדברת עם אנשים
le'a mesokhakhat ito. lele'a yesh yekholet me'anyenet. hi medaberet im anashim
Leah / she converses / with him / Leah has / ability / interesting / she / she talks / with / people

והם מספרים לה כל מה שהיא רוצה לדעת. היא אינה יודעת
vehem mesaprim la kol ma shehi rotsa lada'at. hi eina yoda'at
and they / they tell / to her / all / what / that she / she wants / to know / she / she doesn't / she knows

להסביר איך היא עושה את זה, בדיוק כפי שאני איני יודע
lehasbir eikh hi osa et ze, bediyuk kfi she'ani eini yode'a
to explain / how / she / she does / D.O. / this / exactly / in the same manner / that I / I do not / I know

כיצד פועל הערפול המוחי שלי. אבל זה כישרון נפלא.
keitsad po'el ha'irpul hamokhi sheli. aval ze kisharon nifla
how / it works / the fog / the mental / my / but / this / talent / wonderful

Leah is talking to him. Leah has this interesting ability. She talks with people and they tell her whatever she wants to know. She can't explain how she does it, just like I don't know how my mental fog works. But it's a great talent.

לרוע המזל, הבחור הזה לא יודע הרבה. לאה מגלה את שמו, כי
lero'a hamazal, habakhur haze lo yode'a harbe. le'a megala et shmo, ki
unfortunately / the guy / the this / no / he knows / much / Leah / she finds out / D.O. / his name / that

הוא הגיע מאוקראינה וכי הוא הגיע לישראל לפני עשרה חודשים
hu higi'a mi'ukraina vekhi hu higi'a le'isra'el lifnei asara khodashim
he / he arrived / from Ukraine / and that / he / he arrived / to Israel / ago / ten / months

בטיסה של אירופלוט. הוא מספר לה שיש מספר אוקראינים
betisa shel eiroflot. hu mesaper la sheyesh mispar ukrainim
by flight / of / Aeroflot / he / he tells / to her / that there are / a few / Ukrainians

נוספים העובדים איתו, אבל הוא לא יודע את שמותיהם. הוא
nosafim ha'ovdim ito, aval hu lo yode'a et shmoteihem. hu
additional / that are working / with him / but / he / no / he knows / D.O. / their names / he

נותן לה כתובות של שלוש דירות שבהן עשויים שותפיו
noten la ktovot shel shalosh dirot shebahen asuyim shutafav
he gives / to her / address / of / three / apartments / that in them / they are likely / his partners

להיות, אבל אינו יודע מי מנהל את הפעולה.
lihiyot, aval eino yode'a mi menahel et hape'ula
to be / but / he doesn't / he knows / who / he manages / D.O. / the operation

Unfortunately, this guy doesn't know much. Leah finds out his name, that he comes from the Ukraine and that he arrived in Israel ten months ago on an Aeroflot jet. He tells her that there are a few more Ukrainians working with him, but he doesn't know their names. He gives her three apartment addresses where his associates might be staying, but he doesn't know who is running the operation.

"הוא מקבל את כל הוראותיו באמצעות טלפון נייד," אומרת לי
"hu mekabel et kol hora'otav be'emtsa'ut telefon nayad," omeret li
he / he gets / D.O. / all / his instructions / through / telephone / mobile / she tells / to me

לאה כשהיא מסיימת את החקירה שלה.
le'a kshehi mesayemet et hakhakira shela
Leah / when she / she finishes / D.O. / the interrogation / her

"He gets all his instructions through a cell phone," Leah tells me when she's completed her interrogation.

197

"What do we do with him?" I ask.

מה נעשה בו?" אני שואל.
ma na'ase bo ani sho'el
what we will do with him I I ask

"Throw the mind haze at him again. Make him forget the last few hours."

תפעיל עליו שוב את הערפול המוחי. תגרום לו לשכוח את
tafil alav shuv et ha'irpul hamokhi tigrom lo lishko'akh et
you will activate on him again D.O. the fog the mental you will cause to him to forget D.O.

השעות האחרונות."
hasha'ot ha'akharonot
the hours the last

Leah hands me a gun with a silencer.

לאה מושיטה לי אקדח עם משתיק קול.
le'a moshita li ekdakh im mashtik kol
Leah she hands to me gun with silencer

"This is the gun you used to shoot the first Ukrainian," Leah tells me. "Give it to the guy and drop him off near a police station."

"זה האקדח שבו ירית באוקראיני הראשון," היא אומרת לי. "תן
ze ha'ekdakh shebo yarita ba'ukraini harishon hi omeret li ten
this the gun that with it you shot at the Ukrainian the first she she tells to me give

אותו לבחור ותוריד אותו ליד תחנת משטרה."
oto labakhur vetorid oto leyad takhanat mishtara
it to the guy and you will drop off him near station of police

"Great idea. It would be best if he's naked, so that the police notice him right away."

"רעיון מצוין. יהיה הכי טוב אם הוא יהיה עירום, כך
ra'ayon metsuyan ihiye hakhi tov im hu ihiye eirom kakh
idea excellent it will be the most good if he he will be naked like this

שהמשטרה תבחין בו מיד."
shehamishtara tavkhin bo miyad
that the police she will notice at him immediately

"Sounds good to me," Leah says.

"נשמע לי מצוין," אומרת לאה.
nishma li metsuyan omeret le'a
it sounds to me excellent she says Leah

Leah heads back to our home base. I put the man to sleep in the back of my car and write a confession for him. Then I strip off his clothes, tape the confession to his chest, and drive him to a police station in the next town.

לאה חוזרת לבסיס שלנו. אני מרדים את האיש במושב האחורי של
le'a khozeret labasis shelanu ani mardim et ha'ish bamoshav ha'akhori shel
Leah she returns to the base our I I put to sleep D.O. the man in the seat the rear of

הרכב וכותב עבורו הודאה. לאחר מכן אני מפשיט אותו מבגדיו,
harekhev vekotev avuro hoda'a le'akhar miken ani mafshit oto mibgadav
the car and I write for him confession then I I undress him from his clothes

מדביק את ההודאה לחזהו ומסיע אותו לתחנת משטרה בעיר
madbik et hahoda'a lekhazehu umasi'a oto letakhanat mishtara ba'ir
I attach D.O. the confession to his chest and I drive him to station of police in the town

הסמוכה.
hasmukha
the adjacent

I stop in front of the building and tell him to get out of the car. He's groggy, but manages to hold the gun as he walks naked into the station to talk to the friendly local policemen. Some-

אני עוצר מול חזית הבניין ואומר לו לצאת מהרכב. הוא
ani otser mul khazit habinyan ve'omer lo latset meharekhev hu
I I stop in front of front of the building and I tell to him to get out of the car he

חש	מטושטש,	אבל	מצליח	לאחוז	באקדח	בעודו	צועד	עירום	לתוך
khash	metushtash	aval	matsli'akh	le'ekhoz	ba'ekdakh	be'odo	tso'ed	eirom	letokh
he feels	groggy	but	he succeeds	to hold	by the gun	while he	he walks	naked	into

times I just love my work!

התחנה	כדי	לשוחח	עם	השוטרים	המקומיים	הידידותיים.	לפעמים
hatakhana	kedei	lesokhe'akh	im	hashotrim	hamekomiyim	hayediduti'im	lifamim
the station	in order to	to talk with	with	the policemen	the local	the friendly	sometimes

אני	פשוט	אוהב	את	העבודה	שלי!
ani	pashut	ohev	et	ha'avoda	sheli
I	simply	I love	D.O.	the work	my

---10---

"חשבתי	שהכל	מסודר,"	אני	אומר	לרונן	בטלפון.	"אני	רוצה
khashavti	shehakol	mesudar	ani	omer	leronen	batelefon	ani	rotse
I thought	that everything	settled	I	I say	to Ronen	on the telephone	I	I want

"I thought this was all settled," I say to Ronen over the phone. "I want us to call ourselves 'The Squad'."

שנקרא	לעצמנו	'החוליה'."
shenikra	le'atsmenu	hakhulya
that we will call	to ourselves	The Squad

"עדינה	שכנעה	את	לאה	שאנחנו	צריכים	לערוך	הצבעה	על
adina	shekhne'a	et	le'a	she'anakhnu	tsrikhim	la'arokh	hatsba'a	al
Adina	she convinced	D.O.	Leah	that we	we should	to arrange	voting	about

"Adina convinced Leah that we should vote for a name," he tells me.

השם,"	הוא	אומר	לי.
hashem	hu	omer	li
the name	he	he tells	to me

"מה	עם	'גברים	בשחור'?"
ma	im	gvarim	beshakhor
what	with	men	in black

"How about 'Men in Black'?"

"האם	לאה,	עדינה	ואיילה	נראות	כמו	גברים?"
ha'im	le'a	adina	ve'ayala	nirot	kmo	gvarim
is it that	Leah	Adina	and Ayala	they look	like	men

"Do Leah, Adina, and Ayala look like men?"

"אני	מניח	שלא."
ani	mani'akh	shelo
I	I assume	that no

"I guess not."

רונן	מחליט	לשנות	את	נושא	השיחה.
ronen	makhlit	leshanot	et	nose	hasikha
Ronen	he decides	to change	D.O.	subject of	the conversation

Ronen decides to change the subject.

"איפה	הכסף	שהרווחת	במשחק	הפוקר?"
eifo	hakesef	shehirvakhta	bemiskhak	hapoker
where	the money	that you won	in game of	the poker

"Where is that money you won at the poker game?"

"הוא	בשולחן	במשרד	שלי.	לא	היה	לי	זמן	להפקיד	אותו	בבנק."
hu	bashulkhan	bamisrad	sheli	lo	haya li	zman	lehafkid	oto	babank
it	on the desk	the office	my	no	I had	time	to deposit	it	at the bank

"It's on my office desk. I haven't had time to deposit it at the bank."

199

"Leah is worried you'll use it to go on vacation."

"לאה דואגת שתשתמש בו כדי לצאת לחופשה."
le'a do'eget shetishtamesh bo kedei latset lekhufsha
Leah she worries that you will use with it in order to to go for vacation

Leah is the boss, but sometimes I think she worries about money too much.

לאה היא הבוס, אבל לעתים אני סבור שהיא דואגת יותר מדי
le'a hi habos aval le'itim ani savur shehi do'eget yoter midai
Leah she the boss but sometimes I I am of the opinion that she she worries too much

בענייני כספים.
be'inyanei ksafim
in matters of finance

"Tell her to relax," I say.

"תגיד לה להירגע," אני אומר.
tagid la leheraga ani omer
you will tell to her to relax I I say

"You know I've been studying accounting online," Ronen says.

"אתה יודע שאני לומד ניהול חשבונות באינטרנט," אומר רונן.
ata yode'a she'ani lomed nihul kheshbonot ba'internet omer ronen
you you know that I I study accounting on the internet he says Ronen

"I'm sure you are learning a lot."

"אני בטוח שאתה לומד הרבה."
ani batu'akh she'ata lomed harbe
I sure that you you learn a lot

"Leah is letting me help with our corporate finances," he says.

"לאה מאפשרת לי לעזור בעניינים הכספיים של התאגיד," הוא
le'a me'afsheret li la'azor be'inyanim hakaspiyim shel hata'agid hu
Leah she lets to me to help with matters financial of the corporation he

אומר.
omer
he says

"Why do I need to know about this?" I ask him.

"למה אני צריך לדעת את זה?" אני שואל אותו.
lama ani tsarikh lada'at et ze ani sho'el oto
why I I need to know D.O. this I I ask him

"She put me in charge of the expense reports. I need to keep track of your poker winnings."

"היא מינתה אותי כאחראי לדוחות ההוצאות. אני צריך
hi minta oti ke'akhra'i ledokhot hahotsa'ot ani tsarikh
she she appointed me as the person in charge for reports of the expenses I I need

לעקוב אחרי רווחי הפוקר שלך."
la'akov akharei rivkhei hapoker shelkha
to track after winnings of the poker your

"I have a special system," I tell him. "When I win at poker I keep the money and use it for my business related expenses. That way I don't have to file another expense report until the money runs out."

"יש לי שיטה מיוחדת," אני אומר לו. "כשאני מנצח בפוקר אני
yesh li shita meyukhedet ani omer lo kshe'ani menatse'akh bepoker ani
I have system special I I tell to him when I I win at poker I

שומר את הכסף ומשתמש בו להוצאות הקשורות לעבודה.
shomer et hakesef umishtamesh bo lahotsa'ot hakshurot la'avoda
I keep D.O. the money and I use at it for expenses of that are connected to the job

לכן אני לא צריך להוציא דוח הוצאות נוסף עד שהכסף
lakhen ani lo tsarikh lehotsi dokh hotsa'ot nosaf ad shehakesef
therefore I no I need to take out report of expense additional until that the money

200

ייגמר."

yigamer

it will run out

"זו לא הדרך שבה אתה אמור לעשות את זה," אומר רונן.

ronen omer ze et la'asot amur ata sheba haderekh lo zo

Ronen he says it D.O. to do supposed you that in it the way not this

"That's not how you're supposed to do it," Ronen says.

"למה לא? זה פשוט וחוסך זמן."

zman vekhosekh pashut ze lo lama

time and it saves simple this not why

"Why not? It's simple and it saves time."

"אבל אנחנו לא רואים את ההוצאות האמיתיות שלך. כל מה שאנחנו

she'anakhnu ma kol shelkha ha'amitiyot hahotsa'ot et ro'im lo anakhnu aval

that we what all your the real the expenses D.O. we see no we but

יודעים זה שאתה מרוויח כסף במשחק פוקר ואתה מוציא אותו על

al oto motsi ve'ata poker bemiskhak kesef marvi'akh she'ata ze yodim

on it you spend and you poker in game of money you win that you this we know

פעילויות הקשורות לעסק במהלך השבועות שלאחר מכן. אנחנו

anakhnu shele'akhar miken hashavu'ot bemahalakh le'esek hakshurot pe'iluyot

we that afterward the weeks over the course of to business the related activities

לא יודעים כמה כסף אתה מרוויח ולאן בעצם הכסף הולך."

holekh hakesef be'etsem ule'an marvi'akh ata kesef kama yodim lo

it goes the money actually and to where you win you money how much we know no

"But we don't see your actual expenses. All we know is that you win money in a poker game and you spend it on business related activities over the next few weeks. We don't know how much money you win or where the money actually goes."

"סמוך עלי, אתה לא רוצה לדעת."

lada'at rotse lo ata alai smokh

to know you want no you on me trust

"Trust me, you don't want to know."

"לאה רוצה."

rotsa le'a

she wants Leah

"Leah does."

"תגיד ללאה שאני סוכן שטח, לא רואה חשבון."

ro'e kheshbon lo shetakh sokhen she'ani lele'a tagid

accountant not field agent of that I to Leah you will tell

"Tell Leah I'm a field agent, not an accountant."

"אני לא אומר לה כלום. תדבר איתה אתה," אומר רונן.

ronen omer ata ita tedaber klum la omer lo ani

Ronen he says you with her you will talk nothing to her I tell no I

"I'm not telling her anything. You talk to her," Ronen says.

"לאה בדקה את הכתובות שקיבלנו מהבחור האוקראיני?"

ha'ukraini mehabakhur shekibalnu haktovot et badka le'a

the Ukrainian from the guy that we got the addresses D.O. she checked Leah

"Did Leah check those addresses we got from the Ukrainian?"

"כן, אבל הדירות היו ריקות."

reikot hayu hadirot aval ken

empty they were the apartments but yes

"Yeah, but the apartments were vacant."

אני מנתק בעוד רונן מנסה להזכיר לי מתי יש להגיש את

et lehagish yesh matai li lehazkir menase ronen be'od menatek ani

D.O. to submit there is when to me to remind he tries Ronen as I disconnect I

I disconnect as Ronen tries to remind me when the next expense report is due. Why does running a small business like ours have to be so compli-

---

201

cated? I call Leah a minute later.

צריך	שלנו	כמו	קטן	עסק	ניהול	למה	הבא.	ההוצאות	דוח
tsarikh	shelanu	kmo	katan	esek	nihul	lama	haba	hahotsa'ot	dokh
it needs	ours	like	small	business	management of	why	next	the expenses	report of

ללאה.	מתקשר	אני	אחר כך	דקה?	כל כך?	מסובך	להיות
lele'a	mitkasher	ani	akhar kakh	daka	kol kakh	mesubakh	lihiyot
to Leah	I call	I	later	minute	so	complicated	to be

"Ronen is bothering me about expense reports."

ההוצאות."	דוח	בעניין	אותי	מטריד	"רונן
hahotsa'ot	dokh	be'inyan	oti	matrid	ronen
the expenses	report of	with matter of	me	he bothers	Ronen

"Give him what he wants."

מבקש."	שהוא	מה	לו	"תן
mevakesh	shehu	ma	lo	ten
he requests	that he	what	to him	give

"I like this job," I tell her. "The work is exciting. It's safer than the freelance work I used to do. The pay isn't bad, and we get excellent health care benefits. That's always good to have, in case a bullet happens to penetrate my internal organs."

היא	מלהיבה.	העבודה	לה.	אומר	אני	הזו,"	העבודה	את	אוהב	"אני
hi	malhiva	ha'avoda	la	omer	ani	hazo	ha'avoda	et	ohev	ani
it	exciting	the work	to her	I tell	I	the this	the job	D.O.	I like	I

רע,	לא	התשלום	קודם.	שעשיתי	כעצמאי	מהעבודה	יותר	בטוחה
ra	lo	hatashlum	kodem	she'asiti	ke'atsma'i	meha'avoda	yoter	betukha
bad	not	the pay	before	that I did	as freelancer	than the work	more	safe

ביטוח,	שיש	שתמיד	טוב	תמיד	מצוינת.	בריאות	ביטוח	תוכנית	ויש
bitu'akh	sheyesh	tov	tamid	metsuyenet	bri'ut	bitu'akh	tokhnit	veyesh
insurance	that there is	good	always	excellent	health	insurance of	plan of	and there is

הפנימיים."	לאיבריי	בטעות	יחדור	שכדור	למקרה
hapnimiyim	le'eivarai	beta'ut	yakhdor	shekadur	lemikre
the internal	into my organs	in error	it will penetrate	that bullet	in case

"In addition, we work with a team of great people," she reminds me.

מזכירה	היא	נהדרים,"	אנשים	של	צוות	עם	עובדים	אנחנו	"בנוסף,
mazkira	hi	nehadarim	anashim	shel	tsevet	im	ovdim	anakhnu	benosaf
she reminds	she	great	people	of	team	with	we work	we	additionally

לי.
li
to me

"I was going to say that," I respond. "I was also going to say my job description does not say anything about expense reports."

שהגדרת	לומר	גם	עמדתי	עונה.	אני	זה,"	את	לומר	"עמדתי
shehagdarat	lomar	gam	amadeti	one	ani	ze	et	lomar	amadeti
that description of	to say	also	I was about to	I respond	I	that	D.O.	to say	I was about to

הוצאות."	דוח	שום	כוללת	איננה	שלי	התפקיד
hotsa'ot	dokh	shum	kolelet	einena	sheli	hatafkid
expenses	report of	any	it includes	it doesn't	my	the job

"We don't have a job description for what you do," Leah reminds me.

לאה.	לי	מזכירה	עושה,"	שאתה	למה	תפקיד	הגדרת	לנו	"אין
le'a	li	mazkira	ose	she'ata	lema	tafkid	hagdarat	lanu	ein
Leah	to me	she reminds	you do	that you	for what	job	description of	we don't have	

"When you write one, make sure it says that I don't have to submit expense reports."

להגיש	צריך	לא	שאני	לכתוב	תשכחי	אל	אותה,	"כשתכתבי
lehagish	tsarikh	lo	she'ani	likhtov	tishkekhi	al	ota	kshetikhtevi
to submit	I need	no	that I	to write	you will forget	don't	it	when you will write

דוח הוצאות."
dokh *hotsa'ot*
report of expenses

אני שומע אותה נאנחת.
ani *shome'a* *ota* *ne'enakhat*
I I hear her she sighs

I hear her sigh.

"נוכל לדבר על כך מאוחר יותר?" היא שואלת אותי.
nukhal *ledaber* *al kakh* *me'ukhar* *yoter* *hi* *sho'elet* *oti*
we will be able to talk about it late more she she asks me

"Can we talk about this later?" she asks me.

"או קיי. רק תזכרי שאני לא מתכוון לשנות את דעתי."
o kei *rak* *tizkeri* *she'ani* *lo* *mitkaven* *leshanot* *et* *da'ati*
okay just you will remember that I no I intend to change D.O. my opinion

"OK. Just remember I am not going to change my mind."

— 11 —

אני יושב במשרד הביטוח ביום שלמחרת. לאחר עשר דקות של
ani *yoshev* *bemisrad* *habitu'akh* *bayom shelemokhorat* *le'akhar* *eser* *dakot* *shel*
I I sit in office of the insurance on the following day after ten minutes of

קריאת מאמר על אודות ביטוח אובדן כושר עבודה אני עייף
kri'at *ma'amar* *al odot* *bitu'akh* *ovdan* *kosher* *avoda* *ani* *ayef*
reading of article about insurance of loss of ability of work I tired

כל כך שאני כמעט נופל מהכיסא. אני לוחץ על מקש החיוג המהיר
kol kakh *she'ani* *kimat* *nofel* *mehakise* *ani* *lokhets* *al* *makash* *hakhiyug hamahir*
so that I almost I fall from the chair I I push on key of the speed dial

בנייד שלי כדי לדבר עם לאה.
banayad *sheli* *kedei* *ledaber* *im* *le'a*
on the cellphone my in order to to talk with Leah

I sit in the insurance office the next day. After ten minutes reading an article about Long Term Disability Insurance I am so sleepy I almost fall off my chair. I hit the speed dial on my cell phone to talk to Leah.

"מה?"
ma
what

"What?"

"החוקרת הפרטית שלנו בסביבה?"
hakhokeret *hapratit* *shelanu* *basviva*
the investigator the private our in the area

"Is our private investigator nearby?"

"כן."
ken
yes

"Yes."

"תזכירי לי למה אני צריך בייביסיטר."
tazkiri *li* *lama* *ani* *tsarikh* *beibisiter*
you will remind to me why I I need babysitter

"Remind me why I need a baby sitter."

"אתה צריך גיבוי במקרה שהרעים ישלחו עליך צבא קטן."
ata *tsarikh* *gibui* *bemikre* *shehara'im* *yishlekhu* *aleikha* *tsava* *katan*
you you need backup in case that the bad they will send upon you army small

"You need backup in case the bad guys send a small army after you."

"Did you get my email today? Boris came through with a few names."

"קיבלת את הדוא"ל שלי היום? בוריס העביר לי כמה שמות."
kibalt et hado'ar elektroni sheli hayom boris he'evir li kama shemot
you received D.O. the email my today Boris he transferred to me a few names

"Adina and Ronen are researching those names right now."

"עדינה ורונן בודקים את השמות האלה ממש עכשיו."
adina veronen bodkim et hashemot ha'ele mamash akhshav
Adina and Ronen they check D.O. the names the those exactly now

"Why don't we grab the people Boris told me about, throw them in those holding cells in the office basement, and you pull the truth out of them. That's easier than Adina and Ronen doing computer research."

"למה שלא נתפוס את האנשים שבוריס סיפר לי עליהם, נזרוק
lama shelo nitpos et ha'anashim sheboris siper li aleihem, nizrok
why that no we will catch D.O. the people that Boris he told to me about them we will throw

אותם לתאי הכליאה במרתף המשרד, ואת תוציאי
otam leta'ei hakli'a bemartef hamisrad, ve'at totsi'i
them into the cells of the confinement in basement of the office and you you will take out

מהם את האמת. זה פשוט יותר מאשר תחקיר של עדינה ורונן
mehem et ha'emet. ze pashut yoter me'asher takhkir shel adina veronen
from them D.O. the truth this easy more than investigation of Adina and Ronen

במחשב."
bamakhshev
on the computer

"You want to kidnap senior officers of the police?"

"אתה רוצה לחטוף קצינים בכירים במשטרה?"
ata rotse lakhtof ktsinim b'khirim bamishtara
you you want to kidnap officers senior in the police

"Sure. I can hit them with mind mojo so they don't remember what we look like."

"בודאי. אני יכול להטיל עליהם כישוף מוחי כדי שלא
bevadai. ani yakhol lehatil aleihem kishuf mokhi kedei shelo
of course I I can to throw at them mojo mental in order to that no

יזכרו איך אנחנו נראים."
yizkeru eikh anakhnu nirim
they will remember how we we look

"I prefer to be more subtle," Leah says.

"אני מעדיפה להיות עדינה יותר," אומרת לאה.
ani ma'adifa lihiyot adina yoter, omeret le'a
I I prefer to be subtle more she says Leah

"Do the kids need help with the research?" I say.

"הילדים צריכים עזרה בתחקיר?" אני אומר.
hayeladim tsrikhim ezra batakhkir? ani omer
the kids they need help with the investigation I I say

"No. Stay there and pretend to be an insurance agent. Make telephone calls to potential clients."

"לא. תישאר שם ותעמיד פנים שאתה סוכן ביטוח. תתקשר
lo. tisha'er sham veta'amid panim she'ata sokhen bitu'akh. titkasher
no you will stay there and you will pretend that you agent of insurance you will call

ללקוחות פוטנציאליים."
lelakokhot potentsyali'im
to clients potential

"I hate doing that. Everyone yells at me and hangs up."

"אני שונא את זה. כולם צועקים עליי ומנתקים."
ani sone et ze. kulam tso'akim alai umenatkim
I I hate D.O. that everyone they shout at me and they hang up

"אתה צריך לעבוד על כישורי המכירה שלך."
ata tsarikh la'avod al kishurei hamekhira shelkha
you / you need / to work / on / skills of / the sale / your

"You need to work on your sales skills."

"אין לי אפילו רישיון לעסוק בביטוח. מה יהיה אם מישהו
ein li / afilu / rishayon / la'asok / bevitu'akh / ma / ihiye / im / mishehu
I don't have / even / license / to work at / with insurance / what / it will be / if / someone

ירצה לקנות ממני ביטוח?"
yirtse / liknot / mimeni / bitu'akh
he will want / to buy / from me / insurance

"I don't even have an insurance license. What if someone wants to buy a policy from me?"

"אני לא חושבת שאתה צריך לדאוג בנושא הזה."
ani / lo / khoshevet / she'ata / tsarikh / lidog / banose / haze
I / no / I think / that you / you need / to worry / at the issue / the that

"I don't think you'll have to worry about that."

ביליתי את המשך היום בציפייה לתריסר גברים חמושים
biliti / et / hemshekh / hayom / betsipiya / litreisar / gvarim / khamushim
I spent / D.O. / rest of / the day / with expectation / of dozen of / men / armed

שיפרצו את דלתי, אולם דבר לא קרה. עבודה במסווה
sheyifretsu / et / dalti / ulam / davar / lo / kara / avoda / bemasve
that they will break into / D.O. / my door / however / thing / no / it happened / work / in masking

אינה מסעירה תמיד.
eina / masira / tamid
it isn't / exciting / always

I spent the rest of the day waiting for a dozen armed men to crash through my door, but nothing happens. Undercover work is not always exciting.

לבסוף מגיעה השעה חמש אחר הצוהריים. אני זקוק לקפה, כך
levasof / magi'a / hasha'a / khamesh / akhar / hatsohora'im / ani / zakuk / lekafe / kakh
finally / it arrives / the hour / five / after / the noon / I / in need of / to coffee / so

שאני פונה לבית קפה קרוב. החוקרת הפרטית ככל הנראה מאחוריי.
she'ani / pone / leveit kafe / karov / hakhokeret / hapratit / kekhol hanire / me'akhorai
that I / I turn / to coffee shop / nearby / the investigator / the private / probably / behind me

אני מזמין קפה לאטה עם תוספת קצף, משלם לגברת עשרים שקלים
ani / mazmin / kafe / late / im / tosefet / ketsef / meshalem / lageveret / esrim / shkalim
I / I order / coffee / latte / with / addition of / foam / I pay / to the lady / twenty / shekels

ומתיישב.
umityashev
and I sit down

Finally, five o'clock rolls around. I need coffee, so I head for a nearby cafe. The private investigator is probably close behind. I order a latte with extra foam, pay the lady twenty shekels, and I sit down.

אני מהרהר במחיר הגבוה של קפה ביפו, כשאדם עם עיתון בידו
ani / meharher / bamekhir / hagavoha / shel / kafe / beyafo / kshe'adam / im / iton / beyado
I / I ponder / at the price / the high / of / coffee / in Jaffa / when man / with / newspaper / in his hand

מתיישב בכורסה הסמוכה אליי. הוא רוכן קדימה ונותן בי
mityashev / bekursa / hasmukha / elai / hu / rokhen / kadima / venoten / bi
he sits down / in arm chair / the close to / to me / he / he leans forward / forward / and he gives / at me

מבט חודר.
mabat / khoder
look / penetrating

I reflect on the high cost of coffee in Jaffa when someone holding a newspaper sits on the arm chair next to mine. He leans forward and gives me a fierce look.

205

I let my cup tremble a little bit and spill some of the drink onto the table. Just to let him know that his scowl is working.

אני מניח לכוסי לרעוד מעט, כך שכמות קטנה מהמשקה
ani mani'akh lekhosi lirod me'at, kakh shekamut ktana mehamashke
I I let to my cup to tremble a little so that amount small of the beverage

תישפך על השולחן. רק כדי להבהיר לו שהבעתו
tishafekh al hashulkhan. rak kedei lehavhir lo shehaba'ato
it will be spilled on the table just in order to to clarify to him that his facial expression

המאיימת עובדת.
hame'ayemet ovedet
the threatening it works

"I told the other guy I would bring the money on Tuesday," I whisper.

"אמרתי לבחור השני שאביא את הכסף ביום שלישי," אני
amarti labakhur hasheni she'avi et hakesef beyom shlishi ani
I told to the guy the second that I will bring D.O. the money on Tuesday I

לוחש.
lokhesh
I whisper

The guy looks at me with a bemused expression and shows me a handgun he is hiding under his newspaper.

הבחור מביט בי במבט מבולבל ומראה לי אקדח המוסתר
habakhur mabit bi bemabat mevulbal umare li ekdakh hamustar
the guy he looks at me with look bemused and he shows to me gun the hidden

מאחורי העיתון שהוא אוחז.
me'akhorei ha'iton shehu okhez
behind the newspaper that he he holds

"The other man was found naked outside of a police station. He has been arrested. I think you had something to do with that."

"הבחור השני נמצא עירום מחוץ לתחנת משטרה. הוא
habakhur hasheni nimtsa eirom mikhuts letakhanat mishtara. hu
the man the second he was found naked outside to station of the police he

נעצר. אני חושב שיש לך קשר לכך."
ne'etsar. ani khoshev sheyesh lekha kesher lekhakh.
he was arrested I I think that you have connection to this

I give him a blank look.

אני נותן בו מבט חלול.
ani noten bo mabat khalul.
I I give at him look blank

"I didn't take his clothes off, if that's what you mean," I tell him.

"לא הורדתי לו את הבגדים, אם לזה אתה מתכוון," אני אומר לו.
lo horadeti lo et habgadim, im laze ata mitkaven, ani omer lo.
no I undressed for him D.O. the clothes if to this you you mean I I tell to him

"Let's go somewhere to talk in private," he says. "You will tell me everything."

"בוא נלך למקום שנוכל לשוחח בו בפרטיות," הוא אומר.
bo nelekh lemakom shenukhal lesokhe'akh bo bifratiyut, hu omer.
come we will go to place that we will be able to converse in it with privacy he he says

"תספר לי הכל."
tesaper li hakol.
you will tell to me everything

I give him a worried look and say, "Please don't hurt me."

אני מביט בו בדאגה ואומר, "בבקשה אל תפגע בי."
ani mabit bo bide'aga ve'omer, bevakasha al tifga bi.
I I look at him with worry and I say please don't you will hurt at me

„נצא להליכה," הוא אומר. „תשאיר את המשקה."
netse lehalikha hu omer tashir et hamashke
we will go for walk he he says you will leave D.O. the drink

"We will take a walk," he says. "Leave the drink."

אני מצליח לארגן רעידה או שתיים תוך שאנו יוצאים מבית הקפה.
ani matsli'akh le'argen re'ida o shta'im tokh she'anu yotsim mibeit hakafe
I I succeed to arrange trembling or two while that we we exit from the coffee shop

I manage a tremble or two as we exit the coffee shop. We walk into the parking lot. Sara, the private investigator, leans against a car reading a magazine.

אנחנו צועדים למגרש החנייה. שרה, חוקרת הפרטית, נשענת על
anakhnu tso'adim lemigrash hakhanaya sara khokeret hapratit nishenet al
we we walk into the parking lot Sara investigator the private she leans on on

מכונית וקוראת עיתון.
mekhonit vekoret iton
car and she reads newspaper

ממש כשאנו מגיעים לשרה אני מנחית על הבחור ערפול מוחי מלא.
mamash kshe'anu magi'im lesara ani mankhit al habakhur irpul mokhi male
exactly when we we reach to Sara I I impose on the guy fog mental full

I hit the guy with a full brain fog just as we reach Sara. He stops walking and puts his hands down. I take his gun and help him into the front seat of the car.

הוא נעצר ומוריד את ידיו. אני נוטל את אקדחו ומסייע לו
hu ne'etsar umorid et yadav ani notel et ekdakho umesaye'a lo
he he stops and he lowers D.O. his hands I I take D.O. his gun and I help to him

להיכנס למושב הקדמי של הרכב.
lehikanes lamoshav hakidmi shel harekhev
to get in to the seat the front of the car

שרה מתיישבת במושב הנהג ואילו אני כובל אותו באזיקים לדלת
sara mityashevet bemoshav hanahag ve'ilu ani kovel oto be'azikim ladelet
Sara she sits down in seat the driver whereas I I bind him with handcuffs to the door

Sara gets into the driver's side while I cuff him to the passenger door. I jump in the back and away we go.

בצד הנוסע. אני קופץ למושב האחורי ואנחנו יוצאים לדרך.
betsad hanose'a ani kofets lamoshav ha'akhori ve'anakhnu yotsim laderekh
next to the passenger I I jump into the seat the rear and we we exit to the way

„את נראית טוב במעיל הגשם הזה," אני אומר לשרה.
at niret tov beme'il hageshem haze ani omer lesara
you you look good in the trench coat the that I I say to Sara

"You look very nice in that trench coat," I say to Sara.

„אני שמחה שהוא מוצא חן בעיניך," היא אומרת. „איך קרה
ani smekha shehu motse khen be'eineikha hi omeret eikh kara
I happy that it it finds grace in your eyes she she says how it happened

"I'm glad you like it," she says. "How come this man let us take him without a fight?"

שהבחור הזה אפשר לנו לגבור עליו בלי מאבק?"
shehabakhur haze ifsher lanu ligbor alav bli ma'avak
that the man the this he allowed to us to overpower on him without fight

„שמתי משהו במשקה שלו בבית הקפה."
samti mashehu bemashke shelo beveit hakafe
I put something in drink his in the coffee shop

"I put something into his drink back in the coffee shop."

עדיף שׁשרה לא תדע על כוחותי המיוחדים. אנחנו נוסעים
adif shesara lo teda al kokhotai hameyukhadim anakhnu nosim
preferable that Sara not she will know about my abilities the special we we drive

Sara is better off not knowing about my special abilities. We drive in silence for a few minutes.

207

בשתיקה במשך דקות אחדות.
akhadot dakot bemeshekh beshtika
a few minutes during in silence

"Do you have to fill out expense reports?" I ask her.

"את צריכה למלא דוח הוצאות?" אני שואל אותה.
ota sho'el ani hotsa'ot dokh lemale tsrikha at
her I ask I expenses report of to fill you need you

"When I'm doing a job for Leah I always have to provide an expense report and a time log. Leah insists on it."

"כשאני עושה עבודה עבור לאה אני תמיד צריכה להגיש דוח הוצאות
hotsa'ot dokh lehagish tsrikha tamid ani le'a avur avoda osa kshe'ani
expenses report of to hand in I need always I Leah for job I do when I

ורישום שעות. לאה מתעקשת על כך."
al kakh mitakeshet le'a sha'ot verishum
about it she insists Leah hours and noting of

"What about the security guys?" I ask.

"מה עם אנשי הביטחון?" אני שואל.
sho'el ani habitakhon anshei ma im
I ask I the security people of what about

"I pay them a fixed price for each assignment. They give me receipts for any special items they had to buy."

"אני משלמת להם מחיר קבוע לכל משימה. הם מגישים לי
li magishim hem mesima lekhol kavu'a mekhir lahem meshalemet ani
to me they submit they assignment for each fixed price to them I pay I

קבלות על כל פריט מיוחד שהיה עליהם לקנות."
liknot shehaya aleihem meyukhad parit kol al kabalot
to buy that they were required special item any for receipts

My group owns a security company through a shell corporation. Sara manages the company and is the only full time employee. The security company provides manpower and equipment to do special jobs for our clients. Sara has a long list of mercenaries and ex-army personnel that she can hire for any particular assignment, depending on the skills we need.

הקבוצה שלי מחזיקה בחברת אבטחה דרך חברת קש. שרה
sara kash khevrat derekh avtakha bekhevrat makhzika sheli hakvutsa
Sara straw company of through security in company of it holds my the group

מנהלת את החברה, והיא עובדת החברה היחידה במשרה מלאה.
bemisra mele'a hayekhida hakhevra ovedet vehi hakhevra et menahelet
in full-time job the only the company employee of and she the company D.O. she manages

חברת האבטחה מספקת כוח אדם וציוד לעבודות מיוחדות
meyukhadot le'avodot vetsiyud adam ko'akh mesapeket ha'avtakha khevrat
special for jobs and equipment man power of it provides the security company of

עבור לקוחותינו. לשרה יש רשימה ארוכה של שכירי חרב ואנשי
ve'anshei skhirei kherev shel aruka reshima le'sara yesh lakokhoteinu avur
and people of mercenaries of long list Sara has our clients for

צבא לשעבר שהיא יכולה לשכור לכל אחת מהמשימות, לפי
lefi mehamesimot lekhol akhat liskor yekhola shehi leshe'avar tsava
according to of the assignments for each to hire she can that she former army

הכישורים הנדרשים.
hanidrashim hakishurim
the required the qualifications

"Ronen is starting to help Leah with the office accounting," I tell her. "He's already bugging me about sending in my paperwork on time."

"רונן מתחיל לעזור ללאה בניהול חשבונות המשרד," אני אומר לה.
la omer ani hamisrad benihul kheshbonot lele'a la'azor matkhil ronen
to her I tell I the office with accounting of to Leah to help he starts Ronen

"הוא כבר מציק לי להגיש את הניירת שלי בזמן."
hu kvar metsik li lehagish et hanayeret sheli bazman
he | already | he annoys | to me | to submit | D.O. | the paperwork | my | on time

"זה מה שעושים אנשים בוגרים," אומרת שרה. "הם ממלאים את
ze ma she'osim anashim bogrim, omeret sara. hem memalim et
that | what | that they do | people | grown-up | she says | Sara | they | they fill | D.O.

הניירת שלהם."
hanayeret shelahem.
the paperwork | their

"That's what grown-ups do," Sara says. "They fill out their paperwork."

"אל תתחילי לספר לי על אחריות של מבוגרים," אני אומר לה.
al tatkhili lesaper li al akhrayut shel mevugarim, ani omer la.
don't | you will start | to tell | to me | about | responsibilities | of | adults | I | I say | to her

"אני אפילו לא בטוח שהגעת לגיל החוקי לשתיית אלכוהול."
ani afilu lo batu'akh shehigat lagil hakhuki lishtiyat alkohol.
I | even | not | sure | that you reached | to the age | the legal | for drinking of | alcohol

"Don't start telling me about adult responsibilities," I say to her. "I'm not even sure you are old enough to drink."

שרה היא בת גילו של רונן. הם חברי ילדות. שני הוריה
sara hi bat gilo shel ronen. hem khaverei yaldut. shnei horeiha
Sara | she | same age as | Ronen | they | friends of | childhood | both | her parents

היו חוקרים פרטיים, ובנעורותה סייעה להם בחקירות.
hayu khokrim prati'im, uvena'aruta siya lahem bakhakirot.
they were | investigators | private | and in her youth | she helped | to them | with the investigations

כשהוריה פרשו לגמלאות קיבלה שרה לידיה את העסק
kshehoreiha parshu legimla'ot kibla sara leyadeiha et ha'esek
when her parents | they retired | to pensions | she received | Sara | to her hands | D.O. | the business

המשפחתי.
hamishpakhti.
the family

Sara is the same age as Ronen. They were childhood friends. Her parents were both private investigators, and she grew up helping them with their investigations. She took over the family business when they retired.

זמן קצר לאחר מכן הציג אותה רונן ללאה. במהלך השנים
zman katsar le'akhar miken hitsig ota ronen lele'a. bemahalakh hashanim
time | short | afterward | he introduced | her | Ronen | to Leah | over the course of | the years

הבאות שכרה לאה את שרה למספר עבודות מיוחדות. שרה התגלתה
haba'ot sakhra le'a et sara lemispar avodot meyukhadot. sara hitgalta
the next | she hired | Leah | D.O. | Sara | for several | jobs | special | Sara | she was revealed

כחוקרת פרטית מעולה. בתוך שנים אחדות הפך הצוות שלנו
kekhokeret pratit me'ula. betokh shanim akhadot hafakh hatsevet shelanu
as investigator | private | terrific | within | years | a few | it became | the team | our

ללקוח העיקרי שלה.
lalako'akh ha'ikari shela.
to the client | the main | her

Shortly after that Ronen introduced her to Leah. Leah hired Sara for a number of special jobs over the next few years. Sara turned out to be a great detective. Within a few years, our team became Sara's main client.

בסופו של דבר ביקשה ממנה לאה לנהל את חברת האבטחה.
besofo shel davar biksha mimena le'a lenahel et khevrat ha'avtakha.
in the end | she requested | from her | Leah | to manage | D.O. | company of | the security

שרה עדיין מבצעת עבודות עבור לקוחות אחרים, אולם היא מבלה
sara ada'in mevatsa'at avodot avur lakokhot akherim, ulam hi mevala
Sara | still | she executes | jobs | for | clients | other | but | she | she spends

Finally, Leah asked her to run the security operation. Sara still does work for other clients, but spends most of her time helping our team.

209

את רוב זמנה בסיוע לצוות שלנו.

shelanu latsevet besiyu'a zmana rov et
our the team in helping her time most D.O.

"Why did you need me today?" Sara asks. "All we did was put a harmless guy into a car."

"למה היית צריך אותי היום?" שואלת שרה. "כל מה שעשינו היה

haya she'asinu ma kol sara sho'elet hayom oti tsarikh ha'ita lema
it was that we did what all Sara she asks today me you need you were what for

לשים בחור לא מזיק במכונית."

bimkhonit lo mazik bakhur lasim
in car harmless guy to put

"We weren't sure what would happen," I tell her. "There could have been five men with attack dogs and bazookas. It turns out you were superfluous, but it's always a good idea to be safe."

"לא היינו בטוחים מה יקרה," אני אומר לה. "יכלו להיות כאן

kan lihiyot yakhlu la omer ani yikre ma betukhim ha'inu lo
here to be they could to her I tell I it will happen what sure we were not

חמישה גברים עם כלבי תקיפה ובזוקות. התברר שהנוכחות שלך

shelakh shehanokhekhut hitbarer uvazukot tkifa kalvei im gvarim khamisha
your that the presence it turned out and bazookas attack dogs of with men five

מיותרת, אבל תמיד טוב ללכת על בטוח."

lalekhet al batu'akh tov tamid aval meyuteret
to take no chances good always but superfluous

"Nice word," she tells me. "Superfluous. Where did you learn that one?"

"מילה נחמדה," היא אומרת לי. "מיותרת. איפה למדת את המילה

hamila et lamadeta eifo meyuteret li omeret hi nekhmada mila
the word D.O. you learned where superfluous to me she tells she nice word

הזאת?"

hazot
the that

"I like to surprise people with my vocabulary skills."

"אני אוהב להפתיע אנשים בכישורי אוצר המילים שלי."

sheli otsar hamilim bekhishurei anashim lehafti'a ohev ani
my the vocabulary with skills of people to surprise I like I

Sara drives and we talk a little about the local soccer teams.

שרה נוהגת, ואנחנו משוחחים מעט על קבוצות הכדורגל המקומיות.

hamekomiyot hakaduregel kvutsot al me'at mesokhakhim ve'anakhnu noheget sara
the local the soccer teams of about a little we converse and we she drives Sara

Sara pulls the car into a small parking area next to the warehouse in the town of Or Yehuda. Leah is waiting by an open metal door. A high fence makes it impossible for anyone to see the parking area from the street.

שרה מפנה את המכונית אל תוך מגרש חנייה קטן סמוך למחסן

lamakhsan samukh katan migrash khanaya tokh el hamkhonit et mafna sara
to the warehouse next to small parking lot inside to the car D.O. she turns Sara

באור יהודה. לאה ממתינה ליד דלת פתוחה עשויה מתכת. גדר גבוהה

gvoha gader matekhet asuya ptukha delet leyad mamtina le'a be'or yehuda
high fence metal made of open door next to she waits Leah in Or Yehuda

אינה מאפשרת לאיש לראות את מגרש החנייה מהרחוב.

meharekhov migrash hakhanaya et lirot le'ish me'afsheret eina
from the street the parking lot D.O. to see to person it allows it isn't

I unlock our captive's handcuffs. Leah leads him into the building. By the time the mind fog wears off, he'll be in a holding cell in the basement of the warehouse.

אני פותח את אזיקיו של השבוי שלנו. לאה מובילה אותו אל תוך

tokh el oto movila le'a shelanu hashavui shel azikav et pote'akh ani
inside to him she leads Leah our the captive of his handcuffs D.O. I open I

כליאה בתא יהיה הוא המוחי, הערפול שיתפוגג עד הבניין.
kli'a   beta   ihiye   hu   hamokhi   ha'irpul   sheyitpogeg   ad   habinyan
imprisonment   in cell of   he will be   he   the mental   the fog   that it dissipates   until   the building

המחסן. במרתף
hamakhsan   bemartef
the warehouse   in basement of

קבלה לאה הנראה ככל יהודה? באור המפקדה ממוקמת למה אז
kibla   le'a   kekhol hanire   be'or yehuda   hamifkada   memukemet   lama   az
she received   Leah   probably   in Or Yehuda   the headquarters   it is located   why   so

הבניין. על טובה עסקה
habinyan   al   tova   iska
the building   on   good   deal

So why is headquarters located in Or Yehuda? Leah probably got a good deal on the building.

משם. נוסעים כשאנחנו שרה לי אומרת טובה," צריכה "אני
misham   nosim   kshe'anakhnu   sara   li   omeret   tova   tsrikha   ani
from there   we drive   when we   Sara   to me   she says   favor   I need   I

"I need a favor," Sara says to me as we drive away.

טוב?" קעקועים אמן על לך שאמליץ רוצה "את
tov   ka'aku'im   oman   al   lakh   she'amlits   rotsa   at
good   tattoos   artist of   about   to you   that I will recommend   you want   you

"You want me to recommend a good tattoo artist?"

תודה." "לא,
toda   lo
thanks   no

"No, thank you."

למענך?" לעשות יכול אני עוד "מה
lema'anekh   la'asot   yakhol   ani   od   ma
for you   to do   I can   I   else   what

"What else can I do for you?"

מסוכנים שאחקור רוצה שהוא האנשים חדש. לקוח לי "יש
mesukanim   she'ekh'kor   rotse   shehu   ha'anashim   khadash   lako'akh   yesh li
dangerous   that I will investigate   he wants   that he   the people   new   client   I have

מאוד. תוכל לעזור לי?"
me'od   tukhal   la'azor   li
very   you will be able   to help   to me

"I have a new client. The people he wants me to investigate are very dangerous. Can you help me?"

אני?" "למה
lama   ani
why   I

"Why me?"

באלימות." טוב ממש אתה "כי
be'alimut   tov   mamash   ata   ki
at violence   good   really   you   because

"Because you are really good at violence."

אותי תביני "אל לה. אומר אני יותר," טובה לוחמת "איילה
oti   tavini   al   la   omer   ani   yoter   tova   lokhemet   ayala
me   you will understand   don't   to her   I tell   I   more   good   fighter   Ayala

יותר." טובה היא אבל אנשים. בלהכות למדי טוב אני נכון, לא
yoter   tova   hi   aval   anashim   belehakot   lemadai   tov   ani   nakhon   lo
more   good   she   but   people   at hitting   pretty   good   I   correct   not

"Ayala is a better fighter," I tell her. "Don't get me wrong, I'm pretty good at knocking people around. But she's better."

"This case might require some shooting."

"במקרה הזה יתכן שיהיה צורך ביריות."
biyeriyot tsorekh she'ihiye yitakhen haze bamikre
for shooting need that there will be it is possible the this in the case

"Tell me the details," I say.

"ספרי לי את הפרטים," אני אומר.
omer ani hapratim et li sapri
I say I the details D.O. to me tell

—12—

Two days later ...

יומיים לאחר מכן ...
le'akhar miken yoma'im
later two days

"I count one vote to name ourselves 'The Squad' and four votes against having a name," Leah says.

"אני סופרת קול אחד בעד לקרוא לעצמנו 'החוליה' וארבעה קולות
kolot ve'arba'a hakhulya le'atsmenu likro be'ad ekhad kol soferet ani
votes and four The Squad to ourselves to call in favor of one vote I count I

נגד לקרוא לעצמנו באיזשהו שם," אומרת לאה.
le'a omeret shem be'eizeshehu le'atsmenu likro neged
Leah she says name by some to ourselves to call against

"I want a recount," I tell her.

"אני רוצה ספירה חוזרת," אני אומר לה.
la omer ani khozeret sfira rotse ani
to her I tell I repeat count I want I

"Haim, there are only five votes. I'm not going to count them again."

"חיים, יש רק חמישה קולות. אני לא מתכוונת לספור אותם שוב."
shuv otam lispor mitkavenet lo ani kolot khamisha rak yesh kha'im
again them to count I intend no I votes five only there are Haim

"But every good team needs a name."

"אבל כל צוות טוב צריך שם."
shem tsarikh tov tsevet kol aval
name it needs good team every but

"Looks like you lose again," says Adina. "Just like when you wanted us to buy a cat for a mascot. That vote was four against one also. I think I detect a pattern."

"נראה שאתה מפסיד שוב," אומרת עדינה. "בדיוק כמו אז כשרצית
ksheratsita az kmo bediyuk adina omeret shuv mafsid she'ata nire
when you wanted then like exactly Adina she says again you lose that you it looks

שנקנה חתול כמסמל. ההצבעה ההיא היתה גם ארבעה נגד אחד.
ekhad neged arba'a gam haita hahi hahatsba'a kekame'a khatul shenikne
one against four also it was that one the voting as mascot cat that we will buy

נדמה לי שאני רואה כאן דפוס."
dfus kan ro'a she'ani li nidme
pattern here I see that I to me it seems

Adina is our information expert. She spends her time analyzing tons of data, looking for patterns. When she finds something unusual, she asks Ronen for help. He looks at the data and makes predictions.

עדינה היא מומחית המידע שלנו. היא מבלה את זמנה בניתוח
benitu'akh zmana et mevala hi shelanu hameida mumkhit hi adina
in analysis of her time D.O. she spends she our the information expert of she Adina

הררי נתונים, בחיפוש אחר דפוסים. כשהיא מוצאת משהו
mashehu motset kshehi dfusim akhar bekhipus netunim harerei
something she finds when she patterns after in search data mountains of

ונותן בנתונים מביט הוא לסיוע. לרונן פונה היא יוצא דופן,
venoten *banitunim* *mabit* *hu* *lesiyu'a* *leronen* *pona* *hi* *yotse dofen*
and he gives — at the data — he looks — he — for help — to Ronen — she turns — she — unusual

תחזיות.
takhaziyot
predictions

עדינה בדקה את כל הנתונים הנוגעים לעבירות נגד סוכני
adina — *badka* — *et* — *kol* — *hanetunim* — *hanogim* — *le'averot* — *neged* — *sokhnei*
Adina — she examined — D.O. — all — the data — that concern — of crimes — against — agents of

ביטוח ידועים ביפו ומצאה כמה דפוסים מעניינים. רונן סקר
bitu'akh — *yedu'im* — *beyafo* — *umatsa* — *kama* — *dfusim* — *me'anyenim* — *ronen* — *sakar*
insurance — known — in Jaffa — and she found — a few — patterns — interesting — Ronen — he reviewed

את הדפוסים של עדינה ואמר לנו שהאדם המנהל את מבצע
et — *hadfusim* — *shel* — *adina* — *ve'amar* — *lanu* — *sheha'adam* — *hamenahel* — *et* — *mivtsa*
D.O. — the data — of — Adina — and he told — to us — that the person — that manages — D.O. — operation of

הסחיטה הוא ככל הנראה בעל תפקיד בכיר במשטרה. הוא גם
haskhita — *hu* — *kekhol hanire* — *ba'al* — *tafkid* — *bakhir* — *bamishtara* — *hu* — *gam*
the extortion — he — probably — owner of — job — senior — in the police — he — also

הצליח לגלות מי יהיה המטרה הבאה. סוג כזה של מידע
hitsli'akh — *legalot* — *mi* — *ihiye* — *hamatara* — *haba'a* — *sug* — *kaze* — *shel* — *meida*
he succeeded — to reveal — who — he will be — the target — the next — type — like this — of — information

בהחלט מזרז את עבודתנו.
behekhlet — *mezarez* — *et* — *avodatenu*
certainly — it speeds up — D.O. — our work

Adina examined all the data surrounding the crimes against prominent insurance agents in Jaffa and detected a few interesting patterns. Ronen reviewed Adina's patterns and told us that the person running the extortion operation was probably high up in the Police Department. He also figured out who the next target would be. That kind of information certainly speeds up our work.

עדינה ורונן גם מנהלים את תיק ההשקעות של הקבוצה שלנו,
adina — *veronen* — *gam* — *menahalim* — *et* — *tik* — *hahashka'ot* — *shel* — *hakvutsa* — *shelanu*
Adina — and Ronen — also — they manage — D.O. — portfolio of — the investments — of — the group — our

ומרוויחים סכומים גדולים. לאה משתמשת בסכומים הנוספים
umarvikhim — *skhumim* — *gdolim* — *le'a* — *mishtameshet* — *baskhumim* — *hanosafim*
and they earn — sums of money — big — Leah — she uses — with the sums of money — the extra

לרכישת גאדג'טים חדשים וכלי נשק.
lirkhishat — *gadjetim* — *khadashim* — *ukhlei neshek*
for purchasing — gadgets — new — and weapons

Adina and Ronen also manage our group's investment portfolio, and they make lots of money doing this. Leah uses the extra money to buy new gadgets and weapons.

לרונן יש כישרון נוסף. הוא האקר מעולה. אף מחשב או רשת אינם
leronen yesh — *kisharon* — *nosaf* — *hu* — *haker* — *me'ule* — *af* — *makhshev* — *o* — *reshet* — *einam*
Ronen has — talent — another — he — hacker — terrific — no — computer — or — network — they are not

בטוחים כאשר רונן מחליט שהוא מעוניין בפיסת מידע כלשהי.
betukhim — *ka'asher* — *ronen* — *makhlit* — *shehu* — *me'unyan* — *befisat* — *meida* — *kolshehi*
safe — when — Ronen — he decides — that he — interested — in piece of — information — some

Ronen has another talent. He is an awesome hacker. No computer or network is safe when Ronen decides he wants to look for a certain piece of information.

אתם כבר יודעים שאיילה היא לוחמת מצוינת. תגובותיה מהירות יותר
atem — *kvar* — *yodim* — *she'ayala* — *hi* — *lokhemet* — *metsuyenet* — *tguvoteiha* — *mehirot* — *yoter*
you — already — you know — that Ayala — she — fighter — excellent — her reflexes — fast — more

מהכשת נחש הקוברה, והיא מסוגלת ללמוד כל תנועת קונג פו או
mehakashat — *nekhash* — *hakobra* — *vehi* — *mesugelet* — *lilmod* — *kol* — *tnu'at* — *kung fu* — *o*
than bite of — snake — the cobra — and she — able — to learn — any — movement of — kung fu — or

You already know that Ayala is a great fighter. Her reflexes are faster than a cobra strike and she can learn any kung fu or karate move in a matter of seconds. In addition, she's also a competitive cake decorator.

213

עוגות בקישוט גם עוסקת היא בנוסף, שניות בתוך קראטה
karate / betokh / shniyot / benosaf / hi / oseket / gam / bekishut / ugot
karate / within / seconds / in addition / she / she is involved with / also / in decoration of / cakes

תחרותי.
takharuti
competitive

Leah spent twenty five years working for various law enforcement agencies. As I mentioned, she has the special ability of making people tell the truth. During her career, she used this talent to solve some very high profile cases. It was difficult, but she managed to do this without anyone realizing that she had "extra" abilities.

אכיפת רשויות עבור בעבודה שנה וחמש עשרים בילתה לאה
le'a / bilta / esrim / vekhamesh / shana / be'avoda / avur / rashuyot / akhifat
Leah / she spent / twenty / and five / year / at job / for / authorities of / enforcement of

חוק שונות. כפי שציינתי, היא בעלת יכולת מיוחדת לגרום לאנשים
khok / shonot / kfi / shetsiyanti / hi / ba'alat / yekholet / meyukhedet / ligrom / le'anashim
law / various / as / that I mentioned / she / owner of / ability / special / to cause / to people

לומר אמת. במהלך הקריירה שלה השתמשה לאה בכישרון הזה
lomar / emet / bemahalakh / hakaryera / shela / hishtamsha / shela / le'a / bakisharon / haze
to tell / truth / during / the career / her / she used / her / Leah / with the talent / the this

לפתרון מספר מקרים ידועים מאוד. זה היה קשה, אבל היא
lefitron / mispar / mikrim / yedu'im / me'od / ze / haya / kashe / aval / hi
for the solution of / some / cases / known / very / this / it was / difficult / but / she

הצליחה לעשות זאת בלי שאיש יגלה על אודות יכולותיה
hitslikha / la'asot / zot / bli / she'ish / yegale / al odot / yekholoteiha
she succeeded / to do / this / without / that person / he will find out / about / her abilities

ה"נוספות".
hanosafot
the extra

Leah retired five years ago, when she reached the age of fifty. Rather than learn how to garden, she started to put our team together.

לאה פרשה לפני חמש שנים, כאשר הגיעה לגיל חמישים. במקום
le'a / parsha / lifnei / khamesh / shanim / ka'asher / higi'a / legil / khamishim / bimkom
Leah / she retired / ago / five / years / when / she reached / to age / fifty / instead of

ללמוד גינון, היא החלה להרכיב את הצוות שלנו.
lilmod / ginun / hi / hekhela / leharkiv / et / hatsevet / shelanu
to learn / gardening / she / she started / to put together / D.O. / the team / our

During her career, Leah kept her eyes and ears open to find others with special talents. By the time she retired, she had a list of ten possible candidates for the team. Six of these prospects turned out to be people with normal abilities. Four of us were special. I was the first person on her list.

במהלך הקריירה שלה הקפידה לאה לשמור את עיניה פקוחות
bemahalakh / hakaryera / shela / hikpida / le'a / lishmor / et / eineiha / pkukhot
during / the career / her / she made sure / Leah / to keep / D.O. / her eyes / open

ואוזניה קשובות כדי למצוא אחרים בעלי כשרונות מיוחדים.
ve'ozneiha / kshuvot / kedei / limtso / akherim / ba'alei / kishronot / meyukhadim
and her ears / attentive / in order to / to find / others / possessing / talents / special

כשפרשה, הייתה לה כבר רשימה של עשרה מועמדים אפשריים
ksheparsha / haita la / kvar / reshima / shel / asara / mo'amadim / efshariyim
when she retired / she had / already / list / of / ten / candidates / possible

לצוות. שישה מהמועמדים התגלו כבעלי יכולות רגילות.
latsevet / shisha / mehamo'amadim / hitgalu / keva'alei / yekholot / regilot
for the team / six / of the candidates / it was discovered / as possessing of / abilities / normal

ארבעה מאיתנו היו מיוחדים. אני הייתי הראשון ברשימתה של לאה.
arba'a / me'itanu / hayu / meyukhadim / ani / ha'iti / harishon / birshimata / shel / le'a
four / of us / they were / special / I / I was / the first / on her list / of / Leah

כאשר שוחחה איתי, אמרתי לה שקראה יותר מדי ספרי קומיקס. אולם היא שכנעה אותי שנהנה, נעשה מעשים טובים, נירה בכמה אנשים ונרוויח סכומים נאים. אז הסכמתי. זה היה לפני ארבע שנים.

When she talked to me, I told her that she had been reading too many comic books. But she convinced me that we would have fun, do good deeds, shoot some people, and make a lot of money. So I signed up. That was four years ago.

לאחר מכן, היא גייסה את עדינה ממצוות חשיבה ממשלתי. רונן הצטרף אלינו ממשרה של מומחה מחשבים בגוגל. איילה גויסה אחרונה. היא אימנה סוכני שב"כ בטכניקות הגנה עצמית.

Next, she recruited Adina from a government think-tank. Ronen came to us from a job as a computer specialist at Google. Ayala was the last recruit. She trained Shabak agents in self defense techniques.

אבל אני סוטה מהנושא. בחזרה לסיפור העיקרי.

But I digress. Back to the main story.

אנחנו נפגשים בבסיס הבית היפהפה שלנו. בעבר שימש המקום כמחסן למוצרי אינסטלציה. חלקי צינורות ומחברי מפרק חלודים פזורים עדיין בחלק מהחדרים שאינם בשימוש.

We are meeting in our gorgeous home base. It used to be a plumbing supply warehouse. There are still rusted pieces of pipes and elbow joints scattered around in some of the unused rooms.

"מה שלום האסיר שלנו?" אני שואל.

"How is our prisoner?" I ask.

"הוא בידי שרותי ביטחון הפנים."

"Homeland Security has him."

215

"Why?"

"למה?"

lama
why

"It turns out he is a Russian who has been here illegally for a few years," Leah tells me.

"מתברר שהוא רוסי ששוהה כאן באופן בלתי חוקי כבר כמה
mitbarer *shehu* *rusi* *sheshohe* *kan* *be'ofen* *bilti* *khuki* *kvar* *kama*
it turns out   that he   Russian   who stays   here   in a manner   not   legal   already   a few

שנים," אומרת לי לאה.
shanim *omeret* *li* *le'a*
years   she tells   to me   Leah

"He doesn't know a thing about the Ukrainians. Someone called him a few days ago and hired him to torture you until you told him what happened with the first two men."

"הוא לא יודע דבר על האוקראינים. מישהו התקשר אליו לפני מספר
hu *lo* *yode'a* *davar* *al* *ha'ukrainim* *mishehu* *hitkasher* *elav* *lifnei* *mispar*
he   no   he knows   thing   about   the Ukrainians   someone   he called   to him   ago   a few

ימים ושכר אותו לענות אותך עד שתספר לו מה קרה
yamim *vesakhar* *oto* *le'anot* *otkha* *ad* *shetesaper* *lo* *ma* *kara*
days   and he hired   him   to torture   you   until   that you will tell   to him   what   it happened

לשני הבחורים הראשונים."
lishnei *habakhurim* *harishonim*
to two of   the guys   the first

"Can we trace the phone call?"

"נוכל לאתר את שיחת הטלפון?"
nukhal *le'ater* *et* *sikhat* *hatelefon*
we will be able   to trace   D.O.   call of   the telephone

"The call was made from a disposable phone. The person running this operation is pretty smart."

"השיחה בוצעה מטלפון חד פעמי. האדם שמנהל את
hasikha *butsa* *mitelefon* *khad pa'ami* *ha'adam* *shemenahel* *et*
the call   it was conducted   from telephone   disposable   the man   who (he) manages   D.O.

המבצע הזה חכם למדי."
hamivtsa *haze* *khakham* *lemadai*
the operation   the this   smart   pretty

While Leah and I are talking, Adina and Ronen start discussing whether or not Mendeleev had special evolutionary powers. I ask Ayala if Mendeleev is the prime minister of Russia.

בעוד לאה ואני משוחחים, אדינה ורונן לדון אם
be'od *le'a* *va'ani* *mesokhakhim* *adina* *veronen* *ladun* *im*
while   Leah   and I   we converse   Adina   and Ronen   to discuss   if

מתחילים
matkhilim
they start

למנדלייב היו כוחות אבולוציוניים מיוחדים. אני שואל את איילה אם
lemendeleyev *hayu* *kokhot* *evolutsyoni'im* *meyukhadim* *ani* *sho'el* *et* *ayala* *im*
Mendeleev had   powers   evolutionary   special   I   I ask   D.O.   Ayala   if

מנדלייב הוא ראש ממשלת רוסיה.
mendeleyev *hu* *rosh memshelet* *rusya*
Mendeleev   he   prime minister of   Russia

"No, he invented the periodic table, back in the 19th century," she tells me. "He also predicted the properties of elements that hadn't even been discovered yet."

"לא, הוא המציא את הטבלה המחזורית במאה ה-19," היא
lo *hu* *himtsi* *et* *hatavla* *hamakhzorit* *bame'a* *ha-tsha esre* *hi*
no   he   he invented   D.O.   the table   the periodic   in the century   the nineteenth   she

אומרת לי. "הוא גם ניבא את תכונותיהם של יסודות שאפילו לא
omeret *li* *hu* *gam* *niba* *et* *tkhunoteihem* *shel* *yesodot* *she'afilu* *lo*
she tells   to me   he   also   he predicted   D.O.   their properties   of   elements   that even   not

---

216

התגלו עדיין."
hitgalu ada'in
they were discovered yet

רונן ועדינה מוסיפים להתווכח במשך מספר דקות. אחר כך הם
ronen ve'adina mosifim lehitvake'akh bemeshekh mispar dakot. akhar kakh hem
Ronen and Adina they continue to argue during a few minutes. then they

מתחילים לצעוק. לאחר מכן הם מתגוששים.
matkhilim litsok. le'akhar miken hem mitgosheshim.
they start to yell. then they they wrestle.

Ronen and Adina argue back and forth for a few minutes. Then they start yelling. Next, they are wrestling with each other.

"יאללה מכות, יאללה," אני קורא בקצב.
yala makot, yala, ani kore beketsev.
come on blows come on, I I call out with tempo.

"Fight, fight, fight," I chant.

איילה נעמדת ומכה בעדינה וברונן ברגליהם פעמים אחדות
ayala ne'emedet umaka be'adina uveronen beragleihem pe'amim akhadot
Ayala she stands up and she hits at Adina and at Ronen on their legs times a few

באמצעות מקל עץ שהיא אוהבת לשאת עמה.
be'emtsa'ut makel ets shehi ohevet laset ima.
using staff of wood that she she likes to carry with her.

Ayala stands up and whacks Adina and Ronen on the legs a few times with a wood staff that she likes to carry.

"איי, די, זה כואב," אומר רונן.
ai dai ze ko'ev, omer ronen.
ouch enough that it hurts, he says Ronen.

"Ow. Stop. That hurts," says Ronen.

"בואו נסיים את הישיבה," אומרת איילה.
bo'u nesayem et hayeshiva, omeret ayala.
let's we will finish D.O. the meeting, she says Ayala.

"Let's finish the meeting," Ayala says.

עדינה ורונן קמים מהרצפה, משפשפים את שוקיהם. הם מתיישבים
adina veronen kamim meharitspa, meshafshefim et shokeihem. hem mityashvim
Adina and Ronen they get up from the floor, they rub D.O. their shins. they they sit down

במקומותיהם. עתה כאשר תשומת לבנו נתונה לה, ממשיכה לאה
bimkomoteihem. ata ka'asher tsumat libenu netuna la, ma'amshikha le'a
in their seats. now when our attention given to her, she continues Leah

בדבריה.
bidvareiha.
with her words

Adina and Ronen get off the floor rubbing their shins. They sit down in their seats. Now that she has our attention, Leah continues talking.

"אהרון עדיין בודק את הדנ"א וטביעות האצבע כדי לנסות לאתר
aharon ada'in bodek et ha-DNA utvi'ot ha'etsba kedei lenasot le'ater
Aaron still he checks D.O. the DNA and the fingerprints in order to to try to identify

מאין הגיעו האוקראינים. אולי זה ייתן לנו קצה חוט."
me'a'in higi'u ha'ukrainim. ulai ze yiten lanu ktse khut.
from where they came the Ukrainians. maybe that it will give to us lead.

"Aaron is still checking the DNA and fingerprints to try to pinpoint where the Ukrainians come from. Maybe that will give us a lead."

אהרון הוא ידיד של עדינה. אני חושב שהיא מחבבת אותו. הם נפגשו
aharon hu yadid shel adina. ani khoshev shehi mekhabevet oto. hem nifgeshu
Aaron he friend of Adina. I I think that she she likes him. they they met

Aaron is a friend of Adina's. I think she likes him. They met while she was studying for her PhD. At that time, Aaron already had a doctorate in chemistry and was an expert in proteins and lipids and things like that. We set Aaron up in his own research facility a few years ago and funded some of his projects. In return, he acts as our own private CSI lab.

במהלך לימודי הדוקטורט של עדינה. באותה עת היה כבר לאהרון
bemahalakh limudei hadoktorat shel adina. be'ota et haya kvar le'aharon
during studies of the doctorate of Adina at the same time Aaron already had

תואר דוקטור בכימיה, והוא היה מומחה בחלבונים, שומנים ודברים
to'ar doktor bekhimya vehu haya mumkhe bekhelbonim shumanim udvarim
doctorate degree in chemistry and he he was expert with proteins lipids and things

כאלה. סידרנו לאהרון מתקן מחקר משלו לפני שנים אחדות,
ka'ele sidarnu le'aharon mitkan mekhkar mishelo lifnei shanim akhadot
like those we arranged for Aaron facility of research of his own ago years a few

ומימנו חלק מהפרויקטים שלו. בתמורה, הוא מתפקד כמעבדת
umimanu khelek mehaproyektim shelo bitmura hu metafked kema'abedet
and we funded part of the projects his in return he he functions as lab of

הזיהוי הפלילי הפרטית שלנו.
hazihui haplili hapratit shelanu
the identification of the criminal the private our

"Any progress with those names that I got from Boris?" I ask.

"איזושהי התקדמות עם השמות שקיבלנו מבוריס?" אני שואל.
eizoshehi hitkadmut im hashemot shekibalnu miboris ani sho'el
any progress with the names that I received from Boris I I ask

"Not yet," Ronen answers. "I'm writing a few special programs to try to uncover information about Ukrainians who have been coming to Israel. I'm also looking into all the transactions processed by the Central District people who Haim's friend says are willing to take payoffs. I'll go back as many years as I can to see if there are any links."

"עדיין לא," עונה רונן. "אני כותב כמה תוכנות מיוחדות כדי
ada'in lo one ronen ani kotev kama tokhnot meyukhadot kedei
yet not he answers Ronen I I write a few programs special in order to

לנסות לגלות מידע על אוקראינים שנכנסו לישראל. אני בודק
lenasot legalot meida al ukrainim shenikhnesu le'isra'el ani bodek
to try to find out information about Ukrainians that they entered into Israel I I check

גם את כל העברות הכספים שבוצעו על ידי אנשי מחוז
gam et kol ha'avarot haksafim shebutsu al yedei anshei mekhoz
also all the transfers the financial that (they) were carried out by people of district of

המרכז של המשטרה, שהחבר של חיים טוען שמוכנים לקבל
hamerkaz shel hamishtara shehakhaver shel kha'im to'en shemukhanim lekabel
the central of the police that the friend of Haim he claims that ready to receive

שוחד. אבדוק אחורה ככל הניתן ואראה אם יש קשרים
shokhad evdok akhora kekhol hanitan ve'ere im yesh ksharim
bribe I will check backward as much as the possible and I will see if there are links

כלשהם."
kolshehem
any

"Boris isn't exactly my friend," I say.

"בוריס הוא לא בדיוק חבר שלי," אני אומר.
boris hu lo bediyuk khaver sheli ani omer
Boris he not exactly friend my I I say

"Do we have a client that is paying for this case?" Ayala asks.

"יש לנו לקוח שמשלם עבור החקירה הזאת?" שואלת איילה.
yesh lanu lako'akh shemeshalem avur hakhakira hazot sho'elet ayala
we have client that he pays for the investigation the this she asks Ayala

"No," Leah says, "we're paying for this with our own money."

"לא," אומרת לאה, "אנחנו משלמים על כך מכספנו."
lo omeret le'a anakhnu meshalmim al kakh mekaspenu
no she says Leah we we pay for it from our money

"איך אנחנו מצדיקים את ההוצאה?" שואל רונן.

ronen sho'el hahotsa'a et matsdikim anakhnu eikh
Ronen he asks the expense D.O. we justify we how

"How do we justify the expense?" Ronen asks.

עונה "לפעמים אנחנו עושים דברים כי הם צריכים להיעשות,"

ona lehe'asot tsrikhim hem ki dvarim osim anakhnu lifamim
she answers to be done they need they because things we do we sometimes

"Sometimes we do things because they need to be done," answers Leah. "This is one of those times."

לאה. "זוהי אחת מהפעמים הללו."

halalu mehape'amim akhat zohi le'a
those of the times one this is Leah

"רק שאלתי," אומר רונן.

ronen omer sha'alti rak
Ronen he says I asked just

"I was just asking," Ronen says.

"ובכן, עכשיו אתה יודע."

yode'a ata akhshav uvkhen
you know you now well

"Well, now you know."

רונן דקות. מספר במשך אחרים עניינים על משוחחים אנחנו

ronen dakot mispar bemeshekh akherim inyanim al mesokhakhim anakhnu
Ronen minutes a few during other issues about we talk we

We talk about other issues for a few minutes. Ronen gets bored and starts to play a computer game. Ten minutes later Adina calls over to him.

יותר מאוחר דקות עשר מחשב. במשחק לשחק ומתחיל משתעמם

yoter me'ukhar dakot eser makhshev bemiskhak lesakhek umatkhil mishta'amem
more late minutes ten computer with game of to play and he starts he is bored

עדינה קוראת לו.

lo koret adina
to him she calls out Adina

"רונן, שמעת את הדבר האחרון שלאה אמרה?"

amra shele'a ha'akharon hadavar et shamata ronen
she said that Leah the last the thing D.O. you heard Ronen

"Ronen, did you hear the last thing Leah said?"

"אני בשלב עשר כרגע," הוא ממלמל.

memalmel hu karega eser beshalav ani
he mumbles he right now ten on level I

"I'm on level ten right now," he mumbles.

של הנייד במחשבו הכיבוי כפתור על ללחוץ מנסה עדינה

shel hanayad bemakhshevo hakibui kaftor al lilkhots menasa adina
of the portable on his computer the shutdown button on to press she tries Adina

Adina tries to push the 'Off' button on Ronen's laptop. He pushes her away with one hand and continues to type with his other hand. She pulls him out of his seat.

להקליד וממשיך האחת, בידו הצידה אותה דוחף הוא רונן.

lehaklid umamshikh ha'akhat beyado hatsida ota dokhef hu ronen
to type and he continues the one with his hand aside her he pushes he Ronen

בידו השנייה. היא מושכת אותו החוצה מכיסאו.

mikiso hakhutsa oto moshekhet hi hashniya beyado
of his chair outside him she pulls she the second with his hand

מריבה," אף בלי ישיבה לערוך אחת פעם רק רוצה "הייתי

meriva af bli yeshiva la'arokh akhat pa'am rak ha'iti rotsa
fight not even one without meeting to conduct one time just I would like

"Just once I would like to have a meeting where nobody has a fight," Leah says to me.

אומרת לי לאה.
omeret *li* *le'a*
she says to me Leah

"They're not really fighting," I tell her.

"הם לא באמת רבים," אני אומר לה.
hem *lo* *be'emet* *ravim* *ani* *omer* *la*
they not really they quarrel I I tell to her

"This is your fault," she says.

"זו אשמתך," היא אומרת.
zo *ashmatkha* *hi* *omeret*
this your fault she she says

"Why are you blaming me?"

"למה את מאשימה אותי?"
lama *at* *ma'ashima* *oti*
why you you blame me

"You don't file your reports properly, you encourage the kids when they start to act up, you complain about working in Or Yehuda. I can name other ways that you set a bad example."

"אתה לא מגיש דוחות כמו שצריך, אתה מעודד את הילדים
ata *lo* *magish* *dokhot* *kmo* *shetsarikh* *ata* *me'oded* *et* *hayeladim*
you no you submit reports like that you should you you encourage D.O. the kids

כשהם מתחילים להשתולל, אתה מתלונן על העבודה באור יהודה.
kshehem *matkhilim* *lehishtolel* *ata* *mitlonen* *al* *ha'avoda* *be'or yehuda*
when they they start to go wild you you complain about the work in Or Yehuda

אני יכולה לציין עוד דרכים שבהן אתה משמש דוגמה רעה."
ani *yekhola* *letsayen* *od* *drakhim* *shebahen* *ata* *meshamesh* *dugma* *ra'a*
I I can to point out more ways that with them you you serve example bad

Suddenly we realize the other three are watching us.

לפתע אנחנו קולטים ששלושת האחרים מתבוננים בנו.
lefeta *anakhnu* *koltim* *sheshloshet* *ha'akherim* *mitbonenim* *banu*
suddenly we we realize that three of the others they watch at us

"OK, dad and mom are having a little fight. But don't worry, we still love you," I tell them.

"או קיי, אבא ואמא מתווכחים קצת. אבל אל תדאגו, אנחנו עדיין
o kei *aba* *ve'ima* *mitvak'khim* *ktsat* *aval* *al* *tidagu* *anakhnu* *ada'in*
okay dad and mom we argue a little but don't you will worry we still

אוהבים אתכם," אני אומר להם.
ohavim *etkhem* *ani* *omer* *lahem*
we love you I I tell to them

They roll their eyes.

הם מגלגלים את עיניהם.
hem *megalgelim* *et* *eineihem*
they they roll D.O. their eyes

"One more piece of business," I say, "and then you can continue the fight."

"עוד עניין אחד," אני אומר, "ואז תוכלו להמשיך לריב."
od *inyan* *ekhad* *ani* *omer* *ve'az* *tukhlu* *lehamshikh* *lariv*
another issue one I I say and then you will be able to continue to quarrel

"What?" asks Adina.

"מה?" שואלת עדינה.
ma *sho'elet* *adina*
what she asks Adina

"Sara has a case that she can't handle by herself."

"לשרה יש חקירה שהיא לא יכולה לנהל לבד."
lesara yesh *khakira* *shehi* *lo* *yekhola* *lenahel* *levad*
Sara has investigation that she no she can to manage alone

"ספר לנו," אומרת לאה.

le'a	omeret	lanu	saper
Leah	she says	to us	tell

"Tell us about it," says Leah.

— 13 —

"שרה אמורה לחקור מועדון אופנועים."

ofano'im	mo'adon	lakh'kor	amura	sara
motorcycles	club of	to investigate	she is supposed to	Sara

"Sara has to investigate a motorcycle club."

"מגניב," אומרת איילה.

ayala	omeret	magniv
Ayala	she says	cool

"Cool," Ayala says.

"מי שכר אותה?" שואלת לאה.

le'a	sho'elet	ota	sakhar	mi
Leah	she asks	her	he hired	who

"Who hired her?" Leah asks.

"נשיא המועדון. מישהו מהכנופייה שלו גונב מהם. הוא רוצה
שׁשרה תעקוב אחרי האנשים שלו ותגלה מי לוקח כסף."

rotse	hu	mehem	gonev	shelo	mehaknufiya	mishehu	hamo'adon	nasi
he wants	he	from them	he steals	his	from the gang	someone	the club	president of

kesef	loke'akh	mi	vetegale	shelo	ha'anashim	akharei	ta'akov	shesara
money	he takes	who	and she will find out	his	the people	after	to follow	that Sara

"The president of the club. One of his gang is stealing from them. He wants Sara to watch his people and find out who is taking money."

"איך הוא יודע שחסר כסף?" שואלת לאה.

le'a	sho'elet	kesef	shekhaser	yode'a	hu	eikh
Leah	she asks	money	that missing	he knows	he	how

"How does he know that money is missing?" Leah asks.

"נשיא המועדון מנהל יומן הכנסות חודשי. ההכנסות השנה היו
נמוכות מההכנסות בשנה שעברה, למרות שהמחירים עלו."

hayu	hashana	hahakhnasot	khodshi	hakhnasot	yoman	menahel	hamo'adon	nasi
they were	the year	the revenues	monthly	income	log of	he manages	the club	president of

alu	shehamekhirim	lamrot	she'avra	beshana	mehahakhnasot	nemukhot
they went up	that the prices	even though	that passed	in the year	than the revenues	low

"The club president keeps a monthly log of their income. The income this year was lower than it was last year, even though prices are higher."

"זה נשמע כיף," אומרת עדינה. "תמיד רציתי לרכוב על אופנוע
הארלי דווידסון."

ofano'a	al	lirkov	ratsiti	tamid	adina	omeret	kef	nishma	ze
motorcycle	on	to ride	I wanted	always	Adina	she says	fun	it sounds	this

harli deividson
Harley Davidson

"This sounds like fun," Adina says. "I always wanted to ride around on a big Harley Davidson."

"יש מפגן אופנועים ענק בכנרת בשבוע הבא," אני אומר
להם. "הכנופייה תהיה שם, עסוקה בהרבה עניינים לא חוקיים. שרה

omer	ani	haba	bashavu'a	bakineret	anak	ofano'im	mifgan	yesh
I say	I	next	in the week	in the Sea of Galilee	huge	motorcycles	display of	there is

sara	khukiyim	lo	inyanim	beharbe	asuka	sham	tihiye	haknufiya	lahem
Sara	legal	not	issues	with a lot	busy	there	it will be	the gang	to them

"There's a huge motorcycle rally up at the Sea of Galilee next week," I tell them. "The gang will be there, doing a lot of illegal things. Sara thinks that is the best place to find the thief."

221

חושבת שזה המקום הטוב ביותר למצוא את הגנב."
khoshevet sheze hamakom hatov beyoter limtso et haganav
she thinks that this the place the good most to find D.O. the thief

"Do we all go?" Adina asks.

"כולנו הולכים?" שואלת עדינה.
kulanu holkhim sho'elet adina
all of us we go she asks Adina

"Yes. I convinced Sara that she couldn't keep track of all the gang members by herself. So we'll all go to help. I knew you would like a field trip."

"כן. שכנעתי את שרה שלא תוכל לעקוב אחרי כל חברי
ken shikhnati et sara shelo tukhal la'akov akharei kol khevrei
yes I convinced D.O. Sara that no she will be able to follow after all members of

הכנופייה בעצמה. אז כולנו ניסע לעזור. ידעתי שתרצו טיול
haknufiya be'atsma az kulanu nisa la'azor yadati shetirtsu tiyul
the gang by herself so all of us we will go to help I knew that you will want trip of

שטח."
shetakh
field

"Yay, a weekend at The Sea of Galilee," Ayala says.

"יש, סוף שבוע בכנרת," אומרת איילה.
yesh sof shavu'a bakineret omeret ayala
yay weekend at the Sea of Galilee she says Ayala

—14—

A few days later ...

ימים אחדים לאחר מכן ...
yamim akhadim le'akhar miken
days a few later

"It's Thursday," Ayala reminds us. "Time to go to The Sea of Galilee."

"היום יום חמישי," מזכירה לנו איילה. "הגיע הזמן לנסוע
hayom yom khamishi mazkira lanu ayala higi'a hazman linso'a
today Thursday she reminds to me Ayala it arrived the time to drive

לכנרת."
lakineret
to the Sea of Galilee

"Isn't it a little early?" I ask. "We just finished lunch."

"זה לא מוקדם קצת?" אני שואל. "רק עכשיו סיימנו את
ze lo mukdam ktsat ani sho'el rak akhshav siyamnu et
this not early a little I I ask just now we finished D.O.

ארוחת הצוהריים."
arukhat hatsohora'im
the lunch

"We want to walk around the fair grounds and check out the things the vendors are selling," Ayala says.

"אנחנו רוצים לסייר באתר היריד ולבדוק את המוצרים
anakhnu rotsim lesayer be'atar hayarid velivdok et hamutsarim
we we want to walk around at site of the fair and to check D.O. the products

שנמכרים שם," אומרת איילה.
shenimkarim sham omeret ayala
that (they) are being sold there she says Ayala

עדינה מרימה מעיל עור נוצץ. שרוולי המעיל מקושטים בפרנזים.

adina	merima	me'il	or	notsets	sharvulei	hame'il	mekushatim	bifranzim
Adina	she lifts	coat of	leather	shiny	sleeves of	the coat	adorned	with fringes

Adina holds up a shiny black leather jacket. It has fringes on the sleeves.

"אלה מצוינים," היא אומרת ללאה.

ele	metsuyanim	hi	omeret	lele'a
these	excellent	she	she says	to Leah

"These are excellent," she tells Leah.

"הם היו מוצלחים הרבה יותר אם שם הצוות היה מודפס

hem	hayu mutslakhim	harbe	yoter	im	shem	hatsevet	haya	mudpas
they	they would have been successful	much	more	if	name of	the team	it was	printed

על הגב," אני אומר.

al	hagav	ani	omer
on	the back	I	I say

"They would be a lot better if we had a team name on the back," I say.

"הגיע הזמן לוותר על הרעיון," אומר רונן.

higi'a	hazman	levater	al	hara'ayon	omer	ronen
it arrived	the time	to give up	on	the idea	he says	Ronen

"It's time for you to give up that idea," Ronen says.

"מצאנו עוד רמזים שיסייעו לנו למצוא את הסחטנים?" שואלת

matsanu	od	remazim	sheyesay'u	lanu	limtso	et	hasakhtanim	sho'elet
we found	more	clues	that (they) will help	to us	to find	D.O.	the extortionists	she asks

איילה.

ayala
Ayala

"Have we found any more clues to help us track the extortionists?" Ayala asks.

"לא," אומרת עדינה, "לא קיבלנו עדיין תוצאות מהתוכנות של

lo	omeret	adina	lo	kibalnu	ada'in	totsa'ot	mehatokhnot	shel
no	she says	Adina	no	we received	yet	results	from the programs	of

רונן."

ronen
Ronen

"No," Adina says, "Ronen's programs haven't given us any results yet."

"במהלך הימים הקרובים אנחנו לא צריכים לדאוג לגבי

bemahalakh	hayamim	hakrovim	anakhnu	lo	tsrikhim	lidog	legabei
over the course of	the days	the next	we	no	we need	to worry	about

האוקראינים, אלא להתמקד בכנופיית האופנוענים," אומרת לנו שרה.

ha'ukrainim	ela	lehitmaked	bikhnufiyat	ha'ofno'anim	omeret	lanu	sara
the Ukrainians	but	to focus on	on gang of	the motorcyclists	she tells	to us	Sara

"For the next few days we should not worry about the Ukrainians and focus on the motorcycle gang," Sara tells us.

היא הגיעה לפני דקות אחדות, נושאת מזוודת בגדים קטנה

hi	higi'a	lifnei	dakot	akhadot	noset	mizvedet	bgadim	ktana
she	she arrived	ago	minutes	a few	she carries	suitcase of	clothes	small

לסוף השבוע.

lesof hashavu'a
for the weekend

She arrived a few minutes ago, carrying a small suitcase of clothes for the weekend.

"איפה נשהה?" עדינה שואלת.

eifo	nish'he	adina	sho'elet
where	we will stay	Adina	she asks

"Where are we staying?" Adina asks.

223

"I hacked into the hotel reservation system," Ronen says. "They have a hotel about eight kilometers from the place where the rally is being held. I deleted the names on six existing reservations and replaced them with our names. We've got nice rooms, but a few of the motorcycle people are going to be very upset when they try to check in."

"פרצתי למערכת ההזמנות של המלון," אומר רונן. "יש להם
paratsti lema'arekhet hahazmanot shel hamalon omer ronen yesh lahem
I hacked into the system of the reservations of the hotel he says Ronen they have

מלון בערך שמונה קילומטרים מהמקום שבו ייערך המפגן.
malon be'erekh shmona kilometrim mehamakom shebo ye'arekh hamifgan
hotel about eight kilometers from the place that in it it will be held the display

מחקתי את השמות משש הזמנות קיימות והחלפתי אותם בשמות
makhakti et hashemot mishesh hazmanot kayamot vehekhlafti otam bashemot
I deleted D.O. the names from six reservations existing and I replaced them with the names

שלנו. יש לנו חדרים נחמדים, אבל אופנוענים אחדים עומדים
shelanu yesh lanu khadarim nekhmadim aval ofno'anim akhadim omdim
our we have rooms nice but motorcyclists a few they are going to be

להתרגז מאוד כשינסו להיכנס למלון."
lehitragez me'od ksheyenasu lehikanes lamalon
to become angry very when they will try to enter to the hotel

"Is the equipment ready?" Leah asks me.

"הציוד מוכן?" שואלת אותי לאה.
hatsiyud mukhan sho'elet oti le'a
the equipment ready she asks me Leah

"The weapons are clean, the communications equipment is working well, the computers are functional, and the van is packed. All we need to do is load our suitcases."

"כלי הנשק נקיים, ציוד התקשורת תקין, המחשבים פועלים,
klei haneshek nekiyim tsiyud hatikshoret takin hamakhshevim po'alim
the weapons clean equipment of the communication in order the computers they work

והוואן הועמס. כל מה שאנחנו צריכים לעשות הוא להעמיס את
vehavan hu'amas kol ma she'anakhnu tsrikhim la'asot hu leha'amis et
and the van it is loaded all what that we we need to do is to load D.O.

המזוודות שלנו."
hamizvadot shelanu
the suitcases our

"Adina and Ronen have already identified the four members of the motorcycle club who are most likely to be stealing," Leah says. "One runs the drug selling business. Another is in charge of the gang's gun smuggling operation. The third leads the gang's efforts to hijack trucks and the fourth operates their prostitution business. These are the men we will be following."

"עדינה ורונן כבר זיהו את ארבעת חברי מועדון האופנועים
adina veronen kvar zihu et arba'at khavrei mo'adon ha'ofno'im
Adina and Ronen already they identified D.O. four of group of club of the motorcycles

בעלי הסבירות הגבוהה ביותר לגנוב," אומרת לאה. "אחד מנהל
ba'alei hasvirut hagvoha beyoter lignov omeret le'a ekhad menahel
having the likelihood the high most to steal she says Leah one he manages

עסק למכירת סמים. השני אחראי להברחות הנשק של
esek limkhirat samim hasheni akhra'i lehavrakhot haneshek shel
business for sale of drugs the second responsible for the smuggling of the weapon of

הכנופייה. השלישי מוביל את מאמצי הקבוצה לחטוף משאיות
haknufiya hashlishi movil et ma'amatsei hakvutsa lakhtof masa'iyot
the gang the third he leads D.O. efforts of the gang to hijack trucks

והרביעי מנהל את עסקי הזנות שלהם. אלה האנשים
veharevi'i menahel et iskei haznut shelahem ele ha'anashim
and the fourth he manages D.O. business of the prostitution their these the men

שאחריהם נעקוב."
she'akhareihem na'akov
that after them we will follow

224

"עברנו על זה אתמול, כשחילקת לנו משימות ונתת לנו
avarnu *ze* *al* *etmol* *kshekhilakt* *lanu* *mesimot* *venatat* *lanu*
we went over about this yesterday when you handed out to us assignments and you gave to us

צילומים של כל מטרה," מזכיר לה רונן.
tsilumim *shel* *kol* *matara* *mazkir* *la* *ronen*
photographs of every target he reminds to her Ronen

"We went over this yesterday when you handed out our assignments and gave us pictures of each target," Ronen reminds her.

"לא מזיק להקדיש חמש דקות כדי לעבור שוב על החומר,"
lo *mazik* *lehakdish* *khamesh* *dakot* *kedei* *la'avor* *shuv* *al* *hakhomer*
no it hurts to devote five minutes in order to to go over again about the material

היא אומרת לו.
hi *omeret* *lo*
she she tells to him

"It can't hurt to spend five minutes going over things again," she tells him.

כולם נאנחים בשעה שהיא ממשיכה לחזור על כל הפרטים שמסרה
kulam *ne'enakhim* *besha'a* *shehi* *mamshikha* *lakhzor* *al* *kol* *hapratim* *shemasra*
everyone they groan as she she goes on to repeat about all the details that she gave

לנו ביום הקודם. לאה תופסת אותי עושה פרצופים מאחורי גבה.
lanu *bayom* *hakodem* *le'a* *tofeset* *oti* *ose* *partsufim* *me'akhorei* *gaba*
to us on the day the previous Leah she catches me I make faces behind her back

Everyone groans as she proceeds to repeat everything she told us the day before. Leah catches me making faces behind her back.

"אווו," אני אומר כאשר היא חובטת ברקתי.
auuu *ani* *omer* *ka'asher* *hi* *khovetet* *berakati*
owww I I say when she she hits on my temple

"Owww," I say when she smacks me in the temple.

"לכולכם יש את הוראות ההגעה למלון ולאזור הירד?"
lekhulkhem *yesh* *et* *hora'ot* *hahaga'a* *lamalon* *ule'ezor* *hayarid*
all of you have D.O. instructions of the arrival to the hotel and to the area of the fair

שואלת לאה.
sho'elet *le'a*
she asks Leah

"Do you all have the directions to the hotel and the fair grounds?" Leah asks.

"הדפסתי אותן, למקרה שהניידים שלנו יאבדו קליטה," אומר
hidpasti *otan* *lemikre* *shehanayadim* *shelanu* *ye'abdu* *klita* *omer*
I printed them just in case that the cell phones our they will lose reception he says

רונן.
ronen
Ronen

"I printed them out, just in case our cell phones lose signal," Ronen says.

הוא מוסר עותק לכל אחד מאיתנו. אנחנו אוספים את מזוודותינו
hu *moser* *otek* *lekhol ekhad* *me'itanu* *anakhnu* *osfim* *et* *mizvedoteinu*
he he gives copy to each of us we we collect D.O. our suitcases

ויוצאים מהדלת האחורית של המחסן. שלושה אופנועים מבריקים
veyotsim *mehadelet* *ha'akhorit* *shel* *hamakhsan* *shlosha* *ofano'im* *mavrikim*
and we go out of the door the back of the warehouse three motorcycles shiny

וואן גדול ממתינים במגרש החנייה.
uvan *gadol* *mamtinim* *bemigrash hakhanaya*
and van large they wait in the parking lot

He gives each of us a copy. We pick up our luggage and walk out the back door of the warehouse. Three shiny motorcycles and a large van sit in the parking lot.

The van looks more like a small truck. There are storage panels in the side walls of the truck where all our equipment is stored. The middle section has three chairs and a small desk bolted to the floor. We can use it as an office when we are parked. The front cab has space for four people.

הוואן	נראה	יותר	כמו	משאית	קטנה.	בצדי	המשאית	ממוקמים
havan	nire	yoter	kmo	masa'it	ktana	betsidei	hamasa'it	memukamim
the van	it looks	more	like	truck	small	on the side of	the truck	located

תאי	אחסון,	שבהם	מאוחסן	כל	הציוד	שלנו.	בחלקו	המרכזי
ta'ei	ikhsun	shabahem	me'ukhsan	kol	hatsiyud	shelanu	bekhelko	hamerkazi
cells of	storage	that in them	stored	all	the equipment	our	in part of it	the central

של	הוואן	יש	שלושה	מושבים	ושולחן כתיבה	קטן	מוברג	לרצפה.
shel	havan	yesh	shlosha	moshavim	veshulkhan ktiva	katan	muvrag	laritspa
of	the van	there are	three	chairs	and desk	small	screwed in	to the floor

נוכל	להשתמש	בו	בתור	משרד	כשאנו	חונים.	בתא	הקדמי
nukhal	lehishtamesh	bo	betor	misrad	kshe'anu	khonim	bata	hakidmi
we will be able	to use	with it	as an	office	when we	we park	in the cabin	the front

יש	מקום	לארבעה	אנשים.
yesh	makom	le'arba'a	anashim
there is	space	for four	people

I rented all the vehicles a few days earlier. Leah locks up the building while the kids load our luggage into the van. Adina, Ronen and Ayala put on their leather jackets, jump on their motorcycles, and roar away. Sara, Leah, and I follow in the van. We are all excited about our trip.

שכרתי	את	כל	כלי הרכב	ימים	אחדים	קודם לכן.	לאה	נועלת	את
sakharti	et	kol	klei harekhev	yamim	akhadim	kodem lakhen	le'a	no'elet	et
I rented	D.O.	all	the vehicles	days	a few	before then	Leah	she locks	D.O.

הבניין	בעוד	הילדים	מעמיסים	את	הכבודה	שלנו	בוואן.	עדינה,	רונן
habinyan	be'od	hayeladim	ma'amisim	et	hakvuda	shelanu	bavan	adina	ronen
the building	while	the kids	they load	D.O.	the luggage	our	in the van	Adina	Ronen

ואיילה	לובשים	את	מעילי	העור	שלהם,	קופצים	על	אופנועיהם
ve'ayala	lovshim	et	me'ilei	ha'or	shelahem	koftsim	al	ofno'eihem
and Ayala	they put on	D.O.	coats of	the leather	their	they jump	on	their motorcycles

ומתרחקים	בשאון	מנועים.	שרה,	לאה	ואני	נוסעים	אחריהם	בוואן.
umitrakhakim	bish'on	meno'im	sara	le'a	va'ani	nosim	akhareihem	bavan
and they move away	in noise of	engines	Sara	Leah	and I	we drive	after them	in the van

כולנו	נרגשים	לקראת	הטיול.
kulanu	nirgashim	likrat	hatiyul
all of us	excited	leading up to	the trip

Later that afternoon we cruise into the fair grounds where the rally is being held. We spend the next few hours checking out the concession booths set up around four large tents. For dinner, we buy an assortment of falafel, shawarma, and popcorn.

מאוחר	יותר	אחר	הצוהריים	אנחנו	מגיעים	למתחם	הירידים	שבו
me'ukhar	yoter	akhar	hatsohora'im	anakhnu	magi'im	lemitkham	hayeridim	shebo
late	more	after	the noon	we	we arrive	to site of	the fair	that in it

מתקיים	המפגן.	אנחנו	מבלים	את	השעות	הבאות	בבדיקת	דוכני
mitkayem	hamifgan	anakhnu	mevalim	et	hasha'ot	haba'ot	bivdikat	dukhanei
it takes place	the display	we	we spend	D.O.	the hours	next	with checking of	stands of

המכירה	הממוקמים	סביב	ארבעה	אוהלים	גדולים.	לארוחת הערב	אנחנו
hamekhira	hamemukamim	sviv	arba'a	ohalim	gdolim	la'arukhat ha'erev	anakhnu
the sale	the located	around	four	tents	large	for the dinner	we

קונים	מבחר	של	פלאפל,	שווארמה	ופופקורן.
konim	mivkhar	shel	falafel	shawarma	upopkoren
we bought	variety	of	falafel	shawarma	and popcorn

Bikers from all around the Galilee have already started to arrive. They look mean. I'm glad my gun is fully

אופנוענים	מכל	אזור	הגליל	כבר	החלו	להגיע.	הם	נראים
ofno'anim	mikol	ezor	hagalil	kvar	hekhelu	lehagi'a	hem	nirim
the motorcyclists	from all	area of	the Galilee	already	they started	to arrive	they	they look

נבזיים. אני שמח שהאקדח שלי טעון.
ta'un sheli sheha'ekdakh same'akh ani nivziyim
loaded my that the gun happy I nasty

בשעה תשע רועמים אל תוך מתחם הירידים הלקוח שלנו וקבוצת
besha'a tesha ro'amim el tokh mitkham hayeridim halako'akh shelanu ukvutsat
at hour nine they thunder to inside site of the fair the client our and team of

הנבלים שלו. הם מונים עשרים איש. אנשים מרושעים וכעורים
hanevalim shelo hem monim esrim ish anashim merusha'im ukhe'urim
the scoundrels his they they count twenty man people evil and ugly

למראה.
lemare
in appearance

At nine o'clock, our client and his group of scoundrels roar into the fair grounds. There are twenty of them. Nasty, ugly looking people.

— 15 —

אנחנו מתחלקים כדי לעקוב אחר ארבע המטרות שלנו. הבחור
anakhnu mitkhalkim kedei la'akov akhar arba hamatarot shelanu habakhur
we we split up in order to to follow after four the targets our the guy

שלי משעמם למדי. אני צופה בו שותה כמויות עצומות של
sheli masha'amem lemadai ani tsofe bo shote kamuyot atsumot shel
my boring pretty I watch at him he drinks quantities tremendous of

בירה ומתווכח עם חברתו בעת שהם מטיילים ברחבי מתחם
bira umitvake'akh im khaverto be'et shehem metaylim berakhavei mitkham
beer and he argues with his girlfriend in the time that they they walk all over area of

הירידים. בסביבות השעה אחת עשרה, אני שומע קול מוכר מאחוריי.
hayeridim bisvivot hasha'a akhat esre ani shome'a kol mukar me'akhorai
the fair at around the hour of eleven I I hear voice familiar behind me

אני מסתובב ורואה את עדינה ורונן נשענים על דוכן.
ani mistovev vero'e et adina veronen nishanim al dukhan
I I turn around and I see D.O. Adina and Ronen they lean on on stand

We split up to follow our four targets. My guy is pretty boring. I watch him drink a lot of beer and argue with his girlfriend as they walk around the fairgrounds. At about eleven o'clock, I hear a familiar voice behind me. I turn around and see Adina and Ronen leaning against a concession stand.

"רונן, אל תאכל כל כך הרבה צמר גפן מתוק," אומרת עדינה.
ronen al tokhal kol kakh harbe tsemer gefen matok omeret adina
Ronen don't you will eat so much cotton candy she says Adina

"Ronen, don't eat so much cotton candy," Adina says.

"את לא אמא שלי," עונה לה רונן.
at lo ima sheli one lo la ronen
you not mother my he replies to her Ronen

"You're not my mother," Ronen tells her.

אני חומק לעברם.
ani khomek le'evram
I I slide toward them

I slide over to them.

"אני לא חושב שאתם זקוקים למשקפי השמש, כבר חושך," אני אומר.
ani lo khoshev she'atem zkukim lemishkefei hashemesh kvar khoshekh ani omer
I no I think that you you need to the sunglasses already darkness I I say

"I don't think you need the sunglasses, since it's already dark," I say.

"כן, אבל אנחנו נראים בהם כל כך מגניב," עונה עדינה.
ken aval anakhnu nirim bahem kol kakh magniv ona adina
yes but we we look in them so cool she responds Adina

"Yeah, but we look so cool in them," Adina responds.

227

"Has your guy done anything suspicious?" Ronen asks.

"הבחור שלך עשה משהו חשוד?" שואל רונן.

ronen	sho'el	khashud	_mashehu_	asa	shelkha	habakhur
Ronen	he asks	suspicious	something	he did	your	the guy

"Nothing unusual so far. He just got rid of his girlfriend and walked over to the man you are following."

"שום דבר מיוחד עד כה. הוא בדיוק נפטר מהחברה שלו

shelo	mehakhavera	niftar	bediyuk	hu	ad ko	meyukhad	shum davar
his	of the girlfriend	he got rid of	just	he	so far	special	nothing

והלך אל הבחור שאתם עוקבים אחריו."

akharav	okvim	she'atem	habakhur	el	vehalakh
after him	you follow	that you	the guy	to	and he walked

"Hey, there's a member of another gang going over to talk with them," Ronen says.

"הי, הנה חבר מכנופייה אחרת הולך לדבר איתם," אומר רונן.

ronen	omer	itam	ledaber	holekh	_akheret_	miknufiya	khaver	_hine_	he
Ronen	he says	with them	to talk	he goes	another	of gang	member	here	hey

"I'm going to get closer," Adina says.

"אני אתקרב," אומרת עדינה.

adina	_omeret_	etkarev	ani
Adina	she says	I will get closer	I

"No need," I say. "We can listen to them from here."

"אין צורך," אני אומר. "נוכל להקשיב להם מכאן."

mikan	lahem	lehakshiv	nukhal	omer	ani	_tsorekh_	ein
from here	to them	to listen	we will be able	I say	I	need	there isn't

I pull a small gadget out of my pocket and aim it at the three bikers.

אני מוציא מכשיר אלקטרוני קטן מכיסי ומכוון אותו לעבר

le'ever	oto	umekhaven	mikisi	katan	elektroni	makhshir	motsi	ani
toward	it	and I aim	from my pocket	small	electronic	device	I take out	I

שלושת האופנוענים.

ha'ofno'anim	_shloshet_
the motorcyclists	three of

"This is the latest in microphone technology," I tell them as I plug a little earphone into my left ear.

"זו המילה האחרונה בטכנולוגיית המיקרופונים," אני אומר להם

lahem	omer	ani	hamikrofonim	betekhnologyat	ha'akharona	hamila	zo
to them	I tell	I	the microphones	in technology of	the latest	the word	this

תוך שאני מחבר אוזנייה קטנה לאוזני השמאלית.

hasmalit	le'ozni	ktana	ozniya	mekhaber	tokh she'ani
the left	to my ear	little	earphone	I attach	as I

"What are they saying?" Adina asks me.

"מה הם אומרים?" שואלת אותי עדינה.

adina	oti	sho'elet	omrim	hem	ma
Adina	me	she asks	they say	they	what

"It doesn't seem to be working."

"לא נראה שזה עובד."

oved	sheze	nire	lo
it works	that this	it seems	no

"I thought you tested all the equipment."

"חשבתי שבדקת את כל הציוד."

hatsiyud	kol	et	sheba_dakta_	khashavti
the equipment	all	D.O.	that you tested	I thought

"Well, I tested most of it."

"ובכן, בדקתי את רובו."

rubo	et	ba_dakti_	uvkhen
most of it	D.O.	I tested	well

"אני" אומרת עדינה. "הזאת," המשוכללת הטכנולוגיה כל משהו "לא
ani adina omeret hazot hameshukhlelet hatekhnologya kol lo mashehu
I Adina she says the this the advanced the technology all nothing special

בסביבה." משתלבת אני איך תראו מתקרבת.
basviva mishtalevet ani eikh tiru mitkarevet
with the surroundings I blend in I how you will watch I get close

כשעדינה לרונן אומר אני "היטב, תשתלב שהיא חושב לא אני"
kshe'adina leronen omer ani heitev tishtalev shehi khoshev lo ani
when Adina to Ronen I say I well she will blend in that she I think no I

נעים ריח לה יש שיניים, לה חסרות "לא מאתנו. מתרחקת
na'im rei'akh yesh la shina'im la khaserot lo me'itanu mitrakheket
pleasant smell she has teeth to her missing not from us she moves away

עור." במעיל מהפרברים אמא כמו נראית היא נקיות. וציפורניה
or beme'il mehaparvarim ima kmo niret hi nekiyot vetsiparneiha
leather in coat of from the suburbs mom like she looks she clean and her fingernails

"So much for high technology," Adina says. "I'm getting closer. Watch me blend in with the surroundings."

"I don't think she will blend in well," I tell Ronen as Adina moves away from us. "She has all her teeth, smells nice, and her fingernails are clean. She looks like a soccer mom in a leather jacket."

ועגילים. צמידים למכירת דוכן של בחזיתו עומדים האופנוענים
ve'agilim tsmidim limkhirat dukhan shel bakhazito omdim ha'ofno'anim
and earrings bracelets for sale of stand of in the front of they stand the motorcyclists

מהאופנוענים כמטר של למרחק עד כלאחר יד פוסעת עדינה
meha'ofno'anim kemeter shel lemerkhak ad kile'akhar yad posa'at adina
from the motorcyclists about a meter of to the distance to casually she walks Adina

אחדות, דקות בתוך התכשיטים. את בוחנת שהיא פנים ומעמידה
akhadot dakot betokh hatakhshitim et bokhenet shehi panim uma'amida
several minutes within the pieces of jewelry D.O. she examines that she and she pretends

האחרים. משהו אומר אחד אופנוען מבטים. בה נועצים הגברים שלושת
ha'akherim mashehu omer ekhad ofno'an no'atsim ba mabatim hagvarim shloshet
the others something he says one biker they stare at her the men three of

ואומר בזרוע תופס אחר אופנוען מהם. מתעלמת היא צוחקים.
ve'omer bizro'a tofes akher ofno'an mehem mitalemet hi tsokhakim
and he says at her arm he grabs another biker from them she ignores she they laugh

לו. סוטרת היא משהו עוד
lo soteret hi mashehu od
to him she slaps she something else

The bikers are standing in front of a concession booth that sells bracelets and earrings. Adina casually walks up to within a meter of the bikers and pretends to look at some of the goods. Within several minutes, the three men are staring at her. One biker says something. The others laugh. She ignores them. A second biker grabs her arm and says something else. She slaps him.

רונן. אומר "," כאן "הישאר
ronen omer kan hisha'er
Ronen he says here stay

"Stay here," Ronen says.

משם למשוך ומנסה האופנוענים שלושת אל ניגש הוא
misham limshokh umenase ha'ofno'anim shloshet el nigash hu
from there to pull and he tries the bikers three of towards he approaches he

דוחפים האופנוענים שלושת אותו. תופסים מהם שניים עדינה. את
dokhafim ha'ofno'anim shloshet oto tofsim mehem shna'im adina et
they push the bikers three of him they grab of them two Adina D.O.

את רואה המוכר סמוך. אוהל תוך אל שותפיי שני את ומושכים
et ro'e hamokher samukh ohel tokh el shutafai shnei et umoshkhim
D.O. he sees the vendor nearby tent inside to my partners two of D.O. and they pull

He walks over to the three bikers and tries to pull Adina away. Two of them grab him. The three bikers push and pull my two partners into a nearby tent. The vendor sees what is happening, but does nothing.

I walk into the tent ten seconds later. The tent is empty except for a few musicians warming up for their next performance. One of them sees Adina and Ronen struggling and yells at the bikers. The biker holding Adina lets go of her with one hand. He turns away from her to give the musician his middle finger. This is a mistake.

המתרחש, אולם אינו עושה דבר.
hamitrakhesh ulam eino ose davar
that which is happening / but / he doesn't / he does / thing

אני צועד אל תוך האוהל עשר שניות לאחר מכן. האוהל ריק, מלבד
ani tso'ed el tokh ha'ohel eser shniyot le'akhar miken. ha'ohel reik, milvad
I / I walk / to / inside / the tent / ten / seconds / later / the tent / empty / except for

מספר נגנים המתאמנים לקראת הופעתם הבאה. אחד מהם
mispar naganim hamitamnim likrat hofa'atam haba'a. ekhad mehem
a few / musicians / that are practicing / in preparation for / their appearance / next / one / of them

רואה את עדינה ורונן נאבקים וצועק על האופנוענים. האופנוען
ro'e et adina veronen ne'evakim vetso'ek al ha'ofno'anim. ha'ofno'an
he sees / D.O. / Adina / and Ronen / they struggle / and he yells / at / the bikers / the biker

האוחז בעדינה משחרר את אחיזתו בה בידו האחת. הוא מפנה
ha'okhez be'adina meshakhrer et akhizato ba beyado ha'akhat. hu mafne
that grabs / at Adina / he releases / D.O. / his grasp / on her / with his hand / the one / he / he turns

אליה את גבו כדי להראות לנגן את אצבעו האמצעית.
eleiha et gabo kedei leharot lanagan et etsba'o ha'emtsa'it.
toward her / D.O. / his back / in order to / to show / to the musician / D.O. / his finger / the middle

זו טעות.
zo ta'ut
this / mistake

She whips a little club out of her jacket pocket and swings it at the man's leg. The club smacks against his shinbone. The guy howls and drops to the ground.

היא שולפת אלה מכיס מעילה וחובטת איתה ברגלו של האיש.
hi sholefet ala mikis me'ila vekhovetet ita beraglo shel ha'ish.
she / she pulls out / club / from pocket of / her coat / and she hits / with it / at his leg / of / the man

האלה מכה בעצם השוקה. הבחור מיילל ונופל לקרקע.
ha'ala make be'etsem hashoka. habakhur meyalel venofel lakarka.
the club / make it hits / on the shinbone / the guy / he howls / and he falls / to the ground

Adina reverses her swing and whistles the club toward one of the men who is holding Ronen. He tries to duck but Ronen is struggling so much he has trouble moving out of the way. The club hits him directly on the forehead. He crumbles like an old cookie.

עדינה חובטת בכיוון ההפוך והאלה שורקת לכיוונו של
adina khovetet bakivun hahafukh veha'ala shoreket lekhivuno shel
Adina / she strikes / in the direction / the opposite / and the club / it whistles / to his direction / of

אחד הגברים המחזיקים ברונן. הוא מנסה להתכופף, אולם רונן
ekhad hagvarim hamakhzikim beronen. hu menase lehitkofef, ulam ronen
one / the men / that are holding / at Ronen / he / he tries / to duck / but / Ronen

נאבק בפראות כזו שהוא מתקשה לחמוק מהאלה. האלה
ne'evak bifra'ut kazo shehu mitkashe lakhmok meha'ala. ha'ala
he struggles / savagely / like this / that he / he had difficulty / to evade / from the club / the club

חובטת הישר במצחו. הוא מתפורר כמו עוגייה ישנה.
khovetet haisher bemitskho. hu mitporer kmo ugiya yeshana.
it strikes / directly / on his forehead / he / he crumbles / like / cookie / old

Adina turns back to the first man. He is on the ground holding his leg. She stomps on his other knee with her biker boots and he screams.

עדינה מסתובבת בחזרה לבחור הראשון. הוא על הקרקע, אוחז
adina mistovevet bakhazara labakhur harishon. hu al hakarka, okhez
Adina / she turns around / back to / to the guy / the first / he / on / the ground / he holds

ברגלו. היא רוקעת על ברכו השנייה במגפי האופנוענים שלה והוא
beraglo. hi roka'at al birko hashniya bemagafei ha'ofno'anim shela vehu
at his leg / she / she stomps / on / his knee / the second / with boots of / the bikers / her / and he

צורח.
tsore'akh
he screams

הבחור השלישי תופס בעדינה ומנסה למשוך אותה הצידה לפני
habakhur hashlishi tofes be'adina umenase limshokh ota hatsida lifnei
the man the third he grabs at Adina and he tries to pull her aside before

שתצליח לגרום לנזק נוסף. לפתע הוא נופל. הוא שוכב
shetatsli'akh ligrom lenezek nosaf. lefeta hu nofel. hu shokhev
that she will succeed to cause to damage additional suddenly he he falls he he lies down

על הקרקע, מפרפר. אני מבחין שרונן אוחז בטייזר. רונן בועט
al hakarka, mefarper. ani mavkhin sheronen okhez betaizer. ronen bo'et
on the ground he twitches I notice that Ronen he holds at taser Ronen he kicks

בשניים מהאופנוענים בעת שהוא ועדינה מתרחקים מהמקום.
bishna'im meha'ofno'anim be'et shehu ve'adina mitrakhakim mehamakom.
at two the bikers as he and Adina they move away from the place

The third man grabs Adina and tries to pull her away before she can do any more damage. Suddenly he falls down. He lies on the ground, twitching. I notice that Ronen is holding a Taser. Ronen kicks two of the bikers as he and Adina walk away from them.

"ובכן, אני חושב שהכיסוי שלכם התגלה," אני אומר להם. "למה
"uvkhen, ani khoshev shehakisui shelakhem hitgala," ani omer lahem. "lama
well I think that the cover your it was exposed I tell to them why

שלא תלכו למתחם האוכל ותשתלבו שם בקהל."
shelo telkhu lemitkham ha'okhel vetishtalvu sham bakahal."
that not you will go to site of the food and you will blend in there with the public

"Well, I think your cover is blown," I tell them. "Why don't you go to the food court and blend in over there."

"זה היה נהדר," אומר רונן.
ze haya nehedar," omer ronen.
that it was great he says Ronen

"That was great," Ronen says.

"תודה על עזרתך," אומרת לו עדינה, "אבל הסתדרתי."
"toda al ezratkha," omeret lo adina, "aval histadarti."
thanks for your help she says to him Adina but I managed

"Thanks for your help," Adina tells him, "but I had it covered."

כשהם מתרחקים, הם מתחילים להתווכח האם עדינה יכלה
kshehem mitrakhakim, hem matkhilim lehitvake'akh ha'im adina yakhla
as they they move away they they started to argue whether Adina she could have

להסתדר עם כל שלושת האופנוענים לבדה. אני צועד לאיטי לעבר
lehistader im kol shloshet ha'ofno'anim levada. ani tso'ed le'iti le'ever
to manage with all three of the bikers by herself I stroll slowly toward

הנגנים ומציג את עצמי.
hanaganim umatsig et atsmi.
the musicians and I introduce D.O. myself

As they walk away, they start arguing about whether Adina could have handled all three bikers by herself. I amble over to the musicians and introduce myself.

"כמעט נכנסתם לצרות כאן," אני אומר.
"kimat nikhnastem letsarot kan," ani omer.
almost you got into to troubles here I I say

"You guys almost had a little trouble here," I say.

"אני שונא את ההופעות האלה," אומר נגן הגיטרה. "האופנוענים
"ani sone et hahofa'ot ha'ele," omer nagan hagitara. "ha'ofno'anim
I I hate D.O. the gigs the these he says player of the guitar the bikers

"I hate these gigs," the guitar player says. "The bikers always make trouble."

231

תמיד עושים צרות.״
tamid   osim   tsarot
always   they make   troubles

"But the pay is good, and The Sea of Galilee is nice at this time of the year," the drummer says.

אומר   הזאת,״   בעונה   נעימה   והכנרת   טוב,   התשלום   ״אבל
aval   hatashlum   tov   vehakineret   ne'ima   ba'ona   hazot   omer
but   the pay   good   and the Sea of Galilee   nice   in the season   the this   he says

המתופף.
hametofef
the drummer

"What will happen to the three guys on the ground over there?" I ask.

שואל. אני   שם?״   ששוכבים   הבחורים   לשלושת   יקרה   ״מה
ma   yikre   lishloshet   habakhurim   sheshokhvim   sham   ani   sho'el
what   it will happen   to three of   the guys   that lie down   there   I   I ask

"Eventually they'll get up and go off into the woods to get high."

להתמסטל.״   לחורשה   וילכו   יקומו   הם   ״בסוף
basof   hem   yakumu   veyelkhu   lakhursha   lehitmastel
eventually   they   they will get up   and they will go   to the woods   to get high

"One of them is out cold," I mention.

מציין. אני   הכרה,״   מחוסר   מהם   ״אחד
ekhad   mehem   mekhusar hakara   ani   metsayen
one   of them   unconscious   I   I mention

"There is a security van that swings by every half hour. If he's still here, they'll take him for first aid."

יהיה   עדיין   הוא   אם   שעה.   חצי   כל   כאן   שעובר   אבטחה   ואן   ״יש
yesh   van   avtakha   she'over   kan   kol   khatsi   sha'a   im   hu   ada'in   ihiye
there is   van of   security   that passes   here   every   half   hour   if   he   still   he will be

ראשונה.״   לעזרה   אותו   יקחו   הם   כאן,
kan   hem   yik'khu   oto   le'ezra   rishona
here   they   they will take   him   for aid   first

"I think I'm going to write a song about that girl with the club," the drummer says. "She was amazing."

אומר   האלה,״   עם   הזו   הבחורה   על   שיר   שאכתוב   חושב   ״אני
ani   khoshev   she'ekhtov   shir   al   habakhura   hazo   im   ha'ala   omer
I   I think   that I will write   song   about   the girl   the that   with   the club   he says

המתופף. ״היא היתה מדהימה.״
hametofef   hi   haita   madhima
the drummer   she   she was   amazing

---16---

The next morning we compare notes.

רשמים.   מחליפים   אנחנו   למחרת   בבוקר
baboker   lemokhorat   anakhnu   makhlifim   reshamim
in the morning   the day after   we   we swap   impressions

"The guy in charge of the drug sales is not stealing," Sara says.

שרה. אומרת   גונב,״   לא   הסמים   מכירת   על   האחראי   ״הבחור
habakhur   ha'akhra'i   al   mekhirat   hasamim   lo   gonev   omeret   sara
the guy   that is responsible   for   sale of   the drugs   not   he steals   she says   Sara

"How do you know?" Leah asks.

לאה. שואלת   יודעת?״   את   ״איך
eikh   at   yoda'at   sho'elet   le'a
how   you   you know   she asks   Leah

"איילה ואני בדקנו את הפעילות אמש. הוא מנהל טוב. שני אנשים
מנהלים רישום כמה הם נותנים לכל שליח וכמה כסף
כל שליח מחזיר. בלתי אפשרי למי מהמעורבים לגנוב משהו."

"Ayala and I checked out the operation last night. He's a good manager. Two men keep a log of how much they give to each runner and how much cash the runner brings back. It would be impossible for anyone involved to steal anything."

עדינה ורונן אשפזו את הבחור שלהם בבית החולים עם
פיקת ברך שבורה. והם גרמו לבחור שלי זעזוע מוח. הבחורים
האלה לא גנבו כלום אתמול בלילה," אני אומר.

"Adina and Ronen put their man in the hospital with a broken kneecap. And they gave my man a concussion. Those men didn't do any stealing last night," I say.

לאה כבר סלחה לעדינה ולרונן על הקרב שניהלו
עם האופנוענים. היא מאשימה אותי בכל העניין. רק בגלל
שהמיקרופון לא פעל.

Leah has already forgiven Adina and Ronen for their fight with the bikers. She blames me for the whole thing. Just because that microphone didn't work.

"האיש שאחריו עקבתי הוא הגנב," אומרת לאה. "הוא אחראי על
עסקי הזנות."

"The man I followed is the thief," Leah says. "He's in charge of the prostitution business."

"לא ראיתי שום זונות," אומר רונן.

"I didn't see any prostitutes," Ronen says.

"הן הגיעו במיני ואן נפרד. הכנופייה הקימה חמישה עשר אוהלים
בחורשה. הבנות עבדו מהאוהלים. העסקים שלהם פרחו."

"They arrived in a separate minivan. The gang set up fifteen tents back in the woods. The girls operated out of the tents. They did a booming business."

233

Story 13

"Why wasn't I told about these tents?" I demand to know.

"למה לא נאמר לי דבר על האוהלים הללו?" אני דורש לדעת.

lama lo ne'emar li davar al ha'ohalim halalu? ani doresh lada'at
why not it was told to me thing about the tents the these I demand to know

---

"How do you know the man in charge was stealing?" Sara asks.

"איך את יודעת שהאחראי גונב?" שואלת שרה.

eikh at yoda'at sheha'akhra'i gonev? sho'elet sara
how you you know that the responsible person he steals she asks Sara

---

"I counted the number of men and women who went into each tent," Leah says. "I estimated the total amount of money the prostitutes earned by multiplying the number of customers by the cost of each transaction. The man who runs the operation turned in less than fifty percent of my estimate."

"ספרתי את מספר הגברים והנשים שנכנסו לכל אחד

safarti et mispar hagvarim vehanashim shenikhnesu lekhol ekhad
I counted D.O. number of the men and the women that they entered into each

מהאוהלים," אומרת לאה. "הערכתי את הסכום הכולל שהרוויחו

meha'ohalim, omeret le'a. he'erakhti et haskhum hakolel shehirvikhu
of the tents she says Leah I estimated D.O. the sum the total that they earned

הזנונות על ידי הכפלת מספר הלקוחות במחיר עסקה. הבחור

hazonot al yedei hakhpalat mispar halakokhot bimkhir iska. habakhur
the prostitutes by multiplying number of the customers with price of deal the man

האחראי על העסק מסר פחות מחמישים אחוזים מהההערכה

ha'akhra'i al ha'esek masar pakhot mekhamishim akhuzim mehaha'arakha
that is responsible for the business he turned in less than fifty percent of the estimate

שלי."

sheli
my

"Why couldn't the president of the club figure this out?" I ask.

"למה נשיא המועדון לא יכול היה להבין זאת בעצמו?" אני

lama nesi hamo'adon lo yakhol haya lehavin zot be'atsmo? ani
why president of the club no he could have to figure out this by himself I

שואל.

sho'el
I ask

"He was dead drunk an hour after the gang arrived. There was no way he could know how many customers were serviced."

"הוא היה שיכור כלוט כשעה אחרי שהכנופייה הגיעה. לא הייתה לו

hu haya shikor kalot kesha'a akharei shehaknufiya higi'a. lo haita lo
he he was drunk as Lot about hour after that the gang they arrived not he had

שום אפשרות לדעת כמה לקוחות קיבלו שירות."

shum efsharut lada'at kama lakokhot kiblu sheirut
any possibility to know how many customers they received service

---

A few hours later, I throw a mind haze at the man in charge of the prostitutes and pull him into our van. Leah talks with him for ten minutes and records his answers.

שעות אחדות מאוחר יותר, אני מטיל ערפול מוחי על הבחור

sha'ot akhadot me'ukhar yoter, ani matil irpul mokhi al habakhur
hours a few late more I I throw fog mental at the man

האחראי על עסקי הזנות ומושך אותו אל תוך הוואן

ha'akhra'i al iskei haznut umoshekh oto el tokh havan
that is responsible for business of the prostitution and I pull him to inside the van

שלנו. לאה משוחחת איתו במשך עשר דקות ומקליטה את

shelanu. le'a mesokhakhat ito bemeshekh eser dakot umaklita et
our Leah she talks with with him during ten minutes and she records D.O.

תשובותיו.

tshuvotav
his answers

234

זוכרים שסיפרתי לכם שהיא יכולה להוציא את האמת מכל אחד?
zokhrim shesiparti lakhem shehi yekhola lehotsi et ha'emet mikol ekhad?
you remember that I told to you that she she can to take out D.O. the truth from anyone?

הבחור מספר לה כמה זמן הוא כבר גונב, כמה גנב, ואת
habakhur mesaper la kama zman hu kvar gonev, kama ganav, ve'et
the man he tells to her how much time he he steals already, how much he stole, and D.O.

מיקומה של הכספת שבה הוא שומר את הכסף.
mikuma shel hakasefet sheba hu shomer et hakesef.
its location of the safe that in it he he keeps D.O. the money.

Remember I told you that she can get the truth out of anyone? The man tells her how long he has been stealing, how much he has stolen, and the location of the safe deposit box where he keeps the money.

עם תום החקירה, אני מוחק את קולה של לאה מהההקלטה.
im tom hakhakira, ani mokhek et kola shel le'a mehahaklata.
with completion of the interrogation, I I delete D.O. her voice of Leah from the recording.

לאחר מכן אני מכין שני עותקים לשרה עבור הלקוח שלה. לבסוף,
le'akhar miken ani mekhin shnei otakim lesara avur halako'akh shela. levasof,
then I I prepare two of copies for Sara for the client her. finally,

אני מטשטש את זיכרונו של האופנוען, ואז אני מרדים אותו.
ani metashtesh et zikhrono shel ha'ofno'an, ve'az ani mardim oto.
I I blur D.O. his memory of the biker, and then I I put to sleep him.

After the interrogation, I eliminate Leah's voice from the recording. Then I make two copies for Sara to give to her client. Finally, I scramble the biker's memory, and then I put him to sleep.

כאשר יתעורר, הוא יחשוב שברנש מפחיד בגיל העמידה גרר
ka'asher yitorer, hu yakhshov shebarnash mafkhid begil ha'amida garar
when he will wake up, he he will think that guy scary at middle age he dragged

אותו לתוך וואן, כפת אותו ואיים לנעוץ סכין בעינו אם לא
oto letokh van, kafat oto ve'iyem linots sakin be'eino im lo
him into van, he tied up him and he threatened to insert knife in his eye if no

יודה הודאה מלאה.
yode hoda'a mele'a.
he will admit confession full.

When he wakes up, he will think that some scary middle aged dude dragged him into a van, tied him up and threatened to stick a knife into his eyeball unless he made a full confession.

לאה עוזבת, ואני מתקשר לשרה בטלפון הנייד. כעבור מספר
le'a ozevet, va'ani mitkasher lesara batelefon hanayad. ka'avor mispar
Leah she leaves, and I I call to Sara on the telephone the mobile. after a few

דקות היא מכניסה את נשיא מועדון האופנועים אל הוואן.
dakot hi makhnisa et nesi mo'adon ha'ofno'im el havan.
minutes she she brings in D.O. president of club of the motorcycles to the van.

Leah takes off, and I call Sara on the cell phone. A few minutes later she brings the president of the motorcycle club into the van.

"מי הבחור הזה?" הוא שואל כשהוא רואה אותי.
"mi habakhur haze?" hu sho'el kshehu ro'e oti.
who the guy the this? he he asks when he he sees me.

"Who is this guy?" he asks when he sees me.

"אני הבריון השכיר שלה," אני אומר לו.
"ani habiryon hasakhir shela," ani omer lo.
I the muscular guy the salaried her, I I tell to him.

"I'm her hired muscle," I tell him.

"אתה לא נראה כל כך קשוח."
"ata lo nire kol kakh kashu'akh."
you no you look so tough.

"You don't look so tough."

235

"Tough enough to get a full confession from your man. Here's the recording."

"קשוח מספיק כדי להוציא הודאה מלאה מהאיש שלך. הנה
kashu'akh maspik kedei lehotsi hoda'a mele'a meha'ish shelkha hine
tough enough in order to take out confession full from the man your here is

ההקלטה."
hahaklata
the recording

He looks at his associate who is tied up and sleeping in the corner of the van.

הוא מביט בשותפו הכפות הישן בפינת הוואן.
hu mabit beshutafo hakafut hayashen befinat havan
he he looks at his partner the bound that is sleeping in corner of the van

"What did you do to him?"

"מה עשיתם לו?"
ma asitem lo
what you did to him

"Trust me, you don't want to know."

"סמוך עלי, אינך רוצה לדעת."
smokh alai einkha rotse lada'at
trust on me you don't you want to know

The head of the gang is very happy after he plays the recording. He pulls a wad of hundred shekel bills from his pocket and pays Sara. Then he drags his man out of the van and gives him to a few associates. I notice Sara crying a little bit after the bikers leave.

ראש הכנופייה מאושר מאוד אחרי שהוא שומע את ההקלטה. הוא
rosh haknufiya me'ushar me'od akharei shehu shome'a et hahaklata hu
head of the gang happy very after that he he hears D.O. the recording he

שולף מכיסו חבילת שטרות של מאה שקל ומשלם לשרה.
sholef mikiso khavilat shtarot shel me'a shekel umeshalem lesara
he pulls out from his pocket wad of bills of hundred shekel and he pays to Sara

לאחר מכן הוא גורר את האיש שלו אל מחוץ לוואן ומוסר
le'akhar miken hu gorer et ha'ish shelo el mikhuts lavan umoser
then he he drags D.O. the man his to out of to the van and he gives

אותו למספר חבר'ה. אני מבחין שׂשרה בוכה קצת אחרי שהאופנוענים
oto lemispar khevre ani mavkhin shesara bokha ktsat akharei sheha'ofno'anim
him to a few dudes I I notice that Sara she cries a little after that the bikers

עוזבים.
ozvim
they leave

"What's the matter?"

"מה קרה?"
ma kara
what it happened

"They are going to kill that man. I should have turned him over to the police."

"הם הולכים להרוג את הבחור. הייתי צריכה להסגיר אותו למשטרה."
hem holkhim laharog et habakhur ha'iti tsrikha lehasgir oto lamishtara
they they go to kill D.O. the man I should have to hand over him to the police

"If you didn't give him to the gang, they would have tried to kill us," I tell her. "Besides, the guy told me during the interrogation that he was guilty of a few murders that nobody knows about. So he is getting a rough form of justice."

"אם לא היית מוסרת אותו לכנופייה הם היו מנסים להרוג אותנו,"
im lo ha'it moseret oto laknufiya hem hayu menasim laharog otanu
if no you would give him to the gang they they would have tried to kill us

אני אומר לה. "חוץ מזה, האיש סיפר לי בחקירה שהוא
ani omer la khuts mize ha'ish siper li bakhakira shehu
I I tell to her besides the man he told to me in the interrogation that he

236

שהוא כך עליהם. יודע שאיש אינו רצח מעשי כמה ביצע
shehu kakh aleihem. yode'a she'ish eino retsakh ma'asei kama bitse'a
that he in this way about them he knows that no one murder acts of a few he performed

מקבל מין סוג גס של צדק."
mekabel min sug gas shel tsedek.
he receives kind of type rough of justice

"אני עדיין מרגישה רע."
ani ada'in margisha ra
I still I feel bad

"I still feel bad."

נושא רונן שלנו. הקבוצה חברי ושאר לאה מגיעים אז בדיוק
nose ronen shelanu. hakvutsa khevrei ush'ar le'a magi'im az bediyuk
he carries Ronen our the team group of and rest of Leah they arrive then precisely

שקית גדולה של פופקורן ובקבוק קוקה קולה גדול.
sakit gdola shel popkoren uvakbuk koka kola gadol
bag big of popcorn and bottle of Coca Cola big

Just then, Leah and the rest of our group shows up. Ronen is carrying a big bag of popcorn and a big bottle of Coca Cola.

"אנחנו יכולים להישאר כאן עד סוף המפגן?" שואלת איילה.
anakhnu yekholim lehisha'er kan ad sof hamifgan? sho'elet ayala
we we can to stay here until end of the display she asks Ayala

"Can we stay here for the rest of the rally?" Ayala asks.

"ודאי, החזירי את האופנועים למשרד ההשכרה ביום ראשון ואנחנו
vadai, hakhziri et ha'ofno'im lemisrad hahaskara beyom rishon ve'anakhnu
sure return D.O. the motorcycles to office of the renting on Sunday and we

נאסוף אתכם משם," אומרת לאה.
ne'esof etkhem misham, omeret le'a
we will pick up you from there she says Leah

"Sure, drop off the motorcycles at the rental shop on Sunday and we'll pick you up there," Leah says.

שרה משוחחת עם לאה מספר דקות ומחליטה לשכור רכב ולחזור
sara mesokhakhat im le'a mispar dakot umakhlita liskor rekhev velakhzor
Sara she talks with with Leah a few minutes and she decides to rent car and to go back

ליפו לבד.
leyafo levad
to Jaffa alone

Sara talks with Leah for a few minutes and decides to rent a car and drive back to Jaffa alone.

"היא צריכה קצת זמן לעצמה," מספרת לי לאה לאחר דקות אחדות.
hi tsrikha ktsat zman le'atsma, mesaperet li le'a le'akhar dakot akhadot
she she needs a little time to herself she tells to me Leah after minutes a few

"She needs some time to herself," Leah tells me a few minutes later.

"זה לא שהיא ירתה לבחור בראש," אני אומר. "היא נאלצה להסגיר
ze lo shehi yarta labakhur barosh, ani omer. hi ne'eltsa lehasgir
it not that she she shot to the guy in the head I say he she had to to hand over

אותו לכנופייה."
oto laknufiya
him to the gang

"It's not like she shot the guy in the head," I say. "She had to give him to the gang."

"אבל היא בכל זאת מאוד מצוברחת."
aval hi bekhol zot me'od metsuvrakhat
but she nevertheless very upset

"But she is still very upset."

237

Leah and I drive away in the van. We decide to spend the night at a cute little bed and breakfast in the Galilee.

לאה ואני יוצאים לדרכנו בוואן. אנחנו מחליטים להעביר את הלילה
halaila et leha'avir makhlitim anakhnu bavan ledarkenu yotsim va'ani le'a
the night D.O. to pass we decide we in the van on our way we leave and I Leah

באכסניה קטנה וחמודה, כולל ארוחת בוקר, בגליל.
bagalil arukhat boker kolel vakhamuda ktana be'akhsanya
in the Galilee breakfast including and cute small in an inn

"You know," I tell Leah, "it would have been easier if you had just interrogated each of the four gang members in private. You could have gotten all the answers without us having to spend the weekend at the biker rally."

"את יודעת," אני אומר ללאה, "היה יכול להיות קל יותר אם
im yoter kal haya yakhol lihiyot lele'a omer ani yoda'at at
if more easy it could have been to Leah I tell I you know you

היית פשוט חוקרת כל אחד מארבעת חברי הכנופייה
haknufiya khavrei me'arba'at kol ekhad khokeret pashut ha'it
the gang members of of four of each you interrogate simply you should have

בנפרד. יכולת לקבל את כל התשובות מבלי לבלות את
et levalot mibli hatshuvot kol et lekabel yakholt benifrad
D.O. to spend (time) without the answers all D.O. to get you could have separately

סוף השבוע במפגן האופנוענים."
ha'ofno'anim bemifgan sof hashavu'a
the bikers at display of the weekend

"If I had done it that way, both Sara and the gang leader would have realized that I have special abilities."

"אם הייתי עושה זאת, גם שרה וגם מנהיג הכנופייה היו מבינים
hayu mevinim haknufiya manhig vegam sara gam zot ha'iti osa im
they would have realized the gang leader of and also Sara also this I had done if

שיש לי כוחות מיוחדים."
meyukhadim kokhot sheyesh li
special powers that I have

"Right," I say.

"נכון," אני אומר.
omer ani nakhon
I say I right

"Plus, it was a fun weekend. The kids really enjoyed wearing leather jackets and driving around on giant motorcycles," Leah says.

"ובנוסף, זה היה סוף שבוע נחמד. הילדים ממש נהנו ללבוש
lilbosh nehenu mamash hayeladim nekhmad sof shavu'a haya ze uvenosaf
to wear they enjoyed really the kids lovely weekend it was this and in addition

מעילי עור ולרכוב על אופנועים ענקיים," אומרת לאה.
le'a omeret anakiyim ofano'im al velirkov or me'ilei
Leah she says huge motorcycles on and to ride leather coats of

"Sara kept a copy of the confession for herself," Leah tells me a few minutes later. "She plans to give it to the police, along with other evidence of the gang's illegal activities that she collected this weekend."

"שרה שמרה עותק של ההודאה לעצמה," אומרת לי לאה דקות
dakot le'a li omeret hahoda'a le'atsma shel otek shamra sara
minutes Leah to me she tells the confession for herself of copy she kept Sara

אחדות לאחר מכן. "היא מתכוונת לתת אותו למשטרה, עם ראיות
re'ayot im lamishtara oto latet mitkavenet hi le'akhar miken akhadot
evidence with to the police it to give she plans she later a few

אחרות לפעילות הבלתי חוקית של הכנופייה, שאספה במשך
bemeshekh she'asfa haknufiya shel khukit habilti lape'ilut akherot
during that she collected the gang of legal the non- to the activities other

סוף השבוע."
sof hashavu'a
the weekend

זאת באופן ותעשה חודשים כמה תחכה שהיא "תוודאי
be'ofen zot veta'ase khodashim kama tekhake shehi tevadi
in way this and she will do months a few she will wait that she you will make sure

שהכנופייה לא תוכל לעלות על עקבותיה," אני אומר.
omer ani ikvoteiha al la'alot tukhal lo shehaknufiya
I say I her footprints on to trace it will be able lo that the gang

"אעשה זאת."
zot e'ese
this I will do

"Make sure she waits a few months and does it in a way that the gang can't trace it back to her," I say.

"I will."

— 17 —

יום רביעי מביא עמו חדשות טובות.
tovot khadashot imo mevi yom revi'i
good news with it it brings Wednesday

Wednesday brings good news.

נוספים אוקראינים שלושה של ותמונותיהם שמם את מצא "רונן
nosafim ukrainim shlosha shel utmunoteihem shmam et matsa ronen
additional Ukrainians three of and their pictures their name D.O. he found Ronen

שעשויים להיות חלק מכנופיית הסחיטה," אומרת עדינה.
adina omeret haskhita miknufiyat khelek lihiyot she'asuyim
Adina she says the extortion of gang of part of to be who are likely to

"Ronen found the names and pictures of three additional Ukrainians who might be part of the extortion gang," Adina says.

"איך הוא עשה זאת?" שואלת איילה.
ayala sho'elet zot asa hu eikh
Ayala she asks that he did he how

"How did he do that?" Ayala asks.

חברת נוסעי של נתוניהם את שבדקה תוכנה כתב "הוא
khevrat nosei shel netuneihem et shebadka tokhna katav hu
company of passengers of of their data D.O. that (it) checked program he wrote he

אוקראינה. משטרת של הנתונים למאגר אותם והשוותה ארופלוט
ukraina mishteret shel hanetunim lema'agar otam vehishveta eiroflot
Ukraine police of of the data to pool of them and he compared Aeroflot

לארץ שטסו פלילי עבר בעלי גברים ארבעה זיהתה התוכנה
la'aretz shetasu plili avar ba'alei gvarim arba'a zihata hatokhna
to the country that (they) flew criminal record having men four it identified the program

חקרה שלאה הבחור האחרונה. השנה במהלך ארופלוט עם
khakra shele'a habakhur ha'akharona hashana bemahalakh eiroflot im
she interrogated that Leah the man the last the year during Aeroflot with

עיר." מאותה הגיעו האחרים שלושת מהם. אחד היה בבת ים
ir me'ota higi'u ha'akherim shloshet mehem ekhad haya bevat yam
city from same they arrived the others three of of them one he was in Bat Yam

"He wrote a program that checked Aeroflot passenger records and compared them to Ukrainian police databases. The program identified four men with criminal records who flew into this country via Aeroflot in the last year. The man Leah interrogated in Bat Yam was one of them. The other three come from the same city."

"אנחנו יודעים איך שלושת הגברים הללו נראים?" שואלת איילה.
ayala sho'elet nirim halalu hagvarim shloshet eikh yodim anakhnu
Ayala she asks they look the those the men three of how we know we

"Do we know what the three other men look like?" Ayala asks.

"כן," אומרת עדינה. "למזלנו, ארופלוט מתעדת את תעודת הזהות
te'udat hazehut et meta'edet eiroflot lemazlenu adina omeret ken
the identity card D.O. they document Aeroflot to our luck Adina she says yes

"Yes," says Adina. "Luckily, Aeroflot documents every passenger's photo identification."

239

הנושאת תמונה של כל נוסע."
nose'a kol shel tmuna hanoset
passenger every of picture that carries

"I'm really not looking forward to spending weeks showing pictures of these guys to people all over Jaffa," I say.

"לא ממש מתחשק לי לבלות שבועות בלהראות תצלומים של הבחורים
habakhurim shel tatslumim belehar'ot shavu'ot levalot mitkhashek li mamash lo
the guys of pictures in showing weeks to spend I feel like really not

הללו לאנשים בכל רחבי יפו," אני אומר.
omer ani yafo rakhavei bekhol le'anashim halalu
I say I Jaffa all over to every to people the these

"The Ukrainian immigrants in Jaffa and Tel Aviv are concentrated in two very small areas," Leah tells me. "It won't take too long to find them."

"העולים האוקראינים ביפו ובתל אביב מרוכזים בשני אזורים
azorim bishnei merukazim uvetel aviv beyafo ha'ukrainim ha'olim
areas in two of they are concentrated and in Tel Aviv in Jaffa the Ukrainian the immigrants

קטנים מאוד," אומרת לי לאה. "לא ייקח זמן רב למצוא אותם."
otam limtso rav zman yikakh lo le'a li omeret me'od ktanim
them to find much time it will take no Leah to me she tells very small

That night, Ayala, Sara, and I drive to the Jaffa Ukrainian district, a small section of Jerusalem Avenue. We drive in separate cars.

באותו לילה, איילה, שרה ואני נוסעים לאזור האוקראיני ביפו, מתחם
mitkham beyafo ha'ukraini la'ezor nosim va'ani sara ayala laila be'oto
section in Jaffa the Ukrainian to the area we drive and I Sara Ayala night in same

קטן באזור שדרות ירושלים. אנחנו נוסעים במכוניות נפרדות.
nifradot bimkhoniyot nos'im anakhnu yerushala'im sderot be'ezor katan
separate in cars we drive we Jerusalem avenue in area of small

Ayala hangs out in snooker clubs. Sara checks the grocery stores and laundromats. I work the bars and strip clubs. No luck that first night.

איילה מסתובבת במועדוני הסנוקר. שרה בודקת את חנויות המכולת
hamakolet khanuyot et bodeket sara hasnuker bemo'adonei mistovevet ayala
the grocery stores of D.O. she checks Sara the snooker at clubs of she hangs out Ayala

והמכבסות. אני בודק את הברים ומועדוני הסטריפטיז. אין מזל
mazal ein hastriptiz umo'adonei habarim et bodek ani vehamikhbasot
luck there isn't the striptease and clubs of the bars D.O. I check I and the laundromats

בלילה הראשון.
harishon balaila
the first in the night

"I met two auto mechanics at the snooker club who want to marry me," Ayala tells me on the cell phone as I drive home.

"פגשתי שני מכונאי רכב במועדון הסנוקר שהציעו לי
li shehitsi'u hasnuker bemo'adon rekhev mekhona'ei shnei pagashti
to me that they proposed the snooker at club of automobile mechanics of two of I met

נישואין," מספרת לי איילה בטלפון הנייד כשאני נוהג הביתה.
habaita noheg kshe'ani hanayad batelefon ayala li mesaperet nisu'in
homeward I drive as I the mobile on the phone of Ayala to me she tells marriage

We try the same area the second night. Sara calls me at two a.m.

אנחנו מנסים את אותו אזור בלילה השני. שרה מתקשרת אליי
elai mitkasheret sara hasheni balaila ezor oto et menasim anakhnu
to me she calls Sara the second on the night area same D.O. we try we

בשתיים בלילה.
balaila bishta'im
in the night at two

"מצאת משהו?" היא שואלת.

sho'elet hi mashehu matsata
she asks she something you found

"Did you find anything?" she asks.

"אף אחד לא מזהה את התצלומים," אני אומר לה.

la omer ani hatatslumim et mezahe lo af ekhad
to her I tell I the pictures D.O. he recognizes no no one

"Nobody recognizes the pictures," I tell her.

"קיבלת ריקוד?" היא שואלת.

sho'elet hi rikud kibalta
she asks she dance you got

"Did you get a lap dance?" she asks.

"הבחורות שרוקדות במועדונים האלה הן לא הטיפוס שלי," אני

ani sheli hatipus lo hen ha'ele bamo'adonim sherokdot habakhurot
I my the type not they the these in the clubs who (they) dance the ladies

אומר לה. "וכמה ברמנים הציעו לארגן מחדש את האף שלי

sheli ha'af et mekhadash le'argen hitsi'u barmenim vekhama la omer
my the nose D.O. anew to arrange they offered bartenders and a few to her I tell

אם לא אפסיק להטריד את הלקוחות שלהם."

shelahem halakokhot et lehatrid afsik lo im
their the customers D.O. to bother I will stop no if

"The ladies who dance in these clubs aren't my type," I tell her. "And a few bartenders offered to re-arrange my nose if I didn't stop bothering their customers."

"כמה מרגש," אומרת שרה.

sara omeret meragesh kama
Sara she says exciting how

"How exciting," Sara says.

"איפה את עכשיו?" אני שואל.

sho'el ani akhshav at eifo
I ask I now you where

"Where are you now?" I ask.

"עוזרת לאיילה להראות את התצלומים במועדוני הסנוקר."

hasnuker bamo'adonei hatatslumim et leharot le'ayala ozeret
the snooker at the clubs of the pictures D.O. to show to Ayala I help

"Helping Ayala show the pictures at the snooker clubs."

"אתן נהנות?"

nehenot aten
you have fun you

"Are you having fun?"

"בחור אחד בשם ג'ורג'י לימד אותי איך לאחוז את המקל."

hamakel et le'ekhoz eikh oti limed jorji beshem ekhad bakhur
the cue stick D.O. to hold how me he taught Georgi with name one guy

"Some guy named Georgi taught me to hold the cue."

"נחמד. בעוד כמה שנים תוכלי לצאת לסיבובי תחרויות."

takharuyot lesivuvei latset tukhli shanim kama be'od nekhmad
competitions to circuit of to go out you will be able years a few in another nice

"Nice. You can go on tour in a few years."

"ג'ורג'י אומר שאין לי מספיק ריכוז."

rikuz maspik she'ein li omer jorji
concentration enough that I don't have he says Georgi

"Georgi says I don't have enough concentration."

"את מרגישה טוב יותר לגבי הסגרת הבחור שגנב מכנופיית

miknufiyat sheganav habakhur hasgarat legabei yoter tov margisha at
from the gang of that (he) stole the man handing over of about more good you feel at

"Are you feeling better about turning over the man who was stealing from the motorcycle gang?" I ask.

האופנוענים?" אני שואל.
sho'el · ani · ha'ofno'anim
I ask · I · the bikers

"I guess I can live with it."

"נראה לי שאוכל לחיות עם זה."
ze · im · likhyot · she'ukhal · li · nire
this · with · to live · that I will be able · to me · it seems

"Good."

"יופי."
yofi
good

The next night, we get lucky. I meet a guy at a hole-in-the-wall bar next to a boarded up gas station who recognizes the pictures I show him.

למחרת בלילה מתמזל מזלנו. אני פוגש בחור בבר בחור
bekhor · bebar · bakhur · pogesh · ani · mitmazel mazalenu · balaila · lemokhorat
in hole · at bar · guy · I meet · I · we have a stroke of luck · in the night · the following day

כלשהו, סמוך לתחנת דלק שנאטמה בקרשים, והוא מזהה את
et · mezahe · vehu · bekrashim · shene'etma · delek · letakhanat · samukh · kolshehu
D.O. · he recognizes · and he · with boards · that (it) is sealed · gas · to station of · next to · some

התצלומים שאני מראה לו.
lo · mare · she'ani · hatatslumim
to him · I show · that I · the pictures

"They all live in an apartment in my building," he says. "Very bad men."

"הם גרים כולם בדירה בבניין שלי," הוא אומר. "אנשים
anashim · omer · hu · sheli · babinyan · bedira · kulam · garim · hem
men · he says · he · my · in the building · in apartment · all of them · they live · they

רעים מאוד."
me'od · ra'im
very · bad

— 18 —

Thirty-five minutes later, Ayala and Sara meet me at the building where the three Ukrainians are staying. We get into my car to have a conference call with Leah.

שלושים וחמש דקות מאוחר יותר פוגשות אותי איילה ושרה בבניין
babinyan · vesara · ayala · oti · pogshot · yoter · me'ukhar · dakot · shloshim vekhamesh
at the building · and Sara · Ayala · me · they meet · more · late · minutes · thirty-five

שבו מתאכסנים שלושת האוקראינים. אנחנו נכנסים למכונית שלי
sheli · lamekhonit · nikhnasim · anakhnu · ha'ukrainim · shloshet · mitakhsenim · shebo
my · to the car · we enter · we · the Ukrainians · three of · they are housed · that in it

כדי לערוך שיחת ועידה עם לאה.
le'a · im · ve'ida · sikhat · la'arokh · kedei
Leah · with · conference · call of · to organize · in order to

"We need prisoners," Leah tells me over the phone. "Don't shoot everyone."

"אנחנו צריכים אסירים," אומרת לי לאה בטלפון. "אל תירו
tiru · al · batelefon · le'a · li · omeret · asirim · tsrikhim · anakhnu
you will shoot · don't · on the phone · Leah · to me · she tells · prisoners · we need · we

בכולם."
bekhulam
at everyone

"I'll stay outside in case anyone tries to come down the fire escape," Sara says. "Plus, I can deal with the local police

"אני אשאר בחוץ למקרה שמישהו ינסה לברוח דרך יציאת
yetsi'at · derekh · livro'akh · yenase · shemishehu · lemikre · bakhuts · esha'er · ani
exit of · through · to escape · he will try · that someone · in case · outside · I will stay · I

if they show up unexpectedly."

החירום", אומרת שרה. "אוכל גם לטפל בשוטרים אם הם
hakheirum omeret sara ukhal gam letapel bashotrim im hem
the emergency / she says / Sara / I will be able / also / to deal with / with the policemen / if / they

יופיעו פתאום".
yofi'u pitom
they will show up / suddenly

I use a thin metal bar to break open the front door to the building. I don't make too much noise. Luckily, it's late at night. Everything is quiet as Ayala and I creep up the stairs. My gun has a silencer. No sense waking people up.

אני משתמש במוט מתכת דק כדי לפרוץ את הדלת הראשית
ani mishtamesh bemot matekhet dak kedei lifrots et hadelet harashit
I / I use / with bar / metal / thin / in order to / to break into / D.O. / the door / the main

של הבניין. אני לא עושה הרבה רעש. למרבה המזל, זו שעת לילה
shel habinyan ani lo ose harbe ra'ash lemarbe hamazal zo she'at laila
of / the building / I / no / I make / much / noise / luckily / this / hour of / night

מאוחרת. הכל שקט בזמן שאיילה ואני חומקים במעלה המדרגות.
me'ukheret hakol shaket bizman she'ayala va'ani khomkim bema'ale hamadregot
late / everything / quiet / as / that Ayala / and I / we slip away / going up / the stairs

באקדח שלי מותקן משתיק קול. אין טעם להעיר אנשים.
ba'ekdakh sheli mutkan mashtik kol ein ta'am leha'ir anashim
on the gun / my / installed / silencer / there isn't / reason / to wake up / people

---

Our strategy is simple. Ayala will beat on the bad guys until they give up. If they don't give up, I will shoot them. Hopefully, one of them will live long enough for Leah to talk to him.

האסטרטגיה שלנו פשוטה. איילה תכה את הבחורים הרעים
ha'astrategya shelanu pshuta ayala takhe et habakhurim hara'im
the strategy / our / simple / Ayala / she will beat up / D.O. / the guys / the bad

עד שייכנעו. אם לא ייכנעו, אני אירה בהם. בתקווה
ad sheyikanu im lo yikanu ani ira bahem betikva
until / that they will surrender / if / no / they will surrender / I / I will shoot / at them / hopefully

שאחד מהם יחזיק מעמד בחיים זמן מספיק לאפשר ללאה לדבר
she'ekhad mehem yakhzik ma'amad bakhayim zman maspik le'afsher lele'a ledaber
that one / of them / he will hold on / with life / time / enough / to enable / to Leah / to talk

איתו.
ito
with him

We sneak down the second floor hallway and listen outside the door to apartment 2. Through the door we hear the sound of heavy snoring. Snoring is good. Our opponents are sleeping.

אנחנו חומקים לאורך מסדרון הקומה השנייה ומקשיבים
anakhnu khomkim le'orekh misderon hakoma hashniya umakshivim
we / we sneak / along the length of / hallway of / the floor / the second / and we listen

מעבר לדלת דירה 2. מעבר לדלת נשמעים
me'ever ledelet dira shta'im me'ever ladelet nishma'im
on the other side of / to door of / apartment / two / on the other side of / to the door / we hear

קולות נחירה רמים. נחירה זה טוב. יריבינו ישנים.
kolot nekhira ramim nekhira ze tov yeriveinu yeshenim
sounds of / snoring / loud / snoring / this / good / our opponents / they sleep

---

I notice Ayala slipping brass knuckles onto her right hand.

אני מבחין באיילה מחליקה אגרופן על ידה הימנית.
ani mavkhin be'ayala makhlika egrofan al yada hayemanit
I / I notice / at Ayala / she slips / brass knuckles / on / her hand / the right

---

"Why do you need those?" I ask.

"למה את צריכה את זה?" אני שואל.
lama at tsrikha et ze ani sho'el
why / you / you need / D.O. / that / I / I ask

243

"I don't want to chip my fingernails. I just did them."

"אני לא רוצה לשבור את ציפורניי. רק עכשיו סידרתי אותן."
otan sidarti akhshav rak tsipornai et lishbor rotsa lo ani
them I did now just my fingernails D.O. to break I want no I

"I'm not sure it will work."

"אני לא בטוח שזה יעבוד."
ya'avod sheze batu'akh lo ani
it will work that this sure not I

I use my trusty lock picks to quietly open the door to the apartment. We step inside and see two men sleeping on a couch in front of a small television. I whack them over the head with my club. While I cuff them, Ayala slides down the hall to find their buddy.

אני משתמש במפתח הגנבים הנאמן שלי כדי לפתוח בשקט את
et besheket lifto'akh kedei sheli hane'eman haganavim bemafte'akh mishtamesh ani
D.O. quietly to open in order to my the trusty with the lock pick I use I

דלת הדירה. אנחנו פוסעים פנימה ורואים שני גברים ישנים על
al yeshenim gvarim shnei vero'im pnima posim anakhnu hadira delet
on they sleep men two of and we see inside we walk we the apartment door of

ספה מול טלוויזיה קטנה. אני מכה בראשם באלה שלי. בעוד אני
ani be'od sheli ba'ala berosham make ani ktana televizya mul sapa
I while my with club on their heads I hit I small television in front of sofa

כובל אותם באזיקים, חומקת איילה במורד המסדרון בחיפוש אחר
akhar bekhipus hamisderon bemorad ayala khomeket be'azikim otam kovel
other in search of the corridor down Ayala she sneaks with handcuffs them I handcuff

חברם.
khaveram
their friend

Unfortunately, they have a cat. Who would expect that Ukrainian thugs like cats? The thing yowls as Ayala makes her way down the hall.

לרוע המזל יש להם חתול. מי היה מצפה שבריונים אוקראינים
ukrainim shebiryonim haya metsape mi khatul yesh lahem lero'a hamazal
Ukrainian that thugs he would have expected who cat they have unfortunately

יאהבו חתולים? הדבר הזה משמיע יללה בעת שאיילה
she'ayala be'et yelala mashmi'a haze hadavar khatulim yohavu
that Ayala as yowling it makes a sound the this the thing cats they will like

עושה את דרכה לאורך המסדרון.
hamisderon le'orekh darka et osa
the hallway along the length of her way D.O. she makes

As she gets to the bedroom door, it flies open. The third man, warned by the cat, jumps out at her. The guy is fast.

כשהיא מגיעה אל דלת חדר השינה, נפתחת הדלת בפתאומיות.
befitomiyut hadelet niftakhat khadar hasheina delet el magi'a kshehi
suddenly the door it is opened bedroom door of to she reaches as she

האדם השלישי, שהוזהר על ידי החתול, מזנק עליה. הבחור
habakhur aleiha mezanek hakhatul al yedei shehuzhar hashlishi ha'adam
the guy on her he pounces the cat by who (he) was warned the third the man

זריז.
zariz
fast

He grabs Ayala by the throat before she can move. He is five centimeters taller, and twenty kilograms heavier than Ayala. He pushes her against the wall and starts to choke her. I sit on the couch to watch the fight.

הוא תופס את איילה בגרונה לפני שהיא מספיקה לזוז. הוא גבוה
gavoha hu lazuz maspika shehi lifnei bigrona ayala et tofes hu
tall he to move she manages that she before by her throat Ayala D.O. he grabs he

מאיילה בחמישה סנטימטרים וכבד ממנה בעשרים קילוגרמים. הוא
hu kilogramim be'esrim mimena vekhaved sentimetrim bekhamisha me'ayala
he kilograms by twenty then her and heavy centimeters by five than Ayala

דוחף אותה כנגד הקיר ומתחיל לחנוק אותה. אני יושב על הספה
dokhef ota keneged hakir umatkhil lakhnok ota. ani yoshev al hasapa
he pushes — her — against — the wall — and he starts — to choke — her. — I — I sit — on — the couch

וצופה בקרב.
vetsope bakrav
and I watch — at the fight

איילה חובטת בברכה במפשעתו. הוא משחרר את אחיזתו בצווארה
ayala khovetet bevirka bemifsa'ato hu meshakhrer et akhizato betsavara
Ayala — she strikes — with her knee — at his groin — he — he releases — D.O. — his grip — of her neck

והיא מנסה לשבור את אפו בכף ידה. הוא חוסם את החבטה
vehi menasa lishbor et apo bekhaf yada. hu khosem et hakhavata
and she — she tries — to break — D.O. — his nose — with her palm — he — he blocks — D.O. — the blow

באמת ידו ושולח חבטת מרפק אל עבר לחיה. היא מזיזה את
be'amat yado veshole'akh khavatat marpek el ever lekhya. hi meziza et
with his forearm — and he sends — blow of — elbow — towards — her cheek. — she — she moves — D.O.

ראשה והמרפק פוער חור בקיר שמאחוריה.
rosha vehamarpek po'er khor bakir sheme'akhoreiha.
her head — and the elbow — it opens wide — hole — in the wall — that is behind her.

Ayala crushes her knee into his groin. He lets go of her neck and she tries to break his nose with the palm of her hand. He blocks the blow with his forearm and swings an elbow at her cheek. She moves her head and the elbow pounds a hole in the wall behind her.

איילה פוסעת אחורה אל חדר המגורים כדי להימצא במרחב
ayala posa'at akhora el khadar hamegurim kedei lehimatse bemerkhav
Ayala — she steps — backward — towards — the living room — in order to — to be located in — with space

גדול יותר. יריבה נמצא ממש מעליה. המכה במפשעתו לא
gadol yoter. yeriva nimtsa mamash me'aleiha. hamaka bemifsa'ato lo
big — more — her opponent — he is located — really — on top of her. — the blow — at his groin — no

האטה אותו. הבחור הזה קשוח.
he'eta oto. habakhur haze kashu'akh.
it slowed down — him. — the guy — the this — tough.

Ayala steps back into the living room to get more space. Her opponent is right on top of her. The knee to his groin hasn't slowed him down. This guy is tough.

היא שולחת אגרוף מצויד באגרופן אל סנטרו. הוא בולם את
hi sholakhat egrof metsuyad be'egrofan el santero. hu bolem et
she — she sends — fist — equipped — with brass knuckles — toward — his chin. — he — he blocks — D.O.

המכה וחובט בה בפלג גופו העליון. לאיילה יש שיווי משקל
hamaka vekhovet ba befeleg gufo ha'elyon. le'ayala yesh shivui mishkal
the blow — and he hits — at her — with section of — his body — the upper. — Ayala has — balance

של רקדנית בלט. היא מדלגת אחורה כחצי מטר ונוחתת בעמידת
shel rakdanit balet. hi medaleget akhora kakhatsi meter venokhetet be'amidat
of — dancer of — ballet. — she — she hops — backward — about half of — meter — and she lands — in stance of

קרב מושלמת.
krav mushlemet.
fight — perfect.

She swings an uppercut to his chin with a brass knuckled fist. He blocks the punch and knocks into her with his upper body. Ayala has the balance of a ballet dancer. She hops back half a meter and lands in perfect fighting position.

הוא מניף לכיוונה אגרוף בריוני. היא בולמת אותו באמת ידה.
hu menif lekhivuna egrof biryoni. hi bolemet oto be'amat yada.
he — he swings — in her direction — fist — muscular — she — she blocks — him — with her forearm.

אני שומע עצם מתפצחת. הוא מנסה לשלוח בעיטה סיבובית לצד
ani shome'a etsem mitpatsakhat. hu menase lishlo'akh be'ita sivuvit letsad
I — I hear — bone — it is cracked open. — he — he tries — to send — kick — roundhouse — to side of

He swings a meaty fist at her. She blocks it with her forearm. I hear a bone crack. He tries a roundhouse kick to her side. She lifts her leg and catches the kick on the outside of her thigh.

245

She winces and hops back another step. He shuffles forward, feinting and jabbing. Then he quickly steps back and swings a kick at her head. The kick is fast and ferocious. His leg is a blur as it speeds toward her.

גופה. היא מרימה רגל ותופסת את הבעיטה בירכה.
gufa hi merima regel vetofeset et habe'ita bireikha
her body she she lifts leg and she catches D.O. the kick with her thigh

היא נרתעת ומדלגת צעד נוסף לאחור. הוא מדשדש קדימה בניסיון
hi nirta'at umedaleget tsa'ad nosaf le'akhor hu medashdesh kadima benisayon
she she winces and she hops step another backward he he shuffles forward trying

להטעות ולהכות. ואז הוא נסוג במהירות לאחור ומכוון בעיטה
lehatot ulehakot ve'az hu nasog bimhirut le'akhor umekhaven be'ita
to mislead and to strike and then he he retreats quickly backward and he aims kick

אל ראשה. הבעיטה מהירה ואכזרית. כמעט ולא רואים את רגלו
el rosha habe'ita mehira ve'akhzarit kimat velo ro'im et raglo
at her head the kick fast and ferocious barely they see D.O. his leg

ממהירות תנועתה לכיוונה.
mimhirut tnu'ata lekhivuna
from speed her movement in her direction

But Ayala is an amazing fighter. She ducks under the kick and hammers his other knee with the brass knuckles. I hear a sound like ice being crushed and the guy grunts. Amazingly, he doesn't go down. He gets his other foot back onto the floor and backs up.

אבל איילה היא לוחמת מדהימה. היא מתכופפת אל מתחת לטווח
aval ayala hi lokhemet madhima hi mitkofefet el mitakhat litvakh
but Ayala she fighter amazing she she ducks to under to the range of

הבעיטה והולמת בברכו האחרת באגרופן. אני שומע צליל
habe'ita veholemet bevirko ha'akheret be'egrofan ani shome'a tslil
the kick and she hits at his knee the other with brass knuckles I I hear sound

הדומה לצליל ריסוק קרח והבחור נאנק. למרבה התדהמה, הוא
hadome litslil risuk kerakh vehabakhur ne'enak lemarbe hatadhema hu
that is similar to sound of crushing of ice and the guy he groans amazingly he

אינו נופל. הוא מוריד את רגלו השנייה לקרקע ומתייצב.
eino nofel hu morid et raglo hashniya lakarka umityatsev
he doesn't he falls he he lowers D.O. his foot the second to the ground and he steadies himself

I don't know whether he trips over an area rug on the floor or his cracked knee gives out. But he stumbles just a little bit, just enough to give Ayala an opening. She moves in quickly and knees him in the groin again. Then she snaps his head back with an elbow to the chin. This leaves his neck exposed. She pounds his trachea with the brass knuckles.

אני לא יודע אם הוא מועד על שטיח המונח על הרצפה,
ani lo yode'a im hu mo'ed al shati'akh hamunakh al haritspa
I no I know if he he stumbles on rug that is placed on the floor

או אם ברכו המנופצת כורעת תחתיה. אך הוא מתנודד מעט – רק
o im birko hamenupetset kora'at takhteiha akh hu mitnoded me'at rak
or if his knee the shattered it collapses but he he staggers a little just

מספיק כדי לאפשר לאיילה פרצה. היא פועלת במהירות ומכה
maspik kedei le'efsher le'ayala pirtsa hi po'elet bimhirut umaka
enough in order to to allow to Ayala opening she she works quickly and she strikes

בברכה במפשעתו שוב. ואז היא מעיפה את ראשו לאחור במכת
bevirka bemifsa'ato shuv ve'az hi me'ifa et rosho le'akhor bemakat
with her knee in his groin again and then she she swings D.O. his head backward with hit of

מרפק לסנטרו. צווארו נותר חשוף. היא מכה בגרונו באגרופן.
marpek lesantero tsavaro notar khasuf hi maka bigrono ba'egrofan
elbow to his chin his neck it is left exposed she she hits at his throat with the brass knuckles

The guy goes down. I walk over and look at him. His throat is crushed. He fights for breath that will never come.

הבחור נופל. אני צועד קדימה ומביט בו. גרונו מרוסק. הוא נלחם
habakhur nofel ani tso'ed kadima umabit bo grono merusak hu nilkham
the guy he falls I I walk forward and I look at him his throat crushed he he fights

Interlinear text

עַל נְשִׁימָה שֶׁלֹּא תָּבוֹא לְעוֹלָם. הָאוֹר בְּעֵינָיו מִתְפּוֹגֵג לְאִיטוֹ.
al neshima shelo tavo le'olam. ha'or be'einav mitpogeg le'ito.
for breath that no it will come never. the light in his eyes it fades very slowly.

Slowly, the light fades from his eyes.

אֲנִי שׁוֹלֵחַ לְשָׂרָה הוֹדָעָה בַּטֶּלֶפוֹן הַסֶּלוּלָרִי, וְהִיא מוֹפִיעָה מִיָּד עִם נְיָר דֶּבֶק וְשַׂקִּים. שָׂרָה וַאֲנִי כּוֹפְתִים בִּנְיָר דֶּבֶק אֶת שְׁנֵי הַבַּחוּרִים מְחוּסְרֵי הַהַכָּרָה וְתוֹחֲבִים אוֹתָם אֶל תּוֹךְ שְׁנֵי שַׂקִּים גְּדוֹלִים. לְאַחַר מִכֵּן אֲנַחְנוּ גּוֹרְרִים אוֹתָם לְמַטָּה, לַמְּכוֹנִית שֶׁלִּי.

ani shole'akh lesara hoda'a batelefon haselulari, vehi mofi'a miyad im niyar devek vesakim. sara va'ani koftim beniyar devek et shnei habakhurim mekhusarei hahakara vetokhavim otam el tokh shnei sakim gdolim. le'akhar miken anakhnu gorerim otam lemata, lamekhonit sheli.

I send Sara a message with my cell phone and she comes right up with duct tape and bags. Sara and I tape up the two unconscious guys and stuff them into two large bags. Then we drag them down to my car.

בִּזְמַן שֶׁאֲנַחְנוּ טוֹרְחִים עַל הַעֲבָרַת הַבַּחוּרִים, אַיֶּלֶת בּוֹדֶקֶת אֶת הַדִּירָה. שָׂרָה וַאֲנִי מַשְׁלִיכִים אֶת הַבַּחוּרִים אֶל תּוֹךְ מְכוֹנִיתִי וּמְמַהֲרִים בַּחֲזָרָה לְמַעְלָה לְסַיֵּעַ לְאַיֶּלֶת. שָׂרָה עוֹזֶרֶת לְאַיֶּלֶת לָרֶדֶת בַּמַּדְרֵגוֹת בְּעוֹד אֲנִי נוֹשֵׂא שַׂק מָלֵא בַּחֲפָצִים שֶׁאַיֶּלֶת חָשְׁבָה שֶׁנִּרְצֶה לִבְחוֹן. יָדָהּ הַשְּׂמָאלִית שֶׁל אַיֶּלֶת תְּלוּיָה לְצִדָּהּ.

bizman she'anakhnu torkhim al ha'avarat habakhurim, ayala bodeket et hadira. sara va'ani mashlikhim et habakhurim el tokh mekhoniti umemaharim bakhazara lemala lesaye'a le'ayala. sara ozeret le'ayala laredet bamadregot be'od ani nose sak male bekhafatsim she'ayala khashva shenirtse livkhon. yada hasmalit shel ayala tluya letsida.

While we are taking pains to remove the guys, Ayala checks the apartment. Sara and I drop the guys into my car and run back upstairs to help Ayala. Sara helps her down the steps while I carry a bag full of things that Ayala thought we might want to look at. Ayala's left arm hangs by her side.

בְּדַרְכֵּנוּ לְמַטָּה אֲנַחְנוּ נִתְקָלִים בְּאַחַת מִדַּיָּירוֹת הַבִּנְיָן, שֶׁהִתְעוֹרְרָה בְּעִקְבוֹת הָרַעַשׁ. אֲנִי מְעַרְפֵּל אֶת מוֹחָהּ כְּשֶׁאֲנַחְנוּ חוֹלְפִים עַל פָּנֶיהָ. אֲנַחְנוּ מַשְׁאִירִים בַּדִּירָה אֶת הַבָּחוּר הַמֵּת. כְּשֶׁאֲנַחְנוּ מַגִּיעִים לַמְּכוֹנִית אֲנִי מֵעִיף מַבָּט בַּחֲפָצִים שֶׁאַיֶּלֶת אָסְפָה בַּשַּׂק.

bedarkenu lemata anakhnu nitkalim be'akhat midayarot habinyan, shehitorera be'ikvot hara'ash. ani me'arpel et mokha kshe'anakhnu kholfim al paneiha. anakhnu mashirim badira et habakhur hamet. kshe'anakhnu magi'im lamekhonit ani me'if mabat bekhafatsim she'ayala asfa basak.

On our way down, we encounter one other resident of the building who was awakened by the noise. I throw a mind haze at her as we pass. We leave the dead man in the apartment. When we get to the car I look through the things Ayala threw into the bag.

"A laptop, some cell phones, bills, and a checkbook. Maybe we have some evidence."

makhshev	nayad	telefonim	selulariyim	akhadim	kheshbonot	ufinkas	hamkha'ot
computer	portable	telephones	cellular	some	bills	and notebook of	checks

yitakhen	sheyesh lanu	re'ayot	kolshehen
it may be	that we have	evidence	some

"I need to have my arm x-rayed," Ayala says.

ani	tsrikha	tsilum rentgen	layad	sheli	omeret	ayala
I	I need	x-ray	for the arm	my	she says	Ayala

"Can you drive with one arm?" I ask.

tukhli	linhog	beyad	akhat	ani	sho'el
you will be able	to drive	with arm	one	I	I ask

"Sure," she answers.

vadai	hi	ona
sure	she	she answers

I don't have to remind Ayala to go to the private clinic our team uses for medical emergencies. It's run by a doctor who caters to people who pay in cash and don't use their real names. Before we drive away, Ayala pulls me aside.

ani	lo	tsarikh	lehazkir	le'ayala	lalekhet	lamirpa'a	hapratit	shekvutsatenu
I	no	I need	to remind	to Ayala	to go	to the medical clinic	the private	that our team

ne'ezeret	ba	bemikrei	kheirum	refu'iyim	hi	menohelet	al yedei	rofe
it is helped	by it	in cases of	emergency	medical	it	it is managed	by	doctor

hametapel	be'anashim	hameshalmim	bimzuman	ve'einam	metsayenim	et	shmam
that treats	with people	that pay	with cash	and they don't	they mention	D.O.	their name

ha'amiti	lifnei	she'anakhnu	nosim	misham	moshekhet	oti	ayala	hatsida
the real	before	that we	we drive	from there	she pulls	me	Ayala	aside

"You didn't do that mind clouding thing on the Ukrainian, did you?"

lo	hifalta	et	inyan	ha'irpul	hamakhshavti	al	ha'ukraini	nakhon
no	you activated	D.O.	issue	the fogging	the intellectual	on	the Ukrainian	right

"No way," I say. "I liked watching him smack you around. You beat him without any help from me."

beshum ofen	lo	ani	omer	neheneiti	lirot	oto	khovet	bakh
under no circumstances	not	I	I say	I enjoyed	to see	him	he beats	on you

hekhrat	oto	lelo	kol	ezra	mimeni
you subdued	him	without	any	help	from me

She nods to herself in satisfaction. Ayala is very competitive.

hi	menida	berosha	besipuk	ayala	takharutit	me'od
she	she nods	with her head	in satisfaction	Ayala	competitive	very

—19—

248

למחרת אנחנו עורכים ישיבת צוות נוספת.
lemokhorat *anakhnu* *orkhim* *yeshivat* *tsevet* *nosefet*
the following day — we — we arrange — meeting of — team — another

The next day, we have another meeting.

"מה הוצאת מהמשבויים האוקראינים שלנו?" אני שואל את לאה.
ma *hotset* *mehashvuyim* *ha'ukrainim* *shelanu* *ani* *sho'el* *et* *le'a*
what — you took out — from the captives — the Ukrainians — our — I — I ask — D.O. — Leah

"What did you get from our Ukrainian captives?" I ask Leah.

"הם סיפרו לי על חמישה קורבנות נוספים, ששילמו להם הרבה
hem *sipru* *li* *al* *khamisha* *korbanot* *nosafim* *sheshilmu* *lahem* *harbe*
they — they told — to me — about — five — victims — additional — that (they) paid — to them — a lot of

כסף," היא אומרת.
kesef *hi* *omeret*
money — she — she says

"They told me about five other victims who paid them a lot of money," she says.

"הם עשו זאת הרבה יותר זמן ממה שחשבנו," אני אומר. "גם
hem *asu* *zot* *harbe* *yoter* *zman* *mima* *shekhashavnu* *ani* *omer* *gam*
they — they did — this — much — more — time — than what — that we thought — I — I say — also

הקורבנות הנוספים הם סוכני ביטוח?"
hakorbanot *hanosafim* *hem* *sokhnei* *bitu'akh*
the victims — the other — they — agents of — insurance

"They've been doing this a lot longer than we thought," I say. "Were the other victims insurance agents?"

"לא, הם היו יועצים פיננסיים עצמאיים."
lo *hem* *hayu* *yo'atsim* *finansiyim* *atsma'iyim*
no — they — they were — advisers — financial — independent

"No, they were independent financial advisors."

"זה קרוב למדי," אני אומר. "את יודעת מי הבוס?"
ze *karov* *lemadai* *ani* *omer* *at* *yoda'at* *mi* *habos*
that — close — pretty — I — I say — you — you know — who — the boss

"That's pretty close," I say. "Do you know who the boss is?"

"עדיין לא. רונן עדיין מוציא מידע מהמחשב שמצאתם
ada'in *lo* *ronen* *ada'in* *motsi* *meida* *mehamakhshev* *shematsatem*
yet — not — Ronen — still — he takes out — information — from the computer — that you found

בדירה. החבר'ה האלה היו טיפשים דיים לנהל יומן של
badira *hakhevre* *ha'ele* *hayu* *tipshim* *dayam* *lenahel* *yoman* *shel*
in the apartment — the guys — the these — they were — stupid — enough — to manage — log — of

כל פעולותיהם. אנחנו יודעים איפה הם התאכסנו, עם מי שוחחו,
kol *pe'uloteihem* *anakhnu* *yodim* *eifo* *hem* *hitakhsenu* *im* *mi* *sokhakhu*
all — their activities — we — we know — where — they — they were housed — with — who — they spoke to

מתי קיבלו שיחות טלפון מהבוס, דברים כאלה. אני מקווה שכל
matai *kiblu* *sikhot* *telefon* *mehabos* *dvarim* *ka'ele* *ani* *mekava* *shekol*
when — they received — calls of — telephone — from the boss — things — like these — I — I hope — that all

זה יסייע לנו איכשהו."
ze *yesaye'a* *lanu* *eikhshehu*
this — it will help — to us — somehow

"Not yet. Ronen is still pulling information out of the computer you found at their apartment. These men were foolish enough to keep a log of all their activities. We know where they stayed, who they talked to, when they received phone calls from the boss, things like that. I'm hoping all this will help us somehow."

"אז מתי לדעתך נקבל מידע מבוסס יותר?" שואלת איילה.
az *matai* *leda'atekh* *nekabel* *meida* *mevusas* *yoter* *sho'elet* *ayala*
so — when — in your opinion — we will get — information — proven — more — she asks — Ayala

"So when do you think we'll know something solid?" Ayala asks.

249

She has a cast on her arm and is walking with a slight limp.

ידה נתונה בגבס והליכתה צולעת מעט.
me'at *tsola'at* *vehalikhata* *begeves* *netuna* *yada*
a little / limping / and her gait / in cast / placed / her arm

"A few days, I hope."

"תוך כמה ימים, אני מקווה."
mekava *ani* *yamim* *kama* *tokh*
I hope / I / days / a few / within

Adina calls me two days later.

יומיים לאחר מכן מתקשרת אליי עדינה.
adina *elai* *mitkasheret* *le'akhar miken* *yoma'im*
Adina / to me / she calls / later / two days

"We've got him," she says.

"תפסנו אותו," היא אומרת.
omeret *hi* *oto* *tafasnu*
she says / she / him / we caught

"So who is this great criminal mastermind?"

"אז מי הגאון הקרימינלי הגדול?"
hagadol *hakriminali* *haga'on* *mi* *az*
the great / the criminal / the genius / who / so

"A captain in the Central District Headquarters named David Cohen."

"פקד במשטרת מטה מחוז מרכז, שמו דוד כהן."
kohen *david* *shmo* *merkaz* *makhoz* *mate* *bemishteret* *pakad*
Cohen / David / his name / center / district / headquarters of / for the police of / commander

"How did you find him?"

"איך מצאת אותו?"
oto *matsat* *eikh*
him / you found / how

"Boris gave us his name along with a few others. We looked at all of his credit card receipts. Guess what."

"בוריס נתן לנו את שמו עם כמה שמות נוספים. בדקנו את כל
kol *et* *badaknu* *nosafim* *shemot* *kama* *im* *shmo* *et* *lanu* *natan* *boris*
all / D.O. / we checked / others / names / a few / with / his name / D.O. / to us / he gave / Boris

קבלות כרטיס האשראי שלו. נחש מה."
ma *nakhesh* *shelo* *kartis ha'ashrai* *kabalot*
what / guess / his / the credit card / receipts

"What?"

"מה?"
ma
what

"He paid a dentist to pull a tooth for one of the Ukrainian guys. Can you believe that?"

"הוא שילם לרופא שיניים כדי לעקור שן לאחד מהבחורים
mehabakhurim *le'ekhad* *shen* *la'akor* *kedei* *lerofe shina'im* *shilem* *hu*
of the guys / for one / tooth / to extract / in order to / to dentist / he paid / he

האוקראינים. אתה יכול להאמין?"
leha'amin *yakhol* *ata* *ha'ukrainim*
to believe / you can / you / the Ukrainian

"I'm surprised he didn't pay in cash," I say.

"מפתיע אותי שהוא לא שילם במזומן," אני אומר.
omer *ani* *bimzuman* *shilem* *lo* *shehu* *oti* *mafti'a*
I say / I / in cash / he paid / no / that he / me / it surprises

"That was his only mistake."

"זו היתה הטעות היחידה שלו."
shelo *hayekhida* *hata'ut* *haita* *zo*
only / the only / the mistake / it was / that

אז ביליתי שלושה לילות ביפו, צופה בנשים משופמות מתפשטות, לחינם?"

"So I spent three nights in Jaffa watching women with mustaches take their clothes off for nothing?"

"המאמץ השתלם, כי מצאנו את שאר חברי הכנופייה."

"It was worth the effort because we found the rest of the gang."

"מה לאה עשתה בשני השבויים?"

"What did Leah do with the two captives?"

"עטפה אותם בסרט ושלחה אותם למישהו במטה מחוז מרכז בשם זוהר. העברנו לו גם את שמות הקורבנות האחרים, את היומן שניהלו האוקראינים ואת העובדה שפקד כהן שילם עבור טיפול השיניים של אחד הבחורים."

"Wrapped them up with a bow and sent them to some guy in the Central District Headquarters named Zohar. We also gave him the names of the other victims, the log the Ukrainians kept about their activities, and the fact that Captain Cohen paid for the one man's dental work."

"זה בוודאי יעשה אותו מאושר," אני אומר.

"That should make him happy," I say.

בשבוע שלאחר מכן, מתפרסם סיפור גדול בעיתונים. פקד דוד כהן ממשטרת יפו נעצר והואשם בניהול עסקי סחיטה גדולים ביפו. הכתבות מפרטות את כל הקורבנות ואת שמותיהם של הבריונים האוקראינים שנשכרו לבצע את העבודה המלוכלכת.

The following week, there is a big story in the newspapers. Captain David Cohen of the Jaffa Police has been arrested and charged with running a large extortion operation in Jaffa. The articles go into detail about all of the victims, and lists the names of the Ukrainian thugs who were hired to do all the dirty work.

Two days later, there is another story in the newspapers. The investigators found a safe deposit box and two offshore bank accounts owned by Captain Cohen. The accounts contain several hundred thousand shekels. The safe deposit box is full of uncut diamonds.

החוקרים בעיתונים. נוסף סיפור מתפרסם יותר, מאוחר יומיים
hakhokrim ba'itonim nosaf sipur mitparsem yoter me'ukhar yoma'im
the investigators in the newspapers another story it is published more late two days

כהן. פקד של שמו על בחו״ל בנק חשבונות ושני כספת מצאו
kohen pakad shel al shmo bekhul bank kheshbonot ushnei kasefet matsu
Cohen commander of in his name abroad bank accounts of and two of safe they found

מלאה הכספת שקלים. אלפי מאות כמה נמצאו בחשבונות
mele'a hakasefet shkalim alfei me'ot kama nimtse'u bakheshbonot
full the safe shekels thousands of hundreds a few they were discovered in the accounts

גולמיים. ביהלומים
golmiyim beyahalomim
crude of diamonds

"They never would have found out about the money and the safe deposit box if I hadn't sent Detective Zohar an anonymous email," Ronen says.

לא אם הכספת ואת הכסף את היו מגלים לא "הם
lo im hakasefet ve'et hakesef et hayu megalim lo hem
no if the safe and D.O. the money D.O. they would have found out no they

רונן. אומר אנונימי," דוא״ל זוהר לבלש שולח הייתי
ronen omer anonimi do'ar elektroni zohar labalash ha'iti sholeʻakh
Ronen he says anonymous email Zohar to the detective I had sent

"Too bad the world will never know your talent at finding things with your hacking skills," I tell him.

בעזרת דברים למצוא כישרונך על לעולם ידע לא שאיש "חבל
be'ezrat dvarim limtso kishronkha al le'olam yeda lo she'ish khaval
with things to find your talent about never he will know no that man too bad

לו. אומר אני שלך," המחשבים פריצת כישורי
lo omer ani shelkha hamakhshevim pritsat kishurei
to him I say I your the computers hacking of skills of

Captain Cohen's bail hearing is presided over by a judge who owes him a few favors. He is released from detention after he posts bail for a half million shekels. That's how things work in Jaffa if you have friends.

של באולמו נערך כהן פקד של בערבות השחרור שימוע
shel be'ulamo ne'erakh kohen pakad shel be'arvut hashikhrur shimuʻa
of in his hall it was conducted Cohen commander of on bail the releasing hearing of

לאחר ממעצר משוחרר הוא אחדות. טובות לו החייב שופט
le'akhar mima'atsar meshukhrar hu akhadot tovot lo hakhayav shofet
after from detention he is released he some favors to him that owes judge

מתנהלים כך שקלים. מיליון חצי בסך ערבות שהפקיד
mitnahalim kakh shkalim milyon khatsi besakh arvut shehifkid
they are conducted this way shekels million half of amounting to bail that he deposited

חברים. לך יש אם ביפו הדברים
khaverim yesh lekha im beyafo hadvarim
friends you have if in Jaffa the things

Things quiet down for a few days while Ronen and Adina look through the Ukrainians' computer for more evidence to send to Detective Zohar. And then Captain Cohen swallows half a bottle of poison and dies in his home. We have a team meeting the next day.

עוברים ועדינה רונן בעוד אחדים, ימים למשך נרגעים העניינים
ovrim ve'adina ronen be'od akhadim yamim lemeshekh nirga'im ha'inyanim
they go over and Adina Ronen while a few days for they calm down the issues

לשלוח נוספות ראיות אחר בחיפוש האוקראינים של מחשבם על
lishloʻakh nosafot re'ayot akhar bekhipus ha'ukrainim shel makhshevam al
to send additional evidence after in search of the Ukrainians of their computer regarding

רעל בקבוק חצי כהן פקד בולע ואז זוהר. לבלש
ra'al bakbuk khatsi kohen pakad boleʻa ve'az zohar labalash
poison bottle of half of Cohen commander he swallows and then Zohar to the detective

ומת בביתו. אנחנו עורכים ישיבת צוות למחרת.

umet — and he dies; *beveito* — in his home; *anakhnu* — we; *orkhim* — we arrange; *yeshivat* — meeting of; *tsevet* — team; *lemokhorat* — the next day

"את סבורה שהיו למשטרה ראיות מספיקות לשלוח את פקד כהן לכלא לזמן ממושך?" אני שואל את לאה.

at — you; *svura* — you are of the opinion; *shehayu lamishtara* — that the police had; *re'ayot* — evidence; *maspikot* — enough; *lishlo'akh* — to send; *et* — D.O.; *pakad* — commander; *kohen* — Cohen; *lakele* — to prison; *lizman* — for time; *memushakh* — extended; *ani* — I; *sho'el* — I ask; *et* — D.O.; *le'a* — Leah

"Do you think that the police had enough evidence to send Captain Cohen to prison for a long time?" I ask Leah.

"אני לא חושבת. אם הוא היה שוכר עורך דין טוב, בוודאי

ani — I; *lo* — no; *khoshevet* — I think; *im* — if; *hu* — he; *haya sokher* — he would have hired; *orekh din* — lawyer; *tov* — good; *bevadai* — probably

היה מרצה כמה שנים במקרה הטוב."

haya meratse — he would have served; *kama* — a few; *shanim* — years; *bamikre hatov* — at best

"I don't think so. If he hired a good lawyer, he would probably serve a few years at best."

"אז למה שיתאבד? רונן, צפית את זה?"

az — then; *lama* — why; *sheyitabed* — that he will commit suicide; *ronen* — Ronen; *tsafita* — you predicted; *et* — D.O.; *ze* — that

"Then why would he kill himself? Ronen, did you predict that?"

"אם הייתי חושב שהוא עומד להרעיל את עצמו, הייתי מפסיק

im — if; *ha'iti khoshev* — I would have thought; *shehu* — that he; *omed* — he is about to; *leharil* — to poison; *et* — D.O.; *atsmo* — himself; *ha'iti mafsik* — I would have stopped

לחפש ראיות כבר לפני כמה ימים."

lekhapes — to search for; *re'ayot* — evidence; *kvar* — already; *lifnei* — ago; *kama* — a few; *yamim* — days

"If I thought he was going to take poison, I would have stopped searching for evidence a few days ago."

"אולי אנחנו צריכים לבחון את הדברים מזווית אחרת," מציעה לאה.

ulai — maybe; *anakhnu* — we; *tsrikhim* — we need; *livkhon* — to examine; *et* — D.O.; *hadvarim* — the things; *mizavit* — from angle; *akheret* — different; *matsi'a* — she suggests; *le'a* — Leah

"Maybe we need to look at things from a different angle," Leah suggests.

—20—

שבועיים מאוחר יותר ...

shvu'a'im — two weeks; *me'ukhar* — late; *yoter* — more

Two weeks later ...

"אתה נראה קצת טוב יותר היום," אני אומר למיכאל הרשקו.

ata — you; *nire* — you look; *ktsat* — a little; *tov* — good; *yoter* — more; *hayom* — today; *ani* — I; *omer* — I say; *lemikha'el* — to Michael; *hershko* — Hershko

"You look a little better today," I say to Michael Hershko.

אנחנו אוכלים את הכריכים שהבאתי לביתו.

anakhnu — we; *okhlim* — we eat; *et* — D.O.; *hakrikhim* — the sandwiches; *sheheveti* — that I brought; *leveito* — to his house

We are eating sandwiches that I brought over to his house.

253

Story 13

"Have you stopped taking that medication?"

"הפסקת לקחת את התרופה ההיא?"
hahi hatrufa et lakakhat hifsakta
that one the medication D.O. to take you stopped

"Yeah," he tells me. "I talked to a grief counselor, like you suggested at our last lunch. She has helped me to deal with the loss of my wife. I'm finally getting my life back together."

"כן," הוא אומר לי. "דיברתי עם יועצת אבל, כמו שהצעת
shehitsata kmo evel yo'etset im dibarti li omer hu ken
that you suggested like mourning counselor of with I talked to me he tells he yes

לי בארוחת הצוהריים האחרונה שלנו. היא עזרה לי להתמודד עם
im lehitmoded li azra hi shelanu ha'akharona be'arukhat hatsohora'im li
with to cope to me she helped she our the last at the lunch to me

אובדן אשתי. סוף סוף אני מתחיל להחזיר את חיי חזרה למסלולם."
khazara lemaslulam khayai et lehakhzir matkhil ani sof sof ishti ovdan
back on track my life D.O. to return I start I finally my wife loss of

"That's great."

"זה מצוין."
metsuyan ze
great that

We talk a little more about his therapy sessions. Due to my mind mojo, he still thinks I am his insurance friend. Finally, I get to the point.

אנחנו משוחחים עוד קצת על הפגישות הטיפוליות שלו. הודות
hodot shelo hatipulyot hapgishot al ktsat od mesokhakhim anakhnu
due to his the therapeutic the meetings about a little more we converse we

לכישוף המוחי שלי, הוא עדיין חושב שאני חברו לביטוח. לבסוף
levasof labitu'akh khavero she'ani khoshev ada'in hu sheli hamokhi lakishuf
finally to the insurance his friend that I he thinks still he my the mind to the mojo

אני מגיע לעניין.
la'inyan magi'a ani
to the point I get to I

"You almost succeeded," I tell him.

"כמעט הצלחת," אני אומר לו.
lo omer ani hitslakhta kimat
to him I tell I you succeeded almost

"Huh?" he asks.

"הא?" הוא שואל.
sho'el hu ha
he asks he huh

"You know - the extortions, your wife's murder, even killing Captain Cohen."

"אתה יודע - הסחיטה, רצח אשתך, ואפילו הריגת פקד
pakad harigat va'afilu ishtekha retsakh haskhita yode'a ata
commander the killing of and even your wife murder of the extortion you know you

כהן."
kohen
Cohen

"I don't know what you are talking about," he says.

"אין לי מושג על מה אתה מדבר," הוא אומר.
omer hu medaber ata ma al musag ein li
he says he you talk you what about idea I don't have

"Yes, you do know. We know you ran the whole extortion operation."

"כן, אתה יודע. אנחנו יודעים שאתה ניהלת את כל עסקי
iskei kol et nihalta she'ata yodim anakhnu yode'a ata ken
business of whole D.O. you organized that you we know we you know you yes

254

הסחיטה.
haskhita
the extortion

"אתה מהמשטרה?" הוא שואל.
sho'el hu mehamishtara ata
he asks he from the police you

"Are you with the police?" he asks.

"אני חבר בקבוצה שבילתה את ארבעה עשר הימים האחרונים בבחינת
bivkhinat ha'akharonim hayamim arba'a asar et shebilta bikvutsa khaver ani
looking into the last the days fourteen D.O. that spent in group member I

כל היבט בחייך," אני אומר. "אתה גייסת את פקד כהן
kohen pakad et giyasta ata omer ani bekhayekha heibet kol
Cohen commander D.O. you recruited you I say I in your life aspect every

להביא את האוקראינים. אתה בחרת את קורבנות הסחיטה. אתה
lehavi et ha'ukrainim ata bakharta et korbenot haskhita ata
to bring D.O. the Ukrainians you you selected D.O. victims of the extortion you

ירית בשלושה אנשים, אחת מהם אשתך שלך. ואתה הרעלת את
yarita bishlosha anashim akhat mehem ishtekha shelkha ve'ata hiralta et
you shot at three people one of them your wife your and you you poisoned D.O.

פקד כהן כאשר העניינים התחילו להסתבך."
pakad kohen ka'asher ha'inyanim hitkhilu lehistabekh
commander Cohen when the issues they started to become more complicated

"I'm with a group that has spent the last fourteen days looking into every aspect of your life," I say. "You recruited Captain Cohen to bring over the Ukrainians. You selected the extortion victims. You shot three people, one of them being your own wife. And you poisoned Captain Cohen when things started to fall apart."

"אתה מטורף," הוא אומר לי. "איפה ההוכחות שלך?"
ata metoraf hu omer li eifo hahokhakhot shelkha
you insane he he tells to me where the proof your

"You are insane," he tells me. "Where is your proof?"

"מצאנו את המקום שבו קנית את הרעל. יש להם עדיין את
matsanu et hamakom shebo kanita et hara'al yesh lahem ada'in et
we found D.O. the place that in it you bought D.O. the poison they have still D.O.

סרט המעקב של כל העסקאות שנעשו באותו יום.
seret hama'akav shel kol ha'iska'ot shena'asu be'oto yom
video of the surveillance of all the transactions that (they) were made in same day

פניך נראים בבירור בסרט הזה. בנוסף, הקופאי זוכר
paneikha nirim beverur baseret haze benosaf hakupa'i zokher
your face they are visible clearly on the video the that plus the cashier he remembers

אותך."
otkha
you

"We found the place where you bought the poison. They still have a surveillance video of all the transactions that were made that day. Your face shows up very clearly on that video. Plus, the cashier remembers you."

מר הרשקו שולף אקדח מכיסו ומכוון אותו אליי. אני יושב
mar hershko sholef ekdakh mikiso umekhaven oto elai ani yoshev
Mr. Hershko he pulls out gun from his pocket and he aims it at me I I sit

ללא תנועה בעוד הוא צועד מאחורי שולחן האוכל וטופח עליי
lelo tnu'a be'od hu tso'ed me'akhorei shulkhan ha'okhel vetofe'akh alai
without movement while he he walks behind table of the food and he pats on me

כדי לבדוק אם אני נושא נשק או מכשיר האזנה. לאחר מכן הוא
kedei livdok im ani nose neshek o makhshir ha'azana la'akhar miken hu
in order to to check if I I carry weapon or device of listening then he

Mr. Hershko takes a gun out of his pocket and points it at me. I sit quietly as he comes around the dining room table and pats me to see if I am carrying a weapon or wearing a listening device. Then he sits down and takes another bite out of his turkey sandwich. The gun still points my way.

מתיישב ונוגס שוב בכריך ההודו שלו. האקדח עדיין מכוון
mityashev venoges shuv bekharikh hahodu shelo ha'ekdakh ada'in mekhuvan
he sits down / and he bites / again / in sandwich of / the turkey / his / the gun / still / aimed

אליי.
elai
at me

"You are very stupid to come here and say these things," he tells me. "Did you think I would pay you to keep quiet?"

"אתה טיפש מאוד אם באת הנה להגיד את הדברים הללו," הוא אומר
omer hu halalu hadvarim et lehagid hena bata im me'od tipesh ata
he tells / he / the these / the things / D.O. / to say / here / you came / if / very / stupid / you

לי. "חשבת שאשלם לך כדי שתשתוק?"
shetishtok kedei lekha she'ashalem khashavta li
that you will be quiet / in order to / to you / that I will pay / you thought / to me

"I just wanted the satisfaction of telling you face-to-face that you didn't get away with your crimes."

"רק רציתי את הסיפוק בלומר לך פנים אל פנים שלא תתחמק
titkhamek shelo panim el panim lekha belomar hasipuk et ratsiti rak
you will get away / that no / face / to / face / to you / in to tell / the satisfaction / D.O. / I wanted / just

מפשעיך."
mipsha'eikha
from your crimes

He laughs at me.

הוא צוחק עליי.
alai tsokhek hu
at me / he laughs / he

"You have made a big mistake," he says.

"עשית טעות גדולה," הוא אומר.
omer hu gdola ta'ut asita
he says / he / big / mistake / you made

"Actually, Captain Cohen made the mistake. If he hadn't paid for the Ukrainian's dental work with his credit card, both of you would be in the clear. We didn't have enough evidence to accuse anyone of anything until we found that credit card payment."

"למעשה, פקד כהן עשה את הטעות. אם הוא לא היה משלם
haya meshalem lo hu im hata'ut et asa kohen pakad lema'ase
he had paid / no / he / if / the mistake / D.O. / he made / Cohen / commander / actually

בכרטיס האשראי שלו עבור טיפול השיניים של האוקראיני שניכם
shneikhem ha'ukraini shel hashina'im tipul avur shelo ha'ashrai bekhartis
two of you / the Ukrainian / of / the teeth / treatment of / for / his / the credit / with card of

הייתם יוצאים נקיים. לא היו לנו הוכחות מספיקות להאשים מישהו
mishehu leha'ashim maspikot hokhakhot hayu lanu lo nekiyim ha'item yotsim
anyone / to accuse / enough / evidence / we had / no / clean / you would have emerged

במשהו עד שמצאנו את התשלום בכרטיס האשראי."
ha'ashrai bekhartis hatashlum et shematsanu ad bemashehu
the credit / on card of / the payment / D.O. / that we found / until / of something

"When you say 'we' who are you talking about?" he asks.

"למי אתה מתכוון כשאתה אומר 'אנחנו'?" הוא שואל.
sho'el hu anakhnu omer kshe'ata mitkaven ata lemi
he asks / he / we / you say / when you / you mean / you / to who

"My group. I wanted to call us 'The Squad', but we had a vote and I lost. So we just call ourselves the team. I'm not even allowed to buy team jackets."

"הקבוצה שלי. אני רציתי שנקרא לעצמנו ה'חוליה', אבל ערכנו
arakhnu aval hakhulya le'atsmenu shenikra ratsiti ani sheli hakvutsa
we arranged / but / The Squad / to ourselves / that we will call / I wanted / I / my / the group

הצבעה ואני הפסדתי. כך שאנחנו קוראים לעצמנו סתם הצוות. אני
ani hatsevet stam le'atsmenu korim she'anakhnu kakh hifsadeti va'ani hatsba'a
I the team just to ourselves we call that we so I lost and I vote

לא מורשה אפילו לקנות מעילי צוות."
tsevet me'ilei liknot afilu murshe lo
team coats of to buy even I am allowed no

"עישנת?" הוא שואל אותי. "אין היגיון בדבריך. איזו הצבעה?"
hatsba'a eizo bidvareikha higayon ein oti sho'el hu ishanta
voting what in your words sense there isn't me he asks he you smoked

"Are you high?" he asks me. "You aren't making any sense. What vote?"

"זה לא חשוב."
khashuv lo ze
important not this

"It's not important."

מיכאל הרשקו נאנח.
ne'enakh hershko mikha'el
he sighs Hershko Michael

Michael Hershko sighs.

"אתה עומד לספר לי על הצוות שלך."
shelkha hatsevet al li lesaper omed ata
your the team about to me to tell you about to you

"You're going to tell me about your team."

"לא, אני לא."
lo ani lo
not I no

"No, I'm not."

"אם לא, אני אירה לך בברך, ואז בברך השנייה, ואז
ve'az hashniya baberekh ve'az baberekh lekha ira ani lo im
and then the second in the knee and then in the knee to you I will shoot I not if

במרפק, עד שלבסוף תספר לי."
li tesaper shelevasof ad bamarpek
to me you will tell that finally until in the elbow

"If you don't, I'll shoot you in the knee, and then the other knee, and then the elbow, until you finally tell me."

אני מכה אותו בערפול מוחי מלא. הוא מניח את זרועותיו לצידי
letsidei zro'otav et meni'akh hu male mokhi be'irpul oto make ani
to sides of his arms D.O. he rests he full mind with fogging him I hit I

גופו. אני לוקח את האקדח וכובל אותו באזיקים. לאחר מכן אני
ani le'akhar miken be'azikim oto vekhovel ha'ekdakh et loke'akh ani gufo
I then with handcuffs him and I bind the gun D.O. I take I his body

מתקשר לשרה בטלפון הנייד. היא מגיעה לאחר דקות אחדות.
akhadot dakot le'akhar magi'a hi hanayad batelefon lesara mitkasher
several minutes after she arrives she the mobile on the telephone to Sara I call

I hit him with the full mind cloud. He puts his arms down at his side. I take the gun and cuff him. Then I call Sara on the cell phone. She shows up several minutes later.

"שמת כדור במשקה שלו?" היא שואלת.
sho'elet hi shelo bamashke kadur samta
she asks she his in the drink pill you put

"Did you put a pill in his drink?" she asks.

"מה?" אני אומר.
omer ani ma
I say I what

"What?" I say.

257

"He's almost asleep. How did you do that?"

"הוא כמעט רדום. איך עשית זאת?"
zot asita eikh radum kimat hu
that you did how asleep almost he

"I almost forgot. I spiked his drink."

"כמעט שכחתי. תיבלתי את המשקה שלו."
shelo hamashke et tibalti shakhakhti kimat
his the drink D.O. I spiked I forgot almost

"What next?" Sara asks.

"מה הלאה?" שואלת שרה.
sara sho'elet hala ma
Sara she asks next what

"You tie him up. I'll plant enough evidence to involve him in every crime since the Arlozorov murder. Then I'll call the cops from Hershko's cell phone."

"את תקשרי אותו. אני אשתול ראיות שיקשרו אותו לכל
lekhol oto sheyiksheru re'ayot eshtol ani oto tikshri at
to every him that (it) will connect evidence I will plant I him you will tie up you

פשע אפשרי מאז הרצח של ארלוזורוב. אחר כך אתקשר למשטרה
lamishtara etkasher akhar kakh arlozorov shel haretsakh me'az efshari pesha
to the police I will call then Arlozorov of the murder since possible crime

מהטלפון הנייד של הרשקו."
hershko shel hanayad mehatelefon
Hershko of the mobile from the telephone

21

"This is Detective Sergeant Albert Zohar speaking to you on a recorded line. What is your name please?"

"כאן סמל בלש אלברט זוהר, זהו קו מוקלט. מה שמך בבקשה?"
bevakasha shimkha ma muklat kav zehu zohar albert balash samal kan
please you name what recorded line this is Zohar Albert detective sergeant here

"That's not important."

"זה לא חשוב."
khashuv lo ze
important not that

I talk in a funny voice just to irritate him.

אני מדבר בקול משונה רק כדי להרגיז אותו.
oto lehargiz kedei rak meshune bekol medaber ani
him to irritate in order to just weird in voice I talk I

"You told our receptionist you want to help me with a few of my cases."

"אמרת לפקיד הקבלה שאתה רוצה לעזור לי בכמה מהחקירות
mehakhakirot bekhama li la'azor rotse she'ata lifkid hakabala amarta
of the investigations with a few to me to help you want that you to the receptionist you told

שלי."
sheli
my

"Yes. I solved them for you."

"כן. פתרתי אותן עבורך."
avurkha otan patarti ken
for you them I solved yes

"I won't talk with you unless you tell me your name."

"אני לא אדבר איתך עד שתאמר לי את שמך."
shimkha et li shetomar ad itkha adaber lo ani
your name D.O. to me that you will tell until with you I will talk no I

אז תראה ממש טיפשי כאשר אמסור את המידע
az tera'e mamash tipshi ka'asher emsor et hameida
then / you will look / really / silly / when / I will give / D.O. / the information

שברשותי לעיתונות ואציין שלא היית מעוניין להקשיב."
shebirshuti la'itonut ve'atsayen shelo ha'ita me'unyan lehakshiv
that in my possession / to the press / and I will mention / that no / you were / interested / to listen

> "Then you'll look really silly when I give the newspapers my information and mention that you weren't interested in listening."

שמעתי אותו רוטן מתחת לשפמו.
shamati oto roten mitakhat lisfamo
I heard / him / he mutters / under / to his mustache

> I heard him mutter under his breath.

"או קיי, דבר איתי."
o kei daber iti
okay / talk / with me

> "OK, talk to me."

"אדם בשם מיכאל הרשקו רצח את אשתו לפני כשישה חודשים.
adam beshem mikha'el hershko ratsakh et ishto lifnei keshisha khodashim
man / by name of / Michael / Hershko / he murdered / D.O. / his wife / ago / about six / months

אתם חשבתם שהיא נרצחה בגלל סחיטה שנכשלה, אבל הוא
atem khashavtem shehi nirtsekha biglal skhita shenikhshela aval hu
you / you thought / that she / she was murdered / because of / extortion / that (it) failed / but / he

לחץ על ההדק."
lakhats al hahedek
he squeezed / on / the trigger

> "A man named Michael Hershko murdered his wife about six months ago. You thought she was killed because of a botched extortion payoff, but he pulled the trigger."

"ואיך אתה יודע זאת?"
ve'eikh ata yode'a zot
and how / you / you know / this

> "And how do you know this?"

"הוא מעולם לא נפטר מהאקדח שלו. תשלחו מישהו לביתו.
hu me'olam lo niftar meha'ekdakh shelo tishlekhu mishehu leveito
he / never / he got rid of / of the gun / his / you will send / someone / to his house

אתם יודעים איפה הוא גר. הוא קשור והאקדח מונח על הרצפה
atem yodim eifo hu gar hu kashur veha'ekdakh munakh al haritspa
you / you know / where / he / he lives / he / tied up / and the gun / placed / on / the floor

לידו. טביעות האצבע שלו נמצאות על האקדח."
leyado tvi'ot ha'etsba shelo nimtsa'ot al ha'ekdakh
next to him / fingerprints / his / they are present / on / the gun

> "He never threw away the gun. Send someone to his house. You know where he lives. He's tied up and the gun is on the floor right next to him. His prints are all over it."

זוהר משתהה למשך שניות אחדות, כדי לעכל את המידע.
zohar mishtahe lemeshekh shniyot akhadot kedei le'akel et hameida
Zohar / he is delayed / for / seconds / a few / in order to / to digest / D.O. / the information

> Zohar takes a few seconds to let that sink in.

"אני יכול לשים אותך בהמתנה?" הוא שואל.
ani yakhol lasim otkha behamtana hu sho'el
I / I can / to put / you / on hold / he / he asks

> "Can I put you on hold?" he asks.

"אם תעשה זאת, אני אנתק את השיחה ולא תדע את
im ta'ase zot ani anatek et hasikha velo teda et
if / that / you will do / I / I will hang up / D.O. / the conversation / and no / you will know / D.O.

> "If you do that, I'll hang up and you won't know the whole story. By the way, I'm using Hershko's cell phone."

259

כל הסיפור. דרך אגב, אני מדבר מהטלפון הנייד של הרשקו."
kol hasipur derekh agav ani medaber mehatelefon hanayad shel hershko
all the story / by the way / I / I talk / from the telephone / the mobile / of / Hershko

"OK, keep going."

או קיי, תמשיך."
o kei tamshikh
okay / you will continue

"The same gun killed the two insurance agents, but you already know that."

אותו האקדח הרג את שני סוכני הביטוח, אבל אתה כבר יודע
oto ha'ekdakh harag et shnei sokhnei habitu'akh aval ata kvar yode'a
same / the gun / it killed / D.O. / two of / agents / the insurance / but / you / already / you know

זאת."
zot
that

"Yes."

כן."
ken
yes

"Mr. Hershko was the brains behind the extortion scheme. He recruited Captain David Cohen and murdered him while Captain Cohen was out on bail."

מר הרשקו היה המוח שמאחורי תוכנית הסחיטה. הוא גייס את
mar hershko haya hamo'akh sheme'akhorei tokhnit haskhita hu giyes et
Mr. / Hershko / he was / the brain / that behind / scheme of / the extortion / he / he recruited / D.O.

פקד דוד כהן ורצח אותו כאשר פקד כהן שוחרר
pakad david kohen veratsakh oto ka'asher pakad kohen shukhrar
commander / David / Cohen / and he murdered / him / when / commander / Cohen / he was released

בערבות."
be'arvut
on bail

"How do you know this?"

איך אתה יודע את זה?"
eikh ata yode'a et ze
how / you / you know / D.O. / this

"I left a note next to the gun. It tells you where the poison was purchased. The store has a surveillance camera that shows Hershko buying the poison. The store manager is waiting for you to pick up the tape. Also, the cashier remembers Hershko buying the poison."

השארתי פתק ליד האקדח. כתוב בו איפה נרכש הרעל. לחנות יש
hisharti petek leyad ha'ekdakh katuv bo eifo nirkash hara'al lakhanut yesh
I left / note / next to / the gun / written / on it / where / he bought / the poison / the store has

מצלמת מעקב המראה את הרשקו קונה את הרעל. מנהל החנות
matslemat ma'akav hamar'a et hershko kone et hara'al menahel hakhanut
camera of / surveillance / that shows / D.O. / Hershko / he buys / D.O. / the poison / manager of / the store

מחכה שתאסוף את הווידיאו. בנוסף, הקופאי זוכר את
mekhake shete'esof et havide'o benosaf hakupa'i zokher et
he waits / that you will pick up / D.O. / the video / in addition / the cashier / he remembers / D.O.

הרשקו קונה את הרעל."
hershko kone et hara'al
Hershko / he buys / D.O. / the poison

"What else?" he asks.

מה עוד?" הוא שואל.
ma od hu sho'el
what / more / he / he asks

"Compare Hershko's bank records against Captain Cohen's records. You'll see that there are corresponding withdrawals and deposits."

ערוך השוואה בין רישומי חשבון הבנק של הרשקו ורישומי
arokh hashva'a bein rishumei kheshbon habank shel hershko verishumei
do comparison between recordings of account of the bank of Hershko and recordings of

חשבון הבנק של פקד כהן. אתה תראה שיש משיכות
kheshbon habank shel pakad kohen. ata tire sheyesh meshikhot
account of the bank of commander Cohen you you will see that there are withdrawals

והפקדות תואמות.
vehafkadot to'amot
and deposits corresponding

"Cohen had offshore accounts. We couldn't trace the payments. Money seemed to get there from outer space," he says.

"לכהן היו חשבונות בחו"ל. לא יכולנו לעקוב אחרי התשלומים.
lekhohen hayu kheshbonot bekhul lo yakholnu la'akov akharei hatashlumim
Cohen had accounts outside Israel no we were able to follow after the payments

נראה שהכסף הגיע לשם מהחלל החיצון," הוא אומר.
nire shehakesef higi'a lesham mehekhalal hakhitson, hu omer
it seems that the money it arrived to there from outer space he he says

"You need a better hacker. My man will email you a detailed explanation of how the money was moved from one account into another. After you subpoena all the records you will see that Cohen and Hershko were tied together like conjoined twins."

"אתה צריך האקר טוב יותר. האיש שלי ישלח לך דוא"ל
ata tsarikh haker tov yoter. ha'ish sheli yishlakh lekha do'ar elektroni
you you need hacker good more the man my he will send to you email

עם הסבר מפורט איך הועבר הכסף בין החשבונות.
im hesber meforat eikh hu'avar hakesef bein hakheshbonot
with explanation detailed how it was transferred the money between the accounts

אחרי שתוציא צו לכל הרישומים תראה שכהן והרשקו
ahkarei shetotsi tsav lekhol harishumim tire shekohen vehershko
after that you will issue court order for all the records you will see that Cohen and Hershko

היו קשורים זה לזה כמו תאומים סיאמיים."
hayu kshurim ze leze kmo te'omim siyamim
they were tied one to the other like twins Siamese

"Who is this?"

"מי זה?"
mi ze
who this

I disconnect the call.

ניתקתי את השיחה.
nitakti et hasikha
I disconnected D.O. the call

— 22 —

Five days later, the newspapers run a big story about Michael Hershko and Captain David Cohen. Ayala reads it to all of us.

כעבור חמישה ימים, הופיעה כתבה גדולה בעיתונים על מיכאל
ka'avor khamisha yamim, hofi'a katava gdola ba'itonim al mikha'el
after five days it appeared article big in the newspapers about Michael

הרשקו ופקד דוד כהן. איילה מקריאה את הכתבה לכולנו.
hershko ufakad david kohen. ayala makri'a et hakatava lekhulanu
Hershko and commander David Cohen Ayala she reads aloud D.O. the article to all of us

"You put the first Ukranian's fingers in Hershko's house!" Adina says. "That's gross!"

"שמת את אצבעותיו של האוקראיני הראשון בבית של הרשקו!"
samta et etsbe'otav shel ha'ukraini harishon baba'it shel hershko
you put D.O. his fingers of the Ukrainian the first in the home of Hershko

261

אומרת עדינה. "זה מגעיל!"
omeret adina ze magil
she says Adina that gross

"I thought it was a nice touch," I say.

"חשבתי שזו הייתה תוספת נחמדה," אני אומר.
khashavti shezo haita tosefet nekhmada ani omer
I thought that this it was addition nice I I say

"The cops will realize that Hershko wouldn't cut off his own employee's fingers," Ronen says.

"השוטרים יבינו שהרשקו לא היה קוטע את אצבעותיו
hashotrim yavinu shehershko lo haya kote'a et etsbe'otav
the cops they will realize that Hershko no he would have amputated D.O. his fingers

של מישהו מעובדיו," אומר רונן.
shel mishehu me'ovdav omer ronen
of someone from his employees he says Ronen

"Probably, but it gives the reporters and bloggers something to shout about."

"יכול להיות, אבל זה נותן לעיתונאים ולבלוגרים משהו לצעוק
yakhol lihiyot aval ze noten la'itona'im velablogerim mashehu litsok
it could be but this it gives to the journalists and to the bloggers something to shout

עליו."
alav
about it

"Why did Hershko kill his wife and the two insurance men?" Ayala asks.

"מדוע הרשקו הרג את אשתו ואת שני סוכני הביטוח?" שואלת
madu'a hershko harag et ishto ve'et shnei sokhnei habitu'akh sho'elet
why Hershko he killed D.O. his wife and D.O. two of agents of the insurance she asks

איילה.
ayala
Ayala

"She kept yelling at him to keep the toilet seat down," Ronen jokes.

"היא לא הפסיקה לצעוק עליו שיוריד את מושב האסלה," מתלוצץ
hi lo hifsika litsok alav sheyorid et moshav ha'asla mitlotsets
she no she stopped to yell at him that he will lower D.O. seat of the toilet he jokes

רונן.
ronen
Ronen

I chuckle a little bit.

אני מגחך מעט.
ani megakhekh me'at
I I chuckle a little

"Can we not make fun of murder victims?" Leah asks.

"נוכל לא לצחוק על קורבנות רצח?" שואלת לאה.
nukhal lo litskhok al korbenot retsakh sho'elet le'a
we will be able no to laugh about victims of murder she asks Leah

"He took out a ten million shekel life insurance policy on his wife a few years ago," Adina explains. "That's when he started thinking about how to get rid of her without being caught. Which led to the whole extortion scheme."

"הוא הוציא פוליסת ביטוח חיים על סך עשרה מיליון שקלים
hu hotsi polisat bitu'akh khayim al sakh asara milyon shkalim
he he took out policy of insurance of life in the amount of ten million shekels

על שם אשתו לפני מספר שנים," מסבירה עדינה. "ואז הוא התחיל
al shem ishto lifnei mispar shanim masbira adina ve'az hu hitkhil
on name of his wife ago a few years she explains Adina and then he he started

לתוכנית הוביל וזה להיתפס. בלי ממנה להיפטר איך לחשוב
letokhnit *hovil* *veze* *lehitafes* *bli* *mimena* *lehipater* *eikh* *lakhshov*
to plan of · it led · and this · to be caught · without · of her · to get rid of · how · to think

הסחיטה.״
haskhita
the extortion

חשד ומסיר מאשתו נפטר ״הוא אומר רונן. ״רעיון לא רע,״ אני
khashad *umesir* *me'ishto* *niftar* *hu* *ronen* *omer* *ra* *lo* *ra'ayon* *ani*
suspicion · and he removes · of his wife · he gets rid of · he · Ronen · he says · bad · not · plan · I

מעצמו בו-זמנית.״
bo-zmanit *me'atsmo*
simultaneously · from himself

אני ״,ההם הביטוח סוכני שני את הרג הוא למה יודע לא ״אני
ani *hahem* *habitu'akh* *sokhnei* *shnei* *et* *harag* *hu* *lama* *yode'a* *lo* *ani*
I · the those · the insurance · agents of · two of · D.O. · he killed · he · why · I know · no · I

אומר להם. ״לא טרחתי לשאול אותו.״
oto *lishol* *tarakhti* *lo* *lahem* *omer*
him · to ask · I bothered · no · to them · I tell

שפקד מזל לנו ״היה עדינה. אומרת ״,חכם בחור היה ״הרשקו
shepakad *mazal* *haya lanu* *adina* *omeret* *khakham* *bakhur* *haya* *hershko*
that commander · luck · we had · Adina · she says · smart · guy · he was · Hershko

כהן עשה את הטעות האחת ההיא.״
hahi *ha'akhat* *hata'ut* *et* *asa* *kohen*
that one · the one · the mistake · D.O. · he made · Cohen

בעניין שלי הדוא״ל את מבינה שהמשטרה חושב ״אתה
be'inyan *sheli* *hado'ar elektroni* *et* *mevina* *shehamishtara* *khoshev* *ata*
on issue of · my · the email · D.O. · she understands · that the police · you think · you

העברות הכספים בין הרשקו וכהן?״ שואל רונן.
ronen *sho'el* *vekohen* *hershko* *bein* *haksafim* *ha'avarot*
Ronen · he asks · and Cohen · Hershko · between · the money · transfers of

כדי ימים כמה בעוד זוהר לבלש אתקשר אני ״כנראה.
kedei *yamim* *kama* *be'od* *zohar* *labalash* *etkasher* *ani* *kanire*
in order to · days · a few · in another · Zohar · to the detective · I will call · I · probably

להמשיך בשיחה. הוא כנראה רוצה לדבר איתי שוב.״
shuv *iti* *ledaber* *rotse* *kanire* *hu* *basikha* *lehamshikh*
again · with me · to talk · he wants · probably · he · with the conversation · to continue

״למה?״ שואלת עדינה.
adina *sho'elet* *lama*
Adina · she asks · why

״שרה לא מסתובבת לה במשרד, נכון?״ אני שואל.
sho'el *ani* *nakhon* *bamisrad* *mistovevet la* *lo* *sara*
I ask · I · correct · in the office · she hangs around · no · Sara

---

"Not a bad plan," Ronen says. "He gets rid of his wife and eliminates himself as a suspect simultaneously."

"I don't know why he killed those two insurance men," I tell them. "I didn't bother asking him."

"Hershko was a smart guy," Adina says. "We were lucky that Captain Cohen made that one mistake."

"Do you think the police understand my email about the money transfers between Hershko and Cohen?" Ronen asks.

"Probably. I'll call Detective Zohar in a few days to follow up. He probably wants to talk with me again."

"Why?" Adina asks.

"Sara's not hanging around the office anywhere, is she?" I ask.

"No, she's working another case today," Leah tells me.

לא, היא עובדת על חקירה אחרת היום," אומרת לי לאה.
lo no · *hi* she · *ovedet* she works · *al* on · *khakira* investigation · *akheret* other · *hayom* today · *omeret* she tells · *li* to me · *le'a* Leah

"Good. To answer Adina's question, Sara and I cleaned Hershko's house so that the police wouldn't have our fingerprints. Then I worked a little mind mojo on Hershko to make sure he wouldn't remember anything about ever seeing us. So Zohar is probably very anxious to find out who I am and how I was able to solve the case."

יופי. בתשובה לשאלת עדינה, שרה ואני ניקינו את ביתו
yofi good · *bitshuva* in answer · *lishe'elat* to question of · *adina* Adina · *sara* Sara · *va'ani* and I · *nikinu* we cleaned · *et* D.O. · *beito* his house

של הרשקו, כדי שהמשטרה לא תמצא את טביעות האצבע שלנו.
shel of · *hershko* Hershko · *kedei* so that · *shehamishtara* that the police · *lo* no · *timtsa* she will find · *et* D.O. · *tvi'ot ha'etsba* the fingerprints · *shelanu* our

אחר כך הפעלתי כישוף מוחי קטן על הרשקו כדי לוודא שהוא
akhar kakh then · *hifalti* I applied · *kishuf* mojo · *mokhi* mind · *katan* little · *al* on · *hershko* Hershko · *kedei* in order to · *levade* to confirm · *shehu* that he

לא יזכור שראה אותנו. כך שזוהר בוודאי משתוקק לגלות
lo no · *yizkor* he will remember · *shera'a* that he saw · *otanu* us · *kakh shezohar* so Zohar · *bevadai* probably · *mishtokek* he desires · *legalot* to find out

מי אני ואיך הצלחתי לפתור את החקירה."
mi who · *ani* I · *ve'eikh* and how · *hitslakhti* I succeeded · *liftor* to solve · *et* D.O. · *hakhakira* the investigation

"Between the money and diamonds they got from Captain Cohen and whatever they find in Hershko's accounts, the victims will get most of their money back," Leah says.

"בין הכסף והיהלומים שמצאו אצל פקד כהן,
bein between · *hakesef* the money · *vehayahalomim* and the diamonds · *shematsu* that they found · *etsel* in the possession of · *pakad* commander · *kohen* Cohen

ומה שימצאו בחשבונות הבנק של הרשקו, הקורבנות יקבלו
uma and what · *sheyimtse'u* that they will find · *bekheshbonot* in accounts of · *habank* the bank · *shel* of · *hershko* Hershko · *hakorbanot* the victims · *yekablu* they will get

את רוב כספם בחזרה," אומרת לאה.
et D.O. · *rov* most · *kaspam* their money · *bakhazara* back · *omeret* she says · *le'a* Leah

"Do you think the evidence you left at the house is enough to convict him?" Adina asks.

"אתה חושב שהראיות שהשארת בבית מספיקות כדי
ata you · *khoshev* you think · *shehare'ayot* that the evidence · *shehisharta* that you left behind · *baba'it* at the house · *maspikot* enough · *kedei* in order to

להרשיע אותו?" שואלת עדינה.
leharshi'a to convict · *oto* him · *sho'elet* she asks · *adina* Adina

"I think so. Ronen also fabricated a few financial transactions that link Hershko to the Ukrainians. As the cops unravel Hershko's bank records, those transactions will pop up like red flags," I tell her.

"אני חושב שכן. רונן גם זייף כמה העברות כספים שקושרות את
ani I · *khoshev* think · *sheken* that yes · *ronen* Ronen · *gam* also · *ziyef* he forged · *kama* a few · *ha'avarot* the transfers · *ksafim* financial · *shekoshrot* that (they) link · *et* D.O.

הרשקו לאוקראינים. כשהשוטרים יתירו את סבך חשבונות
hershko Hershko · *la'ukrainim* to the Ukrainians · *kshehashotrim* as the cops · *yatiru* they will unravel · *et* D.O. · *svakh* entanglement of · *kheshbonot* accounts of

הבנק של הרשקו, ההעברות האלה יצוצו כמו דגלים אדומים,"
habank the bank · *shel* of · *hershko* Hershko · *haha'avarot* the transfers · *ha'ele* the those · *yatsutsu* they will pop up · *kmo* like · *dgalim* flags · *adumim* red

אני אומר לה.
ani I · *omer* I tell · *la* to her

"אתם שניכם כל כך לא ישרים," אומרת איילה.

atem	shneikhem	kol kakh	lo	yesharim	omeret	ayala
you	two of you	so	not	honest	she says	Ayala

"You guys are so dishonest," Ayala says.

באותו לילה, לאה ואני שוכבים במיטה ביחד. אני מעסה את

be'oto	laila	le'a	va'ani	shokhvim	bamita	beyakhad	ani	me'ase	et
in same	night	Leah	and I	we lie down	in the bed	together	I	I massage	D.O.

כפות רגליה. היא אוהבת את זה. לאה מספרת לי שהיא רוצה

kapot ragleiha	hi	ohevet	et	ze	le'a	mesaperet	li	shehi	rotsa
her feet	she	she likes	D.O.	that	Leah	she tells	to me	that she	she wants

לחפש מחר מקום חדש למשרד.

lekhapes	makhar	makom	khadash	lamisrad
to look for	tomorrow	place	new	for the office

That night, Leah and I are in bed together. I rub her feet. She likes that. Leah tells me that tomorrow she wants to look for a new location for our office.

"למה?" אני שואל.

lama	ani	sho'el
why	I	I ask

"Why?" I ask.

"נוכל להרוויח הרבה כסף אם נסב את הנכס

nukhal	leharvi'akh	harbe	kesef	im	nasev	et	hanekhes
we will be able	to earn	a lot	money	if	we will convert	D.O.	the property

באור יהודה לבניין דירות ונמכור אותן. שוק הנדל"ן

be'or yehuda	levinyan	dirot	venimkor	otan	shuk	hanadlan
in Or Yehuda	to building of	apartments	and we will sell	them	market of	the real estate

מתחיל להתאושש," היא אומרת.

matkhil	lehitoshesh	hi	omeret
it starts	to recover	she	she says

"We can make a lot of money converting the Or Yehuda property into condos and selling them. The real estate market is starting to come back," she says.

"איפה נחפש?" אני שואל.

eifo	nekhapes	ani	sho'el
where	we will look	I	I ask

"Where should we look?" I ask.

"חשבתי על פרדס חנה. זו עיר קטנה ונחמדה והיא ממוקמת ממש

khashavti	al	pardes khana	zo	ir	ktana	venekhmada	vehi	memukemet	mamash
I thought	about	Pardes Hanna	this	town	little	and nice	and it	located	precisely

על קו הרכבת לתל אביב. חוץ מזה יש שם מסעדות מצוינות. לא

al	kav	harekevet	letel aviv	khuts mize	yesh	sham	misadot	metsuyanot	lo
on	line of	the train	to Tel Aviv	besides	there are	there	restaurants	excellent	no

יצאת אף פעם עם מישהי ששמה חנה, נכון?"

yatsata	af pa'am	im	mishehi	sheshma	khana	nakhon
you went out	never	with	anyone	that her name	Hanna	correct

"I was thinking of Pardes Hanna. It's a nice little town and it's right on the train line for Tel Aviv. Plus, there are great restaurants. You never dated anyone named Hanna, did you?"

"לא שאני זוכר."

lo	she'ani	zokher
not	that I	I remember

"Not that I remember."

אני מעסה את רגליה עוד קצת.

ani	me'ase	et	ragleiha	od	ktsat
I	I massage	D.O.	her feet	more	a little

I rub her feet some more.

Story 13

"I need a new gun," I say.

אני צריך אקדח חדש," אני אומר"
omer ani khadash ekdakh tsarikh ani
I say I new gun I need I

"Is that why you are rubbing my feet?"

זו הסיבה שאתה מעסה את רגליי?"
raglai et me'ase she'ata hasiba zo
my feet D.O. you massage that you the reason this

"Maybe."

אולי."
ulai
maybe

"How about massaging my back for a while. After that we can talk about guns."

מה עם עיסוי גב לזמן מה? אחר כך נוכל לדבר על אקדחים."
ekdakhim al ledaber nukhal akhar kakh lizman ma gav isui ma im
guns about to talk we will be able then for a while back massage of what about

266

Part II

STORIES IN HEBREW ONLY

STORY 1

Garden Variety

טיפוח גינה זה לא דרך טובה לחסוך כסף. נדמה לך שהיבול יוריד את עלות הקניות שלך. אבל אתה שוכח את עלות הטיפול בגינה. לכן, מוטב לגדל ירקות רק בשביל הערך הפסיכולוגי שבדבר.

לא יאומן עד כמה אשתי אוהבת את הגינה שלה. היא נמלאת תחושת סיפוק עצומה מלראות את הירקות גדלים. לעומתה, אני נמלא תחושה אחרת. היא נקראת כאב !

לשים גדר מסביב לגינה זה לא כיף. עלות החומרים לגדר בגובה 2.5 מטרים, המיועדת להקיף גינה בגודל 5 על 6 מטרים, היא כ-1000 שקל. נדרשת גדר בגובה 2.5 מטרים כדי למנוע מהדורבנים להפוך את הגינה למזנון סלטים.

אפילו אז, הם יכולים להיכנס בדרכים אחרות. לפעמים הם מסתובבים ליד השער, מתחבאים מאחורי השיחים. הם חומקים פנימה כשאתה יוצא לנכש עשבים. בקיץ האחרון ניסה דורבן אחד לצנוח פנימה. למרבה המזל כיוון הרוח השתנה והוא סיים את הצניחה בפעירת חור בתקרה של השכנים.

עיבוד הקרקע אינו עניין של מה בכך. ראשית, צריך ללכת למשתלה הקרובה ולמצוא מכונת עיבוד קרקע שנכנסת למכונית שלך. אלא אם יש לך טנדר ארבע על ארבע, תמצא שתוכל לקחת רק מכונה קטנה.

הקטנות שקולות בערך קילו, והן סתם מקפצות על פני השטח. כלומר, אתה צריך לדחוף את להבי המכונה אל תוך האדמה הקשה בזמן שהם מסתובבים.

נסה לעשות זאת במשך שעתיים כששגרת האימון שלך ביום-יום מסתכמת בהנפת כוסות יין וזפזופ מול הטלוויזיה.

ואז אתה צריך לעזור לאישתך לחפור בורות עבור הזרעים. אוקיי, אלה גומות קטנות. אבל חפירה איננה עניין מהנה, אלא אם אתה מוצא אוצר שהוטמן באדמה.

כמה שבועות אחר כך אם לא יורד יותר מדי גשם, אבל יורד מספיק גשם, ואם הארנבות לא מתגנבות דרך הגדר, אתה זוכה לנכש עשבים שוטים ולקטוף קצת יבול.

אני משתדל לצאת מהעיר כשהעשבים השוטים מגיחים מהקרקע, אבל לפעמים אני לא מצליח לקחת חופשה, ואני נאלץ לשנס מותניים ולנכש.

ואז אני זוכה להעביר כמה פגישות אצל הכירופרקט, כדי שיעשה לי כמה תיקונים שאוכל לעמוד שוב באופן נורמלי.

האסיף דורש גם הוא עבודה רבה בכפיפה. רק הרמת שק אחד של שעועית ובחזרה לכירופרקט שזה עתה רכש יאכטה קטנה מהתשלומים שקיבל ממני בעונת הגינון.

כשהילדים היו קטנים הייתה לנו גינה גדולה הרבה יותר, ותמיד שתלנו יותר מדי. נהגנו לגדל ארבעה שיחי קישוא בכל שנה. איזו משפחה נורמלית יכולה לאכול את התוצרת של ארבעה שיחי קישוא?

היו לנו כל כך הרבה קישואים שנאלצנו לחלק לאחרים. העמסנו את הילדים בעגלה קטנה אדומה, כיסינו אותם בקישואים, נתנו להם שנורקלים כדי שלא יחנקו וצעדנו במורד הרחוב.

כל השכנים קיבלו ירקות. שבוע או שבועיים אחר כך, השכנים שמעו שוב את חריקת גלגלי העגלה כשיצאנו לסיבוב שלנו. הם סגרו את הווילונות ונעלו את הדלתות. אף אחד לא היה בבית בשכונה כולה.

מה עושים עם הקישואים המיותרים? הצבנו דוכן קישואים בכביש הגישה לביתנו. בתנו, שיכולה למכור כל דבר לכל אחד, לא הצליחה למכור את התוצרת.

אז האישה גילתה מתכונים למרק קישואים, ללביבות קישואים, עוגיות קישואים, פופקורן קישואים, וכו'. בלילה הייתי מתגנב לגינה ונותן לשיחי הקישואים בחשאי קישואים גלולות למניעת הריון, כל דבר כדי למנוע מהם להתרבות.

אשתי גידלה גם הרבה חצילים. מעולם לא שמעתי על חצילים עד שעברתי ממרכז תל אביב למרחבי הטבע של גבעתיים. כמובן, לרוב תושבי גבעתיים לא היה מושג מהו מוקצ'ינו, כך שהדברים התאזנו מעט.

מאחר ואשתי ממצפה רמון, אין לי מושג מאיפה היא קבלה את הרעיון שחצילים הם משהו שאנשים נורמליים אוכלים. אף אחד במצפה רמון לא אוכל חצילים.

בכל אופן, לא אהבתי את הרעיון לגדל חצילים או לאכול משהו שמכיל חצילים. היה להם צבע מוזר. מי שמע על ירקות סגולים? הם היו רכים מדי כשהיו מבושלים. זה עשה לי כולרה, או יבלות, או משהו כזה.

לא חשוב, גידלנו הרבה חצילים. בכל ערב שיחקנו מחבואים. האישה הייתה מחביאה חצילים איפשהו בארוחה, והילדים ואני ניסינו לזהות אותם ולזרוק אותם על הרצפה.

התלוננו כל כך הרבה שהאישה פצחה בשביתת בישול. זה היה רע. שרדנו שלושה ימים על התבשילים שלי. ואז הילדים נכנעו. החזקתי מעמד עשרים דקות נוספות, כדי להראות להם מאיזה חומר קורצתי. ואז גם אני הרמתי ידיים. אחר כך זה היה חצילים יום ולילה.

העגבניות היו מכת המוות בגינה. בכל שנה שתלנו שנים עשר, כן אמרתי שנים עשר, שיחי עגבניות. ניסיתי לסגור אותם בכלוב. חשבתי שזה יגביל את התפוקה. אבל הממזרות גדלו דרך סורגי הכלובים.

בכל שנה, כל העגבניות הבשילו בתוך שמונה דקות זו מזו, ביום חמישי השלישי של אוגוסט. משמעות הדבר הייתה תמיד – רוטב עגבניות. אני שונא להכין רוטב עגבניות. זה לוקח בערך שלושה ימים.

קודם כל עליך לאסוף בערך שלושת אלפים עגבניות. ואז עליך לזרוק אותן לסיר עם מים רותחים. אנחנו בדרך כלל מקימים מדורה מתחת לג'קוזי בקומה העליונה, ומשתמשים בו בתור סיר.

העגבניות צורחות כשאתה זורק אותן פנימה. זה דבר נוראי לשמוע. כשחושבים על זה הקול בעצם מגיע ממני. אני תמיד זורק את העגבניות לג'קוזי קצת יותר מדי חזק, ומתיז על עצמי רסס רותח. זה כואב!

אחרי כמה דקות, עליך להוציא את העגבניות מהמים הרותחים ולקלף אותן. הן לא אוהבות שמקלפים אותן.

הן מתפתלות ומחליקות ומנסות להתחמק.

אתה לא יכול לתת להן להחליק מהאחיזה שלך או שתקבל את המבט. המבט הוא הבעה שאבא שלי ערך בה ניסויים ואשתי שכללה לכדי שלמות. אני יכול להרגיש את המבט בוער דרכי כשאני רודף אחר עגבניה נמלטת, עירומה למחצה, אל תוך חדר האוכל.

כשהעגבניות מקולפות כולן ושוכבות רועדות על דופן הג'קוזי, עליך להוציא את הגרעינים. אני לא יכול לתאר את הייסורים שאני חש כשאני לוקח בזה אחר זה את היצורים הקטנים והאומללים וסוחט אותם עד שהגרעינים הקטנים והרבים קופצים החוצה. לא אוכל לומר כמה דורות עתידיים של העגבניות האלה נמעכו בין אצבעותיי המחוספסות.

לבסוף אתה מרסק את העגבניות בבלנדר, הופך אותן לפירה ונותן אותן לאשתך, מכינת הרטבים הראשית. אני לא יודע מהם אותם המעשים שאין להעלותם על דל השפתיים שהיא מבצעת בהן מנקודה זו ואילך.

אני בדרך כלל בורח מהמטבח אחרי החלק של הפירה. אבל אני כן יודע שהתוצאה טעימה מאוד כך שזה לא מדיר שינה מעיני. לרוע המזל, שלושה ימי עבודה עם אלפי עגבניות מסתכמים בכחצי כוס רוטב, כך שהשפיצוי הוא קצרצר.

כשאני כותב, אני נזכר בריח רוטב העגבניות המגיע מהמטבח. זה היה ריח נפלא.

בימים אלה הגינה שלנו הרבה יותר קטנה. תודה לאל על חסדים קטנים.

העגלה מחלידה במרתף, הגלגלים עדיין חורקים. הילדים כבר לא כאן לשחק 'החבא את החציל'. השכנים מחוץ לעיר, למקרה שננסה לחלוק איתם ירקות.

אבל תחזוקת הגינה עדיין עולה הרבה יותר משהיא חוסכת בחשבון הקנייה במכולת.

באפריל האחרון עיבדתי את הקרקע לקבלת יבולי השנה, ואני עדיין הולך כמו אדם שסוחב 20 קילו אבנים על הגב. אני חייב לחזור לכירופרקט !

STORY 2

A Good Sport

"תפסיקו לזרוק בוץ אחד על השני," צעקתי.

"תומר השפריץ עלי מבקבוק המים שלו."

"תומר, אל תעשה את זה."

תומר, הבן שלי, היה אמור לשמש דוגמה לילדים האחרים.

"המאמן דן, אני לא יכול לבוא למשחק בשבת," אמר רועי. "אני לא רוצה להתאמן יותר."

"למה לא?" שאלתי.

"אני לא אוהב כדורגל."

"אז למה הצטרפת לקבוצה?"

"אמא שלי הכריחה אותי."

בדיוק אז פגע בי גוש של בוץ.

"תפסיקו לזרוק בוץ," צעקתי. "המשחק הראשון שלנו בעוד יומיים. כולם לשבת ולהקשיב כמה דקות."

קבוצת בני התשע והעשר שלי התיישבה לבסוף על הדשא, מזיעים ועייפים לאחר ריצה מתישה.

דיברתי זריז. בנים אינם מסוגלים לשבת בשקט לאורך זמן. לאחר חמש דקות של הסברים על אסטרטגיה, חזרנו לרוץ.

שעה לאחר מכן, הסתיים האימון. היה עלי להמתין עשרים דקות עד שהופיעה האמא האחרונה לאסוף את בנה.

"אם תאחרי בפעם הבאה, אני מוכר אותו," אמרתי לה.

אחד עשר מתוך חמישה עשר הילדים בקבוצה הגיעו למשחק הראשון.

"איפה כולם?" שאלה אשתי גילת.

"זו בסך הכל הליגה העירונית," אמר אחד האבות. "ההורים והילדים לא לוקחים את זה ברצינות. זה רק עיסוק לשבתות אם אין להם תוכניות אחרות."

"זה לא הוגן כלפי אלה שכן הגיעו," אמרתי.

צור ניגש אליי במהלך החימום.

״אני לא רוצה לשחק היום.״

״למה?״

״הילד הגדול ההוא מהקבוצה השנייה אמר לי שהוא יפיל אותי.״

״גיל ישמור עליך.״

״לא נכון,״ צעק גיל.

״רועי, למה אתה מוריד את נעלי הפקקים שלך?״

״אני לא רוצה לשחק.״

בדיוק אז הגיעה אמא של רועי וצבטה באוזנו. הוא החל לנעול שוב את נעלי הפקקים.

כמה דקות מאוחר יותר, התחיל המשחק. צור רץ מיד אל מחוץ למגרש והסתתר מאחורי כיסא. משם היינו צריכים לשחק עם שחקן אחד פחות.

הורי הקבוצה שלנו היו שקטים מאוד. רוב הזמן הם ישבו על כסאות מתקפלים ושוחחו זה עם זה. תפסתי כמה מהם מציצים על המשחק לשנייה או שתיים אבל רוב הזמן הם לא ממש התעניינו. הם היו מוטרדים במחצית, כשהיה עליהם להפסיק לרכל ולתת לילדים חטיף.

״תסתכל על הצד החיובי,״ אמרה גילת. ״הם היו יכולים להיות כמו ההורים בקבוצה השנייה.״

״האנשים האלה באמת קולניים ולא נעימים. אף פעם לא ראיתי אבא שזורק כיסא על הילד שלו בגלל עבירת יד.״

״הבקענו גול בבעיטת העונשין,״ הזכירה לי גילת.

״תומר יהיה שוב שוער במחצית הזאת?״ המשיכה.

״לא.״

״יופי. אני לא רוצה לראות את הרגליים שלו מסתבכות שוב ברשת.״

״איך הוא הצליח לעשות את זה בדיוק כשהקבוצה השנייה פרצה קדימה?״

״אני לא יודעת, אבל טוב שדוד כל כך מהיר,״ אמרה גילת.

״אם הוא לא היה משיג את החלוץ שלהם ובועט את הכדור החוצה, תומר היה מרגיש נורא,״ אמרתי.

3

הילד הגדול מהקבוצה השנייה היה איטי. איש אחד בצד השני של המגרש התחיל לרוץ הלוך ושוב לאורך המגרש, תוך שהוא צועק עליו לרוץ מהר יותר.

״מי זה המשוגע הזה?״ שאלתי.

"זה אבא שלו," אמרה גילת.

עשר דקות לאחר מכן, הילד כעס כל כך שיצא מהמגרש. הוא התיישב ובכה בעוד אביו ואמו מתווכחים.

"בגלל שהילד הגדול פרש, אני יכול לשחק עכשיו," אמר צור.

"מצוין, תיכנס כבלם. שיחקנו בלי בלם כל המשחק."

שתי דקות לאחר מכן, הבחנתי במשהו.

"אף אחד לא משחק בעמדה שלו," אמרתי. "כולם רצים אחרי הכדור."

"זה קורה הרבה בליגה הזאת," אמר אביו של גיא.

"איך אני עוצר אותם?"

"אני לא יודע. אתה המאמן."

"גילת, תשחררי את ג'סי מהרצועה."

ג'סי הייתה הכלבה שלנו. הבאנו אותה למשחק.

"היא תרוץ למגרש ותרדוף אחרי הכדור," אמרה גילת.

"זה בדיוק מה שאני רוצה שתעשה. השופט יעצור את המשחק ואני אוכל לדבר עם הקבוצה."

"זה לא הוגן. אני לא עושה את זה."

"תגיד לאחד הילדים לזייף פציעה," הציע אביו של גיא.

"גם זה לא יפה," אמרה גילת.

"הם עושים את זה בליגות האירופיות כל הזמן," עניתי לה. "זה ממש אומנות אצל חלק מהמשחקנים המקצוענים האלה."

"אבל אלו ילדים בני עשר. אתה לא רוצה ללמד אותם דברים כאלה בגיל כל כך צעיר."

"ובכן, לא, אבל הם רוצים לנצח."

"לא אכפת להם מהניצחון," אמרה גילת. "לך אכפת."

בדיוק אז, הבקיעה הקבוצה היריבה שער.

4

"זה היה משחק כיפי, לא?" שאלתי את תומר.

"הוא היה ממש מגניב," הוא ענה.

"חבל על המאמן של הקבוצה השנייה," אמרה גילת.

"למה השופט הוציא אותו מהמשחק לקראת הסוף?" שאל תומר.

"המאמן לא חשב שהשופט עושה עבודה טובה," אמרתי.

"הוא אמר הרבה מילים לא יפות שאתה לא אמור לומר בפני אנשים נחמדים," הוסיפה גילת.

"לא ניצחנו," אמר תומר. "אבל שיחקנו טוב. תיקו זה טוב למדי."

"נראית מצחיק כשקפצת למעלה ולמטה אחרי השער שלהם," אמר תומר.

"אתה זוכר מה צעקתי?"

"תישארו בעמדות, תישארו בעמדות."

"נכון. וכולכם עשיתם את זה במשך שאר המשחק. אז הקפיצות עבדו."

"אהבת את הנגיחה שלי?"

"היא הייתה טובה למדי. בפעם הבאה נסה לנגוח בעזרת החלק העליון של הראש. לא הפנים."

"האף שלי עדיין כואב."

"הגלידה תשפר את הרגשתך."

"מתי נלך הביתה?"

"ברגע שהנפיחות תרד והדימום ייפסק," אמרה גילת. "אני לא רוצה שתלכלך את השטיח בדם."

STORY 3

Truth Will Out

התקשרתי לרז, השכן והברוקר שלי, ושאלתי אותו כמה שאלות על אודות אחת מקרנות הנאמנות שמכר לי.

"רפי, אני לא יכול לדבר איתך היום," הוא אמר לי.

"למה לא?" שאלתי.

"אני לוקח תרופה לכאבי גב. יש לה תופעת לוואי מוזרה. היא גורמת לי לומר את האמת."

"זה רע?" שאלתי.

"זה הדבר הגרוע ביותר שיכול לקרות לברוקר. אנחנו אף פעם לא אומרים את האמת. אופס. לא הייתי צריך לומר את זה. אתה רואה איך הגלולות האלה משפיעות עלי?"

"אני חבר ושכן שלך. אתה יכול לספר לי את האמת."

"אני לא מדבר עם אף אחד עד שאסיים עם הגלולות. זה מסוכן מדי. הסיבה היחידה שעניתי לשיחה הזאת היא בגלל שחשבתי שאתה רוצה לארגן משחק גולף. כל השיחות האחרות מגיעות היישר לתא הקולי."

סגרתי את הסלולרי והלכתי למטבח.

"רז לא מוכן לדבר איתי," אמרתי לאשתי גילת.

"זה נשמע מוזר."

"הוא לוקח כדורים לגב שגורמים לו לומר את האמת כל הזמן," אמרתי, "אז הוא מפחד לדבר עם הלקוחות שלו."

גילת ישבה ליד שולחן המטבח ואכלה עוגייה. גבותיה התקמטו. שמתי לב שיש לה רעיון.

"עכשיו זה זמן מצוין לגלות אם רז מכר לנו את ההשקעות הנכונות," אמרה.

חשבתי על זה לרגע.

"את צודקת," אמרתי. "בואי נלך לבקר אותו כשיחזור הביתה. אשתו נסעה בענייני עבודה ולא תוכל להגן עליו."

"אזמין שמרטף לילדים כדי שלא נדאג מכך שהבית יישרף בזמן שאנחנו מוציאים מרז את האמת," אמרה גילת.

שעתיים מאוחר יותר פתח רז את דלת ביתו. גילת ואני יצאנו מאחורי הגדר החיה הגדולה שליד הדלת. רז זינק 60 ס"מ באוויר. ואז הוא זיהה אותנו.

"רפי, כמעט גרמתם לי התקף לב. למה אתה וגילת מתחבאים בשיחים?"

"אנחנו רוצים לשאול אותך כמה שאלות לגבי ההשקעות שלנו," אמרתי.

גילת פתחה את הדלת וליוותה את רז פנימה.

"שב שם, רז," הורתה גילת. היא הצביעה על ספה בסלון.

"אולי כדאי שאשכב," אמר רז. "הגב שלי כואב מדי."

"בבקשה," אמרה גילת.

"הלוואי שאשתי הייתה פה," מלמל רז תוך שהוא שוכב.

"אל תראה כל כך מודאג," אמרתי. "אנחנו חברים שלך."

"מכרת לנו את ההשקעות הנכונות?" דרשה גילת לדעת.

"אסור לי לדבר על העבודה עד שאסיים עם הכדורים," אמר רז.

עיניה של גילת הצטמצמו כשבחנה את שכננו.

"אם לא תשתף פעולה, אספר לכל השכונה על ניתוח האף ושתל שרירי החזה שלך," אמרה גילת.

"זו סחיטה," אמר רז.

"יש לך שתי אפשרויות," אמרתי. "או שתדבר איתנו או שכל השכונה תצחק עליך."

ראיתי מבט כנוע בעיניו של רז.

"או קיי, אני אדבר. בתשובה לשאלתכם, אני מוכר את המוצרים שמשלמים לי את העמלה הגבוהה ביותר. לא מעניין אותי אם הם ההשקעה הנכונה עבורכם."

"זה מה שאנחנו מקבלים על כך שאנחנו בוטחים בשכנים שלנו," אמרה לי גילת.

"מי סיפר לכם על הניתוחים הפלסטיים שלי?" שאל רז.

"זה הסוד שלי," אמרה גילת. "אחרי מה שסיפרת לי עכשיו, מזלך שהאף החדש שלך לא שבור."

היא עמדה מעל הספה והביטה אל תוך עיניו של רז. ראיתי זיעה מבצבצת על מצחו.

"מה הדרך הטובה ביותר להשקיע את הכסף שלנו?" שאלה גילת.

"לקנות קרן אגרות חוב, קרן שמתמחה במניות מקומיות וקרן נוספת שמשקיעה במניות זרות."

"כמה כסף אנחנו שמים בכל קרן?" שאלתי.

"בגילכם, הייתי שם שלושים אחוז באגרות חוב, חמישה עשר אחוזים במניות זרות והשאר במניות מקומיות."

גילת ואני עיכלנו את המידע החדש במשך זמן מה.

"אני באמת לא רוצה לענות על שאלות נוספות," אמר רז.

"אולי אאלץ לספר לאשתך על הביקורים השבועיים שלך במכון העיסוי ליד המשרד שלך," ציינה גילת.

"עקבת אחרי?" התנשף רז.

גילת המשיכה בחקירה חסרת הרחמים.

"מהן ההשקעות הטובות ביותר שאנחנו יכולים לקנות?" שאלה.

"תעודת סל בעלות נמוכה."

"זה גם מה שקנית בשביל עצמך?" שאלתי.

"כמובן. כל הברוקרים משתמשים בתעודות סל בתיק ההשקעות שלהם."

"איך זה שמעולם לא סיפרת לנו על כך?" שאלתי.

"אני לא מוכר תעודות סל."

גילת תפסה אגרטל גדול שהיה מונח על שולחן סמוך.

"אל תחשבי אפילו לשבור את זה על הראש שלו," אמרתי לה.

רז נראה מתוח מאוד כשגילת אחזה באגרטל. לבסוף הניחה אותו בחזרה על השולחן.

"אנחנו צריכים להחליף קרנות בכל שנה?" שאלתי.

"לא, רוב האנשים שמחליפים קרנות בכל שנה מפסידים כסף בטווח הארוך."

"אז למה אתה מעביר את הכסף שלנו מקרן לקרן כל כמה חודשים?" צעקה גילת.

"אני מקבל עמלה בכל פעם שאתם מבצעים עסקאות פעולה. ככל שאתם עושים יותר עסקאות אני מרוויח יותר כסף."

גילת העיפה בי מבט זועף. "החבר שלך עומד להיקשר לפגוש המכונית שלנו בתחתוניו ולהיגרר ברחבי העיר."

"בבקשה אל תפגעי בי," אמר רז. "אני רק מנסה להרוויח מספיק כסף למּן את הבית היפה הזה, בית נופש בגליל ושתי מכוניות יקרות."

פניה של גילת הפכו אדומים ממש. עיניה הוצפו בדם. זה היה מפחיד. רז ואני הבטנו בה בפה פעור. היא נשמה נשימות עמוקות עד ששליטתה העצמית שבה אליה. לבסוף הייתה מסוגלת לדבר בקול רגיל.

"אני עוזבת עכשיו. רז, אם אראה אותך שוב אחקוק את ראשי התיבות של שמי על שרירי החזה המזוייפים שלך."

היא יצאה החוצה מהדלת בקריעת רגליים.

"צדקת," אמרתי לרז. "הכדורים האלה באמת מסוכנים. אל תצא מהבית עד שתסיים לקחת אותם."

"איך היא יודעת עלי את כל הדברים האלה?" שאל רז.

יכולתי לומר לרז את האמת. שאחותה של גילת עובדת אצל המנתח הפלסטי שלו, ואחיה הוא בעל מכון העיסוי. היות שגילת מדברת עם אחיה כל הזמן, היא יודעת אילו שכנים עברו מתיחת בטן ואיזה סוג עיסוי הם אוהבים. אבל רציתי שרז יתפתל קצת.

"היא עובדת בסוכנות ממשלתית סודית," אמרתי לו.

הלכתי לכיוון הדלת.

"עוד דבר אחד," אמרתי. "אני מתכוון להעביר את כל הכסף שלי לתעודות סל בעלות נמוכה. אני לא צריך

שתהיה הברוקר שלי יותר. ״

STORY 4

Child's Play

"למה אתה מקלל?" שאלה אותי גילת.

"האינטרנט לא עובד."

"המחשב מחובר לחשמל?"

"למחשבים ניידים יש סוללה. בניגוד לטוסטרים, אין צורך לחבר אותם לחשמל."

"רפי, אין צורך להיות סרקסטי. אני רק מנסה לעזור. למה שלא תתקשר לתמיכה הטכנית?"

"אולי קובי יוכל לעזור לי."

"בפעם האחרונה שקובי עזר לך עם בעיה במחשב הוא שרף את הדיסק הקשיח."

"אה, נכון. אני אבקש מאחד הילדים לתקן את זה."

"אני לא רוצה שהם יתעסקו עם המחשב שלנו. בפעם האחרונה שביקשת מהם לעזור סיימנו עם בובספוג בתור תמונת הרקע."

"אתקשר לחברת המחשבים," אני אומר.

אני ממתין בטלפון במשך עשרים דקות לנציג פנוי. הוא מכריח אותי לחזור על כל הפעולות שכבר ניסיתי. לאחר כמה דקות, אנחנו מגלים את הבעיה.

"אני אשלח לך בדוא"ל תוכנה להורדה שתפתור את הבעיה," הוא אומר לי.

"זה לא יעזור, מכיוון שאני לא יכול להיכנס לאינטרנט."

"שכחתי מזה," הוא אומר.

"במחשבה שנייה, שלח לי את המייל. אני אפתח אותו אצל השכנים, אעתיק את התוכנה לדיסק און קי ואתקין אותה במחשב שלי."

"מצוין."

רצתי לביתו של קובי לקבל את הדוא"ל. ארבעים דקות אחר כך המחשב שלי היה מעודכן.

"תראי את זה," אמרתי לגילת.

"האינטרנט עדיין לא עובד?"

"זה בסדר עכשיו, אבל בדיוק קיבלתי הודעה ממיקרוסופט. הם מודיעים לי לא להוריד את העדכון האחרון של התוכנה כי זה מפריע לאינטרנט."

"עשית את זה לפני יומיים."

281

"וזו הסיבה שהאינטרנט הפסיק לעבוד."

"אתה רוצה כוס יין?"

"נראה לי שכן."

2

יומיים מאוחר יותר, גילת תולשת את שיערה.

"המדפסת לא עובדת."

"ניתקת את המחשב הנייד מהמדפסת היום?"

"כן, השתמשתי בו במטבח."

"לפעמים זה משבש את העניינים," אני אומר.

"אתה יכול לתקן את זה?"

"כבר הראיתי לך איך לתקן את הבעיה הזאת."

"שכחתי."

"אני קורא עכשיו," אני אומר לה.

"רפי, בוא לכאן ותתקן את המדפסת הזאת, או שלא אבשל ארוחת ערב היום."

אני מתקן את הבעיה מיד. גילת טבחית מעולה. אני לא רוצה שתשבות.

"למה את לא מצליחה לזכור כשאני מראה לך איך לתקן בעיות קטנות במחשב ובמדפסת?" אני שואל את גילת בארוחת הערב.

"זה התפקיד שלך. אני לא רוצה להתעסק עם תיקון מכשירי אלקטרוניקה."

"זה לא הוגן," אני אומר.

"החיים קשים. תתמודד עם זה."

3

"אתה יכול להוסיף את דוד עמוס לרשימת אנשי הקשר בטלפון שלי?" אני שואל את בני בן השש.

"כבר הראיתי לך איך לעשות את זה," הוא אומר לי.

"תראה לי שוב."

"יש ספר הוראות הפעלה על השולחן שלך," הוא אומר.

"הרגל שלי כואבת. אני לא יכול ללכת לשולחן שלי."

"אתה עושה את עצמך?" הוא שואל אותי.

"אולי."

"אם אתה לא אוהב שאמא לא זוכרת דברים שאתה מראה לה במחשב, למה אני צריך להסביר לך כל פעם איך לעדכן את רשימת אנשי הקשר?"

ככל הנראה יש לבני שמיעה חדה מאוד וזיכרון מצוין. אני רושם בזכרוני להיזהר בדבריי בעתיד כשהוא בסביבה.

"כי אני אבא שלך, ואני מסיע אותך לאימוני כדורגל," אני אומר לו.

"זו הפעם האחרונה שאני עושה את זה. עכשיו תסתכל טוב."

הוא מוסיף את מספר הטלפון של אחי לרשימת אנשי הקשר שלי. אני מעמיד פנים שאני מרוכז מאוד. למעשה, אני שם לב שהוא זקוק לניקוי ציפורניים. מספיק גרוע שאני צריך לבקש מילד שבקושי סיים את הגן לעזור לי עם הטלפון הסלולרי שלי. זה גרוע אפילו יותר כשאני אומר לו לתקן את מערכת הסראונד שעתיים לאחר מכן.

"מה הבעיה?" הוא שואל.

"אין צליל בארבעת הרמקולים הנוספים," אני אומר.

הוא מזדחל לו מאחורי הטלוויזיה בפינת הסלון, ובוחן את ארבע מאות הכבלים המחוברים לטלוויזיה, לדי וי די ולממיר.

"מישהו לחץ בטעות על הכפתור הזה," הוא אומר.

אני מציץ מאחורי הטלוויזיה ורואה אותו יושב בתוך קן של חוטים וכבלים. הוא מצביע על מתג קטן בחלקו האחורי של הטיונר.

"זה במצב סגור," הוא אומר.

"אז תדליק אותו."

הוא לוחץ על הכפתור וארבעת הרמקולים הנוספים מתעוררים לחיים.

"אל תיגע בכפתור הזה שוב," הוא אומר.

"לא נגעתי בו."

"אם יהיו לך עוד בעיות תשאל את החנונית," הוא אומר לי.

"תפסיק לקרוא כך לאחותך. ולמה אני צריך לשאול אותה?"

"היא יודעת יותר ממני. מר סלזר, השכן, משלם לה עשרים שקלים לשבוע שתדאג שהקולנוע הביתי והאזעקה שלו יעבדו כמו שצריך."

"הטכנולוגיה מתקדמת מהר מדי בשבילנו," אני אומר לגילת מאוחר יותר באותו לילה.

"אתה שוב מסתבך עם כיוון השעון המעורר?" היא שואלת.

"כן. למה קנינו את הדבר הדיגיטלי הזה? צריך תואר שני באלקטרוניקה כדי להפעיל אותו."

"אתה סתם כועס כי הילדים יודעים יותר ממך."

"לבת שלנו יש חוזה ייעוץ טכני עם מר סלזר."

"אין לו ילדים, אז הוא צריך את המומחיות שלה."

אני מתיישב במיטה ומניד בראשי בפליאה.

"המחשבון שהיא משתמשת בו בשיעורי המתמטיקה יכול לפתור משוואות," אני אומר לגילת. "אני לא ידעתי אפילו לאיית את המילה 'משוואה' כשהייתי בן עשר."

"הילדים שלנו גדלים עם טכנולוגיה מתקדמת," אומרת גילת. "הם לא חוששים ללחוץ על כל הכפתורים והם לומדים הרבה יותר מהר מאיתנו."

"מעניין איך קשישים מסתדרים," אני אומר.

"הם מתקשרים לנכדים שלהם שיעזרו, או שהם פשוט לא מתעסקים עם גאדג'טים מתוחכמים."

"כמו אימא שלך, שמסרבת לגעת במחשב ולא קונה טלפון סלולרי."

"בדיוק," היא אומרת.

"אבל מה יקרה אם המכונית שלה תתקלקל והיא תצטרך להזמין גרר?"

"היא כבר לא נוהגת."

"נכון, שכחתי."

"מה תעשה כשהילדים יצאו מהבית?" שואלת גילת.

"עד אז היצרנים ייצרו מכשירים פשוטים כל כך שאפילו מבוגרים יצליחו להפעיל אותם. או זה, או שתצטרכי ללדת עוד כמה ילדים."

"אני חושבת ששניים זה מספיק," אמרה גילת.

STORY 5

Selling Low

השעה שמונה וחצי בשבת בבוקר. מוקדם מכדי להיות ער. ובכל זאת, הנה אני עם אשתי גילת, סוחבים שולחנות עמוסים גרוטאות מהחנייה הפרטית אל כביש הגישה.

"איך הצלחנו לצבור את כל הגרוטאות האלה?" היא שואלת.

"זה מעגל קסמים. אנחנו קונים דברים שאנחנו לא צריכים כי הם במבצע. בסוף אנחנו מאחסנים את הדברים במחסן. אחרי כמה שנים המחסן מלא. אנחנו עורכים מכירת חצר כדי להיפטר מהדברים במחסן, והמעגל מתחיל שוב."

לפתע אני שומע קול נוסף.

"אתן לכם שמונה שקלים עבור המנורה הזאת."

אני מסתובב. אישה קטנה ואפורת שיער המרכיבה משקפי ראייה גדולים ניצבת סמוך לאחד השולחנות שגררנו מהחנייה. היא אוחזת באחד מהפריטים שאנחנו מנסים למכור.

"זו מנורת טיפאני מקורית," אני אומר. "המחיר הוא שמונים שקלים."

"לא תצליחו לקבל שמונים שקלים. תיקחו עשרים?"

"גברת, המכירה מתחילה בעוד שלושים דקות. תחזרי אז ונדבר."

"חוט החשמל בלוי," היא אומרת.

היא מחזיקה את החוט בידה השמאלית ומצביעה על קטע שחוק.

"היא עשתה את זה עם השיניים כשהוצאנו את השולחן הזה," אומרת גילת. "ראיתי אותה."

"העונש על פגיעה בסחורה הוא תשלום כפול מהמחיר המסומן בתג המחיר," אני אומר לגברת. "מאה שישים שקלים עבור המנורה."

הגברת מתרחקת בכבדות, ממלמלת לעצמה דבר-מה. בקצה כביש הגישה היא בועטת בעמוד התאורה שלנו.

עשר דקות אחר כך מגיע קהל ציידי מציאות במגוון כלי רכב. הם מפשפשים בפיצ׳פקס ומכשירי החשמל הקטנים שגילת ואני סידרנו על השולחנות.

גילת צועדת לעבר שני אדונים מבוגרים הכפופים מעל הסחורה שלנו. "ראיתי שהחלפתם את תגי המחיר," היא אומרת להם. פניהם מאדימים, והם פונים לדרכם, נבוכים.

גילת גוררת לכיווני נערה בת עשרה בעלת שיער קוצים כתום. על זרועותיה כתובות קעקע אחדות, ושפתיה

צבועות בליפסטיק שחור. בשתי גבותיה פירסינג עם טבעות רבות.

"היא ניסתה להגניב את הדיסק הזה לתוך הארנק שלה," אומרת לי גילת.

אני מביט בדיסק. "הבינ׳ בויז – המיטב," אני אומר לנערה. "זה לא מוזיקה קלילה קצת בשבילך?"

"זה בשביל חבר שלי," היא מייבבת.

"הוא בן שישים?"

"הוא בן עשרים. הוא אוהב מוזיקת גלישה."

"לכי תגנבי דיסק של בלאק סבאת׳ מהמכירה בהמשך הרחוב."

"רוצי הביתה, שרה, לפני שאתקשר לאימא שלך," אומרת גילת.

"אנחנו מכירים אותה?" אני שואל בעוד אנו מביטים בנערה רצה במורד הרחוב.

"היא הייתה עושה בייביסיטר לילדים."

"מפחיד."

בעשרים הדקות הבאות גילת ואני עסוקים מאוד. הגרוטאות שלנו נמכרות מהר יותר מכפי שציפינו.

"המכירה הזאת הולכת כל כך טוב שאני חושבת שאעלה את מחיר החפצים שנותרו בשלושים אחוז," אומרת גילת תוך שהיא מחזיקה את עט הסימון.

"עדיף שלא," אני אומר לה. "האנשים האלה באמוק. עלולה להתעורר מהומה אם תנסי לחלוב מהם יותר כסף."

גבר לבוש בהידור ניגש אלי.

"אני רוצה לקנות את השולחן המתרחב," הוא אומר במבטא קל.

"הוא עולה מאה עשרים ושמונה שקלים."

"תוכל לשים שלט ׳נמכר׳ על השולחן ולשמור לי אותו עד שאחזור מאוחר יותר היום?"

"בהחלט, אם תשלם לי מאה עשרים ושמונה שקלים."

"אתן לך מקדמה של עשרים שקלים."

"לא. שלם את כל הסכום אם אתה רוצה שאשמור לך אותו."

"אבל אני צריך ללכת הביתה להביא עוד כסף."

"אתה מנסה להגיד לי שבאת למכירת חצר עם פחות ממאה עשרים ושמונה שקלים?"

"לא חשבתי שאקנה משהו יקר."

"אני מכיר את הטריק הזה," אמרתי. "אני שומר לך את השולחן עד סוף היום. אתה חוזר ומסרב לשלם את הסכום שהוסכם. אתה חושב שתוכל לגנוב אותו ממני בארבעים שקלים, כי אין יותר קונים. זה תרגיל ישן. לך מכאן."

"אתה לא אדם נחמד. אני לא אבוא למכירת החצר הבאה שלך."

"אוריד אותך מרשימת התפוצה שלנו," אני אומר בסרקזם.

האיש הולך לדרכו ובועט בעמוד התאורה שלנו. אני מכריז:

"אם עוד מישהו יבעט בעמוד התאורה שלי, אנעל אותו בבגאז' של המכונית שלי למשך שבוע."

אף אחד לא שם לב אלי.

"אוכל להחזיר את הטוסטר אם הוא לא ימצא חן בעיני?" שואלת גברת אחת את גילת.

"זה טוסטר," אומרת גילת. "תחליטי עכשיו אם הוא מוצא חן בעינייך."

"יכול להיות שהוא לא יתאים על השיש שלי."

"כל המכירות סופיות. אין החזרות."

"אשלם לך שני שקלים עבורו."

"אני מעדיפה לרסק אותו בפטיש ולהשליך אותו לזבל מאשר למכור אותו בשני שקלים," אומרת גילת. "המחיר הוא חמישה שקלים."

"מה דעתך על ארבעה?"

"נמכר. מזומן בלבד, בלי המחאות בבקשה."

הגברת משלמת עם שקית מלאה בכסף קטן. היא הולכת עם הטוסטר.

"את אשת מכירות מצוינת," אני אומר לגילת.

היא זורחת מנחת.

לקראת סוף היום נותרים רק חפצים אחדים. גילת ואני תשושים. התמקחות עם קונים והתגוששות עם גנבים הם עבודה קשה. אנחנו קרובים לנקודת השבירה. מכירת חצר יכולה לגרום לבודדה לרצוח.

נותר קונה אחד.

"אשלם לך שנים עשר שקלים עבור המסגרת הזאת," הוא אומר לי.

"המחיר הוא ארבעים ושמונה שקלים. מאחר ואתה הלקוח האחרון אתן לך אותה בעשרים וארבעה."

"יש לי רק שנים עשר שקלים."

אני חושב רגע. אני מוכן לבקבוק יין נחמד. אולי אני צריך פשוט למכור את המסגרת בשנים עשר שקלים ולהיפטר מהבחור הזה.

"או קיי, שנים עשר שקלים," אומרת גילת. כנראה קראה את מחשבותיי.

"אפשר לשלם באגורות?" הוא שואל.

אני פותח את בקבוק היין בזמן שגילת, עם את חפירה בידיה, רודפת אחרי האיש במורד הרחוב.

STORY 6

Don't Stop and Smell the Roses

"הרגתי עוד שלושה," צעקתי לגילת.

"תמשיך להילחם, אולי נצא מזה בחיים," היא צורחת בחזרה.

הפניתי את ראשי מתוקפיי לשבריר שנייה וראיתי שהאויב מקיף את גילת מכל הכיוונים. מיהרתי לעזרתה, מתעלם מביטחוני האישי.

"בואו, דפוקים," צעקתי לעבר יריבינו.

ניצבנו גב אל גב, חובטים ומכים ביריבינו, בעוד הם ממשיכים בהתקפתם. לאחר דקות אחדות היינו מותשים. אויבינו המשיכו במתקפה.

"רפי, אין לנו ברירה," התנשפה גילת. "אנחנו חייבים להשתמש בכימיקלים רעילים."

"נשאר ממש מעט."

"זה הסיכוי היחיד שלנו."

היאוש בקולה גרם לי להסב את ראשי ולהביט באשתי היפה. עיניה היו מלאות דמעות. שיערה היה פרוע. הוצאתי את מכל דוחה היתושים מכיס מכנסיי הקצרים. ריססתי מעט על זרועותיה ורגליה החשופות של גילת. לאחר מכן ריססתי את החומר הנותר על עצמי. השלכתי את המכל על נחיל היצורים הקטלניים הזעירים שריחף מולנו.

היתושים נסוגו כדי לארגן את השורות מחדש. הם חכמים מכדי לנחות על עור שזה עתה כוסה בתרסיס. יכולתי לראות את היתושים הקצינים אוספים את הכוחות להסתערות נוספת.

"ההגנה מספיקה רק לכמה דקות," אמרה גילת. "רוץ למכונית מהר ככל שתוכל."

היינו שני קילומטר ממגרש החנייה. עמוק בביצה בעמק החולה. לפנינו ראינו שלט עץ קטן שעליו מסומן חץ. המילה "כרוז" הייתה כתובה עליו.

"בואי אחרי!" צעקתי. היה קשה להישמע בתוך זמזומם של מיליוני כנפי יתושים. רצתי בכיוון שעליו הורה החץ. גילת הייתה מעט אחרי.

"האם "כרוז" אומר שזו הדרך למגרש החנייה?" התנשמה.

"יכול להיות שהכוונה שיש בהמשך כרוב ענק," עניתי. "הערבית שלי לא טובה במיוחד."

בתחילת הטיול דרכתי על שורש של עץ ונקעתי את הקרסול. רגלי הלמה בכאב. ועדיין, הכאב לא עצר בעדי מלהימלט במלוא המהירות. זיעה מעורבת בקרם הגנה טיפטפה במורד מצחי אל תוך עיניי, שהחלו לצרוב. היער

הפך מטושטש.

"אני לא רואה," אמרתי לגילת בקול שהכיל מידה רבה של תבהלה. "לכי את ראשונה."

חלפנו על פני אדם שישב על כיסא ומכר בקלאווה ושתייה בקרון צבעוני.

"רוץ," אמרתי לו. "הם מאחורינו."

"רוצים לקנות קוקה קולה?" שאל האיש.

לא היה לי זמן לאיש מטורף שלא דואג לביטחון שלו. עזבנו אותו והמשכנו לרוץ.

קבוצה של שבעה ילדים בגיל בית ספר ושני מורים מבוגרים חלפה על פנינו, מפטפטים בעליזות תוך שהם צועדים אל עבר גורלם המר.

גילת עצרה לשנייה ואחזה בזרועו של אחד המלווים. "תחזרו. אף אדם לא יכול לשרוד בביצה."

הוא הביט בנו בשלווה. אני מניח שהיה מורגל לראות תיירים מזיעים העוטים הבעה פראית על פניהם, ואלפי עקיצות יתושים על פניהם, ידיהם ורגליהם.

"עזבי אותם," אמרתי לגילת. "אולי רודפינו יטרפו אותם. זה ייתן לנו כמה שניות נוספות לחזור למכונית השכורה שלנו."

"אבל הם רק ילדים," קראה גילת.

"זה הם או אנחנו," אמרתי ומשכתי אותה הרחק מקבוצת בית הספר.

מעבר לעיקול הדרך הפך שביל העפר העמוס בסלעים לשביל סלול.

"יש בניין לפנינו," צעקה גילת.

רצנו עוד עשרים מטרים, פתחנו את הדלת המרושתת ומעדנו אל תוך חדר גדול. שבעה אנשים היו בחדר. הם הרימו את מבטם כששרטקתי את הדלת מאחורינו.

"תתקשרו למשטרה ולבית החולים," אמרתי, מתנשם בכבדות. "אנחנו צריכים טיפול רפואי ופסיכיאטרי."

איש זקן דידה לעברנו.

"הסתבכתם עם החרקים," אמר בעברית צחה.

"כן," התנשפתי, "היינו תחת התקפה מאז שעזבנו את אזור קני הסוף."

"לא הבאתם דוחה יתושים?" שאל הזקן.

"הבאנו. זה היה אמור להספיק לשש שעות, אבל זה הרתיע את האויב רק לכמה דקות," אמרתי. "תהיה בטוח שאשלח מכתב חריף ליצרן ואדרוש החזר מלא. ריססנו שוב ושוב, עד שהמכל התרוקן. ואז רצנו אל מגרש החניה. הצלחנו להגיע לכאן לפני שהנחיל השיג אותנו שוב."

"יש שם ילדים," אמרה גילת. "מישהו צריך להציל אותם."

"יהיה בסדר," הסביר האיש. "אנחנו רגילים לחרקים."

"איפה אנחנו?" שאלתי.

"במרכז המידע. יש לנו ספרייה קטנה, שאתם יכולים לקרוא בה על הביצה ועל סוגי הצמחייה השונים בגנים שלנו. מגרש החנייה נמצא כמה מטרים מכאן. תרצו לשתות משהו?"

"יש לכם ערק?"

הוא צחק. "אתם כל כך מצחיקים. יש לנו מיץ, מים, תה וקפה."

גילת ואני התיישבנו על שרפרפים, לגמנו מבקבוקי המים וניסינו להשיב את רוחנו. דפדפנו בדפי הספר, שהסביר על אודות סוגי הצמחים השונים בגן הבוטני. עיניי צרבו עדיין והקרסול שלי החל להתנפח.

"איך פיספסנו את הבניין הזה כשהגענו?" שאלה גילת.

"אין שלטים," אמרתי. "החניתי את המכונית בצד הלא נכון של מגרש החנייה."

"היינו צריכים לשאול את האנשים בכפר הנופש אם יש להם מפה של המקום," אמרה גילת.

"תוכלי לנהוג בדרך חזרה?" שאלתי אותה.

"אני לא יודעת לנהוג בהילוכים," ענתה גילת.

"אבל הרגל שלי כואבת," התבכיינתי.

"תוכל לטבול אותה באמבטיה חמה אחר כך."

זמן מה מאוחר יותר היינו מוכנים לרוץ למכונית השכורה.

"אני לא חוצה את כל מגרש החנייה," אמרה גילת. "היתושים בטח הכינו לנו איזו מלכודת."

התווכחתי איתה, אבל זה היה חסר טעם. כשגילת מחליטה משהו, היא לא תשנה את דעתה.

רצתי אל עבר המכונית הכי מהר שיכולתי, מסתכל מעבר לכתפי אם האויב מתקרב. למרבה המזל, הם היו עסוקים במקום אחר. מן הסתם באכילת גווייתו של תייר אחר שצדו בביצה. הסעתי את המכונית לכניסת מרכז המידע וגילת קפצה פנימה.

כשמיהרנו חזרה למלון, ניסתה גילת לספור את העקיצות שעל גופה. היא הפסיקה במאתיים וחבטה בזרועי.

"איי," אמרתי. "מה זה היה?"

"על זה שהבאת אותי לגן הבוטני הטיפשי הזה," אמרה.

"את הכרחת אותי לבוא לכאן," אמרתי. "אני רציתי לשבת ליד הבריכה ולשתות יין."

"זה מה שהיינו צריכים לעשות. זו אשמתך."

STORY 7

Fool's Gold

"תיזהר מהמשאית!" צעקה גילת אשתי.

"אני רואה אותה. את רוצה לנהוג?"

"לא, רפי, נהיגה במנהטן מלחיצה אותי מדי."

"אז תפסיקי להתלונן. את מפריעה לי," אמרתי תוך שאני חותך נהג מונית בשדרה העשירית.

"נהג המונית עשה תנועה מגונה לעברנו," אמרה גילת. "איזה חצוף."

"הוא רק נופף לשלום."

"למה כולם צופרים? יש בכל פינה שלטים שאומרים שזה קנס של שלוש מאות וחמישים דולר."

"השוטרים לא נותנים דוחות לנהגים מקומיים. בגלל שאין לנו לוחיות רישוי של ניו יורק, אנחנו נקבל דוח. אני מבטיח לך שאם אצפור, תנחת עלינו להקת שוטרים ותרשום לנו דוחות ככל שנוכל לשאת."

"איך זה שאף אחד מהנהגים האלה לא נשאר בנתיב שלו?" שאלה גילת.

"הם עסוקים מדי בהתחמקות מהמהמורות בכביש, מכוניות בחניה כפולה ורוכבי האופניים המטורפים האלה מכדי לשים לב לקווים על הכביש."

"עברת עכשיו באור אדום."

"וגם שלוש המכוניות שמאחורינו. אם הייתי עוצר, הם היו נכנסים בנו."

"אני כל כך שמחה שאנחנו נוסעים במכונית ישנה. יש בה כל כך הרבה מכות שכל מכה נוספת תהיה שיפור."

"כן, האנשים במכוניות החדשות והיקרות נמצאים בעמדת נחיתות. הם לא יכולים להרשות לעצמם להיות אגרסיבים," אמרתי.

"למה אתה עוצר?"

"אני רוצה נקניקייה."

"לא צריך להחנות את המכונית?"

"כל מקומות החניה תפוסים. זה בסדר לחנות בחניה כפולה כאן, ליד המוכר."

"אבל יש שני אוטובוסים ושלוש משאיות תקועים מאחורינו וצופרים. הם לא יכעסו?"

"זו מנהטן. הם צריכים לצפות לכמה עיכובים," אמרתי.

פתחתי את חלון הנהג. הריח שעלה מדוכן הנקניקיות מילא את חלל המכונית.

"נקניקייה עם כרוב כבוש וקטשופ," צעקתי באנגלית מבעד לרעש פטישי האוויר.

293

"אתה חושב שבטוח לאכול כאן?" שאלה גילת.

"בוודאי. זה אתר בנייה. רק לדוכני הנקניקיות הטובים ביותר מותר למכור כאן. את רוצה משהו?"

"אני חושבת שאחכה לאחר כך."

"את מפסידה מעדן אמיתי," אמרתי תוך שאני לוקח את המנה מהמוכר הידידותי ומשלם לו ארבעה דולרים.

"נהג האוטובוס מאחורינו יצא מהאוטובוס והולך לעברך," אמרה גילת בפחד.

"בוודאי גם הוא רוצה נקנקייה," אמרתי.

לחצתי על דוושת הגז והתרחקתי משם ממש כשנהג האוטובוס הגיע לחלון שלי.

"הוא מנופף לעברך באגרוף," אמרה גילת.

"תפסיקי להסתכל בחלון האחורי," אמרתי. "ייתפס לך הצוואר."

אכלתי את הנקנִיקייה בעודי נוהג בשדרה העשירית עם יד אחת על ההגה. גילת השמיעה צווחות מבוהלות אחדות. אני לא יודע למה. התנועה הייתה יחסית סבירה היום. פניתי פנייה חדה שמאלה לרחוב ארבעים ותשע.

"תראה את האנשים האלה שבורחים מהנתיב שלנו," אמרה גילת.

"הנזירות האלה זריזות למדי. אפילו זאת המבוגרת עם מקל ההליכה יודעת לרוץ די מהר."

נכנסתי לתוך בניין חנייה. הוא נראה כאילו גמר את הקריירה לפני עשר שנים, אבל היו להם המחירים הטובים ביותר בניו יורק. שילמנו לשומר הרוסי החביב וצעדנו מזרחה.

"אתה חושב שבטוח בשכונה הזאת?" שאלה גילת.

"אל תדאגי. הפושעים באזור הזה עובדים רק בלילה," אמרתי.

"אתה אומר את זה בסרקזם?" שאלה גילת.

"כן."

עשר דקות מאוחר יותר היינו במתחם היהלומים. רחוב ארבעים ושבע, בין השדרה החמישית והשישית. עצרתי ונשענתי על ואן חונה.

"תני לי קצת זמן להסדיר את הנשימה," אמרתי לגילת.

"אתה באמת לא בכושר," אמרה גילת.

"איך זה שהיינו צריכים לרוץ את כל הדרך מהשדרה השמינית עד לכאן?" שאלתי. "חשבתי שמישהו עוקב אחרינו."

"כמעט נדרסתי על ידי לימוזינה כשחצינו את רחוב ברודווי בריצה. אנחנו אמורים לחכות לאור הירוק." לקח קצת זמן לפלוט את המילים, מאחר שעדיין נאבקתי להכניס אוויר לריאותיי.

"תפסיק להתלונן," אמרה גילת. "הגענו עד לכאן בלי לאבד את שרשראות הזהב. בוא נעלה ונראה כמה הן שוות."

לאחר מספר דקות נוספות הצלחתי לנשום כרגיל. צעדנו אל תוך בניין בן עשר קומות באמצע הבלוק ועלינו

במעלית לקומה השישית. על דלת חדר מספר 604 היה תלוי שלט עם שם העסק חרוט עליו באותיות מוזהבות. נשמע זמזום מהדלת והוכנסנו פנימה לחדר קבלה קטן. גברת צעירה ישבה ליד שולחן שהוצב מאחורי מחיצה חסינת כדורים.

"אנחנו רוצים למכור כמה שרשראות זהב," אמרה גילת לגברת.

"תיכנסו לתא מספר אחת. תנעלו את הדלת מאחוריכם ואני אשלח מישהו."

על הקיר משמאלה של פקידת הקבלה היו שלוש דלתות ממוספרות. נכנסנו בדלת מספר אחת. מולנו ניצבה מחיצה חסינת כדורים נוספת. תוך שלוש דקות הופיע מאחורי המחיצה גבר נמוך ורזה בעל שפמפם.

"היי," אמר. "יש לכם זהב בשבילי?"

"יש לך מבטא מעניין," אמרתי בזמן שגילת דגה שקית פלסטיק מתוך ארנקה. "מאיפה אתה?"

"ליטא," ענה האיש.

"זה ליד שיקגו?" שאלתי.

"לא," הוא צחק.

גילת הוציאה את השקית המלאה בשרשראות זהב ודחפה אותה בעד חרך במחיצה אל הדלפק. עשרים דקות מאוחר יותר יצאנו עם ארבע מאות דולר במזומן.

"הם שילמו לנו חמישים אחוז יותר ממה שחנויות התכשיטים בניו ג'רזי היו מוכנות לשלם," אמרה גילת. "בוא נתפנק בארוחת ערב טובה."

"כדאי לנו ללכת לאכול המבורגרים," אמרתי. "אחרת נבזבז את כל הרווח על אוכל ויין יקרים שאנחנו לא צריכים."

"הזמנתי מקומות במסעדה לפני שיצאנו מהמלון," אמרה גילת. "זו מסעדה צרפתית שני צמתים מכאן." חשבתי לרגע.

"כל ההרפתקה הזאת הייתה חלק מתוכנית מתוחכמת לאכול ארוחת ערב במסעדה יוקרתית במנהטן, נכון?" אמרתי לגילת.

"ואם כן?"

"נלך לשם, בתנאי שלא תכריחי אותי לרוץ," אמרתי.

STORY 8

Dumbbells Everywhere

"תוריד קצת במשקל, רפי."

"זה הכל?" שאלתי. "ארבע מאות וחמישים שקלים עבור בדיקה מקיפה, וכל מה שאתה אומר לי זה שאני צריך לרדת במשקל? בסכום הזה היית צריך למצוא לפחות ארבע בעיות נוספות. אני רוצה חוות דעת נוספת."

"או קיי," אמר חברי הטוב, ד"ר מיכה ווגנר, "גם האף שלך נראה מוזר."

"אתה עושה הופעות סטנד אפ בבית החולים בימי חמישי בערב?" שאלתי.

"תשמע," הוא אמר, "אנחנו מכירים מאז האוניברסיטה. אתה יכול לסמוך עליי. אני אומר לך שאתה צריך להתחיל להתאמן כל יום."

"אני עובד כרגע חמישים שעות בשבוע," אמרתי. "יש לי שלושה ילדים קטנים שאני מנסה לבלות איתם קצת זמן יחד. וגילת, אשתי החביבה, רוצה שאדבר איתה מדי פעם. אין לי זמן פנוי להתאמן."

"מה אתה עושה אחרי העבודה?"

"אני מקווה שאתה לא מתכוון לשלוח לי חשבון על השיחה הזאת," אמרתי. "שמעתי על זה שרופאים מחייבים מטופלים רק על שיחה."

"אתה רוצה שאתן לך כמה זריקות שאתה לא צריך?" הוא שאל.

לא הוגן. הוא ידע שאני מפחד ממחטים.

"בסדר, אני אדבר," אמרתי בעודי מנופף מעלי מחטים דמיוניות. "אחרי העבודה אנחנו אוכלים ארוחת ערב. אנחנו משחקים עם הילדים, משכיבים אותם לישון, ואז אנחנו צופים בטלוויזיה כמה שעות."

"והרי התשובה שלך. במקום לצפות בטלוויזיה אתה יכול להתאמן שעה."

"כל כך מאוחר בלילה?" שאלתי.

"זה לא מושלם, אבל זה עדיף על להפוך למרשמלו."

"רק עכשיו קניתי טלוויזיה בעלת מסך גדול ומערכת סראונד."

"תקליט את התוכניות האהובות עליך בזמן שאתה מתאמן ותצפה בהן בסופי השבוע," הוא אמר.

"זה לא אותו דבר בסוף השבוע," התלוננתי.

ד"ר מיכה נתן בי מבט חודר.

"תפסיק להמציא תירוצים ותמצא דרך להתאמן קצת במקום לצפות בטלוויזיה."

הוא נטל פנקס מרשמים והחל לכתוב. "זה שם של ספר כושר מצוין. יש שלוש או ארבע סדרות פשוטות

שאתה יכול לעשות כדי לגוון את האימון. תקנה את הספר הזה ותתחיל להזיע."

"אני לא אוהב להזיע," אמרתי לו. "כשאני מזיע זה גורם לי להרגיש איכסה."

"אני לא רוצה לשמוע תירוצים," הוא אמר.

"התחתונים שלי נדבקים לי לעור," המשכתי. "יש ריח מוזר מבתי השחי שלי."

"תתקלח אחרי שאתה מתאמן. גילת תעריך את זה," הוא ענה.

"מי רוצה להתקלח יותר מפעם בשבוע? אף אחד! זה בזבוז של מים טובים."

"עכשיו הרגזת אותי באמת," הוא אמר. "רק בגלל זה, אני עורך אצלך ביקור בית ביום שבת הבא בשעה אחת."

"הביטוח מכסה את זה?"

"לא. אני אביא את תיק הרופא שלי ואבדוק את לחץ הדם שלך. אני גם אשאר למשחק הכדורגל, מאחר שיש לך טלוויזיה כל כך נחמדה. בנוסף, אני אשב על כורסת הטלוויזיה החביבה עליך בזמן שאצפה במשחק."

"זאת עם מחזיק הכוסות המובנה במשענת היד בשביל פחית הבירה?"

"זאת. תוודא שיהיו לך הרבה בירות וחטיפים," הוא אמר.

"ומה אם לחץ הדם שלי לא ירד?"

"אני אבוא כל שבת עד שאראה שיפור משמעותי. אולי אביא את המשפחה. החטיפים יעלו לך הון."

2

"למה כל ריהוט הסלון במחסן מלבד הטלוויזיה ושתי הכורסאות?" שאלה אותי גילת מאוחר יותר באותו ערב.

"אני צריך מקום להתאמן."

"אתה לא יכול להתאמן בחוץ?"

"אני מתכוון להתאמן אחרי שנשכיב את הילדים לישון. עד אז נהיה חשוך מדי."

"לך למכון כושר."

"אני רוצה להתאמן בבית, איפה שאני יכול לצפות בתוכניות הטלוויזיה שאני אוהב."

"זה לא נשמע טוב," היא אמרה.

"מיכה ווגנר אמר שיבוא כל שבת לצפות בספורט ולאכול את כל האוכל שלנו עד שאתחיל להיכנס לכושר."

"עדיף אותו מאשר ההורים שלך," היא אמרה.

"אל תתחילי עם ההורים שלי," אמרתי. "בואי נתרכז באימון."

"אתה תתרכז באימון. אני לא מתכוונת להצטרף," אמרה.

"למה לא?" שאלתי.

"אני מתאמנת במכון כושר חמש פעמים בשבוע בהפסקת הצוהריים שלי."

"יכולנו לחסוך הרבה כסף אם היית מתאמנת בבית."

"לא תודה. אני אוהבת להתאמן בצוהריים. אחר כך אני אוכלת ארוחת צוהריים בריאה. פירות ויוגורט. אתה צריך לנסות לאכול אוכל בריא יותר."

"אני נהיה עצבני אם אני לא אוכל לפחות שני המבורגרים עם צ׳יפס כל יום," אמרתי.

גילת נטלה את הספר שהיה מונח על כורסת הטלוויזיה והחלה לדפדף בו.

"מיכה המליץ על ספר הכושר הזה. אני אעשה את החלק האירובי של האימון בחלל הפנוי שבין הכורסה לטלוויזיה בזמן שאנחנו צופים בתוכניות שלנו בכל ערב."

"הסדרה בעמוד עשרים וחמש אומרת שאתה צריך ללכת במהירות תוך הנפת משקולות יד," אמרה. "איך אתה מתכוון לעשות את זה כאן?"

"יש מספיק מקום ללכת הלוך חזור כמה צעדים."

"מה יהיה אם תפגע באחד הילדים בראש בזמן שאתה עושה את זה? משקולת יד יכולה להרוג אותם."

"הילדים יישנו."

היא הביטה בתרגילים שוב.

"קפיצות פישוק," אמרה. "הם רוצים שתעשה עשרים דקות של קפיצות פישוק."

"מה לא בסדר בזה?"

"זה מרעיש. כל הבית ירעד. אני לא אוכל לשמוע את הטלוויזיה."

"יש שטיח בחדר. זה יעמעם את הרעש. ואני אקפוץ ממש בקלילות, כמו נינג׳ה."

גילת הנידה בראשה.

"אני אצפה בטלוויזיה בחדר השינה כשאתה מתאמן," החליטה. "כך יהיה קל יותר לשנינו."

"מה עם זמן האיכות שלנו יחד?"

"יש לנו זמן איכות כשאנחנו משחקים עם הילדים. צפייה בטלוויזיה זה זמן הרגעות. אני ארגע טוב יותר בחדר השינה."

"אז אשים את אחת הכורסאות במחסן. כך יהיה לי יותר מקום," אמרתי.

3

ד״ר מיכה הופיע בשבת הבאה עם בקבוק יין ושקית בייגלה. גילת הובילה אותו לחדר האורחים. כל הריהוט עמד שוב במקומו. אודי ונתי, שני חברים נוספים מהאוניברסיטה, כבר ישבו על הספה ושתו בירה. ישבתי בכורסת הטלוויזיה כשהתחבושת גדולה מכסה את ראשי.

"מה קרה לך?" שאל מיכה.

"אתה עשית לי את זה," אמרתי. "יש לך מזל שאני לא תובע אותך על רשלנות מקצועית."

"איך עשיתי את זה?"

"אתה צריך לשמוע את כל הסיפור, מיכה," אמרה גילת.

"כדאי שאחזק את עצמי במעט אלכוהול."

הוא התיישב ופתח את פקק ההברגה של בקבוק היין.

"אתה לא יכול להרשות לעצמך יין עם פקק שעם?" שאל אודי.

"זה יין מצוין," ענה מיכה. "והרבה יותר קל לפתוח את הבקבוק."

מיכה נטל כוס יין ריקה משולחן הסלון, מזג והושיט את הכוס החצי מלאה לגילת.

"תודה, מיכה. איך ידעת שאני צריכה את זה?"

"כשאני רואה תחבושת על הראש של רפי ומגלה שיש סיפור מאחורי זה, אני יודע שיהיה לך ככל הנראה שבוע קשה," אמר.

הוא מזג כוס נוספת לעצמו, התיישב והביט בי.

"ספר לי את הסיפור."

"יש עשר דקות עד שהמשחק מתחיל," אמר נתי. "ספר מהר."

"חכה רגע," אמר מיכה. "מה קרה לתקרה?" הוא הצביע על חור גדול בתקרה, ממש מעל הספה.

"זה חלק מהסיפור," אמר נתי. "רפי לא רצה לספר לנו עד שתגיע."

עמדתי להסביר הכל כשגילת נכנסה לדבריי. "אני צריכה עוד יין," היא אמרה.

היא נטלה את הבקבוק ומילאה שוב את הכוס שבידה.

"זה יעזור לי להקשיב שוב לסיפור בלי לזרוק על רפי את השלט," אמרה לחבריי.

4

לרגע קצר תהיתי למה אשתי תרצה להשליך עליי חפץ קטן וקשיח. החלטתי להתעלם מההערה ולספר את הסיפור.

"קניתי את הספר שרשמת לי, רכשתי כמה משקולות והתחלתי להתאמן."

"מצוין," אמר מיכה.

"לא כל כך מצוין," אמרה גילת. "הוא החליט שהוא יכול להתאמן בחדר הזה בזמן שהוא צופה בטלוויזיה בלילה."

עיניו של מיכה התרחבו. "אהה," אמר, "פתאום הכל נהיה ברור."

"אחת מסדרות האימון כללה צעידה במקום והנפת משקולות. החלטתי לשלב את התרגיל הזה עם תרגיל מדרגה אירובי, אז שמתי שרפרף קטן על הרצפה."

"הוא צפה באחת מתוכניות הריאליטי האלה," הפסיקה אותי גילת.

"אפילו לא שמתי לב לזה שאני מניף את המשקולות לכיוון התקרה," המשכתי.

"הוא עלה על השרפרף ותקע משקולת של קילו וחצי ישר לתוך התקרה," סיכמה גילת.

מיכה, אודי ונתי התחילו לצחוק עליי.

"מי מספר את הסיפור?" תבעתי לדעת.

"הייתי במיטה וצפיתי בדרמה רפואית מצוינת," אמרה גילת. "היה רעש חזק, ופתאום היד של רפי הופיעה דרך הרצפה."

הבחורים צחקו חזק יותר.

"איזו הגזמה," צעקתי.

גילת הרימה את השלט ונתנה בי מבט מרושע. החלטתי לשתוק.

מיכה הרים את ידו. "נפלה לך חתיכה מהתקרה על הראש?"

"גילת לא הרשתה לי להשתמש שוב במשקולות, אז בחרתי סדרת תרגילים אחרת מהספר."

"תרגול אירובי שדורש הרמת ברכיים ובעיטות," הוסיפה גילת.

"זה היה אימון לא רע," אמרתי.

"עד שהוא התקרב מדי לטלוויזיה," אמרה גילת.

"תפסיקי להפריע," התלוננתי.

"הוא תקע את הרגל ישר לתוך הטלוויזיה," אמרה גילת.

עכשיו שלושת חבריי מהאוניברסיטה התגלגלו מצחוק. אודי אחז בברכיו והתנודד מצד לצד. דמעות זלגו מעיניו של נתי.

רתחתי בשקט. מה יכולתי לומר?

"הייתי צריכה ללכת לחנות ביום שלישי לקנות טלוויזיה חדשה למשחק של היום. רפי היה נבוך מדי," סיכמה גילת.

לקח לחבריי מספר דקות להרגע ולשלוט בעצמם.

"עדיין לא סיפרת לי איך נפגעת בראש," אמר מיכה.

"גילת אמרה לי שאני צריך להתאמן בפינה רחוקה מהטלוויזיה החדשה. עברתי לצד ההוא של החדר," הצבעתי על נקודה ליד האח.

"וגם בחרתי סדרת תרגול אירובי אחרת."

"קפיצות פישוק," אמרה גילת.

"איך נפצעת מקפיצות פישוק?" שאל מיכה.

"הייתה לנו מנורה יפה מזכוכית על התקרה, שהאירה את החלק הזה של החדר," אמרה גילת.

היא הצביעה על חוטי חשמל שהידלדלו להם בעצבות מהתקרה, סמוך לאח.

"לא נכון," אמר לה מיכה.

"הוא צפה בסדרה ההיא עם הערפדים," ענתה גילת.

"זאת שמראים בה את החזה של הערפדיות," הוספתי, בתקווה להסביר למה פישלתי בפעם השלישית.

"הוא היה מרותק כל כך לחזה שהוא לא שם לב שהוא קופץ קרוב יותר למנורה," אמרה גילת.

"הוא מחא כפיים בחוזקה והרס את המנורה," סיכם מיכה.

"חתיכות גדולות של זכוכית נפלו על הראש שלו," אמרה גילת.

"הדבר הבא שאני זוכר זה שעשו לי עשרה תפרים בבית החולים," אמרתי.

הם המשיכו לצחוק עליי במהלך כל המחצית הראשונה של המשחק. באחד מפסקי הזמן אמר לי מיכה: "ברצינות, אתה לא יכול להמשיך לנסות להתאמן בחדר הזה. אתה יכול לשבור הכל."

"גילת אמרה לי שאני צריך ללכת איתה למכון הכושר בהפסקת הצוהריים. כך היא תוכל להשגיח עליי ולוודא שאני אוכל הרבה יוגורט."

"תוכנית מצוינת," אמרו כולם.

STORY 9

In Good Repair

"אנחנו צריכים לקרוא לשרברב," אמרה לי אשתי גילת.

"למה?"

"טוחן האשפה התקלקל."

"שרברבים הם יקרים," עניתי. "אני יכול לקנות טוחן אשפה חדש ולהרכיב אותו בעצמי."

"רפי, אני חושבת שאתה צריך לתת לבעל מקצוע לעשות את העבודה הזאת."

"אין לך אמון בכישורים הטכניים של בעלך?" שאלתי.

"אתה טוב בגיזום הגדר החיה ובכיסוח הדשא," ענתה לי.

"אני יכול לבצע גם עבודות טכניות," התעקשתי.

"מה עם עמוד התאורה שהחלפת בגינה?" שאלה.

"הוא עובד מצוין."

"הוא נוטה חמישה עשר סנטימטרים שמאלה," אמרה. "כך יש יותר אור על שביל הכניסה."

"והנתיך נשרף אם מדליקים את הטלוויזיה כשהאור בגינה דולק."

"תאשימי את החשמלאי שהתקין את החיווט בבית," אמרתי. "הוא יצר עומס יתר על המערכת."

"אני בכל זאת חושבת שצריך להזמין שרברב."

לא המשכתי בויכוח עם גילת. תכננתי בחשאי לבצע את העבודה בעצמי. אני אראה לה כמה קל לתקן דברים בבית.

2

שבת היום. הילדים מבלים את סוף השבוע אצל הוריי. גילת יצאה זה עתה לבקר חברות מימי האוניברסיטה. אהיה לבד למשך שש שעות לפחות. זה הזמן להוציא לפועל את התוכנית שלי. התקשרתי לשכני יעקב, מהנדס בגמלאות.

"תוכל לעזור לי להתקין טוחן אשפה חדש היום?"

"ודאי."

"בוא אלי עכשיו. כבר קניתי טוחן חדש. הוא מוחבא במחסן."

"גילת לא רוצה שאתה תעשה את העבודה הזו, נכון?"

"למה אתה אומר את זה?"

"מכיוון שהיית צריך להסתיר את טוחן האשפה החדש במחסן. חוץ מזה, אני זוכר את הפעם שגרמת להצפה בחדר האמבטיה בקומה השנייה כשניסית להתקין ברז מים קרים חדש בכיור."

"זו היתה תאונה," אמרתי.

"שכחת להבריג את הידית לצינור."

"זו לא היתה אשמתי. הילדים הפריעו לי."

"כשפתחת את ברז המים הראשי הידית עפה מהצינור בכזו עוצמה, שהיא נתקעה בתקרה."

"אל תזכיר לי."

"בינתיים, היית במחסן ולא שמעת את המים ניתזים על הרצפה באמבטיה."

"השארתי את הסיפור הזה מאחוריי."

"הנזק מהמים היה גדול כל כך שהיה צריך להחליף את התקרה בחדר המגורים," אמר יעקב.

"אתה רוצה לעזור לי או לא?"

"אשמח לעזור לך. אני רק מסביר איך אני יודע שגילת לא רוצה שתעשה את העבודה. אני תיכף מגיע."

3

כעבור עשרים דקות דקות היינו במטבח שלי, פורסים בפנינו את כלי העבודה. יעקב הוציא את טוחן האשפה החדש מהאריזה.

"קודם כל אנחנו צריכים לפרק את טוחן האשפה הישן," אמר יעקב.

הוא התכופף והכניס את ראשו בארון שמתחת לכיור. כבר הוצאנו מהארון את כל בקבוקי הפלסטיק, חומרי הניקוי ושאר הפריטים המאוחסנים בו, כדי שלא יפריעו לנו. יעקב בילה מספר דקות כשראשו בתוך הארון, עושה דבר מה.

ואז אמר, "בוא תראה את זה."

הכנסתי את ראשי לתוך הארון.

"זה צינור הניקוז שפירקתי עכשיו מטוחן האשפה." הוא הצביע על צינור פלסטיק לבן שהיה תלוי ליד טוחן האשפה.

"טוחן האשפה מוצמד לתחתית הכיור כאן." הוא הצביע על משהו אחר. אביזר מתכתי כלשהו. "שים את המברג שלך על הסגר בדיוק במקום שבו הוא מתקפל כלפי מטה, ואז תן מכות בפטיש כדי לפתוח את הסגר ולשחרר את טוחן האשפה."

עשיתי כדבריו. שום דבר לא קרה.

"הסגר כנראה תקוע בגלל חלודה," אמרתי.

יעקב נעמד. קשה להתכופף ולהסתכל בארון.

"תן מכות חזקות יותר," אמר.

הלמתי בחוזקה במברג. הצלחה! הסגר השתחרר. טוחן האשפה נפל מטבעת התושבת.

"מה קרה?" שאל יעקב.

"לא תאמין איזה חור גדול עושה טוחן אשפה כבד כשהוא נופל על רצפת ארון מטבח," עניתי.

"כנראה שהייתי צריך להחזיק את הטוחן כשאתה שחררת את הסגר."

נעמדתי כדי שיעקב יוכל להסתכל פנימה לתוך הארון.

"זה חור רציני," הסכים. "זה נראה כאילו פגז קטן עבר דרך רצפת הארון. יש לי בבית חתיכה קטנה של דיקט שנוכל להשתמש בה כדי לתקן את החור. אל תעשה כלום עד שאחזור."

בזמן שיעקב הלך, התחלתי לדאוג מה תגיד גילת כשתחזור הביתה. הייתי זקוק לכוס מים כדי לנקות את הראש. פתחתי את ברז המים הקרים והנחתי למים לזרום אל תוך הכיור. לאחר מספר שניות המים היו נעימים וקרים. מילאתי כוס וישבתי לשולחן המטבח. יעקב חזר כעבור מספר דקות.

"לא הצלחתי למצוא את חתיכת הדיקט הזאת," אמר. "תצטרך לקנות דיקט בחנות. היי, למה יש שלולית גדולה על רצפת המטבח?"

"איזו שלולית?"

יעקב הבחין בכוס המים שבידי. "אתה לא הזרמת מים לתוך הכיור, נכון?"

שנינו הבטנו לתוך הארון שמתחת לכיור.

"תראה איזה בלגן," אמר יעקב.

"שכחתי שצינור הניקוז לא מחובר."

"יש כאן כמה ליטרים טובים של מים שזרמו מהכיור אל תוך החור. עכשיו זה דולף אל הרצפה."

"אני אנקה את זה."

"עשה זאת. אחר כך לך לחנות ותקנה חתיכת דיקט. אני הולך הביתה לנוח. תתקשר אלי כשתחזור מהחנות."

— 4 —

לקח לי יותר משעה לנקות את המטבח ולקנות חתיכה קטנה של דיקט כדי לכסות את החור בארון. כשחזרתי הביתה התקשרתי ליעקב.

"יעקב היה צריך ללכת לבן שלנו," אמרה לי אשתו. "הם היו צריכים מישהו שישגיח על התינוק כשהם עושים קניות."

"הוא היה אמור לעזור לי לתקן משהו," התבכיינתי.

"הנכדים קודמים לכל," אמרה לי. "בכל מקרה, חשבתי שאסור לך לתקן עוד דברים בבית."

"אני מעדיף לא לדבר על זה."

"אני זוכרת כשניסית לסתום את החור ההוא בגג מעל חדר השינה שלכם. החלקת מהגג ישר על השיחים."

"הגג היה הרבה יותר חלקלק משחשיפתי."

"לפחות היית מספיק חכם לקשור את עצמך לעץ בגינה לפני שטיפסת לגג. התנדנדת מהענף העליון די הרבה זמן עד שהשוטר הציל אותך, לא?"

"זה היה תרגול טוב עבורו," אמרתי. "אני באמת צריך לנתק עכשיו."

ניתקתי את הטלפון. עכשיו הייתה לי בעיה. יעקב איננו וגילת תגיע הביתה בעוד שלוש שעות.

"נראה שאצטרך לעשות את העבודה לבד," אמרתי לכלבה, שישבה והביטה בי כשהבט מוזר נסוך על פניה. בדקתי את הוראות ההתקנה. הן היו כתובות ביפנית. חיפוש מהיר גילה שאין חוברת הוראות נוספת. הבהלה החלה להזדחל במעלה בטני.

5

אחרי חמש דקות של חשיבה קדחתנית, הגעתי למסקנה שיש לי אפשרות אחת בלבד. בחוסר רצון הרמתי את הטלפון וחייגתי למספר אחר.

הטלפון צלצל צלצול אחד. חרדתי מפני השיחה. צלצול שני. הביטחון העצמי שלי היה בשפל הנמוך ביותר מאז כיתה ז'. צלצול שלישי נשמע באזני. ייתכן שאין אף אחד בבית. לרוע המזל, הצלצול נענה.

"הלו," אמר קול שייסר אותי במשך שנים.

"היי מירה. אני צריך קצת עזרה."

"רפי, נחמד מאוד לשמוע ממך," המתה אחותי מירה לתוך הטלפון. "מה הבעיה?"

בלעתי את גאוותי. "תוכלי להסביר לי בטלפון איך להתקין טוחן אשפה?"

"מתי החלטת להיות שרברב?"

"מאז ששרברבים התחילו לנהוג במכוניות יקרות יותר מהמכונית שלי."

"אתה זוכר את הפעם ההיא כשניסית לעזור לי לבנות את מדפי הספרים ההם?" שאלה מירה.

אחותי מבוגרת ממני בשנה. היא תמיד ידעה לבנות ולתקן דברים. כשהיינו בגיל העשרה ניסיתי לעזור לה כמה פעמים.

"אל תזכירי לי," אמרתי.

"הכית את הבוהן שלך בפטיש בלי הפסקה. היא התנפחה כל כך שאמא נאלצה להחזיק בשבילך את המסמרים."

"היא החזיקה רק מסמר אחד," אמרתי.

"נכון," צחקה מירה. "היא פרשה כשהכית גם את הבוהן שלה."

"אני הרבה יותר טוב עם הפטיש עכשיו," אמרתי. "יכולתי לעשות את העבודה בעצמי אבל הוראות ההתקנה כתובות ביפנית."

"שים את הטלפון על רמקול," נאנחה אחותי. "אני אדריך אותך לאורך כל העבודה."

6

גילת הגיעה הביתה ממש כשהחזרתי את כלי העבודה למקומם.

"יש לנו טוחן אשפה חדש," אמרתי לה.

היא ניגשה למטבח והביטה מתחת לכיור.

"זה באמת חדש," אמרה. "לאיזה שרברב קראת?"

"עשיתי את זה בעצמי."

"לא נכון," אמרה אשתי החביבה. "שום דבר במטבח לא שבור."

"תסתכלי בארון שוב," אמרתי לה. "מתחת לפח האשפה."

"איזה חור גדול!" קראה כעבור מספר שניות. "אפשר להכניס לתוכו דלעת."

"התכוונתי לתקן אותו עם חתיכת דיקט, אבל לא היה לי זמן."

"אם זה הנזק היחיד שגרמת זה מרשים," אמרה גילת. "אתה בטוח שלא קיבלת שום עזרה?"

"יעקב היה כאן בהתחלה אבל הוא היה צריך ללכת."

"זה מצריך חגיגה. בוא נפתח בקבוק יין."

היא נטלה בקבוק שרדונה מהמקרר ומזגה שתי כוסות. הרמנו לחיים.

"לחיי התיקונצ'יק שלי," אמרה גילת בעודנו לוגמים מהשרדונה.

נשארנו במטבח, שותים יין ומכינים את ארוחת הערב. גילת בישלה. ערכתי את השולחן והכנתי סלט. גילת סיפרה לי על חבריה מהאוניברסיטה.

"הלכנו לקניון ואכלנו סושי לארוחת הצוהריים," אמרה.

"זה נחמד."

גילת ואני היינו כבר בכוס היין השלישית כשהתיישבנו לארוחת הערב. הרגשתי מאוד נינוח.

"ובכן, דיברת היום עם מישהו מעניין מלבד יעקב?" שאלה גילת.

"התקשרתי לאחותי מירה," ציינתי.

"אהה," אמרה גילת כשהיא זוקפת אצבע לעברי. "מירה עזרה לך."

"לא הוגן," התלוננתי. "השקית אותי באלכוהול כדי לסחוט ממני את האמת."

"זו לא אשמתי שאתה לא יודע לשתות יין," היא גיחכה.

"ניצלת אותי באופן לא הוגן," התלוננתי.

"אתה לא צריך להתבייש," אמרה גילת. "זה היה חכם מצדך לבקש עזרה ממישהו."

"הוראות ההתקנה היו כתובות ביפנית."

"לא כל אחד נולד להיות מומחה לשימוש בכלי עבודה ודברים מכניים," אמרה גילת. "יש לך הרבה כשרונות אחרים שאין לאחותך."

"כמו מה?"

היא חשבה לרגע. "אתה באמת טוב בעיסוי הרגליים שלי."

"אני לא רוצה שאנשים ידעו על זה. הם עלולים לחשוב שאני מוזר."

"סודך שמור עמי. זה רק שאני הרבה יותר מאושרת עם בעל שעושה לי עיסוי ברגליים מאשר בעל שמתקן דברים. אתה לא צריך להרגיש חסר בטחון בגלל שאתה לא יודע לתקן דברים בבית. בוא נשכור אנשים שיעשו את העבודות האלה."

"זה נשמע כמו תוכנית טובה," אמרתי. "אין לך מושג כמה הייתי מתוח היום."

STORY 10

All Inclusive

אכלנו ארוחת ערב עם יוסי ומירה, זוג נחמד מצפת. פגשנו אותם בבר הבריכה מוקדם יותר אחר הצוהריים. היה כל כך כיף איתם שהזמנו אותם להצטרף אלינו לארוחת הערב.

"אז מה עשיתם שניכם היום?" שאל יוסי.

"רפי שתה עשר מרגריטות ונרדם על החוף," אמרה גילת. "עכשיו יש לו כוויות שמש."

מירה הביטה בי. "אתה נראה ורוד קצת," העירה.

"השמש כאן בקנקון ממש חזקה. צריך להיזהר," אמר יוסי. "תשתה כמה מרגריטות נוספות ותרגיש טוב יותר."

"המקום הזה ממש נהדר," אמרה מירה. "אנחנו יכולים לאכול ולשתות כאוות נפשנו, והכל כלול במחיר. וחוץ מזה, יש להם פעילויות מים נהדרות, קיאקים, שיט בסירות וצלילה בשנורקלים ממש כאן באתר הנופש."

"אני מקווה שאמא שלי מסתדרת עם הילדים," אמרה גילת.

"היא תסתדר," אמרתי.

"מה אם יקרה משהו?"

"שום דבר רע לא יקרה," אמרתי. "אבל יש לאמא שלך את מספר הטלפון של המלון. היא תמיד יכולה להתקשר ולבקש שימצאו אותנו."

"האימון האירובי במים היה מתיש," ציינה גילת. "רפי ניסה, אבל הוא לא הצליח לעמוד בקצב."

"זה היה לפני או אחרי האלכוהול?" שאל יוסי.

"לפני," אמרתי. "עומר מדריך את האימון האירובי. הוא כמו סמל מחלקה בתרגיל צבאי. אני לא מבין איך כל הנשים האלה בבריכה מסוגלות לנפנף בזרועותיהן ולהקפיץ את רגליהן במשך שעה שלמה."

"עומר מלמד גם שיעורי סלסה בשעה ארבע בכל יום," אמרה גילת. "הוא נתן לי שיעור כשרפי נחר על החוף."

"לא סיפרת לי שעומר נתן לך שיעור ריקוד," אמרתי. "אני לא בטוח שזה מוצא חן בעיניי."

"ובעיניי לא מוצאת חן הדרך שבה נעצת מבטים בשתי הבחורות הצעירות בחוטיני בזמן האימון האירובי במים," אמרה גילת.

עצמתי את עיניי ונזכרתי בשתי הנשים היפהפיות שגילת הזכירה. היה להן שיזוף מושלם, כמה קעקועים קלאסיים, וציפורניים צבועות בצבע בהיר. די היה במחשבה עליהן כדי להעלים את כאב כוויות השמש למשך

שניות אחדות.

"היו להן עגילי טבור ממש יפים," נאנחתי.

גילת חבטה בי. "היית צריך להסתכל ממש מקרוב כדי לדעת את זה," אמרה.

"אני יודעת לאיזה בחורות אתה מתכוון," קטעה אותה מירה. "יש לי נעליים יותר מבוגרות מהן."

"שמתם לב לשני הבחורים בכובעי בוקרים שעמדו בבריכה כל אחר הצוהריים?" שאל יוסי.

"הם היו באימון האירובי במים," אמרה גילת. "שתו בירה מכוסות תרמיות גדולות ביד אחת, ועשו תרגילים ביד השנייה. זה היה כל כך מצחיק."

"אתם מתכוונים ללכת לשמוע את הלהקה שתנגן כאן הלילה?" שאל יוסי.

"אני חושב שנישאר בחדר ונקרא. כוויות השמש הורגות אותי. תהנו שניכם," אמרתי.

<hr>

— 2 —

הגענו למסיבת הקוקטייל של המנהל בחמש בערב. יוסי ומירה כבר ישבו ליד הבר. הצטרפנו אליהם לכמה משקאות.

"אתה לא נראה טוב במיוחד," אמרתי ליוסי.

"הוא פגש כמה בחורים אירים בבר הקריוקי אתמול בלילה," אמרה מירה. "הם שתו שוטים ושרו שירים עד חצות."

"והיינו צריכים לקום ממש מוקדם היום לצלילה בשונית," הוסיף יוסי.

"האלכוהול, הצלילה וטלטולי הסירה במים עשו את יוסי ממש חולה," אמרה מירה.

"הם בטח עדיין מנקים את הסירה," אמר יוסי.

"רב החובל אסר עלינו לעלות על הסירה שלו ליתר השבוע," התלוננה מירה. "עכשיו לא נוכל לצלול יותר."

"לא יכולת להוציא את הראש מחוץ לסירה?" שאלתי.

"ניסיתי, אבל לא הספקתי."

"אז מה אתה שותה עכשיו?" שאלה גילת.

"רק בירה. אני מקווה שעוד אלכוהול ירגיע את הבטן שלי."

"מה אתם עשיתם היום?" שאלה מירה.

"רפי למד איך להכניס את המכונית השכורה להילוך אחורי," אמרה גילת בגאווה.

יוסי ומירה הביטו בי במבט מוזר מעט.

"נסענו לטולום לראות את העתיקות," אמרתי. "בדרך עצרנו במינימרקט והחניתי את המכונית כשהחזית בכיוון החנות. כשניסינו לנסוע משם לא הצלחתי להכניס להילוך אחורי."

"למה לא?"

"לא ידעתי איך. כתוב על ידית ההילוכים איפה נמצא ההילוך האחורי, אבל הידית לא עברה לשם."

"שילמנו לבחור צעיר ונחמד כדי שיראה לנו," אמרה גילת.

"עשרה פסו כדי שיראה לנו איך להפעיל את ההילוכים ושלושים פסו כדי שלא יצחק עליי," אמרתי.

"אף פעם לא נהגת במכונית עם מוט הילוכים ידני?" שאלה מירה.

"כן, אבל למכונית הזאת הייתה טבעת קטנה בחלק התחתון של מוט ההילוכים. הייתי צריך למשוך את הטבעת מעלה כדי להכניס להילוך אחורי," אמרתי.

"זה טריק חדש," אמר יוסי.

"אתם מתכוונים ללכת לארוחת הערב במזנון?" שאלה גילת את מירה.

"החלטנו להזמין שרות חדרים, למקרה שיוסי יחלה שוב. בטח נראה אתכם שוב מתישהו מחר."

3

"מה עבר לך בראש?" צעקה גילת.

"זו לא הייתה אשמתי," אמרתי.

"אתה אפילו לא יודע להשיט סירת צעצוע באמבטיה. למה שתיקח אחת מהסירות של אתר הנופש לתוך אוקיינוס גלי?"

"זה נראה כל כך קל. נראה שכל האורחים האחרים הצליחו להסתדר עם הסירות."

"אבל אתה הרסת איכשהו את הסירה."

"הצוות בדוכן ספורט המים היה מאוד נחמד. אף אחד לא צעק עליי. איך זה שאת כל כך כועסת?"

"כי אנחנו צריכים לשלם לאתר הנופש עבור מפרש חדש."

"הם לא יכולים פשוט לתפור את החור במפרש?"

"החור היה גדול יותר מהמכונית השכורה שלנו."

גילת הלכה לאורך החוף שעות אחדות קודם לכן כשנתקלה בסירה המסכנה שלי, מוטלת אופקית על המים. אני עמדתי על הרציף, צופה בעובדי ספורט המים משחררים את המפרש מהתורן. עמוד גדול חדר דרך המפרש. העמוד היה מקובע לסלעים על הרציף. שתי הבחורות עם הלכה על ציפורניהן, הקעקועים ובגדי הים הזעירים עמדו בסמוך אליי. גילת ניחשה נכון, שלקחתי את הגברות לשיט תענוגות שהסתיים באופן גרוע. היא כעסה עליי מאותו רגע ואילך.

היא חבטה בי בעורף. "למה אמרת לצוות ספורט המים שאתה שייט מומחה?"

"רציתי להרשים את הבחורות," הודיתי.

"ולמה הפלגת עם שתי בנות שהן צעירות מכדי להצביע בבחירות במקום עם אשתך?"

"לא היית מסכימה להפליג אלא אם היינו מבקשים מאחד מחברי הצוות לעזור לי להשיט את הסירה," רטנתי.

"ברור. אני מניחה שהיית זקוק לעזרה, לא?"

למרבה המזל ישבנו כבר הראשים בתוך אתר הנופש. בעוד שתי דקות עמד להתחיל שיעור. עמדנו ללמוד כיצד להכין מרטיני.

"בואי נשכח מהעבר," אמרתי לגילת. "אני כבר לא יכול לחכות ללמוד איך להכין מרטיני."

היא חבטה בעורפי פעם נוספת, למזל. אבל לא חזק כמו החבטה הקודמת, כך שפירשתי זאת שהיא כבר אינה כועסת כל כך. קיוויתי שאחרי שתשתה כמה כוסות מרטיני היא תשכח מכל העניין.

כל המקומות על הבר היו תפוסים. בשעה ארבע הופיע עומר ליד לוצ'יאנו, הברמן החביב עלינו.

"כולם מוכנים ללמוד על מרטיני?" צעק.

"כן!" צעקנו כולנו בחזרה.

הוא צעד לאורך הבר. כשראה את גילת, נטל את ידה ונישק את פרקי אצבעותיה.

"כל מדריכי האירובי כאלה ידידותיים?" שאלתי.

"זו הייתה נשיקה מתוך רחמים. הוא שמע על הגבר חסר התקווה שנישאתי לו."

"בואי נתמקד במרטיני," אמרתי.

למדנו איך להכין יותר סוגי מרטיני ממה שידעתי שיש. עומר לא נישק שוב את ידה של גילת. אני חושב שהוא הבחין במבט הזועף שנעצתי בו.

"בוא נחתור בקיאק לאתר הנופש הסמוך," אמר לי יוסי.

"אני נהנה לשבת כאן, מול הים ולשתות פינה קולדה," אמרתי. "למה שארצה להזיע?"

"שמעתי שבגדים הם בגדר רשות באתר הנופש ההוא. נוכל להסתכל על כל האנשים הערומים."

"מי אמר לך?"

"הבחורים עם כובעי הקאובוי," אמר יוסי.

"הם לא יצאו מהבריכה כבר ארבעה ימים. איך הם יודעים?"

"הנשים שלהם הן סוכנות נסיעות. הן יודעות הכל על האזור הזה."

"אי אפשר פשוט ללכת על החוף?"

"יש גדר גדולה שחוסמת את הדרך," אמר יוסי.

הנחתי את המשקה שלי. "קצת כושר לא יזיק לי."

עשר דקות מאוחר יותר יוסי ואני חתרנו בקיאקים שלנו במרץ לכיוון אתר הנופש הסמוך. כשהגענו לשם, ציפתה לנו אכזבה מרה.

"יש להם מסך גדול מול חוף הנודיסטים," אמר יוסי.

"לא הוגן. קרעתי את עצמי בחתירה נגד כיוון הרוח כדי להגיע לכאן, ועכשיו אני לא יכול לראות אף פיסת עור," הוספתי.

ישבנו במים, שלושים מטר מהחוף, מתנודדים מעלה ומטה בקיאקים שלנו.

"בוא נרד לחוף," הצעתי.

יוסי היסס.

"אני לא בטוח שאני רוצה להתפשט," אמר.

"לא כולם באתר עירומים. האנשים שלפני המסך לובשים בגדי ים."

יכולתי לראות שיוסי חוכך בדעתו.

"יש קיאק כפול על החוף ליד הכיסאות ההם," אמרתי. "נוכל לגרור את שלנו ממש לידו."

"הקיאק הזה הוא מאתר הנופש שלנו," אמר יוסי. "יש לו אותו סימן ואותו צבע."

"אתה רואה, אנחנו לא היחידים שחשבו על הרעיון הזה. יהיה בסדר. בוא נעשה את זה."

לקח ליוסי חמש דקות נוספות לאזור אומץ לעגון את הקיאק שלו.

"חבל שלא שתיתי עוד כמה משקאות," אמר תוך שגררנו את הקיאקים שלנו אל מחוץ למים.

"אז, נוריד את בגדי הים או שנשאיר אותם?" שאלתי.

לאחר דיון קצר החלטנו להישאר בבגדי הים שלנו. התהלכנו בנחת אל מאחורי המסך שהוצב על החוף. היו שם עשרה או חמישה עשר קשישים וקשישות, שרועים על כיסאות נוח. אחדים מהם לבשו בגדי ים, אולם רובם היו עירומים לחלוטין.

"תראה את כל הקמטים על האנשים האלה," לחש יוסי.

אנשים קשישים לא נראים סקסיים במיוחד בעירום. הבטחתי לעצמי ללבוש הרבה בגדים כשאגיע לגיל שבעים.

"בוא ננסה את הג'קוזי," אמרתי.

הלכנו אל עבר ג'קוזי גדול שניצב סמוך לחוף. לפחות עשרים אנשים כבר היו בג'קוזי, מפטפטים ונחים. כולם נראו נטולי קמטים למדי. רובם היו עירומים. הבחנתי בנשים אחדות בעלות מראה יוצא דופן.

"זה עומד להיות כל כך טוב," אמרתי תוך שאנחנו נכנסים כבדרך אגב למים ומתיישבים.

כשהתחלתי לבחון את הרוחצים האחרים, החל יוסי לגעת בכתפי.

"מה?" אמרתי, מתבונן בו.

מבטו היה נעוץ בשתי נשים חשופות חזה שישבו בשמש, כשלושה מטרים מהג׳קוזי. עקבתי אחר מבטו ונשימתי נעתקה. גילת ומירה ישבו שם, אוחזות בקוקטייל מאי טאי ולוטשות בנו מבט בחזרה.

5

"אתה כזה סוטה," אמרה לי גילת כשהשמטוס המריא משדה התעופה של קנקון.

"רק רגע, גם את היית שם. בלי חלק עליון, אם יורשה לי להוסיף."

"הלכתי לשם כדי להשתזף. אתה סתם רצית לראות בחורות עירומות."

"אתמול חשבת שזה די מצחיק."

היא צחקקה ונשקה ללחיי. "אני סתם מקניטה אותך."

"לא היה אכפת לך שיוסי יראה את החזה שלך?" שאלתי.

"לא ממש. איבדתי את הביישנות כשהנקתי את הילדים."

"מירה נראתה נחמד מאוד בלי חלק עליון," אמרתי.

גילת צחקה וחבטה בזרועי. אשתי היכתה אותי במהלך השבוע הזה יותר מאשר במהלך כל שנות נישואינו. נשענתי לאחור בכסאי והבטתי מהחלון. חצי האי יוקטן החל להיעלם מעיניי כשהשמטוס פנה לכיוון מפרץ מקסיקו.

"זו הייתה חופשה מוצלחת, למרות כל הדברים המטורפים שקרו," אמרתי.

STORY 11

Murder Mystery in L.A.

"זה רעיון גרוע," אני צועק אל תוך אוזנו של נתי.

"לשתות בבר?" הוא שואל.

"לא אכפת לי לשתות בבר," אני אומר לו. "רק לא הבר הזה."

אודי חוזר עם שתי בירות וכוס יין עבורי.

"יש הרבה אנשים עם פרוסה גדולה של גבינה מפלסטיק על הראש," הוא צועק.

להקה של מתבגרים על הבמה מקימה רעש חזק ממה שעור התוף שלי יכול לסבול. אני חש מסוחרר מעט בגלל הצלילים. קשה לשמוע מישהו מדבר.

"זו הסיבה שאני לא רוצה לשתות בבר הזה," אני משיב בצעקה. "בואו נמצא מקום ניטרלי."

עשרים דקות מאוחר יותר אנחנו הולכים באוויר הלילה החם של קליפורניה. אנחנו מנסים למצוא בר שאיננו עמוס באנשים ממדינת ויסקונסין.

"למה הם תמיד חובשים את משולשי גבינת הפלסטיק המזויפים האלה על הראש לפני כל משחק פוטבול חשוב?" אני שואל.

"מה?" אומרים נתי ואודי. אוזנינו עדיין מצלצלות מהרעש החזק שהקימה הלהקה.

"אמרתי שאני זקן מכדי להאזין לרוקנ'רול גרוע," אני צועק אליהם.

שלושתינו נמצאים בחופשה בת שבוע בלוס אנג'לס עם הנשים. הילדים בבית עם סבא וסבתא. הערב הנשים היו עייפות מדי מכדי לצאת אחרי ארוחת הערב. נתי, אודי ואני החלטנו לצאת ולבלות קצת כברים. לא ידענו שנבחרת הפוטבול של אוניברסיטת ויסקונסין משחקת נגד אוניברסיטת קליפורניה מחר. חצי ממדינת ויסקונסין פלש ללוס אנג'לס לקראת המשחק. בכל מקום שאליו אנו מסבים את מבטנו אנחנו רואים אנשים בעלי עור לבנבן בגוון חלבי ופרוסת גבינת פלסטיק לראשם.

"אין להם הרבה שמש בויסקונסין, נכון?" שואל אודי.

"אני חושב שהעור שלהם בהיר כל כך בגלל שהמתיישבים הראשונים היו ויקינגים," אומר נתי. "תראו את הגודל של האנשים האלה."

אכן, נראה שגובהו ומשקלו הממוצעים של תושב ויסקונסין הם כפולים מגובהו ומשקלו של אדם רגיל מלוס אנג'לס.

"הבר האחרון היה מטורף," אומר אודי. "הייתי בשרותי הגברים ושני אוהדי ויסקונסין החזיקו בחור עם

315

חולצה של אוניברסיטת קליפורניה. הם טבלו את ראשו באסלה שוב ושוב ושרו."

"אוהדי ספורט הם מטורפים," אני אומר להם. "הנה בר שנראה שקט למדי."

אנחנו פוסעים אל תוך מקום שאורותיו מעומעמים. חמישה אנשים יושבים על הבר, מדברים בקולות שקטים. שאר המקום ריק.

אנחנו מתיישבים בבר ומזמינים סיבוב משקאות. "המקום הזה הרבה פחות מלחיץ," אני אומר.

אנחנו דנים בפעיליויות הצפויות למחר. הנשים רוצות ללכת למוזיאון לוס אנג'לס לאומנות. אנחנו רוצים לראות את אתר הזפת הטבעית בלה-בריאה.

אני מבחין בשלולית על הרצפה סמוך למקום שבו אנחנו יושבים.

"יש לכם משהו על הרצפה," אני אומר לברמן.

"אל תדאג, זה יבש," הוא אומר.

"מה זה?" אני שואל.

"דם. איזה בחור נורה כאן לפני שעה. הוא ישב על הכיסא שלך."

"זה מסביר למה המקום שקט כל כך," אומר נתי.

"מה הסיכוי שיהיה כאן קרב יריות נוסף הלילה?" שואל אודי.

"ככל הנראה אפס. כדאי לנו להישאר," אני אומר.

מספר דקות לאחר מכן מישהו טופח קלות בכתפי. אני מביט מסביב ורואה אישה יפהפייה. היא מגישה לי חבילה.

"הנה הכסף ופרטים על המטרה שלך," היא אומרת, והולכת לדרכה.

אני מופתע ממראה האישה הנהדר הזה מכדי להגיב עד שהיא כמעט יוצאת.

"הי," אני צועק, "על מה את מדברת?"

אני פותח את המעטפה. היא מלאה בשטרות של מאה דולר.

"תראו את זה, חבר'ה. אנחנו יכולים לשתות בחינם כל הלילה."

אנחנו מוציאים את הכסף. בנוסף, יש שם תצלומים של אדם בעל מראה מרושע שצלקת מעטרת את לחיו, ותדפיס מחשב הכולל את פרטיו האישיים של הבחור.

"מה זה?" שואל נתי.

ואז, המשטרה פורצת דרך הדלת.

2

"הייתי בטוח למדי שאתם לא רוצחים שכירים כשהתחלתם לבכות," אומר לנו הבלש.

"אז למה לקח ארבע שעות וחמשת אלפים דולר שכר טרחת עורך דין עד ששחררת אותנו?" שואל נתי.

אנחנו אוספים את חפצינו האישיים, חגורות ושרוכי נעליים בדלפק הקבלה במתקן משטרה שמור כלשהו סמוך להוליווד.

"התובע המחוזי היה במסיבה. הוא לא הסכים לחתום על מסמכי השחרור לפני שהמסיבה נגמרה."

"מה הכתובת שלו?" אני שואל. "אני רוצה לשלוח לו מתנה לחג המולד."

"אל תתחכם," אומר השוטר בדלפק הקבלה. "יכולנו להשאיר אתכם כאן כל הלילה."

"פשוט נמאס לנו לשמוע אתכם צורחים שהעצורים האחרים מפחידים אתכם," אומר הבלש.

"הכנסתם אותנו לתא מעצר עם שני סוחרי סמים, אופנוען מטורף ובחור שזה עתה קטע אוזן של מישהי בנשיכה," אומר אודי.

"אין לנו מגורים מיוחדים לחנונים מישראל," אומר השוטר בדלפק. "לפחות לא זרקו אתכם לתא עם המטורפים האלה עם הגבינה על הראש."

"כשאתה מציג את זה כך, היה לנו מזל," אני אומר לשוטרים.

"מה עם הכסף?" אני שואל.

"הוא לא שלכם. הוא נועד לרוצח השכיר האמיתי."

"הוא בטח היה הבחור שנורה לפני שהגענו לבר," אומר אודי.

"אם הסוכנים החשאיים שלכם שמו מארב על הבר, איך זה שלא ידעתם על היריות שהיו שם קודם?" שואל נתי.

"לא היה לנו מארב על הבר. עקבנו אחרי האישה. ואף אחד לא דיווח על היריות קודם. תשאלנו את הברמן במשך שעתיים עד שהודה שפשוט השליך את הבחור מכל האשפה."

"איזה מין אנשים גרים בעיר הזאת?" אני שואל. "מישהו נורה ממש לנגד עיניהם והם ממשיכים לשתות בזמן שהברמן משליך את הגופה למכל האשפה ושוטף את הרצפה."

"הם היו מן הסתם שחקנים מובטלים," אומר הבלש.

"ומה לגבי האישה שעקבתם אחריה?"

"איבדנו אותה כשהמשטרה נכנסה לבר."

"נפלא," אני אומר.

אנחנו עוזבים את תחנת המשטרה ומנסים להשיג מונית. השעה ארבע וחצי בבוקר, כך שלא היה לנו הרבה מזל. בעוד אנחנו ממתינים ברחוב, אני חש בנקישה נוספת בכתפי. שוב האישה היפהפייה.

הפעם יש לי מספיק תושייה לתפוס אותה. היא תוקעת אקדח קטן בפניי ואני משחרר את אחיזתי.

"סם הגדול אומר שאתם צריכים להחזיר את הכסף עד הצוהריים, או שתהיו בצרה צרורה," היא אומרת שלושתנו לוטשים בה מבט. היא נסוגה אל תוך מכונית שהמתינה לה והפליגה משם.

"אנחנו באמת בצרות עכשיו," אומר אודי.

שעתיים מאוחר יותר אנחנו עוזבים את תחנת המשטרה בפעם השנייה.

"אני לא מאמין שהם לא מאמינים לנו," אני אומר.

"אני לא מאמין שבחורה איימה עלינו באקדח ממש בחזית התחנה שלהם ואף אחד לא ראה," אומר אודי.

"זה מזכיר לי סרט רע במיוחד," אומר נתי.

"אתם חושבים שסם הגדול הזה יעשה לנו צרות?" שואל אודי.

"פשוט נסביר שהבחורה נתנה את הכסף לאנשים הלא נכונים. זו אשמתה," אני אומר.

המזל היחידי שלנו הוא שבשעה שש וחצי בבוקר יש שוב מוניות בכבישים. בזמן שנהג ישנוני אחד מסיע אותנו בחזרה למלון שלנו, אנחנו מסכימים שלא לספר לנשים דבר. אני חומק אל חדר המלון ממש כשגילת מתעוררת משנת לילה מרעננת.

"נהנית, רפי?" היא שואלת.

"אין לך מושג כמה."

3

אני עייף מכדי להתווכח עם גילת על האתרים שנראה, וזו הסיבה שאני מוצא את עצמי עומד לצידה שעות אחדות מאוחר יותר, מביט בציורים בני שלוש מאות שנה. אודי, נתי והנשים שלהם נמצאים איתנו.

"מוזיאון האמנות הזה הרבה יותר נחמד מבורות הזפת, לא?" גילת שואלת אותי.

אני בקושי ממלמל תשובה. מספיק קשה לי לשמור על עיניי פקוחות, שלא לדבר על להוציא מילה. אני מבחין כי אודי ונתי חווים בעיות דומות.

הנשים מחליטות שאנחנו צריכים לאכול את ארוחת הצוהריים במוזיאון.

"תראו, יש להם תפריט צמחוני במזנון," אומרת אשתו של נתי.

"אתם כל כך שקטים היום," אומרת אשתו של אודי בעודנו אוכלים את בורגר הטופו שלנו. "מה עשיתם בחוץ כל כך מאוחר, בכל אופן?"

"עשינו חיים," אני ממלמל.

"זו כוס הקפה השלישית שלך," אשתו של נתי אומרת לו. "לא תצליח לישון הלילה."

"אני רק מנסה לצלוח את היום," הוא אומר.

אחרי ארוחת הצוהריים, אנחנו אומרים לנשים שעלינו לגשת לשירותים.

"ניפגש בתערוכת כלי החרס מהמזרח התיכון," אומרת גילת.

אנחנו מתיזים מים על פנינו בניסיון להישאר ערים.

לפני שאנו פונים לעזוב, נכנסים שני גברים בעלי חזות מרושעת וחוסמים את דרכנו.

"איפה הכסף?" אומר הגבוה ביניהם.

"המשטרה לקחה אותו כראיה," אני מייבב. "הם לא היו מוכנים להחזיר לנו אותו."

"סם הגדול לא יאהב את זה," הוא אומר.

"הבחור שהיה אמור לקבל את הכסף נורה שעה לפני שהגענו לבר," אומר נתי. "האישה הזאת טעתה ונתנה את הכסף של סם הגדול לאנשים הלא נכונים."

"למה שרוצח שכיר יאפשר למישהו לירות בו כשהוא מחכה לכסף שלו?" מגחך הנמוך מבין השניים.

"ככל הנראה דברים כאלה קורים בלוס אנג'לס כל הזמן," עונה אודי.

"יש לכם מזל שהיא נתנה את הכסף לבחור הלא נכון," אני אומר להם. "המשטרה עקבה אחריה. אם היו תופסים את הרוצח השכיר האמיתי הוא היה מספר להם על סם הגדול. מצד שני, אנחנו לא יודעים כלום על סם הגדול, כך שהכל הסתדר על הצד הטוב ביותר בשבילו."

"כדאי שאתקשר לסם הגדול," אומר הבחור הגבוה. "אתם תישארו כאן."

הוא יוצא להתקשר, בעוד שותפו נשאר איתנו בשירותים. אנחנו מנצלים את ההזדמנות לשבת בשלושה תאים נפרדים ולנוח מעט.

לאחר חמש דקות חוזר הבחור הגבוה.

"אתם בואו איתנו. סם הגדול רוצה לראות אתכם."

אנחנו מהססים, אבל שני הגברים מראים לנו את האקדחים שבנרתיקי הכתף שלהם, כך שאנחנו יוצאים איתם מחדר השירותים.

ארבעה קשישים ממתינים בתור להיכנס לשירותים.

"הגיע הזמן שתסיימו לנקות את המקום," אומר אחד מהם. "אוטובוס הסיור שלנו עומד לצאת ואנחנו נאלצים לחכות עשר דקות לשירותים. זה לא בסדר."

"מי אמר שאנחנו מנקים?" אני שואל.

"הבחור הגבוה," עונה קשיש אחר.

"הוא שיקר לך," צועק נתי.

לפתע תוקפים ארבעת הקשישים בעלי השלפוחיות המלאות את אנשיו של סם הגדול.

"אין לי מושג באיזה סיור הם משתתפים, אבל הם כולם יודעים ג'ודו," אומר נתי.

"תזכיר לי להיות נחמד לקשישים מעכשיו והלאה," אומר לי אודי תוך שאנו צופים בבחור בהליכון תופס את הנמוך בין שני אנשיו של סם הגדול בתפיסת חנק.

בתוך שתי דקות, הרעים מחוסרי הכרה וכבולים באזיקים.

היום הנשים שלנו מבקרות בפסדינה. אודי, נתי ואני ישנים עד השעה אחת עשרה בערך וסועדים ארוחת צוהריים עם מכרנו בלש המשטרה.

"לא ידענו שעקבתם אחרינו אתמול," אומר נתי.

"גם אנשיו של סם הגדול לא ידעו. לכן היה קל כל כך לעצור אותם מחוץ לחדר השירותים."

"היה לאנשיכם מסווה מצוין," אני אומר.

"למעשה, פשוט נעזרנו בכמה חבר'ה שקרובים לפרישה," הוא אומר.

"אז מה עם סם הגדול?" מתעניין אודי.

"התובע המחוזי עשה עסקה עם אחד מאנשיו של סם. הוא אמר לנו איפה מתחבא סם הגדול והודה שסם הוציא חוזה על אחד ממתחריו. עצרנו את סם הבוקר, עם האישה שנתנה לכם את הכסף."

"איזו הקלה," אני אומר. "עכשיו נוכל לסיים את החופשה שלנו בלי שהנשים שלנו יצפו במישהו חונק אותנו או דורס אותנו בבולדוזר."

"רק תבטיחו שבחופשה הבאה שלכם תצאו למקום אחר," אומר הבלש.

"אולי ננסה את ויסקונסין," אומר נתי. "האנשים שם נראים נורמלים למדי."

STORY 12

Mommy and Me

"אתה חייב לעצור אותה, מר לוי."

"מה בדיוק אמא שלי עושה?"

"עדנה מספרת לכולם בכפר הגמלאים שהיא נקשרה לשולחן למשך שעתיים ולא הורשתה ללכת לשירותים."

נשמע כאילו ד"ר נחמה אנגל, רופאת השיניים שלי, כרסמה תוך דיבור בטלפון. אולי חרקה בשיניה. התפתיתי לומר לה שפעולות כאלה אינן בריאות לשיניים, אבל היא מן הסתם כבר ידעה זאת.

במקום זאת אמרתי, "היא לא נקשרה לשולחן. היא ישבה בכיסא רופא השיניים שלך. אפשרה לה לקום אחרי שעה כדי לגשת לשירותים."

"אני יודעת. אבל עדנה מספרת לשכניה שעיניתי אותה. ארבעה אנשים מכפר הגמלאים כבר התקשרו לבטל את התור שלהם. גברת אחת אמרה ששמעה שאין לי אפילו רישיון."

ד"ר אנגל נשמעה נואשת. מחצית מלקוחותיה התגוררו בקהילה שבה חיה אמי. אם יאמינו לדברים שמספרת אמי, ד"ר אנגל תפסיד חלק ניכר מעבודתה.

עדנה לוי, אמי, היא בת שמונים ושמונה. היא איננה סובלת ממחלות כלשהן. היא הולכת ללא מקל. מוחה עדיין חד. יש לה בעיות רפואיות קלות אחדות, אולם היא במצב גופני מעולה לגילה.

לרוע המזל, אמא איננה מאושרת בחייה. היא מאמינה שאם היא איננה מאושרת, אף אחד לא צריך להיות מאושר. לכן, היא יוצאת מגדרה כדי לאמלל את חייהם של כל הסובבים אותה. עכשיו היה זה תורה של ד"ר אנגל לחוש בחמת זעמה של עדנה.

"אני אתקשר לאמא מיד," אמרתי.

"כבר ניסיתי. הטלפון שלה תפוס. תוכל לנסוע לשם ולדבר איתה? בבקשה."

סגרתי את הטלפון הסלולרי שלי ונכנסתי למכוניתי. בעודי נוסע את שלושת הקילומטרים אל דירתה של אמי, יכולתי לחוש באשמה ההולכת וממלאת אותי. בעייתה הגדולה של ד"ר אנגל הייתה באשמתי. שבועות אחדים קודם לכן החלו חלו שיניה של אמי לכאוב. היא לא ביקרה אצל רופא השיניים כבר שנים.

"למה להוציא כסף על השיניים שלי, אני אמות בתוך כמה שנים," נהגה לומר לי.

התעקשתי שתלך לראות את רופאת השיניים שלי, ד"ר אנגל.

"אני אלך, אבל בלי צילומי רנטגן," אמרה אמא.

"ד"ר אנגל צריכה לבצע צילומי רנטגן כדי שתוכל לראות אם יש בעיות נסתרות," אמרתי לה.

"כמה יעלו צילומי הרנטגן?" שאלה.

"זה לא משנה. את זקוקה להם."

"אני לא יכולה להרשות לעצמי צילומי רנטגן."

"יש לך הרבה כסף."

"אתה לא יודע כמה כסף יש לי," אמרה אמא.

"אני יודע הכל על אודות הכספים שלך. אני משלם את החשבונות שלך."

אמא ניסתה טיעון חדש.

"אני צריכה את הכסף למקרה שאצטרך לעבור למוסד סיעודי."

"את גם צריכה להיות מסוגלת ללעוס את האוכל שלך ללא כאבים," אמרתי לה.

לבסוף גררתי את אמא לד"ר אנגל. היא נזקקה לטיפול שורש ולכתר באחת משיניה הקדמיות. בשלוש שיניים אחרות היו חורים שהיה צורך לסתום.

לפני יומיים עשתה ד"ר אנגל את טיפול השורש והתאימה לאמא כתר זמני על השן הקדמית. התהליך כולו ארך כולו שעתיים. אמא הייתה צריכה לחזור לשתי פגישות נוספות עד שיורכב הכתר הקבוע.

עכשיו אמא מספרת לאנשים שד"ר אנגל מענה את מטופליה. אם לא הייתי גורר את אמא לרופאת השיניים שלי, הבעיה הזו לא הייתה מתעוררת. כן, חשתי אשמה רבה.

2

כשנכנסתי לדירתה של אמא, היא דיברה בטלפון.

"אני אומרת לך, היא קשרה אותי לשולחן למשך שעתיים. תארי לך מה זה עשה לגב שלי. אני עדיין לא יכולה להזיז את רגליי כמו שצריך," סיפרה אמא למישהי.

"נתקי את הטלפון, אמא," צעקתי.

היא קפצה מעט למשמע קולי.

"הבן שלי בדיוק הגיע לבקר," אמרה לתוך השפופרת. "תודה שהתקשרת."

"זו הייתה אחת משכנותיי," אמרה תוך שהיא מניחה את שפופרת הטלפון על כנה. "היא רצתה לדעת הכל על הכתר שלי."

"למה את מספרת לאנשים שרופאת השיניים הכריחה אותך לשכב על שולחן?"

"זה מה שהיא עשתה. הגב שלי הורג אותי."

"ישבת בכיסא של רופא שיניים. היא רק היטתה אותו לאחור."

"איך אתה יודע?" שאלה אמא, כעוסה.

״הייתי שם. זוכרת שהסעתי אותך למרפאת השיניים ונשארתי שם במהלך הביקור כולו?״

היא העווותה את פניה בניסיון להיזכר. אמא נמוכה מאוד. כשהיא עושה העוויה כזו בפניה, היא נראית כאילו היא אחותי הגדולה של יודה. שיערה המתולתל והלבן גזור בתספורת קצרה. כל הנשים בנות השמונים שראיתי מעודי הן בעלות שיער קצר ומתולתל. אולי זה מין חוק כזה.

אמא גם מרכיבה משקפיים גדולים, שצבעם הופך סגול באור השמש. הם מסתירים את רוב תווי פניה. כאשר היא בחוץ, כל שניתן לראות הוא השיער הלבן המתולתל ופנים סגולות. זה מעניין למדי.

צפיתי בה מהרהרת במשך שניות אחדות. לבסוף אמרה, ״לא היית שם.״

״כן הייתי. לא היה שולחן עיניים. וד״ר אנגל אפשרה לך ללכת לשירותים אחרי שעה.״

״לא נכון. היא השאירה אותי קשורה לדבר הזה במשך שעתיים.״

״אני עזרתי לך ללכת לשירותים.״

״היא הניחה פיסת בטון גדולה על החזה שלי.״

״זה היה סינר עופרת. כדי להגן עלייך מפני קרני הרנטגן.״

פניה של אמא התכרכמו. היא שונאת שחולקים עליה.

״את חייבת להפסיק לספר לאנשים שד״ר אנגל עינתה אותך,״ המשכתי. ״הם מבטלים את התורים שלהם.״

״סיפרתי רק לשלושה או ארבעה אנשים.״

״חדשות רעות מתפשטות מהר בכפר הגמלאים שלך. עד מחר אפילו ראש העיר ישמע את הסיפור שלך אם לא תתקשרי לכולם שוב ותאמרי להם שהגזמת.״

אמא שינתה את הנושא. ״כדאי מאוד שרופאת השיניים לא תשלח לי חשבון מנופח.״

״היא כבר נתנה לך תדפיס של עלות הטיפול כולו.״

״למה היא מכריחה אותי לחזור בשבוע הבא? כבר יש לי שן חדשה.״

״זו שן זמנית. תצטרכי לחזור עוד כמה פעמים עד שיורכב הכתר הקבוע. היא אמרה לך את זה.״

״לא נכון. היא סתם רוצה עוד כסף!״

״אני הייתי שם כשהיא אמרה לך.״

״בפעם הבאה, אני רוצה שאודליה תיקח אותי.״

״לא. אני הייתי זה ששכנע אותך ללכת לרופא השיניים. אני אקח אותך לשם.״

״תמיד היית בן רע,״ אמרה לי. זה היה הביטוי החביב עליה.

נשארתי בדירתה של אמא כשעה כשעוד היא מתקשרת לכל מכריה ומספרת להם שהגזימה בסיפורה על אודות רופאת השיניים.

אתם בוודאי תוהים בעניין אודליה. האם היא קרובת משפחה? עובדת סוציאלית? לא. אודליה היא פצצת אנרגיה בת שבעים וחמש.

היא מבלה את מרבית זמנה בהתרוצצות ברחבי העיר בשליחויות עבור האנשים הקשישים יותר המתגוררים בכפר הגמלאים שבו מתגוררת אמי. היא תעשה כל מה שיעלה על דעתך. היא מסיעה את הקשישים לחנויות, מרפאות ובתי חולים. היא קונה מצרכי מזון עבור אנשים שאינם יכולים לערוך קניות בעצמם. ואז היא מקשיבה לתלונותיהם על כך שהבזיאה קופסת שימורי אפונה בגודל הלא נכון ועל כך שהבננות יקרות מדי. לעתים אודליה אף לוקחת את בגדיהם של אנשים חולים לביתה ומכבסת אותם.

אודליה איננה מקבלת הרבה תודות על כל עבודתה הברוכה. במיוחד מאנשים כמו אמי, שנראה כי הם סבורים שהמחוות הנדיבות הללו מגיעות להם. רק בשבוע שעבר שוחחתי על כך עם אמא.

"אודליה באה לבקר הבוקר. היא הרסה לי את כל היום."

"איך היא עשתה זאת?"

"היא ישבה שם שעה ודיברה איתי," אמרה אמא.

"זה טוב שהייתה לך אורחת. כמעט אף אחד לא מגיע לבקר בדירה שלך."

"היא אף פעם לא מקשיבה לי."

"למה את אומרת זאת?"

"הזכרתי את התקף הלב שהיה לי ביום ראשון האחרון, והיא אמרה שזה שום דבר. איך היא יודעת?"

"היא אחות מוסמכת, אמא."

"אז מה? היא לא רופאה."

"אפילו אני יודע שלא היה לך התקף לב. את זוכרת שהתקשרת אליי ביום ראשון אחר הצהריים וסיפרת לי על התסמינים שלך?"

"כן."

"עצירות וכאב בטן אינם תסמינים של התקף לב."

"זה היה יותר מזה. היו לי גם כאבים בחזה."

"את ממציאה את זה. שאלתי אותך על כאבים בחזה כשהתקשרת אליי ואמרת שהחזה שלך בסדר."

"ובכן, היא בכל זאת לא צריכה להגיד לי שהבריאות שלי טובה. היא לא יודעת על כל הכאבים והמכאובים שלי."

"היא כן יודעת," אמרתי. "היא לוקחת אותך לרופא ויושבת בחדר הבדיקה איתך."

"היא מדברת עם הרופא כל כך הרבה, שהוא גובה עוד כסף עבור הביקור. אני תמיד אומרת לה לא להגיד לו כלום, אבל היא לא מקשיבה."

"זה בגלל שכשאת הולכת לרופא, את שוכחת לספר לו על כל הבעיות הרפואיות שלך, אז אודליה צריכה

לספר לו."

"אם כך, היא צריכה לשלם עבור הזמן הנוסף שהוא גובה ממני."

"אמא, אודליה היא האדם הנחמד ביותר בעולם. אל תבקשי ממנה לשלם חלק ממחיר ביקור הרופא שלך. היא עלולה להיפגע."

"אולי אבקש ממנה להתחיל לכבס עבורי," המשיכה.

אמא באמת כעסה על כך שאודליה מעולם לא הציעה לכבס עבורה. היא הרגישה שנוהגים בה בזלזול.

"היא מכבסת רק עבור אנשים שחולים באמת. את לא באמת חולה. את יכולה לדחוף את העגלה שלך לחדר הכביסה ולכבס בעצמך," אמרתי.

"אני למעשה נכה. אין לך מושג כמה הברכיים שלי כואבות."

"הברכיים שלך בסדר גמור," אמרתי לה.

"תמיד היית בן רע!" אמרה אמא.

שוב. הביטוי החביב עליה.

4

לאחר ששה שבועות ...

ערב שבת הוא זמן האחווה הגברית. זה מה שעשיתי. שיחקתי פוקר עם שכניי אשר, בני וגבי. בילינו ביחד נינוחים, שותים בירה ומשוחחים.

החיים היו לחוצים למדי עבורי ועבור אמי. נדרשו ארבע פגישות נוספות אצל רופאת השיניים במהלך ארבעה שבועות עד שהותקן לה כתר קבוע ובוצעו שלוש סתימות חדשות בשלוש שיניים אחרות. עשרים ושמונה ימים של האזנה לתלונותיה על עבודתה הגרועה של רופאת השיניים ועל מה שהכל צפוי לעלות. לפחות היא לא התקשרה לאנשים בעיר והאשימה את ד"ר אנגל בעריכת טקסי וודו.

"מה שלום אמך?" שאל חברי גבי.

"היא ממשיכה להגיד לי שהיא רוצה לגור אצלי בבית," אמרתי.

"שמישהו יחלק את הקלפים, בבקשה," אמר בני. "אני מרגיש בר מזל."

"אתה באמת שוקל לאפשר לאמא שלך לגור אתך בבית?" שאל גבי.

הנדתי בראשי מצד לצד. "אין סיכוי. הנישואים שלי לא יעמדו בכך. חוץ מזה, היא תשגע אותי. אני אומר לה את זה בכל פעם שהיא מעלה את הנושא."

"לא ידעתי שאמך קשה כל כך," אמר גבי.

"זה בגלל שאתה חדש בעיר," אמר אשר.

"יש הרבה אנשים שיש להם סיפורי עדנה," אמר גבי. "היא באמת צרה."

"אתה זוכר את המסיבה ההיא אצל קובי בקיץ שעבר?" צחק בני. "עדנה התחילה לצעוק עלינו שאכלנו כל כך הרבה."

"היא רצתה לקחת את השאריות הביתה," הוסיף אשר. "היא אילצה את אשתי להחזיר סלט תפוחי אדמה בחזרה לקערה."

"אתה ודאי חש אשמה כשאתה אומר לה שהיא לא יכולה לבוא לגור איתך," אמר גבי וגרף את הקופה.

"אני חש אשמה כבר שנים. שום דבר שאני עושה אינו מספיק טוב עבורה. אם אני מתקשר חמש פעמים בשבוע, היא מתלוננת שאשתי גילת לא מתקשרת. אם אני מבקר פעמיים בשבוע, היא מספרת לי שילדיהם של השכנים מבקרים בכל יום."

"איך היא יודעת מה עושים ילדיהם של אנשים אחרים?" שאל בני.

"כולם בכפר הגמלאים משקרים זה לזה על כמה יפה ילדיהם מטפלים בהם. הם גם מתרברבים בנכדיהם הגאונים," אמרתי. "זו תחרות - למי יש את הקרובים הטובים ביותר."

"די עם הדיבורים," קטע אותי גבי. "חלק את הקלפים."

חילקתי סיבוב נוסף. הסתכלתי בקלפים שלי. שני מלכים. אולי אזכה בקופה פעם אחת. בעצם זכיתי ביד הזאת בכך ששלפתי מלך שלישי. ועדיין, בסוף הערב, חזרתי הביתה עם פחות כסף בארנקי. אני אף פעם לא מנצח בפוקר.

כעבור שבועיים ...

"אתה יודע שעדנה גזרה את הפרחים במגרש החנייה."

הקשבתי למגי, מנהלת כפר הגמלאים, מתלוננת על אמי.

"איך היא יכלה לעשות זאת?" שאלתי. "אמא לא יכולה להתכופף מבלי ליפול על הפנים. בכל אופן, היא אומרת שלא הייתה שם."

"היא הסתדרה איכשהו. יש שמונה עדים. הם בדיוק יצאו ממשחק הבינגו השבועי כשהיא הניחה את הפרחים בתוך קופסת קרטון. לפחות היא גזרה רק את הפרחים ליד שפת המדרכה."

"לא נוכל להעמיד פנים שהיא עזרה למועדון הגינון בגיזום כמה צמחים?" שאלתי.

"אני לא חושבת שמועדון הגינון יתמוך בתירוץ כזה. הנשיאה שלהם התעלפה כשראתה את הנזק הבוקר. היינו צריכים להזמין אמבולנס."

"לפחות הדירה של אמא מקושטת יפה. את צריכה לראות את סידור הפרחים שהיא הכינה," אמרתי.

"לעדנה גם הייתה תאונה במטבח בשבוע שעבר," המשיכה מגי.

"היא רק שכחה לכבות את האש מתחת למחבת. אני באמת מצטער על כך שמכבי האש הגיעו."

"היא נעשית סכנה לקהילה," אמרה מגי.

"אף אחד לא נפגע. בבקשה תני לאמא הזדמנות נוספת."

היא נאנחה ושפשפה את מצחה. זו בוודאי משימה קשה לנהל מקום מלא קשישים.

"או קיי, מר לוי. אבל אני מתעקשת שאמך תפסיק לבשל. היא יכולה לאכול בחדר האוכל הראשי שלנו בכל ערב. זה עולה רק עשרים וחמישה שקלים והאוכל מצוין."

"לא עוד בישולים או קטיפת פרחים," הבטחתי.

— 6 —

שמתי פעמיי אל דירתה של אמא וסיפרתי לה על פגישתי עם מגי.

"היא אינה מחבבת אותי," אמרה אמא. "מאז שהחטפתי לכלבלב שלה עם המקל של רחל."

"בבקשה אל תגידי לי שפגעת בכלב הקטן והחמוד שלה," אמרתי.

"רק רציתי להפסיק את הנביחות. החטפתי לו מאהבה."

"היא ראתה אותך עושה זאת?"

"לא, האשמתי את רחל. זה המקל שלה."

"אז הכנסת את רחל לצרה."

"מגי לא האמינה לי. היא אמרה שרחל חלשה מכדי להניף את המקל. היה לנו ויכוח גדול."

"בואי נשכח את רחל והכלב. הבטחתי למגי שתאכלי את ארוחת הערב בחדר האוכל כל ערב. זה אומר שאין יותר בישולים. אסור גם לקטוף פרחים או שיחים. אין גדיעת עצים."

"אל תהיה כזה טיפש. אין לי בכלל גרזן. הי, אני לא יכולה להרשות לעצמי ארוחה בעשרים וחמישה שקלים כל ערב. אני ענייה."

בחמש הדקות הבאות ניהלנו ויכוח סוער. אמא הסכימה לבסוף לתנאיה של מגי, אבל הייתי צריך להבטיח לשלם עבור ארוחותיה בחדר האוכל. העובדה שלא הייתי צריך לדאוג שאמא תשרוף את בניין הדירות שבו התגוררה הייתה שווה עשרים וחמישה שקלים לערב.

אמא הביטה ברשימה שהייתה מונחת על שולחן המטבח שלה. לעתים קרובות הכינה רשימת תלונות.

"אתה אף פעם לא לוקח אותי לשום מקום."

חשבתי לרגע.

"מדוע איננו הולכים לקולנוע?"

"הסרט האחרון שהלכנו אליו היה מגעיל. אתה צריך להתבייש בעצמך."

"זו אינה אשמתי שיש מילים גסות בסרטים," עניתי.

"בואי נלך לפארק. נוכל לשבת על ספסל ולצפות בציפורים."

"בסדר, זה נשמע טוב."

לקח לה עשר דקות להתכונן, ללגום שתי לגימות מים, ולהיכנס לשירותים שיהיה על כל מקרה. נסענו לפארק מקומי. מרחק ההליכה ממגרש החנייה עד לספסל שהיה מוצל על ידי עצים לא היה גדול. אמא הייתה צריכה להחזיק בי לכל אורך הדרך.

מהספסל יכולנו לראות אגם קטן. לצד האגם היה ממוקם מגרש משחקים. ילד קטן רדף אחרי ברווזים ליד המים.

"זה נחמד," אמרתי.

"למי אכפת מברווזים?" אמרה אמא. "הביטוח הרפואי שלי לא שילם עבור הביקור האחרון שלי אצל הרופא."

נאנחתי. "דיברנו על זה מספר פעמים," הזכרתי לה. "הביטוח הרפואי שלך שלח לך הצהרה שאומרת כי דמי הביקור נכללים בהשתתפות העצמית."

"מה זה השתתפות עצמית?"

"הסברתי לך שלוש פעמים על השתתפות עצמית. מדוע אינך כותבת את זה?"

"מעולם לא דיברת איתי על השתתפות עצמית. מה עם רופא העיניים שלי? הוא שלח לי חשבון על תשעים וחמישה שקלים. הוא גנב."

"הוא עשה לך בדיקה כללית מקיפה," אמרתי לה.

"איזו בחורה צעירה עשתה הכל. היא כנראה רק אחות. אני לא משלמת."

"אודליה אמרה לי שהוא עשה את רוב העבודה והבחורה רק רשמה הערות," אמרתי.

"הרופא אכל בייגל'ה. הוא רק הסתכל. אני אתבע אותו."

העין שלי התחילה לרעוד. חום החל להציף את פניי. לקחתי מספר נשימות עמוקות. באורח נס הצלחתי להגיע להרגיע את עצמי, למרות שהיא המשיכה להתלונן על רופאיה. אחרי עשר דקות נגמרו לה הנושאים להתלונן עליהם.

בילינו עוד שעה בישיבה על הספסל, נהנים מהשמש ומשוחחים על החיים.

7

"הייתי ילד טוב, אז למה אמא שלי מנסה כל כך לאמלל אותי?"

"היא איננה זוכרת איזה ילד נהדר היית," אמר ד"ר רוזנברג.

ד״ר רוזנברג הוא הפסיכיאטר שלי. אני נפגש איתו כל שבוע. הוא עוזר לי להתמודד עם הבעיות שיש לי עם אמי.

״לפחות לא השלכתי אותה לאגם,״ אמרתי.

״זה מוכיח שאתה ילד נהדר,״ הוא אמר.

״היא סתם אשה מרושעת, נכון?״ שאלתי.

״כבר עברנו על זה. היא אינה מאושרת בחייה והיא מוציאה את זה על כל מי שמתקרב אליה.״

״היא לעולם לא תשתנה,״ אמרתי.

״זו הסיבה שאתה לומד להתמודד איתה.״

״היא עדיין משגעת אותי.״

״כן, אבל אתה מתמודד טוב יותר. לפני שנה לא יכולת לישון בלילה אחרי ביקור אצלה. אתמול קיבלת את כל הצער שהסבה לך בלי שמרטת את שערותיך. אחר כך בילית איתה זמן בנעימים. זה מראה על התקדמות ניכרת.״

״כן, נהנינו למדי אחרי שהפסיקה לבכות לי על ענייני רופאים.״

״על מה דיברתם?״

״על דברים נחמדים. על הגודל והצורה של היציאה שלה באותו בוקר. עודפי הליחה המצטברים באפה. השכנה ממול שהולכת לארוחת הצהריים השבועית המוגשת בחינם בכפר הגמלאים שלה ודוחפת לתיקה כמה שיותר אוכל.״

״זה לא היה משעשע?״ אמר ד״ר רוזנברג.

8

״אתה מתקדם בטיפול מכיוון שלא חנקת את אמך בפארק ולא השתכרת כשחזרת הביתה?״ שאלה גילת.

״זה מה שד״ר רוזנברג אמר.״

״זו סיבה לחגוג. בוא נזמין את אמא שלך לארוחת ערב.״

״לא הלילה.״

״היא יודעת שאתה נפגש עם פסיכיאטר מכיוון שהיא כה מרושעת אליך?״

״איזו טובה תצמח מכך שאספר לה? היא חושבת שהיא נחמדה לכולם.״

״אז מה אתה מתכוון לעשות?״

״מה שעשיתי עד עכשיו. אבלה איתה זמן, אקשיב לתלונותיה, אנסה לשפר מעט את חייה האומללים, ואתגבר על הדחף לקבור אותה בחיים.״

״אתה עדיין זקוק לפגישות עם הפסיכיאטר?״

״כנראה שיהיה עלי לפגוש אותו כל שבוע עד מותה.״

״היא תחיה עוד עשרים שנה!״

״אני מקווה. תוכלי לסבול אותי עד אז?״ אמרתי.

גילת התחלחלה.

״אני מניחה שאתה שווה את זה,״ אמרה.

STORY 13

Evolution

"אני מאמין באלוהים, אבל אני לא חושב שהוא מעורב מדי בחיי היום יום שלנו. הוא ברא את העולם והתניע עניינים לפני כמה מיליארד שנים. ואז הוא נשען לאחור להתבונן."

אני מהרהר מספר שניות, ואז ממשיך.

"האבולוציה היא דרכו של אלוהים לשמור על הסדר בעולם. אם משהו מתחיל להשתבש, האבולוציה מוצאת תשובה. לפעמים זה לוקח מאה או שתיים, אבל בסופו של דבר האבולוציה מסייעת לעולם לפתור את בעיותיו."

אני מביט בבחור שאתו אני משוחח. הוא לא נראה מתעניין.

"לפני מאות שנים," אני ממשיך, "אנשים דאגו מפני מוות ממגיפות. עוד לפני כן, בני האדם לא עיכלו חלב של בעלי חיים. ואז האבולוציה נכנסה לתמונה. הגנטיקה שלנו השתנתה צעד אחר צעד. בנוסף, טכנולוגיות חדשות המריצו את התגובה האבולוציונית שלנו. לימים אנחנו נפתח עמידות לרבות מהמחלות שקוטלות אותנו היום. אלו הן דוגמאות מצוינות לאופן שבו אבולוציה יוצרת פתרונות לבעיות."

האיש עדיין איננו מגיב.

"אני יודע מה אתה חושב," אני אומר לו. "מחלות קטלניות אינן דוגמא טובה, מכיוון שבני אדם מתים בימינו מאיידס, מלריה, וכולרה. אבל אני בטוח שהאבולוציה תמצא תשובה איך להילחם גם במחלות הללו."

אני שולף בקבוק מים מכיס המעיל ולוגם לגימות אחדות.

"הנה דוגמה נוספת לפתרון בעיה על ידי האבולוציה," אני אומר לאיש. "אתה טפיל הגורם מצוקה וסבל לאנשים אחרים. האבולוציה פיתחה מרפא. זה אני!"

אני מבין שאני מבזבז את זמני. אחרי הכל, לבחור לא אכפת מהתאוריה שלי על אודות היקום. יש לו שלושה נקבי כדורים בלבו!

2

ימים אחדים קודם לכן ...

אני נשען לאחור בכיסא המסתובב ומביט החוצה מחלון המשרד. זהו בוקר סתווי יפה. הכל שלו ורגוע.

ואז אני שומע פסיעות כבדות במסדרון. הדלת נפתחת וגבר גדול בעל מבנה מרובע פוסע פנימה. הוא מביט בי כאילו הייתי צורת חיים נחותה שהוא עומד לבצע בה ניתוח מחקרי.

"תרצה להגיש בקשה לפוליסת ביטוח חיים?" אני שואל אותו. "אם אתה בריא ואינך מעשן תוכל לקבל כיסוי של מיליון שקלים לפחות. אני יכול להשיג לך פרמיות מצוינות."

מבטו נודד מהרהיטים היקרים שלי לתמונות המהודרות שעל הקיר.

"משרד נחמד," הוא אומר.

"נכון. יש לי מכונת קפה חדשה. תרצה קפה נטול? מאיפה קיבלת את כל הצלקות האלה ואת האף המעוקם? אם אתה עובד במקצוע מסוכן, אתה צריך להצהיר על כך בטופס הבקשה."

"תפסיק לדבר על ביטוח חיים," הוא אומר לי.

"אני לא מצליח לזהות את המבטא," אני מציין. "רוסיה? הבלקן אולי?"

"אני מרמת גן."

הוא מכניס את ידו לכיסו, מוציא תצלום קטן ומניח אותו על שולחני. אני מביט בתצלום, ורואה אישה צעירה, בת עשרים וארבע או עשרים וחמש.

"היא יפה מאוד, הבת שלך, נכון?" הוא שואל.

אני מבין שזהו ביקור רציני. אנחנו בוהים זה בזה למשך שניות אחדות.

"אתה לא מדבר כל כך הרבה עכשיו, נכון?" הוא שואל. "זה מפני שאתה אוהב את הבת שלך ואתה לא רוצה שיקרה לה משהו."

"אתה מאיים עליי?" אני שואל.

"לא. אני אומר שתעשה הכל כדי להגן על הבת שלך."

הוא מושיט לי פיסת נייר. כתוב בה: "תתכונן. יומיים. שטרות קטנים לא מסומנים."

על הפתק מצוין גם סכום כסף גדול. הוא קם ויוצא.

3

איש בתחנת המשטרה העירונית לא מוכן להקשיב לבעיה שלי. אין להם משאבים לטיפול בפשעים מסוג זה. לפחות הם נחמדים מספיק כדי לתת לי את מספר הטלפון של מטה מחוז מרכז.

לאחר מכן אני מדבר עם מישהו, שמעביר אותי למישהו אחר, שמעביר אותי לבלש הסמל אלברט זוהר. הוא עובד ביחידה המטפלת במקרי סחיטה. אני מספר לו את סיפורי. כשאני מסיים, אני שואל אותו מספר שאלות.

"יש לך מישהו שיחקור?" אני שואל.

"בהחלט."

"שמעתי שהיו לפחות שלושה סוכני ביטוח נוספים כמוני שהיו קורבן לסחיטה בששת החודשים האחרונים. המחלקה שלך חוקרת את המקרים הללו?"

"כן."

"איך זה שעדיין לא עצרתם אף אחד?"

"יש לנו מספר כיווני חקירה רציניים."

"אבל שניים מהקורבנות נורו למוות, לא?" אני שואל.

"כן," הוא אומר.

"ואשתו של הקורבן השלישי נרצחה באותו אקדח, לא?"

"כן. כל זה דווח בתקשורת."

"למה אין לכם חשודים?"

"אני לא יכול לדון בחקירה שעדיין מתנהלת."

"סמל זוהר, אני חושש שהעבריינים האלה חכמים יותר מהמשטרה."

"אני לא יכול להגיב."

"אולי עדיף שאשלם להם את הסכום שביקשו. אני יכול להרשות לעצמי."

"שני אנשים שילמו. הם נרצחו בידי הכנופייה בכל זאת."

"אולי הם נרצחו בגלל שהחליטו לשתף פעולה עם המשטרה והעבריינים גילו את זה."

"גם על זה אני לא יכול להגיב."

"אתה לא עוזר. כל פעם שאני אומר משהו חשוב אתה אומר לי שאתה לא יכול להגיב."

"המחלקה שלי עובדת מסביב לשעון כדי למצוא את הכנופייה הזאת. תוכל לעזור לנו בכך שתשתף איתי פעולה. אני יכול לבוא למשרד שלך ולחפש טביעות אצבע?"

"הוא לבש כפפות," אני אומר.

"אז לפחות תיפגש איתי ותגיש תלונה רשמית."

"אני לא בטוח שאני רוצה לעשות את זה. שלושה אנשים מתים ולא נראה שאתם מתקדמים."

"אז למה התקשרת?"

"זו שאלה טובה. תן לי לחשוב על המצב ולחזור אליך."

חמש דקות לאחר שיחתי עם סמל זוהר, אני מתקשר למיכאל הרשקו. הוא סוכן הביטוח שאשתו נרצחה לפני חמישה חודשים. אני מבקש ממנו להיפגש איתי לארוחת צוהריים למחרת.

4

מיכאל הרשקו נראה נורא. פניו כחושים, זקנו מוזנח. הוא מתקשה להתרכז בתפריט.

"התרופה מקשה עליי לעשות דברים," הוא אומר. "אני מנומנם כל הזמן."

אנחנו מדברים על כמה עצוב הוא מאז שאשתו נרצחה. לאחר מספר דקות אני משנה את הנושא ומספר לו שאותה קבוצת עבריינים מאיימת על בתי.

"כדאי לי לערב את המשטרה?" אני שואל.

"לא. תשלם להם."

"לשלם לנצח?"

"הם אמרו לי שיעזבו אותי בשקט אחרי שאשלם במשך שנה," הוא אומר.

"האמנת להם?"

"לא. אז הלכתי למשטרה."

"למה אשתך נרצחה?" אני שואל.

"איכשהו, העבריינים ידעו שאני עובד עם המשטרה."

"איך הם ידעו?"

"התשלום הבא שלי היה אמור להימסר בתחנת דלק על הכביש המהיר. כמה בלשים עקבו אחריי. הם לבשו בגדים אזרחיים כדי להשתלב בין האנשים בתחנת הדלק. העבריינים בוודאי ראו אותם, כי אף אחד לא הופיע לקחת את הכסף."

הוא ממתין רגע, לוגם לגימות אחדות מהקפה.

"כמה ימים אחר כך אשתי נורתה מטווח קצר. זה היה רצח מקצועי."

הוא מתחיל לבכות.

"היא עדיין הייתה בחיים אם לא הייתי הולך למשטרה."

אחרי ארוחת הצוהריים העגומה שלנו אני מסיע אותו בחזרה לביתו.

"אני לא הולך יותר למשרד," הוא אומר לי. "אני יותר מדי מדוכא מכדי לעבוד."

"אתה צריך לקחת משרה בסוכנות גדולה," אני אומר לו. "רוב המקומות ישמחו לקבל לעבודה סוכן מכירות מצליח כמוך. חוץ מזה, יעשה לך טוב להיות עם אנשים."

הוא מושך בכתפיו בתבוסה.

"לפחות תיפגש עם יועץ אבל מקצועי," אני אומר.

אני עוצר בחניית הבית.

הוא יוצא מהמכונית, מנופף נפנוף קטן לשלום וגורר רגליו בדרכו אל ביתו. אני חוזר למשרד ומנמנם. עליי להיות רענן לקראת משחק הפוקר.

5

אני מביט סביב השולחן בשחקנים האחרים. מיקי, סוחר הסמים, יושב לימיני. נודף ממנו ריח של ג'ל לשיער

ואפטר שייב. חברתו עומדת מאחוריו, רוכנת ונושקת לאוזנו. אני מתקשה להביט בקלפים שלי.

גיא, רואה חשבון, יושב מולי. חליפתו מקומטת, עניבתו מעוקמת ושני הכפתורים העליונים בחולצתו פתוחים. בקבוק הוויסקי שלו כבר ריק בחציו, ועדיין לא שיחקנו יותר משעה.

"יום קשה במשרד, גיא?" אני שואל אותו.

"כמה עורכי דין מפרקליטות המדינה עושים לי חיים קשים," הוא עונה.

בוריס, החבר הרביעי בקבוצה, יושב לשמאלי. בוריס מלווה כסף לאנשים שאינם יכולים לקבל הלוואה בבנק. הוא גובה ריביות גבוהות מאוד. אם לקוחותיו אינם משלמים את החזרי ההלוואה במועד, העוזר שלו שובר להם את הרגליים.

עוזרו של בוריס יושב בפינה, צופה בטלוויזיה במסך גדול. תוכנית עיצוב בתים כלשהי.

מדוע בחור המכה אנשים למחייתו נהנה מתוכניות הריאליטי המטופשות האלה? על טעם ועל ריח אין להתווכח.

אנחנו משחקים פוקר בחדר בתחנת כיבוי האש למתנדבים בחולון. מפקד התחנה מחלק עבורנו את הקלפים, ולוקח חמישה אחוזים עמלה מכל קופה. אם לשפוט על פי הריהוט הנחמד בתחנת הכיבוי, העמלה הזו הכניסה לתחנה כסף רב במהלך השנים. מעניין כמה שומר מפקד התחנה לעצמו.

שותפתי, איילה, יושבת על ספה בסמוך לטלוויזיה. היא קוראת ספר מאת סטיבן הוקינג. משהו על הכוכבים וכוכבי הלכת.

גיא מעיף מבטים לעבר איילה ללא הרף. מיקי היה מציץ גם הוא, אלא שהחברה שלו חסמה את שדה ראייתו. בוריס אינו מביט. נדמה שהוא מרוכז ביד שקיבל. מפקד תחנת הכיבוי ממקד את מבטו בקלפים ובכסף.

איילה נמוכה ממני בכחמישה סנטימטרים, כלומר גובהה מטר ושמונים. היא בעלת שיער חום באורך בינוני. מצחה מתקמט מעט כאשר היא מתרכזת בספרה. היא לובשת אימונית נוחה, ללא איפור או תכשיטים.

"היא לא חברה שלך," אומר בוריס. "למה אתה מביא אותה?"

"למזל," אני אומר לו. "אני צריך הרבה מזל הלילה. בוא נקווה שארוויח הרבה כסף."

"בוא נקווה שלא," אומר בוריס.

"מה שלום אשתך, גיא?" אני שואל.

"בסדר."

אשתו של גיא היא בתו של עבריין ידוע מתל אביב. חמו נקרא אריה הגרזן. גיא עושה את כל עבודת הכספים עבור עסקיו של אריה.

"מישהו ראה את המשחק ביום שני האחרון?" אני שואל.

אני נענה במספר נהמות וקללות. זו איננה קבוצה ידידותית.

מיקי מזיז מעליו את חברתו בעדינות. "מיטל, אני לא יכול לחשוב כשאת תלויה מעליי. לכי תראי טלוויזיה."

היא מחליקה לדרכה ומתיישבת לצד איילה.

"למישהו מכם היה פעם עסק עם המשטרה?" אני שואל.

"למי לא?" שואל בוריס.

"יש לי איזה עניין עכשיו," אני אומר להם. "אתם יודעים אם מישהו בצמרת יהיה מוכן לעשות טובות לאנשים כמונו?"

אנחנו משחקים קלפים דקות אחדות.

"אם המחיר נכון, תוכל לשכנע מישהו לעשות משהו," אומר בוריס.

"מי?"

"תלוי מה אתה רוצה."

"אני רוצה להפסיק חקירה," אני אומר.

"אולי יש לי שם. תן לי את הסלולרי שלך."

אני כותב את מספר הטלפון על פיסת נייר ומחליק אותה אליו.

"תן לי כמה ימים," הוא אומר.

"אני חייב לך," אני אומר לו.

גיא זורק את קלפיו על השולחן ופורש. גם אני. בוריס ומיקי מושכים קלפים אחדים.

"מישהו רוצה בירה?" אני שואל.

מיקי מהנהן לעברי. אני צועד לכיוון המקרר ולוקח שני בקבוקי בירה. כשאני שב לשולחן, מיקי גורף את הזיתונים.

"הקלפים קרים הערב," אומר בוריס.

מפקד התחנה מחלק יד נוספת. אנחנו מתחילים לשוחח על כדורסל. ארבע שעות מאוחר יותר, אני מחליט לסיים את הערב.

"הרווחת הרבה כסף," אומר גיא כשאיילה ואני פונים לצאת. "תישאר בסביבה, כדי שנוכל לקבל חלק ממנו בחזרה."

"תודה, גיא, אבל אני צריך את הכסף עכשיו למשהו אחר."

"כן. העניין עם חקירת המשטרה," הוא אומר.

אנחנו יוצאים מתחנת הכיבוי וצועדים במורד הרחוב לכיוון המכונית. בדרכנו אנחנו חולפים על פני גדר חיה ארוכה וגבוהה. אני מחפש בכיסי את שלט המכונית.

לפתע, איילה מסתובבת על רגלה השמאלית. היא מטיחה את רגלה הימנית בפניו של בחור גדול, שהופיע מאחורי הגדר החיה. הוא שומט את האלה שבידיו ונופל לאחור על ישבנו.

אני נשען על המכונית כששני גברים נוספים מזנקים מתוך החשכה. אחד מהם אוחז במחבט קטן. האחר

אוחז בידיו סכין. הם צעירים - אולי בני 19 או 20. מעט נמוכים ממני, אבל שוקלים כחמישה עשר קילוגרם יותר ממני.

איילה ניצבת בפניה אליהם. ברכיה כפופות מעט. אמות ידיה מורמות ומרפקיה צמודים לגופה. אגרופיה קמוצים ברפיון. רגלה השמאלית מושטת קדימה ואצבעות רגלה הימנית פונות הצידה. שני העקבים מורמים מהרצפה. זוהי עמידת קרב המואי-תאי המסורתית.

שני הבחורים הקשוחים מביטים בחברם היושב על הקרקע. ידיו מורמות אל פניו. דם ניגר מבין אצבעותיו. הם מהססים ואיילה תוקפת. הבחור האוחז במחבט מנסה להניפו. מאוחר מדי.

מרפקה של איילה מרסק את אפו ורגלה השמאלית שומטת את רגליו מתחתיו לפני שהמחבט נע יותר מחמישה סנטימטרים.

בעודו נופל, היא חומקת בצעדי ריקוד המונפת מסכינו של הבחור האחר. הוא הולם חזק מדי ומאבד את שיווי משקלו. לפני שהוא מספיק להתאושש, איילה סוגרת עליו.

היא נותנת לו ברכייה בכליות ומכה בצד הלסת שלו בעוצמה. גופו קורס מעוצמת המכה.

בעודו נופל, היא מרקדת אל עבר הבחור עם המחבט ודורכת על אשכיו. הוא מייבב ומאבד את הכרתו.

היא חומקת בחזרה לבחור עם הסכין, השרוע כעת על הקרקע. היא בועטת בראשו. הוא שומט את הסכין ושוכב ללא תזוזה.

בשלב זה, התוקף הראשון שלנו גרר עצמו בחזרה למצב עמידה. הוא ממשש אקדח התחוב בכיס מכנסיו. ידיו חלקלקות מהדם הניגר מאפו ומפיו, דבר המקשה עליו לאחוז באקדח.

אני חובט בצד ראשו ללא מאמץ עם אלה שאני מחזיק בכיסי. הוא מתמוטט חזרה אל המדרכה.

"אתה צריך נרתיק כתף," אני אומר לבחור מחוסר ההכרה. "יותר קל לשלוף את האקדח."

"הוא לא יכול לשמוע אותך," אומרת איילה.

נשימתה אפילו אינה כבדה. שנינו נכנסים למכוניתי ונוסעים משם.

"איך הם ידעו על משחק הפוקר?" היא שואלת.

"אולי הם חברים בקבוצת המתנדבים של מכבי האש," אני אומר.

— 6 —

האיש מרמת גן, בעל המבטא המצחיק מתקשר אליי למחרת בבוקר. בטלפון הנייד שלי! איך הוא השיג את המספר?

"תביא את המתנה שלי לחניה של פארק רמת גן בשעה שתיים," הוא אומר.

"לא," אני עונה.

יש הפסקה על הקו.

"אין לך את המתנה?" הוא שואל.

"היא אצלי, אבל אני לא נוסע את כל הדרך עד לשם כדי לפגוש אותך."

"אני לא צוחק. אתה חייב לעשות מה שאני אומר לך."

"אם אתה רוצה את הכסף שלך, אני אתן לך אותו במקום שאני אבחר."

הוא מהרהר שניות אחדות.

"אם המשטרה תהיה שם, אני אדע. אני מאוד זהיר."

"אל תדאג," אני אומר לו, "שום משטרה לא תהיה שם."

כעבור עשרים שניות של שתיקה הוא אומר, "או קיי, לאן אתה רוצה להביא את המתנה?"

"אני אפגוש אותך ברציף 5 בתחנת הרכבת בעג'מי. התחנה ביפו, לא תחנת ההגנה. זה מקום ציבורי נחמד."

"אתה דואג שאני אעשה לך משהו?"

"אני רוצה שיהיו עדים."

"תזכור," הוא אומר לי, "אם המשטרה תופיע, אני אדע."

"אני מבין," אני אומר.

"דרך אגב, אתה מקבל המחאות?"

הוא לא מגחך אפילו.

שעות אחדות מאוחר יותר אני עומד ברציף 5, קורא עיתון. רכבת עוצרת, ועשרה נוסעים יורדים ממנה. הרכבת רועמת הלאה לכיוון לוד. איש לא שם לב אליי. ידידי החדש צועד לאורך הרציף ונעמד מולי.

"איפה המתנה שלי?" הוא שואל.

זו שאלה טובה, מאחר שאיני נושא מזוודה או תיק.

"היא כאן קרוב," אני אומר. "לפני שאני מביא אותה, נוכל לעשות עסקה?"

הוא נראה משועשע.

"תוריד את הז'קט," הוא אומר.

לאחר שאני עושה כדבריו הוא טופח בידיו סביב חזי, בטני, גבי וירכיי. כעבור דקות אחדות הוא עוצר.

"אין עליך שום ציוד אלקטרוני. אנחנו יכולים לדבר. העסקה היא שאתה חייב לשלם לי כל חודש."

"זה הרבה כסף," אני אומר. "נוכל להתקשר לבוס שלך ולדון בסידור אחר?"

"הבוס לא עושה עסקאות."

"יש אפשרות שאשלם אחוזים מהרווחים שלי? יש חודשים שאני מרוויח פחות."

"מספיק לדבר. קח אותי לכסף," הוא עונה.

הבחור נראה נחוש, אז אני מוביל אותו אל מאחורי רציף 5 ובמורד גרם מדרגות. במחצית הדרך במורד

המדרגות מונח תרמיל גב על הרצפה. קופסת חשמל מחוברת לקיר כשני מטרים מעל המדרגות. בעוד הוא מביט בתרמיל הגב, אני נוטל את האקדח המונח על קופסת החשמל ויורה בו שלוש פעמים בליבו.

"היית צריך לקחת את ביטוח החיים ההוא," אני אומר לגופתו.

7

האקדח מצויד במשתיק קול, כך שאיש אינו ממהר במורד המדרגות לראות מה קרה. אני מתקשר במהירות לללאה.

"זה נעשה," אני אומר לה.

עשרים שניות מאוחר יותר אני שומע צלצול מתחתי. חברי הצוות שלי סוגרים את הדלתות בראש המדרגות ובתחתיתו בשרשראות. זה מעניק לי זמן לחקור. אני בודק את כיסיו. כלום. אני פושט את בגדיו ומחפש כתובות קעקע או צלקות. כלום.

בעודי עוסק בחיפוש, אני מסביר לו את תיאוריית האבולוציה שלי. אתם זוכרים את המונולוג מתחילת הסיפור, לא?

אני קוצץ את אצבעותיו ומניח אותן בשקית ניילון. נוכל להשיג טביעות ודנ"א מהאצבעות, וקל הרבה יותר לשאת אותן מאשר את הגופה כולה.

אני צועד במורד גרם המדרגות ונוקש על הדלת הסגורה שבתחתיתו. עדינה פותחת מנעול שרשרת ופותחת את הדלת לרווחה. היא סוגרת את הדלת בשרשרת שוב ואנחנו פונים אל הרכב. עם מעט מזל, הגופה לא תתגלה במשך מספר שבועות. אחרי הכל, זו עג'מי.

8

עדינה מסיעה אותנו הרחק מתחנת הרכבת. היא לובשת חליפת עסקים. הקוקו שלה הוחלף בתסרוקת בוגרת יותר.

"למה את לובשת את החליפה הזאת?" אני שואל אותה.

"אני מתערה בין הנוסעים," היא עונה.

"תורידי אותי בסוכנות הביטוח. יש לי פגישה בארבע וחצי. את יכולה לקחת את האצבעות בחזרה למפקדה. קחי גם את האקדח. תגידי לללאה להיפטר ממנו."

"ערפלת את הבחור במדרגות?"

"ערפלתי אותו כשהיינו על הרציף. למה את חושבת שהוא הסכים לבוא איתי?"

"וזה הפך את היריה בו לקלה."

"ודאי. נתתי לו דחיפה מנטלית להסתכל על תרמיל הגב. הוא אפילו לא שם לב שאני לוקח את האקדח. אבל יכולתי ככל הנראה לעשות זאת בלי לערפל אותו."

"אני יודעת כמה אתה מהיר," היא אומרת.

"לא הפכתי איטי יותר בגיל העמידה," אני מזכיר לה.

"מישהו במצב רוח רע."

"אני פשוט שונא לירות באנשים."

"אבל אתה עושה את זה בכל זאת."

"אני סוכן השטח, זוכרת? מישהו צריך לעשות את העבודה הקשה."

"תזכיר לי שוב למה כולם חושבים שאתה סוכן ביטוח אמיתי," היא אומרת.

"היכולת המיוחדת שלי יכולה להתבטא בכמה צורות. אני יכול לערפל את מוחו של אדם כך שלא ידע מה קורה. אני יכול לשנות את זכרונותיו לגבי ארועים. אני יכול לשכנע אותו לעשות דברים פשוטים, כמו להביט בתרמיל גב או לשמוט אקדח. ואני יכול לגרום לו להאמין שאני מישהו אחר."

"אתה יכול להפנט חדר שלם?" היא שואלת.

"זו לא היפנוזה. אני אפילו לא יודע איך לתאר את הכישרון שלי, אבל הוא עובד רק על אנשים בודדים וקבוצות קטנות."

"איפה האדם שהתחזית לו?" שואלת עדינה.

"שלחתי אותו ואת בתו לטיול נחמד בספרד למספר שבועות. הם שמחו לנסוע כשהסברתי לו שהאנליסט הראשי שלנו סבור שהוא עומד להיות המטרה הבאה."

"מי האנליסט הראשי שלכם?"

"רונן."

"לא אני?"

"את האנליסטית הבכירה הראשית."

"יופי," היא אומרת.

יש רגע שקט בעוד אני מתבונן בהתפעלות באזור היפהפה של מרכז שכונת עג'מי.

"אני מקווה שאתה לא באמת מוכר פוליסות ביטוח," אומרת עדינה.

"עדיין לא מכרתי אף אחת. אנשים לא מאמינים לי כשאני מסביר את יתרונות ביטוח החיים. כנראה שאין לי פרצוף אמין."

יש רגע נוסף של שקט כשאנחנו משתלבים בנתיבי איילון.

"את שואלת הרבה שאלות היום," אני אומר לעדינה.

״אני מתאמנת על כישורי השיחה שלי.״

״את מתכננת להיות עורכת דין?״

״לא, אני רק מנסה להיות חברה טובה יותר בצוות.״

״לאה אמרה לך משהו?״

״היא ציינה שאני צריכה לעבוד על יחסי האנוש שלי.״

״בגלל שזרקת את המסך ההוא על רונן?״

״הוא כל כך מעצבן לפעמים.״

אני מגחך.

״עבור מי עבד הבחור המת לדעתך?״ היא שואלת.

״רונן בטוח למדי שזה מישהו בכיר מאוד במטה מחוז מרכז.״

״ואתה מאמין לו?״

״הוא מעולם לא טעה באף אחת מהתחזיות שלו. אחד מהבחורים שאני משחק איתם פוקר ישלח לי כמה שמות לבדיקה.״

״למה העבריינים האלו נותנים לך לשחק איתם פוקר?״

״נהגתי לעשות הרבה עבודות עצמאיות. מדי פעם עשיתי עבודות עבור עבריינים. הם מכירים את המוניטין שלי.״

״אם אתה יכול לערפל את מוחם של אנשים, איך זה שאתה לא מרוויח ערמות של כסף בכל פעם שאתה משחק פוקר?״

״אני לא רוצה.״

״למה לא?״

״אני משחק עם החבר׳ה האלה כדי לאסוף מידע, לא כדי להרוויח כסף. זו הסיבה שאני משחק במקומות שונים, עם קבוצות שונות של אנשים. בדרך כלל אני מנסה להרוויח קצת או להפסיד קצת. מה שאני לא רוצה לעשות זה למשוך אליי תשומת לב רבה בכך שאנצח כל הזמן.״

״הרווחת הרבה כסף אתמול בלילה.״

״נסחפתי. ניסיתי להרשים את הבחורה שהיית שם.״

״איילה?״

״מישהי אחרת. היא הייתה חתיכה.״

״יותר מדי מידע!״ מרימה עליי עדינה את קולה.

המכונית הופכת שוב שקטה. עדינה מתרגלת את כישורי המעקב והחלפת המסלולים שלה. נהגים אחדים צופרים לעברנו.

"תנפנף באקדח שלך מולם," היא אומרת לי.

"זו יפה. בטח יש להם אקדחים גדולים יותר."

"סיפרת לגופה את התאוריה שלך על האבולוציה?" היא שואלת.

"הסברתי לו את התאוריה שלי בזמן שערכתי חיפוש בבגדיו."

"אתה לא חושב שזה מוזר קצת לדבר לאנשים מתים?" היא שואלת.

"כל מי שמבקר בבית קברות מדבר לאנשים מתים," אני אומר.

"זה שונה. הם לא מסבירים את דעותיהם על היקום. בכל אופן, לא קיבלנו את הכוחות המיוחדים שלנו מהאבולוציה."

"אז איך קיבלנו את הכישרונות המוזרים האלה?"

"חוצנים מהחלל החיצון הוסיפו את הדנ"א שלהם לכרומוזומים אנושיים בתקופת האבן. בכל כמה דורות מאז צץ משהו ייחודי - כמונו."

"זה טיפשי," אני אומר.

"לא טיפשי כמו האמונה שלך באלוהים שאיננו קיים."

"אני לא מאמין שאני עובד עם אתאיסטית," אני קורא. "שאר החבר'ה 'בחוליה' ישמעו על זה."

"אף אחד לא הסכים לקרוא לצוות שלנו 'החוליה'," היא אומרת.

"אף אחד גם לא התנגד."

"לא רצינו לפגוע ברגשותיך. זה שם אדיוטי."

"אני אוהב אותו. אולי נוכל להזמין ז'קטים עם כיתוב 'החוליה' על הגב."

"אני חושבת שאנחנו צריכים לערוך הצבעה על השם," היא אומרת.

"נראה."

9

באותו לילה מצלצל הטלפון הנייד. אני עונה ושומע קול נוסף בעל מבטא מוזר.

"איפה הוא?"

"מי זה?"

"אל תהיה טיפש. אני אשאל שוב - איפה הוא?"

"אתה מדבר על הבחור שהייתי אמור לפגוש היום ברציף 5?" אני שואל.

"תפסיק לבזבז זמן. תענה על השאלה."

"אני לא יודע," אני אומר. "בזבזתי חצי שעה בתחנת הרכבת בעג'מי, מתפלל שלא ישדדו אותי, והאיש שלך לא הופיע."

"הוא היה שם. מה קרה לו?"

"אני לא יודע."

השיחה ממשיכה כך למשך מספר דקות. הוא ממשיך לטעון שעשיתי משהו ואני ממשיך לומר לו שלא עשיתי כלום. אני משקר, אבל הבחור בטלפון לא ידע את זה. לבסוף, הוא מחליט שאני אומר אמת. אחרי הכל, מי יאמין שמישהו בעל אישיות עליזה כשלי יכול לירות במישהו בליבו ולקצוץ את אצבעותיו?

"אני אחזור אליך," הוא אומר.

"אני שומע את זה מהרבה בנות," אני אומר כשהוא מנתק את השיחה.

למחרת, אני קורא בעיתון שהבחור שירתי בו כבר נמצא. איש תחזוקה חרוץ כלשהו ניסר את השרשרת שסגרה את הדלת וגילה את הגופה.

הכתבה מרמזת שזה היה רצח של המאפיה. אני חושב להתקשר לכתבת ולתקן את סיפורה, אבל מחליט שלא. היא לא תאמין לי.

מאוחר יותר באותו יום אני פוסע למזנון מקומי לארוחת צוהריים נחמדה. המזנון מעוצב ברוח מלחמת העצמאות. לפריטים בתפריט יש שמות חמודים.

מלצרית בת תשעים, לבושה כמו פולה בן-גוריון, ניגשת לקחת ממני הזמנה.

"מה מנת היום?" אני שואל.

"מרק בצל ונקניק טלה."

"זה טעים?"

"איך אני יכולה לדעת? אני לא אוכלת כאן."

"למה לא?"

"אני צריכה לשמור על הכולסטרול."

"אתם עדיין מגישים ארוחת בוקר?"

"אין ארוחת בוקר אחרי אחת עשרה. כתוב על התפריט."

"אני חושב על סלט הטונה. הוא טרי?"

"אתה מתכוון להזמין משהו היום, או שאתה כאן כדי לערוך מחקר?"

"חשבתי שתהני מקצת שיחה," אני אומר לה. "אחרי הכל, המקום לא ממש עמוס."

"טוב, הרגליים שלי כואבות," היא אומרת לי, "אז תמהר ותזמין."

"אני אקח המבורגר וקוקה-קולה."

המלצרית רושמת את ההזמנה בפנקסה והולכת לדרכה. עשר דקות מאוחר יותר מתיישב בחור מכוער על הדלפק לצדי. זה מוזר, מכיוון שיש שרפרפים פנויים רבים. בדרך כלל אנשים ביפו לא רוצים לשבת זה ליד זה אלא אם אין להם ברירה.

"בשבוע הבא אתה משלם כפול," הוא אומר לי. "אני אגיע למשרד שלך ביום שלישי. בלי שינויי מקום."

ואז הוא עוזב. אני מדבר אל תוך סיכה בז'קט שלי.

"הוא בדרכו החוצה. שיער חום, מטר שמונים וחמש, שוקל כתשעים וחמישה קילו. הוא לובש מעיל כהה וג'ינס. נראה כאילו הלך מכות עם רכבת והפסיד."

באוזני מותקן מקלט קטן, כך שאני יכול לשמוע את האדם שבצדו השני של הקו. חוקרת פרטית שעוקבת אחריי מאז אתמול.

"מצאתי אותו," מדווחת החוקרת הפרטית. "אני אתקשר אליך מאוחר יותר לדווח לך לאן הוא הולך."

בדיוק אז מביאה המלצרית את ההמבורגר שלי. הוא טעים. כשאני עוזב אני משאיר לה תשר נאה.

המשך היום נטול התרחשויות מיוחדות. אני קורא מדריכים אחדים העוסקים במכירת ביטוח שיניים לאנשים שאינם מעוניינים בו. אני משחק קצת במחשב במשרד. אני פותר תשבץ. לאחר מכן אני מנמנם. לבסוף, אני גולש באינטרנט וקורא רכילות על אודות כוכבי הוליווד. ישנם אלפי אתרים שמוקדשים לנושא.

בשעה שש וחצי מתקשרת החוקרת הפרטית.

"הבחור הלך לבניין דירות ישן בחולון, אסף את הכביסה שלו וכיבס אותה במכבסה אוטומטית ליד הבניין."

"שמת לב אם היו ארנבונים על אחת מהפיג'מות שהוא כיבס?"

"ארנבונים?"

"כן. גורי ארנבים. אני אוהב פיג'מות עם ארנבונים."

"לא התקרבתי כל כך."

"את אמורה לשים לב לדברים כאלה. אני מתכוון לשלוח מכתב תלונה לאחראי שלך."

"חיים, אין לי אחראי."

"שכחתי. איפה הבחור עכשיו?"

"שותה במסעדה בראשון."

"תני לי את הכתובת. אהיה שם בתוך חצי שעה."

"אתה צריך הוראות הגעה?"

"ברור שלא. יש לי ג'י.פי.אס."

כשאני מגיע למסעדה אני מזהה את האיש שלי יושב בקצה הבר. אני מתיישב במושב שלצידו. הוא מביט בי. אני מחייך. הוא איננו מזהה אותי. כפי שציינתי קודם, היכולת המיוחדת שלי מאפשרת לי לשלוט במה שאנשים רואים ושומעים.

"מערכות הניווט האלה מדהימות, לא?" אני שואל את הבחור.

"עזוב אותי בשקט," הוא רוטן.

"לג'י.פי.אס שלי יש קול בריטי. אני אוהב לדמיין שאני נוסע עם וינסטון צ'רצ'יל."

"אם תדבר איתי שוב אני אחטיף לך."

בשלב זה אני מכה בו במלוא כוחו של הערפול המוחי שלי.

"למה שלא תסיים את המשקה הזה ונצא לנסיעה," אני אומר לו.

הוא גומע את שארית הבירה שלו ויוצא אחריי החוצה אל מכוניתי.

"היכנס והירגע," אני אומר לו. "אני אנהג."

אני קושר את האדון באזיקים לדלת בצד הנוסע ומתקשר ללאה. אנחנו מחליטים להיפגש באתר בנייה נטוש סמוך לבת ים. עשרים דקות לאחר מכן ראשו של הבחור צלול, אבל ידיו ורגליו קשורות.

לאה משוחחת איתו. ללאה יש יכולת מעניינת. היא מדברת עם אנשים והם מספרים לה כל מה שהיא רוצה לדעת. היא אינה יודעת להסביר איך היא עושה את זה, בדיוק כפי שאני איני יודע כיצד פועל הערפול המוחי שלי. אבל זה כישרון נפלא.

לרוע המזל, הבחור הזה לא יודע הרבה. לאה מגלה את שמו, כי הוא הגיע מאוקראינה וכי הוא הגיע לישראל לפני עשרה חודשים בטיסה של אירופלוט. הוא מספר לה שיש מספר אוקראינים נוספים העובדים איתו, אבל הוא לא יודע את שמותיהם. הוא נותן לה כתובות של שלוש דירות שבהן דירות עשויים להיות שותפיו להיות, אבל אינו יודע מי מנהל את הפעולה.

"הוא מקבל את כל הוראותיו באמצעות טלפון נייד," אומרת לי לאה כשהיא מסיימת את החקירה שלה.

"מה נעשה בו?" אני שואל.

"תפעיל עליו שוב את הערפול המוחי. תגרום לו לשכוח את השעות האחרונות."

לאה מושיטה לי אקדח עם משתיק קול.

"זה האקדח שבו ירית באוקראיני הראשון," היא אומרת לי. "תן אותו לבחור ותוריד אותו ליד תחנת משטרה."

"רעיון מצוין. יהיה הכי טוב אם הוא יהיה עירום, כך שהמשטרה תבחין בו מיד."

"נשמע לי מצוין," אומרת לאה.

לאה חוזרת לבסיס שלנו. אני מרדים את האיש במושב האחורי של הרכב וכותב עבורו הודאה. לאחר מכן אני מפשיט אותו מבגדיו, מדביק את ההודאה לחזהו ומסיע אותו לתחנת משטרה בעיר הסמוכה.

אני עוצר מול חזית הבניין ואומר לו לצאת מהרכב. הוא חש מטושטש, אבל מצליח לאחוז באקדח בעודו צועד עירום לתוך התחנה כדי לשוחח עם השוטרים המקומיים הידידותיים. לפעמים אני פשוט אוהב את העבודה שלי!

10

"חשבתי שהכל מסודר," אני אומר לרונן בטלפון. "אני רוצה שנקרא לעצמנו 'החוליה'."

"עדינה שכנעה את לאה שאנחנו צריכים לערוך הצבעה על השם," הוא אומר לי.

"מה עם 'גברים בשחור'?"

"האם לאה, עדינה ואיילה נראות כמו גברים?"

"אני מניח שלא."

רונן מחליט לשנות את נושא השיחה.

"איפה הכסף שהרווחת במשחק הפוקר?"

"הוא בשולחן במשרד שלי. לא היה לי זמן להפקיד אותו בבנק."

"לאה דואגת שתשתמש בו כדי לצאת לחופשה."

לאה היא הבוס, אבל לעתים אני סבור שהיא דואגת יותר מדי בענייני כספים.

"תגיד לה להירגע," אני אומר.

"אתה יודע שאני לומד ניהול חשבונות באינטרנט," אומר רונן.

"אני בטוח שאתה לומד הרבה."

"לאה מאפשרת לי לעזור בעניינים הכספיים של התאגיד," הוא אומר.

"למה אני צריך לדעת את זה?" אני שואל אותו.

"היא מינתה אותי כאחראי לדוחות ההוצאות. אני צריך לעקוב אחרי רווחי הפוקר שלך."

"יש לי שיטה מיוחדת," אני אומר לו. "כשאני מנצח בפוקר אני שומר את הכסף ומשתמש בו להוצאות הקשורות לעבודה. לכן אני לא צריך להוציא דוח הוצאות נוסף עד שהכסף ייגמר."

"זו לא הדרך שבה אתה אמור לעשות את זה," אומר רונן.

"למה לא? זה פשוט וחוסך זמן."

"אבל אנחנו לא רואים את ההוצאות האמיתיות שלך. כל מה שאנחנו יודעים זה שאתה מרוויח כסף במשחק פוקר ואתה מוציא אותו על פעילויות הקשורות לעסק במהלך השבועות שלאחר מכן. אנחנו לא יודעים כמה כסף אתה מרוויח ולאן בעצם הכסף הולך."

"סמוך עלי, אתה לא רוצה לדעת."

"לאה רוצה."

"תגיד ללאה שאני סוכן שטח, לא רואה חשבון."

"אני לא אומר לה כלום. תדבר איתה אתה," אומר רונן.

"לאה בדקה את הכתובות שקיבלנו מהבחור האוקראיני?"

"כן, אבל הדירות היו ריקות."

אני מנתק בעוד רונן מנסה להזכיר לי מתי יש להגיש את דוח ההוצאות הבא. למה ניהול עסק קטן כמו שלנו צריך להיות מסובך כל כך? דקה אחר כך אני מתקשר ללאה.

"רונן מטריד אותי בעניין דוח ההוצאות."

"תן לו מה שהוא מבקש."

"אני אוהב את העבודה הזו," אני אומר לה. "העבודה מלהיבה. היא בטוחה יותר מהעבודה כעצמאי שעשיתי קודם. התשלום לא רע, ויש תוכנית ביטוח בריאות מצוינת. תמיד טוב שיש ביטוח, למקרה שכדור יחדור בטעות לאיבריי הפנימיים."

"בנוסף, אנחנו עובדים עם צוות של אנשים נהדרים," היא מזכירה לי.

"עמדתי לומר את זה," אני עונה. "עמדתי גם לומר שהגדרת התפקיד שלי איננה כוללת שום דוח הוצאות."

"אין לנו הגדרת תפקיד למה שאתה עושה," מזכירה לי לאה.

"כשתכתבי אותה, אל תשכחי לכתוב שאני לא צריך להגיש דוח הוצאות."

אני שומע אותה נאנחת.

"נוכל לדבר על כך מאוחר יותר?" היא שואלת אותי.

"או קיי. רק תזכרי שאני לא מתכוון לשנות את דעתי."

—11—

אני יושב במשרד הביטוח ביום שלמחרת. לאחר עשר דקות של קריאת מאמר על אודות ביטוח אובדן כושר עבודה אני עייף כל כך שאני כמעט נופל מהכיסא. אני לוחץ על מקש החיוג המהיר בנייד שלי כדי לדבר עם לאה.

"מה?"

"החוקרת הפרטית שלנו בסביבה?"

"כן."

"תזכירי לי למה אני צריך בייביסיטר."

"אתה צריך גיבוי במקרה שהרעים ישלחו עליך צבא קטן."

"קיבלת את הדוא"ל שלי היום? בוריס העביר לי כמה שמות."

"עדינה ורונן בודקים את השמות האלה ממש עכשיו."

"למה שלא נתפוס את האנשים שבוריס סיפר לי עליהם, נזרוק אותם לתאי הכליאה במרתף המשרד, ואת תוציאי מהם את האמת. זה פשוט יותר מאשר תחקיר של עדינה ורונן במחשב."

"אתה רוצה לחטוף קצינים בכירים במשטרה?"

"בוודאי. אני יכול להטיל עליהם כישוף מוחי כדי שלא יזכרו איך אנחנו נראים."

"אני מעדיפה להיות עדינה יותר," אומרת לאה.

"הילדים צריכים עזרה בתחקיר?" אני אומר.

"לא. תישאר שם ותעמיד פנים שאתה סוכן ביטוח. תתקשר ללקוחות פוטנציאליים."

"אני שונא את זה. כולם צועקים עליי ומנתקים."

"אתה צריך לעבוד על כישורי המכירה שלך."

"אין לי אפילו רישיון לעסוק בביטוח. מה יהיה אם מישהו ירצה לקנות ממני ביטוח?"

"אני לא חושבת שאתה צריך לדאוג בנושא הזה."

ביליתי את המשך היום בציפייה לתריסר גברים חמושים שיפרצו את דלתי, אולם דבר לא קרה. עבודה במסווה אינה מסעירה תמיד.

לבסוף מגיעה השעה חמש אחר הצוהריים. אני זקוק לקפה, כך שאני פונה לבית קפה קרוב. החוקרת הפרטית ככל הנראה מאחוריי. אני מזמין קפה לאטה עם תוספת קצף, משלם לגברת עשרים שקלים ומתיישב.

אני מהרהר במחיר הגבוה של קפה ביפו, כשאדם עם עיתון בידו מתיישב בכורסה הסמוכה אליי. הוא רוכן קדימה ונותן בי מבט חודר.

אני מניח לכוסי לרעוד מעט, כך שכמות קטנה מהמשקה תישפך על השולחן. רק כדי להבהיר לו שהבעתו המאיימת עובדת.

"אמרתי לבחור השני שאביא את הכסף ביום שלישי," אני לוחש.

הבחור מביט בי במבט מבולבל ומראה לי אקדח המוסתר מאחורי העיתון שהוא אוחז.

"הבחור השני נמצא עירום מחוץ לתחנת משטרה. הוא נעצר. אני חושב שיש לך קשר לכך."

אני נותן בו מבט חלול.

"לא הורדתי לו את הבגדים, אם לזה אתה מתכוון," אני אומר לו.

"בוא נלך למקום שנוכל לשוחח בו בפרטיות," הוא אומר. "תספר לי הכל."

אני מביט בו בדאגה ואומר, "בבקשה אל תפגע בי."

"נצא להליכה," הוא אומר. "תשאיר את המשקה."

אני מצליח לארגן רעידה או שתיים תוך שאנו יוצאים מבית הקפה. אנחנו צועדים למגרש החנייה. שרה, חוקרת הפרטית, נשענת על מכונית וקוראת עיתון.

ממש כשאנו מגיעים לשרה אני מנחית על הבחור ערפול מוחי מלא. הוא נעצר ומוריד את ידיו. אני נוטל את אקדחו ומסייע לו להיכנס למושב הקדמי של הרכב.

שרה מתיישבת במושב הנהג ואילו אני כובל אותו באזיקים לדלת בצד הנוסע. אני קופץ למושב האחורי ואנחנו יוצאים לדרך.

"את נראית טוב במעיל הגשם הזה," אני אומר לשרה.

"אני שמחה שהוא מוצא חן בעיניך," היא אומרת. "איך קרה שהבחור הזה אפשר לנו לגבור עליו בלי

מאבק?"

"שמתי משהו במשקה שלו בבית הקפה."

עדיף שׁשׂרה לא תדע על כוחותי המיוחדים. אנחנו נוסעים בשתיקה במשך דקות אחדות.

"את צריכה למלא דוח הוצאות?" אני שואל אותה.

"כשאני עושה עבודה עבור לאה אני תמיד צריכה להגיש דוח הוצאות ורישום שעות. לאה מתעקשת על כך."

"מה עם אנשי הביטחון?" אני שואל.

"אני משלמת להם מחיר קבוע לכל משימה. הם מגישים לי קבלות על כל פריט מיוחד שהיה עליהם לקנות." הקבוצה שלי מחזיקה בחברת אבטחה דרך חברת קש. שרה מנהלת את החברה, והיא עובדת החברה היחידה במשרה מלאה. חברת האבטחה מספקת כוח אדם וציוד לעבודות מיוחדות עבור לקוחותינו. לשׂרה יש רשימה ארוכה של שכירי חרב ואנשי צבא לשעבר שהיא יכולה לשכור לכל אחת מהמשימות, לפי הכישורים הנדרשים.

"רונן מתחיל לעזור ללאה בניהול חשבונות המשרד," אני אומר לה. "הוא כבר מציק לי להגיש את הניירת שלי בזמן."

"זה מה שעושים אנשים בוגרים," אומרת שרה. "הם ממלאים את הניירת שלהם."

"אל תתחילי לספר לי על אחריות של מבוגרים," אני אומר לה. "אני אפילו לא בטוח שהגעת לגיל החוקי לשתיית אלכוהול."

שרה היא בת בגילו של רונן. הם חברי ילדות. שני הוריה היו חוקרים פרטיים, ובנערותה סייעה להם בחקירות. כשׁהוריה פרשו לגמלאות קיבלה שרה לידיה את העסק המשפחתי.

זמן קצר לאחר מכן הציג אותה רונן ללאה. במהלך השנים הבאות שכרה לאה את שרה למספר עבודות מיוחדות. שרה התגלתה כחוקרת פרטית מעולה. בתוך שנים אחדות הפך הצוות שלנו ללקוח העיקרי שלה.

בסופו של דבר ביקשה ממנה לאה לנהל את חברת האבטחה. שׂרה עדיין מבצעת עבודות עבור לקוחות אחרים, אולם היא מבלה את רוב זמנה בסיוע לצוות שלנו.

"למה היית צריך אותי היום?" שואלת שרה. "כל מה שעשינו היה לשים בחור לא מזיק במכונית."

"לא היינו בטוחים מה יקרה," אני אומר לה. "יכלו להיות כאן חמישה גברים עם כלבי תקיפה ובזוקות. התברר שהנוכחות שלך מיותרת, אבל תמיד טוב ללכת על בטוח."

"מילה נחמדה," היא אומרת לי. "מיותרת. איפה למדת את המילה הזאת?"

"אני אוהב להפתיע אנשים בכישורי אוצר המילים שלי."

שרה נוהגת, ואנחנו משוחחים מעט על קבוצות הכדורגל המקומיות.

שרה מפנה את המכונית אל תוך מגרש חנייה קטן למחסן סמוך למחסן באור יהודה. לאה ממתינה ליד דלת פתוחה עשויה דלת מתכת. גדר גבוהה אינה מאפשרת לאיש לראות את מגרש החנייה מהרחוב.

אני פותח את אזיקיו של השבוי שלנו. לאה מובילה אותו אל תוך הבניין. עד שיתפוגג הערפול המוחי, הוא יהיה בתא כליאה במרתף המחסן.

אז למה ממוקמת המפקדה באור יהודה? ככל הנראה לאה קבלה עסקה טובה על הבניין.

"אני צריכה טובה," אומרת לי שרה כשאנחנו נוסעים משם.

"את רוצה שאמליץ לך על אמן קעקועים טוב?"

"לא, תודה."

"מה עוד אני יכול לעשות למענך?"

"יש לי לקוח חדש. האנשים שהוא רוצה שאחקור מסוכנים מאוד. תוכל לעזור לי?"

"למה אני?"

"כי אתה ממש טוב באלימות."

"איילה לוחמת טובה יותר," אני אומר לה. "אל תביני אותי לא נכון, אני טוב למדי בלהכות אנשים. אבל היא טובה יותר."

"במקרה הזה יתכן שיהיה צורך ביריות."

"ספרי לי את הפרטים," אני אומר.

—12—

יומיים לאחר מכן ...

"אני סופרת קול אחד בעד לקרוא לעצמנו 'החוליה' וארבעה קולות נגד לקרוא לעצמנו באיזשהו שם," אומרת לאה.

"אני רוצה ספירה חוזרת," אני אומר לה.

"חיים, יש רק חמישה קולות. אני לא מתכוונת לספור אותם שוב."

"אבל כל צוות טוב צריך שם."

"נראה שאתה מפסיד שוב," אומרת עדינה. "בדיוק כמו אז כשרצית שנקנה חתול כמקמע. ההצבעה ההיא הייתה גם ארבעה נגד אחד. נדמה לי שאני רואה כאן דפוס."

עדינה היא מומחית המידע שלנו. היא מבלה את זמנה בניתוח הררי נתונים, בחיפוש אחר דפוסים. כשהיא מוצאת משהו יוצא דופן, היא פונה לרונן לסיוע. הוא מביט בנתונים ונותן תחזיות.

עדינה בדקה את כל הנתונים הנוגעים לעבירות נגד סוכני ביטוח ידועים ביפו ומצאה כמה דפוסים מעניינים. רונן סקר את הדפוסים של עדינה ואמר לנו שהאדם שמבצע את הסחיטה הוא ככל הנראה בעל תפקיד בכיר במשטרה. הוא גם הצליח לגלות מי יהיה המטרה הבאה. סוג כזה של מידע מזרז את החלטת עבודתנו.

עדינה ורונן גם מנהלים את תיק ההשקעות של הקבוצה שלנו, ומרוויחים סכומים גדולים. לאה משתמשת בסכומים הנוספים לרכישת גאדג׳טים חדשים וכלי נשק.

לרונן יש כישרון נוסף. הוא האקר מעולה. אף מחשב או רשת אינם בטוחים כאשר רונן מחליט שהוא מעוניין בפיסת מידע כלשהי.

אתם כבר יודעים שאיילה היא לוחמת מצוינת. תגובותיה מהירות יותר מהכשת נחש הקוברה, והיא מסוגלת ללמוד כל תנועת קונג פו או קראטה בתוך שניות. בנוסף, היא עוסקת גם בקישוט עוגות תחרותי.

לאה בילתה עשרים וחמש שנה בעבודה עבור רשויות אכיפת חוק שונות. כפי שציינתי, היא בעלת יכולת מיוחדת לגרום לאנשים לומר אמת. במהלך הקריירה שלה השתמשה לאה בכישרון הזה לפתרון מספר מקרים ידועים מאוד. זה היה קשה, אבל היא הצליחה לעשות זאת בלי שאיש יגלה על אודות יכולותיה ה"נוספות".

לאה פרשה לפני חמש שנים, כאשר הגיעה לגיל חמישים. במקום ללמוד גינון, היא החלה להרכיב את הצוות שלנו.

במהלך הקריירה שלה הקפידה לאה לשמור את עיניה פקוחות ואוזניה קשובות כדי למצוא אחרים בעלי כישרונות מיוחדים. כשפרשה, הייתה לה כבר רשימה של עשרה מועמדים אפשריים לצוות. שישה מהמועמדים התגלו כבעלי יכולות רגילות. ארבעה מאיתנו היו מיוחדים. אני הייתי הראשון ברשימתה של לאה.

כאשר שוחחה איתי, אמרתי לה שקראה יותר מדי ספרי קומיקס. אולם היא שכנעה אותי שנהנה, נעשה מעשים טובים, ניריה בכמה אנשים ונרוויח סכומים נאים. אז הסכמתי. זה היה לפני ארבע שנים.

לאחר מכן, היא גייסה את עדינה מצוות חשיבה ממשלתי. רונן הצטרף אלינו ממשרה של מומחה מחשבים בגוגל. איילה גויסה אחרונה. היא אימנה סוכני שב"כ בטכניקות הגנה עצמית.

אבל אני סוטה מהנושא. בחזרה לסיפור העיקרי.

אנחנו נפגשים בבסיס הבית היהפהפה שלנו. בעבר שימש המקום כמחסן למוצרי אינסטלציה. חלקי צינורות ומחברי מפרק חלודים פזורים עדיין בחלק מהחדרים שאינם בשימוש.

"מה שלום האסיר שלנו?" אני שואל.

"הוא בידי שרותי ביטחון הפנים."

"למה?"

"מתברר שהוא רוסי ששוהה כאן באופן בלתי חוקי כבר כמה שנים," אומרת לי לאה.

"הוא לא יודע דבר על האוקראינים. מישהו התקשר אליו לפני מספר ימים ושכר אותו לענות אותך עד שתספר לו מה קרה לשני הבחורים הראשונים."

"נוכל לאתר את שיחת הטלפון?"

"השיחה בוצעה מטלפון חד פעמי. האדם שמנהל את המבצע הזה חכם למדי."

בעוד לאה ואני משוחחים, מתחילים עדינה ורונן לדון אם למנדלייב היו כוחות אבולוציוניים מיוחדים. אני שואל את איילה אם מנדלייב הוא ראש ממשלת רוסיה.

"לא, הוא המציא את הטבלה המחזורית במאה ה־19," היא אומרת לי. "הוא גם ניבא את תכונותיהם של יסודות שאפילו לא התגלו עדיין."

רונן ועדינה מוסיפים להתווכח במשך מספר דקות. אחר כך הם מתחילים לצעוק. לאחר מכן הם מתגושמים.

"יאללה מכות, יאללה," אני קורא בקצב.

איילה נעמדת ומכה בעדינה וברונן ברגליהם פעמים אחדות באמצעות מקל עץ שהיא אוהבת לשאת עמה.

"איי, די. זה כואב," אומר רונן.

"בואו נסיים את הישיבה," אומרת איילה.

עדינה ורונן קמים מהרצפה, משפשפים את שוקיהם. הם מתיישבים במקומותיהם. עתה כאשר תשומת לבנו נתונה לה, ממשיכה לאה בדבריה.

"אהרון עדיין בודק את הדנ"א וטביעות האצבע כדי לנסות לאתר מאין הגיעו האוקראינים. אולי זה ייתן לנו קצה חוט."

אהרון הוא ידיד של עדינה. אני חושב שהיא מחבבת אותו. הם נפגשו במהלך לימודי הדוקטורט של עדינה. באותה עת היה כבר לאהרון תואר דוקטור בכימיה, והוא היה מומחה בחלבונים, שומנים ודברים כאלה. סידרנו לאהרון מתקן מחקר משלו לפני שנים אחדות, ומימנו חלק מהפרויקטים שלו. בתמורה, הוא מתפקד כמעבדת הזיהוי הפלילי הפרטית שלנו.

"איזושהי התקדמות עם השמות שקיבלנו מבוריס?" אני שואל.

"עדיין לא," עונה רונן. "אני כותב כמה תוכנות מיוחדות כדי לנסות לגלות מידע על אוקראינים שנכנסו לישראל. אני בודק גם את כל העברות הכספים שבוצעו על ידי אנשי המרכז של מחוז המשטרה, שהחבר של חיים טוען שמוכנים לקבל שוחד. אבדוק אחורה ככל הניתן ואראה אם יש קשרים כלשהם."

"בוריס הוא לא בדיוק חבר שלי," אני אומר.

"יש לנו לקוח שמשלם עבור החקירה הזאת?" שואלת איילה.

"לא," אומרת לאה, "אנחנו משלמים על כך מכספנו."

"איך אנחנו מצדיקים את ההוצאה?" שואל רונן.

"לפעמים אנחנו עושים דברים כי הם צריכים להיעשות," עונה לאה. "זוהי אחת מהפעמים הללו."

"רק שאלתי," אומר רונן.

"ובכן, עכשיו אתה יודע."

אנחנו משוחחים על עניינים אחרים במשך מספר דקות. רונן משתעמם ומתחיל לשחק במשחק מחשב. עשר דקות מאוחר יותר עדינה קוראת לו.

"רונן, שמעת את הדבר האחרון שלאה אמרה?"

"אני בשלב עשר עשר כרגע," הוא ממלמל.

עדינה מנסה ללחוץ על כפתור הכיבוי במחשבו הנייד של רונן. הוא דוחף אותה הצידה בידו האחת, וממשיך להקליד בידו השנייה. היא מושכת אותו החוצה מכיסאו.

"הייתי רוצה רק פעם אחת לערוך ישיבה בלי אף מריבה," אומרת לי לאה.

"הם לא באמת רבים," אני אומר לה.

"זו אשמתך," היא אומרת.

"למה את מאשימה אותי?"

"אתה לא מגיש דוחות כמו שצריך, אתה מעודד את הילדים כשהם מתחילים להשתולל, אתה מתלונן על העבודה באור יהודה. אני יכולה לציין עוד דרכים שבהן אתה משמש דוגמה רעה."

לפתע אנחנו קולטים ששלושת האחרים מתבוננים בנו.

"או קיי, אבא ואמא מתווכחים קצת. אבל אל תדאגו, אנחנו עדיין אוהבים אתכם," אני אומר להם. הם מגלגלים את עיניהם.

"עוד עניין אחד," אני אומר, "ואז תוכלו להמשיך לריב."

"מה?" שואלת עדינה.

"לשרה יש חקירה שהיא לא יכולה לנהל לבד."

"ספר לנו," אומרת לאה.

13

"שרה אמורה לחקור מועדון אופנועים."

"מגניב," אומרת איילה.

"מי שכר אותה?" שואלת לאה.

"נשיא המועדון. מישהו מהכנופייה שלו גונב מהם. הוא רוצה ששרה תעקוב אחרי האנשים שלו ותגלה מי לוקח כסף."

"איך הוא יודע שחסר כסף?" שואלת לאה.

"נשיא המועדון מנהל יומן הכנסות חודשי. ההכנסות השנה היו נמוכות מההכנסות בשנה שעברה, למרות שהמחירים עלו."

"זה נשמע כיף," אומרת עדינה. "תמיד רציתי לרכוב על אופנוע הארלי דווידסון."

"יש מפגן אופנועים ענק בכנרת בשבוע הבא," אני אומר להם. "הכנופייה תהיה שם, עסוקה בהרבה עניינים לא חוקיים. שרה חושבת שזה המקום הטוב ביותר למצוא את הגנב."

"כולנו הולכים?" שואלת עדינה.

"כן. שכנעתי את שרה שלא תוכל לעקוב אחרי כל חברי הכנופייה בעצמה. אז כולנו ניסע לעזור. ידעתי שתרצו טיול שטח."

"יש, סוף שבוע בכנרת," אומרת איילה.

—14—

ימים אחדים לאחר מכן ...

"היום יום חמישי," מזכירה לנו איילה. "הגיע הזמן לנסוע לכנרת."

"זה לא מוקדם קצת?" אני שואל. "רק עכשיו סיימנו את ארוחת הצוהריים."

"אנחנו רוצים לסייר באתר היריד ולבדוק את המוצרים שנמכרים שם," אומרת איילה.

עדינה מרימה מעיל עור נוצץ. שרוולי המעיל מקושטים בפרנזים.

"אלה מצוינים," היא אומרת ללאה.

"הם היו מוצלחים הרבה יותר אם שם הצוות היה מודפס על הגב," אני אומר.

"הגיע הזמן לוותר על הרעיון," אומר רונן.

"מצאנו עוד רמזים שיסייעו לנו למצוא את הסחטנים?" שואלת איילה.

"לא," אומרת עדינה, "לא קיבלנו עדיין תוצאות מהתוכנות של רונן."

"במהלך הימים הקרובים אנחנו לא צריכים לדאוג לגבי האוקראינים, אלא להתמקד בכנופיית האופנוענים," אומרת לנו שרה.

היא הגיעה לפני דקות אחדות, נושאת מזוודת בגדים קטנה לסוף השבוע.

"איפה נשהה?" עדינה שואלת.

"פרצתי למערכת ההזמנות של המלון," אומר רונן. "יש להם מלון בערך שמונה קילומטרים מהמקום שבו ייערך המפגן. מחקתי את השמות משש הזמנות קיימות והחלפתי אותם בשמות שלנו. יש לנו חדרים נחמדים, אבל אופנוענים אחדים עומדים להתרגז מאוד כשינסו להיכנס למלון."

"הציוד מוכן?" שואלת אותי לאה.

"כלי הנשק נקיים, ציוד התקשורת תקין, המחשבים פועלים, והוואן הועמס. כל מה שאנחנו צריכים לעשות הוא להעמיס את המזוודות שלנו."

"עדינה ורונן כבר זיהו את ארבעת חברי מועדון האופנוענים בעלי הסבירות הגבוהה ביותר לגנוב," אומרת לאה. "אחד מנהל עסק למכירת סמים. השני אחראי להברחות הנשק של הכנופייה. השלישי מוביל את מאמצי הקבוצה לחטוף משאיות והרביעי מנהל את עסקי הזנות שלהם. אלה האנשים שאחריהם נעקוב."

"עברנו על זה אתמול, כשחילקת לנו משימות ונתת לנו צילומים של כל מטרה," מזכיר לה רונן.

"לא מזיק להקדיש חמש דקות כדי לעבור שוב על החומר," היא אומרת לו.

כולם נאנחים בשעה שהיא ממשיכה לחזור על כל הפרטים שמסרה לנו ביום הקודם. לאה תופסת אותי עושה פרצופים מאחורי גבה.

"אוו," אני אומר כאשר היא חובטת ברקתי.

"לכולכם יש את הוראות ההגעה למלון ולאזור היריד?" שואלת לאה.

"הדפסתי אותן, למקרה שהניידים שלנו יאבדו קליטה," אומר רונן.

הוא מוסר עותק לכל אחד מאיתנו. אנחנו אוספים את מזוודותינו ויוצאים מהדלת האחורית של המחסן. שלושה אופנועים מבריקים וואן גדול ממתינים במגרש החנייה.

הוואן נראה יותר כמו משאית קטנה. בצדי המשאית ממוקמים תאי אחסון, שבהם מאוחסן כל הציוד שלנו. בחלקו המרכזי של הוואן יש שלושה מושבים ושולחן כתיבה קטן מוברג לרצפה. נוכל להשתמש בו בתור משרד כשאנו חונים. בתא הקדמי יש מקום לארבעה אנשים.

שכרתי את כל כלי הרכב ימים אחדים קודם לכן. לאה נועלת את הבניין בעוד הילדים מעמיסים את הכבודה שלנו בוואן. עדינה, רונן ואיילה לובשים את מעילי העור שלהם, קופצים על אופנועיהם ומתרחקים בשאון מנועים. שרה, לאה ואני נוסעים אחריהם בוואן. כולנו נרגשים לקראת הטיול.

מאוחר יותר אחר הצוהריים אנחנו מגיעים למתחם היריידים שבו מתקיים המפגן. אנחנו מבלים את השעות הבאות בבדיקת דוכני המכירה הממוקמים סביב ארבעה אוהלים גדולים. לארוחת הערב אנחנו קונים מבחר של פלאפל, שווארמה ופופקורן.

אופנוענים מכל אזור הגליל כבר החלו להגיע. הם נראים נבזיים. אני שמח שהאקדח שלי טעון.

בשעה תשע רועמים אל תוך מתחם היריידים הלקוח שלנו וקבוצת הנבלים שלו. הם מונים עשרים איש. אנשים מרושעים וכעורים למראה.

אנחנו מתחלקים כדי לעקוב אחר ארבע המטרות שלנו. הבחור שלי משעמם למדי. אני צופה בו שותה כמויות עצומות של בירה ומתווכח עם חברתו בעת שהם מטיילים ברחבי מתחם היריידים. בסביבות השעה אחת עשרה, אני שומע קול מוכר מאחוריי. אני מסתובב ורואה את עדינה ורונן נשענים על דוכן.

"רונן, אל תאכל כל כך הרבה צמר גפן מתוק," אומרת עדינה.

"את לא אמא שלי," עונה לה רונן.

אני חומק לעברם.

"אני לא חושב שאתם זקוקים למשקפי השמש, כבר חושך," אני אומר.

"כן, אבל אנחנו נראים בהם כל כך מגניב," עונה עדינה.

"הבחור שלך עשה משהו חשוד?" שואל רונן.

"שום דבר מיוחד עד כה. הוא בדיוק נפטר מהחברה שלו והלך אל הבחור שאתם עוקבים אחריו."

"הי, הנה חבר מכנופייה אחרת הולך לדבר איתם," אומר רונן.

"אני אתקרב," אומרת עדינה.

"אין צורך," אני אומר. "נוכל להקשיב להם מכאן."

אני מוציא מכשיר אלקטרוני קטן מכיסי ומכוון אותו לעבר שלושת האופנוענים.

"זו המילה האחרונה בטכנולוגיית המיקרופונים," אני אומר להם תוך שאני מחבר אוזנייה קטנה לאוזני השמאלית.

"מה הם אומרים?" שואלת אותי עדינה.

"לא נראה שזה עובד."

"חשבתי שבדקת את כל הציוד."

"ובכן, בדקתי את רובו."

"לא משהו כל הטכנולוגיה המשוכללת הזאת," אומרת עדינה. "אני מתקרבת. תראו איך אני משתלבת בסביבה."

"אני לא חושב שהיא תשתלב היטב," אני אומר לרונן כשעדינה מתרחקת מאתנו. "לא חסרות לה שיניים, יש לה ריח נעים וציפורניה נקיות. היא נראית כמו אמא מהפרברים במעיל עור."

האופנוענים עומדים בחזיתו של דוכן למכירת צמידים ועגילים. עדינה פוסעת כלאחר יד עד למרחק של כמטר מהאופנוענים ומעמידה פנים שהיא בוחנת את התכשיטים. בתוך דקות אחדות, שלושת הגברים נועצים בה מבטים. אופנוען אחד אומר משהו. האחרים צוחקים. היא מתעלמת מהם. אופנוען אחר תופס בזרועה ואומר עוד משהו. היא סוטרת לו.

"הישאר כאן," אומר רונן.

הוא ניגש אל שלושת האופנוענים ומנסה למשוך משם את עדינה. שניים מהם תופסים אותו. שלושת האופנוענים דוחפים ומושכים את שני שותפיי אל תוך אוהל סמוך. המוכר רואה את המתרחש, אולם אינו עושה דבר.

אני צועד אל תוך האוהל עשר שניות לאחר מכן. האוהל ריק, מלבד מספר נגנים המתאמנים לקראת הופעתם הבאה. אחד מהם רואה את עדינה ורונן נאבקים וצועק על האופנוענים. האופנוען האוחז בעדינה משחרר את אחיזתו בה בידו האחת. הוא מפנה אליה את גבו כדי להראות לנגן את אצבעו האמצעית. זו טעות.

היא שולפת אלה מכיס מעילה וחובטת איתה ברגלו של האיש. האלה מכה בעצם השוקה. הבחור מיילל ונופל לקרקע.

עדינה חובטת בכיוון ההפוך והאלה שורקת לכיוונו של אחד הגברים המחזיקים ברונן. הוא מנסה להתכופף, אולם רונן נאבק בפראות כזו שהוא מתקשה לחמוק מהאלה. האלה חובטת הישר במצחו. הוא מתפורר כמו

עוגייה ישנה.

עדינה מסתובבת בחזרה לבחור הראשון. הוא על הקרקע, אוחז ברגלו. היא רוקעת על ברכו השנייה במגפי האופנועים שלה והוא צורח.

הבחור השלישי תופס בעדינה ומנסה למשוך אותה הצידה לפני שתצליח לגרום לנזק נוסף. לפתע הוא נופל. הוא שוכב על הקרקע, מפרפר. אני מבחין שרונן אוחז בטייזר. רונן בועט בשניים מהאופנועים בעת שהוא ועדינה מתרחקים מהמקום.

״ובכן, אני חושב שהכיסוי שלכם התגלה,״ אני אומר להם. ״למה שלא תלכו למתחם האוכל ותשתלבו שם בקהל.״

״זה היה נהדר,״ אומר רונן.

״תודה על עזרתך,״ אומרת לו עדינה, ״אבל הסתדרתי.״

כשהם מתרחקים, הם מתחילים להתווכח האם עדינה יכלה להסתדר עם כל שלושת האופנועים לבדה. אני צועד לאיטי לעבר הנגנים ומציג את עצמי.

״כמעט נכנסתם לצרות כאן,״ אני אומר.

״אני שונא את ההופעות האלה,״ אומר נגן הגיטרה. ״האופנועים תמיד עושים צרות.״

״אבל התשלום טוב, והכנרת נעימה בעונה הזאת,״ אומר המתופף.

״מה יקרה לשלושת הבחורים ששוכבים שם?״ אני שואל.

״בסוף הם יקומו וילכו לחורשה להתמסטל.״

״אחד מהם מחוסר הכרה,״ אני מציין.

״יש וואן אבטחה שעובר כאן כל חצי שעה. אם הוא עדיין יהיה כאן, הם יקחו אותו לעזרה ראשונה.״

״אני חושב שאכתוב שיר על הבחורה הזו עם האלה,״ אומר המתופף. ״היא הייתה מדהימה.״

בבוקר למחרת אנחנו מחליפים רשמים.

״הבחור האחראי על מכירת הסמים לא גונב,״ אומרת שרה.

״איך את יודעת?״ שואלת לאה.

״איילה ואני בדקנו את הפעילות אמש. הוא מנהל טוב. שני אנשים מנהלים רישום כמה הם נותנים לכל שליח וכמה כסף כל שליח מחזיר. בלתי אפשרי למי מהמעורבים לגנוב משהו.״

״עדינה ורונן אשפזו את הבחור שלהם בבית החולים עם פיקת ברך שבורה. והם גרמו לבחור שלי זעזוע מוח. הבחורים האלה לא גנבו כלום אתמול בלילה,״ אני אומר.

לאה כבר סלחה לעדינה ולרונן על הקרב שניהלו עם האופנוענים. היא מאשימה אותי בכל העניין. רק בגלל שהמיקרופון לא פעל.

"האיש שאחריו עקבתי הוא הגנב," אומרת לאה. "הוא אחראי על עסקי הזנות."

"לא ראיתי שום זונות," אומר רונן.

"הן הגיעו במיני וואן נפרד. הכנופייה הקימה חמישה עשר אוהלים בחורשה. הבנות עבדו מהאוהלים. העסקים שלהם פרחו."

"למה לא נאמר לי דבר על האוהלים הללו?" אני דורש לדעת.

"איך את יודעת שהאחראי גונב?" שואלת שרה.

"ספרתי את מספר הגברים והנשים שנכנסו לכל אחד מהאוהלים," אומרת לאה. "הערכתי את הסכום הכולל שהרוויחו הזונות על ידי הכפלת מספר הלקוחות במחיר עסקה. הבחור האחראי על העסק מסר פחות מחמישים אחוזים מההערכה שלי."

"למה נשיא המועדון לא יכול היה להבין זאת בעצמו?" אני שואל.

"הוא היה שיכור כלוט כשעה אחרי שהכנופייה הגיעה. לא הייתה לו שום אפשרות לדעת כמה לקוחות קיבלו שירות."

שעות אחדות מאוחר יותר, אני מטיל ערפול מוחי על הבחור האחראי על עסקי הזנות ומושך אותו אל תוך הוואן שלנו. לאה משוחחת איתו במשך עשר דקות ומקליטה את תשובותיו.

זוכרים שסיפרתי לכם שהיא יכולה להוציא את האמת מכל אחד? הבחור מספר לה כמה זמן הוא כבר גונב, כמה גנב, ואת מיקומה של הכספת שבה הוא שומר את הכסף.

עם תום החקירה, אני מוחק את קולה של לאה מההקלטה. לאחר מכן אני מכין שני עותקים לשרה עבור הלקוח שלה. לבסוף, אני מטשטש את זיכרונו של האופנוען, ואז אני מורידים אותו.

כאשר יתעורר, הוא יחשוב שברנש מפחיד בגיל העמידה גרר אותו לתוך וואן, כפת אותו ואיים לנעוץ סכין בעינו אם לא יודה הודאה מלאה.

לאה עוזבת, ואני מתקשר לשרה בטלפון הנייד. כעבור מספר דקות היא מכניסה את נשיא מועדון האופנוענים אל הוואן.

"מי הבחור הזה?" הוא שואל כשהוא רואה אותי.

"אני הבריון השכיר שלה," אני אומר לו.

"אתה לא נראה כל כך קשוח."

"קשוח מספיק כדי להוציא הודאה מלאה מהאיש שלך. הנה ההקלטה."

הוא מביט בשותפו הכפות הישן בפינת הוואן.

"מה עשיתם לו?"

"סמוך עלי, אינך רוצה לדעת."

ראש הכנופייה מאושר מאוד אחרי שהוא שומע את ההקלטה. הוא שולף מכיסו חבילת שטרות של מאה שקל ומשלם לשרה. לאחר מכן הוא גורר את האיש שלו אל מחוץ לוואן ומוסר אותו למספר חבר'ה. אני מבחין ששרה בוכה קצת אחרי שהאופנועים עוזבים.

"מה קרה?"

"הם הולכים להרוג את הבחור. הייתי צריכה להסגיר אותו למשטרה."

"אם לא היית מוסרת אותו לכנופייה הם היו מנסים להרוג אותנו," אני אומר לה. "חוץ מזה, האיש סיפר לי בחקירה שהוא ביצע כמה מעשי רצח שאיש אינו יודע עליהם. כך שהוא מקבל מין סוג גס של צדק."

"אני עדיין מרגישה רע."

בדיוק אז מגיעים לאה ושאר חברי הקבוצה שלנו. רונן נושא שקית גדולה של פופקורן ובקבוק קוקה קולה גדול.

"אנחנו יכולים להישאר כאן עד סוף המפגן?" שואלת איילה.

"ודאי, החזירי את האופנועים למשרד ההשכרה ביום ראשון ואנחנו נאסוף אתכם משם," אומרת לאה.

שרה משוחחת עם לאה מספר דקות ומחליטה לשכור רכב ולחזור ליפו לבד.

"היא צריכה קצת זמן לעצמה," מספרת לי לאה לאחר דקות אחדות.

"זה לא שהיא ירתה לבחור בראש," אני אומר. "היא נאלצה להסגיר אותו לכנופייה."

"אבל היא בכל זאת מאוד מצוברחת."

לאה ואני יוצאים לדרכנו בוואן. אנחנו מחליטים להעביר את הלילה באכסניה קטנה וחמודה, כולל ארוחת בוקר, בגליל.

"את יודעת," אני אומר ללאה, "היה יכול להיות קל יותר אם היית חוקרת כל אחד מארבעת חברי הכנופייה בנפרד. יכולת לקבל את כל התשובות מבלי לבלות את סוף השבוע במפגן האופנוענים."

"אם הייתי עושה זאת, גם שרה וגם מנהיג הכנופייה היו מבינים שיש לי כוחות מיוחדים."

"נכון," אני אומר.

"ובנוסף, זה היה סוף שבוע נחמד. הילדים ממש נהנו ללבוש מעילי עור ולרכוב על אופנועים ענקיים," אומרת לאה.

"שרה שמרה עותק של ההודאה לעצמה," אומרת לי לאה דקות אחדות לאחר מכן. "היא מתכוונת לתת אותו למשטרה, עם ראיות אחרות לפעילות הבלתי חוקית של הכנופייה, שאספה במשך סוף השבוע."

"תודאי שהיא תחכה כמה חודשים ותעשה זאת באופן שהכנופייה לא תוכל לעלות על עקבותיה," אני אומר. "אעשה זאת."

יום רביעי מביא עמו חדשות טובות.

"רונן מצא את שמם ותמונותיהם של שלושה אוקראינים נוספים שעשויים להיות חלק מכנופיית הסחיטה," אומרת עדינה.

"איך הוא עשה זאת?" שואלת איילה.

"הוא כתב תוכנה שבדקה את נתוניהם של נוסעי חברת ארופלוט והשוותה אותם למאגר הנתונים של משטרת אוקראינה. התוכנה זיהתה ארבעה גברים בעלי פלילי שטסו לארץ עם ארופלוט במהלך השנה האחרונה. הבחור שלאה חקרה בבת ים היה אחד מהם. שלושת האחרים הגיעו מאותה עיר."

"אנחנו יודעים איך שלושת הגברים הללו נראים?" שואלת איילה.

"כן," אומרת עדינה. "למזלנו, ארופלוט מתעדת את תעודת הזהות הנושאת תמונה של כל נוסע."

"לא ממש מתחשק לי לבלות שבועות בלהראות תצלומים של הבחורים הללו לאנשים בכל רחבי יפו," אני אומר.

"העולים האוקראינים ביפו ובתל אביב מרוכזים בשני אזורים קטנים מאוד," אומרת לי לאה. "לא ייקח זמן רב למצוא אותם."

באותו לילה, איילה, שרה ואני נוסעים לאזור האוקראיני ביפו, מתחם קטן באזור שדרות ירושלים. אנחנו נוסעים במכוניות נפרדות.

איילה מסתובבת במועדוני הסנוקר. שרה בודקת את חנויות המכולת והמכבסות. אני בודק את הברים ומועדוני הסטריפטיז. אין מזל בלילה הראשון.

"פגשתי שני מכונאי רכב במועדון הסנוקר שהציעו לי נישואין," מספרת לי איילה בטלפון הנייד כשאני נוהג הביתה.

אנחנו מנסים את אותו אזור בלילה השני. שרה מתקשרת אליי בשתים בלילה.

"מצאת משהו?" היא שואלת.

"אף אחד לא מזהה את התצלומים," אני אומר לה.

"קיבלת ריקוד?" היא שואלת.

"הבחורות שרוקדות במועדונים האלה הן לא הטיפוס שלי," אני אומר לה. "וכמה ברמנים הציעו לארגן מחדש את האף שלי אם לא אפסיק להטריד את הלקוחות שלהם."

"כמה מרגש," אומרת שרה.

"איפה את עכשיו?" אני שואל.

"עוזרת לאיילה להראות את התצלומים במועדוני הסנוקר."

"אתן נהנות?"

"בחור אחד בשם ג'ורג'י לימד אותי איך לאחוז את המקל."

"נחמד. בעוד כמה שנים תוכלי לצאת לסיבובי תחרויות."

"ג'ורג'י אומר שאין לי מספיק ריכוז."

"את מרגישה טוב יותר לגבי הסגרת הבחור שגנב מכנופיית האופנוענים?" אני שואל.

"נראה לי שאוכל לחיות עם זה."

"יופי."

למחרת בלילה מתמזל מזלנו. אני פוגש בחור בבר בחור כלשהו, סמוך לתחנת דלק שנאטמה בקרשים, והוא מזהה את התצלומים שאני מראה לו.

"הם גרים כולם בדירה בבניין שלי," הוא אומר. "אנשים רעים מאוד."

18

שלושים וחמש דקות מאוחר יותר פוגשות אותי איילה ושרה בבניין שבו מתאכסנים שלושת האוקראינים. אנחנו נכנסים למכונית שלי כדי לערוך שיחת ועידה עם לאה.

"אנחנו צריכים אסירים," אומרת לי לאה בטלפון. "אל תירו בכולם."

"אני אשאר בחוץ למקרה שמישהו ינסה לברוח דרך יציאת החירום," אומרת שרה. "אוכל גם לטפל בשוטרים אם הם יופיעו פתאום."

אני משתמש במוט מתכת דק כדי לפרוץ את הדלת הראשית של הבניין. אני לא עושה הרבה רעש. למרבה המזל, זו שעת לילה מאוחרת. הכל שקט בזמן שאיילה ואני חומקים במעלה המדרגות. באקדח שלי מותקן משתיק קול. אין טעם להעיר אנשים.

האסטרטגיה שלנו פשוטה. איילה תכה את הבחורים הרעים עד שייכנעו. אם לא ייכנעו, אני אירה בהם. בתקווה שאחד מהם יחזיק מעמד בחיים זמן מספיק לאפשר ללאה לדבר איתו.

אנחנו חומקים לאורך מסדרון הקומה השנייה ומקשיבים מעבר לדלת דירה 2. מעבר לדלת נשמעים קולות נחירה רמים. נחירה זה טוב. יריבינו ישנים.

אני מבחין באיילה מחליקה אגרופן על ידה הימנית.

"למה את צריכה את זה?" אני שואל.

"אני לא רוצה לשבור את ציפורניי. רק עכשיו סידרתי אותן."

"אני לא בטוח שזה יעבוד."

אני משתמש במפתח הגנבים הנאמן שלי כדי לפתוח בשקט את דלת הדירה. אנחנו פוסעים פנימה ורואים שני גברים ישנים על ספה מול טלוויזיה קטנה. אני מכה בראשם באלה שלי. בעוד אני כובל אותם באזיקים, חומקת איילה במורד המסדרון בחיפוש אחר חברם.

לרוע המזל יש להם חתול. מי היה מצפה שבריונים אוקראינים יאהבו חתולים ? הדבר הזה משמיע יללה בעת שאיילה עושה את דרכה לאורך המסדרון.

כשהיא מגיעה אל דלת חדר השינה, נפתחת הדלת בפתאומיות. האדם השלישי, שהוזהר על ידי החתול, מזנק עליה. הבחור זריז.

הוא תופס את איילה בגרונה לפני שהיא מספיקה לזוז. הוא גבוה מאיילה בחמישה סנטימטרים וכבד ממנה בעשרים קילוגרמים. הוא דוחף אותה כנגד הקיר ומתחיל לחנוק אותה. אני יושב על הספה וצופה בקרב.

איילה חובטת בברכה במפשעתו. הוא משחרר את אחיזתו בצווארה והיא מנסה לשבור את אפו בכף ידה. הוא חוסם את החבטה באמת ידו ושולח חבטת מרפק אל עבר לחיה. היא מזיזה את ראשה והמרפק פוער חור בקיר שמאחוריה.

איילה פוסעת אחורה אל חדר המגורים כדי להימצא במרחב גדול יותר. יריבה נמצא ממש מעליה. המכה במפשעתו לא האטה אותו. הבחור הזה קשוח.

היא שולחת אגרוף מצויד באגרופן אל סנטרו. הוא בולם את המכה וחובט בה בפלג גופו העליון. לאיילה יש שיווי משקל של רקדנית בלט. היא מדלגת אחורה כחצי מטר ונוחתת בעמידת קרב מושלמת.

הוא מניף לכיוונה אגרוף בריוני. היא בולמת אותו באמת ידה. אני שומע עצם מתפצחת. הוא מנסה לשלוח בעיטה סיבובית לצד גופה. היא מרימה רגל ותופסת את הבעיטה בירכה.

היא נרתעת ומדלגת צעד נוסף לאחור. הוא מדשדש קדימה בניסיון להטעות ולהכות. ואז הוא נסוג במהירות לאחור ומכוון בעיטה אל ראשה. הבעיטה מהירה ואכזרית. כמעט ולא רואים את רגלו ממהירות תנועתה לכיוונה.

אבל איילה היא לוחמת מדהימה. היא מתכופפת אל מתחת לטווח הבעיטה והולמת בברכו האחרת באגרופן. אני שומע צליל הדומה לצליל ריסוק קרח והבחור נאנק. למרבה התדהמה, הוא אינו נופל. הוא מוריד את רגלו השנייה לקרקע ומתייצב.

אני לא יודע אם הוא מועד על שטיח המונח על הרצפה, או אם ברכו המנופצת כורעת תחתיה. אך הוא מתנודד מעט – רק מספיק כדי לאפשר לאיילה פרצה. היא פועלת במהירות ומכה בברכה במפשעתו שוב. ואז היא מעיפה את ראשו לאחור במכת מרפק לסנטרו. צווארו נותר חשוף. היא מכה בגרונו באגרופן.

הבחור נופל. אני צועד קדימה ומביט בו. גרונו מרוסק. הוא נלחם על נשימה שלא תבוא לעולם. האור בעיניו מתפוגג לאיטו.

אני שולח לשרה הודעה בטלפון הסלולרי, והיא מופיעה מיד עם נייר דבק ושקים. שרה ואני כופתים בנייר דבק את שני הבחורים מחוסרי ההכרה ותוחבים אותם אל תוך שני שקים גדולים. לאחר מכן אנחנו גוררים אותם למטה, למכונית שלי.

בזמן שאנחנו טורחים על העברת הבחורים, איילה בודקת את הדירה. שרה ואני משליכים את הבחורים אל תוך מכוניתי וממהרים בחזרה למעלה לסייע לאיילה. שרה עוזרת לאיילה לרדת במדרגות בעוד אני נושא שק

מלא בחפצים שאיילה חשבה שנרצה לבחון. ידה השמאלית של איילה תלויה לצידה.

בדרכנו למטה אנחנו נתקלים באחת מדיירות הבניין, שהתעוררה בעקבות הרעש. אני מערפל את מוחה כשאנחנו חולפים על פניה. אנחנו משאירים בדירה את הבחור המת. כשאנחנו מגיעים למכונית אני מעיף מבט בחפצים שאיילה אספה בשק.

"מחשב נייד, טלפונים סלולריים אחדים, חשבונות ופנקס המחאות. יתכן שיש לנו ראיות כלשהן."

"אני צריכה צילום רנטגן ליד שלי," אומרת איילה.

"תוכלי לנהוג ביד אחת?" אני שואל.

"ודאי," היא עונה.

אני לא צריך להזכיר לאיילה ללכת למרפאה הפרטית שקבוצתנו נעזרת בה במקרי חירום רפואיים. היא מנוהלת על ידי רופא המטפל באנשים המשלמים במזומן ואינם מציינים את שמם האמיתי. לפני שאנחנו נוסעים משם, מושכת אותי איילה הצידה.

"לא הפעלת את עניין הערפול המחשבתי על האוקראיני, נכון?"

"בשום אופן לא," אני אומר. "נהניתי לראות אותו חובט בך. הכרעת אותו ללא כל עזרה ממני."

היא מנידה בראשה בסיפוק. איילה תחרותית מאוד.

למחרת אנחנו עורכים ישיבת צוות נוספת.

"מה הוצאת מהמחשבים האוקראינים שלנו?" אני שואל את לאה.

"הם סיפרו לי על חמישה קורבנות נוספים, ששילמו להם הרבה כסף," היא אומרת.

"הם עשו זאת הרבה יותר זמן ממה שחשבנו," אני אומר. "גם הקורבנות הנוספים הם סוכני ביטוח?"

"לא, הם היו יועצים פיננסים עצמאיים."

"זה קרוב למדי," אני אומר. "את יודעת מי הבוס?"

"עדיין לא. רונן עדיין מוציא מידע מהמחשב שמצאתם בדירה. החבר'ה האלה היו טיפשים דיים לנהל יומן של כל פעולותיהם. אנחנו יודעים איפה הם התאכסנו, עם מי שוחחו, מתי קיבלו שיחות טלפון מהבוס, דברים כאלה. אני מקווה שכל זה יסייע לנו איכשהו."

"אז מתי לדעתך נקבל מידע מבוסס יותר?" שואלת איילה.

ידה נתונה בגבס והליכתה צולעת מעט.

"תוך כמה ימים, אני מקווה."

יומיים לאחר מכן מתקשרת אליי עדינה.

"תפסנו אותו," היא אומרת.

"אז מי הגאון הקרימינלי הגדול?"

"פקד במשטרת מטה מחוז מרכז, שמו דוד כהן."

"איך מצאת אותו?"

"בוריס נתן לנו את שמו עם כמה שמות נוספים. בדקנו את כל קבלות כרטיס האשראי שלו. נחש מה."

"מה?"

"הוא שילם לרופא שיניים כדי לעקור שן לאחד מהבחורים האוקראינים. אתה יכול להאמין?"

"מפתיע אותי שהוא לא שילם במזומן," אני אומר.

"זו הייתה הטעות היחידה שלו."

"אז ביליתי שלושה לילות ביפו, צופה בנשים משופמות מתפשטות, לחינם?"

"המאמץ השתלם, כי מצאנו את שאר חברי הכנופייה."

"מה לאה עשתה בשני השבויים?"

"עטפה אותם בסרט ושלחה אותם למישהו במטה מחוז מרכז בשם זוהר. העברנו לו גם את שמות הקורבנות האחרים, את היומן שניהלו האוקראינים ואת העובדה שפקד כהן שילם עבור טיפול השיניים של אחד הבחורים."

"זה בוודאי יעשה אותו מאושר," אני אומר.

בשבוע שלאחר מכן, מתפרסם סיפור גדול בעיתונים. פקד דוד כהן ממשטרת יפו נעצר והואשם בניהול עסקי סחיטה גדולים ביפו. הכתבות מפרטות את כל הקורבנות ואת שמותיהם של הבריונים האוקראינים שנשכרו לבצע את העבודה המלוכלכת.

יומיים מאוחר יותר, מתפרסם סיפור נוסף בעיתונים. החוקרים מצאו כספת ושני חשבונות בנק בחו"ל על שמו של פקד כהן. בחשבונות נמצאו כמה מאות אלפי שקלים. הכספת מלאה ביהלומים גולמיים.

"הם לא היו מגלים את הכסף ואת הכספת אם לא הייתי שולח לבלש זוהר דוא"ל אנונימי," אומר רונן.

"חבל שאיש לא ידע לעולם על כשרונך למצוא דברים בעזרת כישורי פריצת המחשבים שלך," אני אומר לו.

שימוע השחרור בערבות של פקד כהן נערך באולמו של שופט החייב לו טובות אחדות. הוא משוחרר ממעצר לאחר שהפקיד ערבות בסך חצי מיליון שקלים. כך מתנהלים הדברים ביפו אם יש לך חברים.

העניינים נרגעים למשך ימים אחדים, בעוד רונן ועדינה עוברים על מחשבם של האוקראינים בחיפוש אחר ראיות נוספות לשלוח לבלש זוהר. ואז בולע פקד כהן חצי בקבוק רעל ומת בביתו. אנחנו עורכים ישיבת צוות למחרת.

"את סבורה שהיו למשטרה ראיות מספיקות לשלוח את פקד כהן לכלא לזמן ממושך?" אני שואל את לאה.

"אני לא חושבת. אם הוא היה שוכר עורך דין טוב, בוודאי היה מרצה כמה שנים במקרה הטוב."

"אז למה שיתאבד? רונן, צפית את זה?"

"אם הייתי חושב שהוא עומד להרעיל את עצמו, הייתי מפסיק לחפש ראיות כבר לפני כמה ימים."

"אולי אנחנו צריכים לבחון את הדברים מזווית אחרת," מציעה לאה.

20

שבועיים מאוחר יותר ...

"אתה נראה קצת טוב יותר היום," אני אומר למיכאל הרשקו.

אנחנו אוכלים את הכריכים שהבאתי לביתו.

"הפסקת לקחת את התרופה ההיא?"

"כן," הוא אומר לי. "דיברתי עם יועצת אבל, כמו שהצעת לי בארוחת הצוהריים האחרונה שלנו. היא עזרה לי להתמודד עם אובדן אשתי. סוף סוף אני מתחיל להחזיר את חיי חזרה למסלולם."

"זה מצוין."

אנחנו משוחחים עוד קצת על הפגישות הטיפוליות שלו. הודות לכישוף המוחי שלי, הוא עדיין חושב שאני חברו לביטוח. לבסוף אני מגיע לעניין.

"כמעט הצלחת," אני אומר לו.

"הא?" הוא שואל.

"אתה יודע - הסחיטה, רצח אשתך, ואפילו הריגת פקד כהן."

"אין לי מושג על מה אתה מדבר," הוא אומר.

"כן, אתה יודע. אנחנו יודעים שאתה ניהלת את כל עסקי הסחיטה."

"אתה מהמשטרה?" הוא שואל.

"אני חבר בקבוצה שבילתה את ארבעה עשר הימים האחרונים בבחינת כל היבט בחייך," אני אומר. "אתה גייסת את פקד כהן להביא את האוקראינים. אתה בחרת את קורבנות הסחיטה. אתה ירית בשלושה אנשים, אחת מהם אשתך שלך. ואתה הרעלת את פקד כהן כאשר העניינים התחילו להסתבך."

"אתה מטורף," הוא אומר לי. "איפה ההוכחות שלך?"

"מצאנו את המקום שבו קנית את הרעל. יש להם עדיין את סרט המעקב של כל העסקאות שנעשו באותו יום. פניך נראים בבירור בסרט הזה. בנוסף, הקופאי זוכר אותך."

מר הרשקו שולף אקדח מכיסו ומכוון אותו אליי. אני יושב ללא תנועה בעוד הוא צועד מאחורי שולחן האוכל וטופח עליי כדי לבדוק אם אני נושא נשק או מכשיר האזנה. לאחר מכן הוא מתיישב ונוגס שוב בכריך ההודו שלו. האקדח עדיין מכוון אליי.

"אתה טיפש מאוד אם באת הנה להגיד את הדברים הללו," הוא אומר לי. "חשבת שאשלם לך כדי שתשתוק?"

"רק רציתי את הסיפוק בלומר לך פנים אל פנים שלא תתחמק מפשעיך."

הוא צוחק עליי.

"עשית טעות גדולה," הוא אומר.

"למעשה, פקד כהן עשה את הטעות. אם הוא לא היה משלם בכרטיס האשראי שלו עבור טיפול השיניים של האוקראיני שניכם הייתם יוצאים נקיים. לא היו לנו הוכחות מספיקות להאשים מישהו במשהו עד שמצאנו את התשלום בכרטיס האשראי."

"למי אתה מתכוון כשאתה אומר 'אנחנו'?" הוא שואל.

"הקבוצה שלי. אני רציתי שנקרא לעצמנו ה'חוליה', אבל ערכנו הצבעה ואני הפסדתי. כך שאנחנו קוראים לעצמנו סתם הצוות. אני לא מורשה אפילו לקנות מעילי צוות."

"עישנת?" הוא שואל אותי. "אין היגיון בדבריך. איזו הצבעה?"

"זה לא חשוב."

מיכאל הרשקו נאנח.

"אתה עומד לספר לי על הצוות שלך."

"לא, אני לא."

"אם לא, אני אירה לך בברך, ואז בברך השנייה, ואז במרפק, עד שלבסוף תספר לי."

אני מכה אותו בערפול מוחי מלא. הוא מניח את זרועותיו לצידי גופו. אני לוקח את האקדח וכובל אותו באזיקים. לאחר מכן אני מתקשר לשרה בטלפון הנייד. היא מגיעה לאחר דקות אחדות.

"שמת כדור במשקה שלו?" היא שואלת.

"מה?" אני אומר.

"הוא כמעט רדום. איך עשית זאת?"

"כמעט שכחתי. תיבלתי את המשקה שלו."

"מה הלאה?" שואלת שרה.

"את תקשרי אותו. אני אשתול ראיות שיקשרו אותו לכל פשע אפשרי מאז הרצח של ארלוזורוב. אחר כך אתקשר למשטרה מהטלפון הנייד של הרשקו."

"כאן סמל בלש אלברט זוהר, זהו קו מוקלט. מה שמך בבקשה?"

"זה לא חשוב."

אני מדבר בקול משונה רק כדי להרגיז אותו.

"אמרת לפקיד הקבלה שאתה רוצה לעזור לי בכמה מהחקירות שלי."

"כן. פתרתי אותן עבורך."

"אני לא אדבר איתך עד שתאמר לי את שמך."

"אז תראה ממש טיפשי כאשר אמסור את המידע שברשותי לעיתונות ואציין שלא היית מעוניין להקשיב."

שמעתי אותו רוטן מתחת לשפמו.

"או קיי, דבר איתי."

"אדם בשם מיכאל הרשקו רצח את אשתו לפני כשישה חודשים. אתם חשבתם שהיא נרצחה בגלל סחיטה שנכשלה, אבל הוא לחץ על ההדק."

"ואיך אתה יודע זאת?"

"הוא מעולם לא נפטר מהאקדח שלו. תשלחו מישהו לביתו. אתם יודעים איפה הוא גר. הוא קשור והאקדח מונח על הרצפה לידו. טביעות האצבע שלו נמצאות על האקדח."

זוהר משתהה למשך שניות אחדות, כדי לעכל את המידע.

"אני יכול לשים אותך בהמתנה?" הוא שואל.

"אם תעשה זאת, אני אנתק את השיחה ולא תדע את כל הסיפור. דרך אגב, אני מדבר מהטלפון הנייד של הרשקו."

"או קיי, תמשיך."

"אותו האקדח הרג את שני סוכני הביטוח, אבל אתה כבר יודע זאת."

"כן."

"מר הרשקו היה המוח שמאחורי תוכנית הסחיטה. הוא גייס את פקד דוד כהן ורצח אותו כאשר פקד כהן שוחרר בערבות."

"איך אתה יודע את זה?"

"השארתי פתק ליד האקדח. כתוב בו איפה נרכש הרעל. לחנות יש מצלמת מעקב המראה את הרשקו קונה את הרעל. מנהל החנות מחכה שתאסוף את הווידיאו. בנוסף, הקופאי זוכר את הרשקו קונה את הרעל."

"מה עוד?" הוא שואל.

"ערוך השוואה בין רישומי חשבון הבנק של הרשקו ורישומי חשבון הבנק של פקד כהן. אתה תראה שיש משיכות והפקדות תואמות."

"לכהן היו חשבונות בחו"ל. לא יכולנו לעקוב אחרי התשלומים. נראה שהכסף הגיע לשם מהחלל החיצון," הוא אומר.

"אתה צריך האקר טוב יותר. האיש שלי ישלח לך דוא"ל עם הסבר מפורט איך הועבר הכסף בין החשבונות. אחרי שתוציא צו לכל הרישומים תראה שכהן והרשקו היו קשורים זה לזה כמו תאומים סיאמיים."

"מי זה?"

ניתקתי את השיחה.

— 22 —

כעבור חמישה ימים, הופיעה כתבה גדולה בעיתונים על מיכאל הרשקו ופקד דוד כהן. איילה מקריאה את הכתבה לכולנו.

"שמת את אצבעותיו של האוקראיני הראשון בבית של הרשקו!" אומרת עדינה. "זה מגעיל!"

"חשבתי שזו הייתה תוספת נחמדה," אני אומר.

"השוטרים יבינו שהרשקו לא היה קוטע את אצבעותיו של מישהו מעובדיו," אומר רונן.

"יכול להיות, אבל זה נותן לעיתונאים ולבלוגרים משהו לצעוק עליו."

"מדוע הרשקו הרג את אשתו ואת שני סוכני הביטוח?" שואלת איילה.

"היא לא הפסיקה לצעוק עליו שיוריד את מושב האסלה," מתלוצץ רונן.

אני מגחך מעט.

"נוכל לא לצחוק על קורבנות רצח?" שואלת לאה.

"הוא הוציא פוליסת ביטוח חיים על סך עשרה מיליון שקלים על שם אשתו לפני מספר שנים," מסבירה עדינה. "ואז הוא התחיל לחשוב איך להיפטר ממנה בלי להיתפס. וזה הוביל לתוכנית הסחיטה."

"רעיון לא רע," אומר רונן. "הוא נפטר מאשתו ומסיר חשד מעצמו בו-זמנית."

"אני לא יודע למה הוא הרג את שני סוכני הביטוח ההם," אני אומר להם. "לא טרחתי לשאול אותו."

"הרשקו היה בחור חכם," אומרת עדינה. "היה לנו מזל שפקד כהן עשה את הטעות האחת ההיא."

"אתה חושב שהמשטרה מבינה את הדו"ח שלי בעניין העברות הכספים בין הרשקו וכהן?" שואל רונן.

"כנראה. אני אתקשר לבלש זוהר בעוד כמה ימים כדי להמשיך בשיחה. הוא כנראה רוצה לדבר איתי שוב."

"למה?" שואלת עדינה.

"שרה לא מסתובבת לה במשרד, נכון?" אני שואל.

"לא, היא עובדת על חקירה אחרת היום," אומרת לי לאה.

"יופי. בתשובה לשאלת עדינה, שרה ואני ניקינו את ביתו של הרשקו, כדי שהמשטרה לא תמצא את טביעות האצבע שלנו. אחר כך הפעלתי כישוף מוחי קטן על הרשקו כדי לוודא שהוא לא יזכור שראה אותנו. כך שזוהר בוודאי משתוקק לגלות מי אני ואיך הצלחתי לפתור את החקירה."

"בין הכסף והיהלומים שנמצאו אצל פקד כהן, ומה שנמצאו בחשבונות הבנק של הרשקו, הקורבנות יקבלו את רוב כספם בחזרה," אומרת לאה.

"אתה חושב שהראיות שהשארת בבית מספיקות כדי להרשיע אותו?" שואלת עדינה.

"אני חושב שכן. רונן גם זייף כמה העברות כספים שקושרו את הרשקו לאוקראינים. כשהשוטרים יתירו את סבך חשבונות הבנק של הרשקו, ההעברות האלה יצוצו כמו דגלים אדומים," אני אומר לה.

"אתם שניכם כל כך לא ישרים," אומרת איילה.

באותו לילה, לאה ואני שוכבים במיטה ביחד. אני מעסה את כפות רגליה. היא אוהבת את זה. לאה מספרת לי שהיא רוצה לחפש מחר מקום חדש למשרד.

"למה?" אני שואל.

"נוכל להרוויח הרבה כסף אם נסב את הנכס באור יהודה לבניין דירות ונמכור אותן. שוק הנדל"ן מתחיל להתאושש," היא אומרת.

"איפה נחפש?" אני שואל.

"חשבתי על פרדס חנה. זו עיר קטנה ונחמדה והיא ממוקמת ממש על קו הרכבת לתל אביב. חוץ מזה שם יש מסעדות מצוינות. לא יצאת אף פעם עם מישהי ששמה חנה, נכון?"

"לא שאני זוכר."

אני מעסה את רגליה עוד קצת.

"אני צריך אקדח חדש," אני אומר.

"זו הסיבה שאתה מעסה את רגליי?"

"אולי."

"מה עם עיסוי גב לזמן מה? אחר כך נוכל לדבר על אקדחים."

Made in the USA
Coppell, TX
29 March 2024

30725063R00212